W9-CDA-423

NUMERICAL METHODS
WITH APPLICATIONS
(Abridged Edition)

Authors

AUTAR KAW, University of South Florida

http://www.autarkaw.com

E. ERIC KALU, Florida A&M University

http://www.eng.fsu.edu/~ekalu/

Contributors

GLEN BESTERFIELD, University of South Florida

SUDEEP SARKAR, University of South Florida

HENRY WELCH, Milwaukee School of Engineering

ALI YALCIN, University of South Florida

*There is nothing noble about being superior
to another man; the true nobility lies in being
superior to your previous self* - Upanishads.

NUMERICAL METHODS WITH APPLICATIONS

(Abridged Edition)

Second Edition

....

AUTAR KAW

University of South Florida

E. ERIC KALU

Florida A&M University

To Sherrie, Candace and Angelie
AKK

To Ngozi, Ola, Erinma and Egwuchukwu
EEK

AUTAR K KAW

Autar K. Kaw is a Professor of Mechanical Engineering at the University of South Florida, Tampa. Professor Kaw obtained his B.E. (Hons.) degree in Mechanical Engineering from Birla Institute of Technology and Science, India in 1981. He received his Ph.D. degree in 1987 and M.S. degree in 1984, both in Engineering Mechanics from Clemson University, SC. He joined the faculty of University of South Florida, Tampa in 1987. He has also been a Maintenance Engineer (1982) for Ford-Escorts Tractors, India, and a Summer Faculty Fellow (1992) and Visiting Scientist (1991) at Wright Patterson Air Force Base.

Professor Kaw's main scholarly interests are in engineering education research, bridge design, thermal stresses, engineering software, computational nanomechanics, and fracture. His research has been funded by National Science Foundation, Air Force Office of Scientific Research, Florida Department of Transportation, Research and Development Laboratories, Systran, Wright Patterson Air Force Base, and Montgomery Tank Lines.

Professor Kaw is a Fellow of the American Society of Mechanical Engineers (ASME) and a member of the American Society of Engineering Education (ASEE). He has written more than forty journal papers and developed several software instructional programs for courses such as Mechanics of Composites and Numerical Methods.

Professor Kaw has published textbooks on *Mechanics of Composite Materials* (CRC press), and *Introduction to Matrix Algebra* (autarkaw.com).

Professor Kaw received the Florida Professor of the Year Award from the Council for Advancement and Support of Education (CASE) and Carnegie Foundation for Advancement of Teaching (CFAT) in 2004, American Society of Mechanical Engineers (ASME) Curriculum Innovation Award in 2004, Archie Higdon Mechanics Educator Award from the American Society of Engineering Education (ASEE) in 2003, State of Florida Teaching Incentive Program Award in 1994 and 1997, American Society of Engineering Education (ASEE) New Mechanics Educator Award in 1992, and the Society of Automotive Engineers (SAE) Ralph Teetor Award in 1991.

E. ERIC KALU

E. Eric. Kalu is an Associate Professor of Chemical & Biomedical Engineering at the Florida A&M University-Florida State University College of Engineering, Tallahassee. Dr Kalu received a B.Sc (Hons) degree with First Class in Chemical Engineering from University of Lagos, Nigeria in 1984 and in 1988 was awarded a MASc (Chemical Engineering) from the University of British Columbia, Canada. He also received a Ph.D. degree from Texas A&M University, TX in Chemical Engineering in 1991. Before joining the faculty at Florida A&M University in 1995, he worked as a Senior Research Engineer (1991 – 1993) for Monsanto Chemical Company in St Louis, MO and Research Assistant Professor at University of South Carolina, Columbia (1994). He has also been a Summer Faculty Fellow (2007) at Sandia National Laboratories.

Dr Kalu's research interests are in electrochemical & nanomaterials engineering for sustainable energy and environmental systems, engineering education and mentoring. Mathematical modeling of electrochemical and thermochemical systems research are areas of key interest. Dr Kalu has written several journal papers in his areas of interest.

He is a member of the American Institute of Chemical Engineers (AIChE) and a member of the Electrochemical Society (ECS).

Dr Kalu received the NASA Faculty Fellowship Award (2004), Lockheed Martin E&M Minority Institution Award (1998) and High Merit Award for Pioneering Nanotechnology Research Masscal Scientific Instruments (2007). He was also awarded Florida State University First year Assistant Professor Research Award in 1996.

PREFACE

This textbook is written for an undergraduate course in numerical methods for engineering and science. The book has been written in a holistic manner so that the student gets a strong fundamental knowledge of various numerical methods and their applications. Combined with the freely accessible web-based resources at http://numericalmethods.eng.usf.edu, the student can adapt their learning styles and preferences to learn numerical methods.

In 2002, National Science Foundation funded a prototype proposal on Holistic Numerical Methods to develop various resources for typical numerical methods topics of interpolation and solution of nonlinear equations. With the success of this proposal, NSF continued to fund the proposal for other topics of numerical methods via three more multi-university grants in 2004-07, 2008-10, 2009-10. This funding has so far resulted in complete resources on a typical Numerical Methods course. These resources include textbook chapters, PowerPoint presentations, worksheets in MATLAB, MATHEMATICA, Maple and MathCAD, multiple-choice tests, experiments, video lectures, and a blog (http://autarkaw.wordpress.com). All these resources are available at http://numericalmethods.eng.usf.edu.

The book is abridged because of the following reasons:

1) It is being written primarily for Arizona State University, University of South Florida and Old Dominion University and follows their respective complete syllabi.

2) The book needs to be kept under the 740-page limit set by the publisher for perfect-bound binding.

3) We believe in keeping textbook prices low.

However, the abridged nature does not sacrifice the level of content available. The chapters that are not in the printed book can be viewed at http://numericalmethods.eng.usf.edu/topics/textbook_index.html.

If you are an instructor of a numerical methods course and you are interested in adopting the book and want to customize it based on your syllabus, please contact the first author at autarkaw@yahoo.com.

We continue to provide the resources free of charge while selling the printed book to gain sustainability as required by our sponsor

The book is divided into eight topics:
1. Introduction to Scientific Computing,
2. Differentiation,
3. Nonlinear Equations,
4. Simultaneous Linear Equations,
5. Interpolation,
6. Regression,
7. Integration, and
8. Ordinary Differential Equations.

Each topic is covered in several separate chapters because we intend to keep the chapters short and independent. This allowed us to customize the book based on your needs.

Supplemental material is always available from the website. Just go to the main website http://numericalmethods.eng.usf.edu and click on the numerical method of your choice. You will have access to PowerPoint presentations, worksheets, additional examples, and multiple-choice tests. We have added broadcast quality (http://numericalmethods.eng.usf.edu/videos/numerical_methods_course.html) instructional audiovisual content for each numerical method. A blog on numerical methods and MATLAB is also available at http://autarkaw.wordpress.com.

By December 2010, we will have additional topics of Optimization, Partial Differential Equations, and Fast Fourier Transforms available.

The chapters in the book are numbered as Chapter XX.YY. The XX stands for the topic number while YY is the chapter number within that topic. Most of the chapters are followed by a multiple-choice test based on Bloom's taxonomy (you should take these tests online at http://numericalmethods.eng.usf.edu/assessment_text.html) and a problem set.

Chapter 01.YY introduces scientific computing by taking a real-life example to show that solving an engineering problem requires one to develop a mathematical model, solve the model, and then implement the corresponding solution. This is followed by discussion of sources of numerical error and their measurement, binary and floating-point representation of numbers, and propagation of errors.

Chapters 02.YY through **Chapter 08.YY** cover Differentiation, Nonlinear Equations, Simultaneous Linear Equations, Interpolation, Regression, Integration, and Ordinary Differential Equations, respectively. Each of these topics start with an example of application of the mathematical procedure (e.g. differentiation, nonlinear equations, etc) from each of the seven engineering majors. Background information needed to understand the numerical method is also given. For example, for differentiation, a primer chapter (available online) has been written to review the background from the differential calculus course; for nonlinear equations, quadratic equations are reviewed from the college algebra course; for integration, a primer chapter (available online) has been written to review the background from the integral calculus course. Then numerical methods used to solve the mathematical procedure are shown complete with examples from general engineering. If you want to see how a numerical method works with examples from a different engineering major of your choice, go to http://numericalmethods.eng.usf.edu/numerical_methods_topic_major_language.html. Each chapter is followed by a multiple-choice test and a problem set.

We would like to thank - Sri Harsha Garapati, Luke Snyder, Eric Marvella, Sue Britten, and Matthew Emmons for reformatting and typing the textbook. Sean Rodby's painstaking proofreading has been critical in maintaining accuracy of the contents of the book. We would like to thank Cuong Nguyen, Praveen Chalasani, Michael Keteltas, and Luke Snyder for contributions to the book. Kaw would like to thank his spouse, Sherrie, and children Candace and Angelie, who encouraged him to co-write this textbook.

We would like to thank Professors Melvin Corley of Louisiana Technical University, Duc Nguyen of Old Dominion University, Tianxia Zhao of Indiana University-Purdue University, Fort Wayne, and Xudong Jia of California State Polytechnic University for reviewing the contents of the website which included the textbook notes that are in this book.

The first author has written the major portion of the material in this book. The second author has written most of the chapters on regression. The four contributors to this book have written the real-life problems from their engineering majors of expertise. All the authors and contributors are acknowledged at the end of each chapter.

For further information, please visit the book website at http://autarkaw.com/books/numericalmethods/index.html. There you will find links to the additional resources on each numerical method topic and answers to selected problems.

We would appreciate feedback, questions, or comments that you may have on the book or the numerical methods project. You can contact the first author, Autar Kaw, via
      Email: autarkaw@yahoo.com
      URL: http://autarkaw.com
      Tel: 813.974.5626
      Mailing Address: Department of Mechanical Engineering Department, University of South Florida, 4202 East Fowler Avenue, ENB118, Tampa, FL 33620-5350.

TABLE OF CONTENTS

NONLINEAR EQUATIONS   **122**

INTEGRATION   486

Chapter 01.01
Introduction to Numerical Methods

After reading this chapter, you should be able to:
1. *understand the need for numerical methods, and*
2. *go through the stages (mathematical modeling, solving and implementation) of solving a particular physical problem.*

Mathematical models are an integral part in solving engineering problems. Many times, these mathematical models are derived from engineering and science principles, while at other times the models may be obtained from experimental data.

Mathematical models generally result in need of using mathematical procedures that include but are not limited to
  (A) differentiation,
  (B) nonlinear equations,
  (C) simultaneous linear equations,
  (D) curve fitting by interpolation or regression,
  (E) integration, and
  (F) differential equations.

These mathematical procedures may be suitable to be solved exactly as you must have experienced in the series of calculus courses you have taken, but in most cases, the procedures need to be solved approximately using numerical methods. Let us see an example of such a need from a real-life physical problem.

To make the fulcrum (Figure 1) of a bascule bridge, a long hollow steel shaft called the trunnion is shrink fit into a steel hub. The resulting steel trunnion-hub assembly is then shrink fit into the girder of the bridge.

Figure 1 Trunnion-Hub-Girder (THG) assembly.

This is done by first immersing the trunnion in a cold medium such as a dry-ice/alcohol mixture. After the trunnion reaches the steady state temperature of the cold medium, the trunnion outer diameter contracts. The trunnion is taken out of the medium and slid through the hole of the hub (Figure 2).

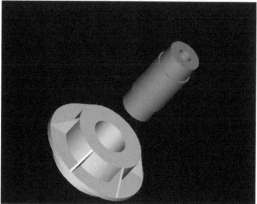

Figure 2 Trunnion slided through the hub after contracting

When the trunnion heats up, it expands and creates an interference fit with the hub. In 1995, on one of the bridges in Florida, this assembly procedure did not work as designed. Before the trunnion could be inserted fully into the hub, the trunnion got stuck. Luckily, the trunnion was taken out before it got stuck permanently. Otherwise, a new trunnion and hub would needed to be ordered at a cost of $50,000. Coupled with construction delays, the total loss could have been more than a hundred thousand dollars.

Why did the trunnion get stuck? This was because the trunnion had not contracted enough to slide through the hole. Can you find out why?

A hollow trunnion of outside diameter 12.363" is to be fitted in a hub of inner diameter 12.358". The trunnion was put in dry ice/alcohol mixture (temperature of the fluid - dry ice/alcohol mixture is $-108°F$) to contract the trunnion so that it can be slid through the hole of the hub. To slide the trunnion without sticking, a diametrical clearance of at least 0.01" is required between the trunnion and the hub. Assuming the room temperature is $80°F$, is immersing the trunnion in dry-ice/alcohol mixture a correct decision?

To calculate the contraction in the diameter of the trunnion, the thermal expansion coefficient at room temperature is used. In that case the reduction ΔD in the outer diameter of the trunnion is

$$\Delta D = D\alpha\Delta T \qquad (1)$$

where

D = outer diameter of the trunnion,

α = coefficient of thermal expansion coefficient at room temperature, and

ΔT = change in temperature,

Given

$D = 12.363"$

$\alpha = 6.47\times10^{-6}$ in/in/°F at 80°F

$\Delta T = T_{fluid} - T_{room}$

$= -108 - 80$

$$= -188°F$$

where

T_{fluid} = temperature of dry-ice/alcohol mixture

T_{room} = room temperature

the reduction in the outer diameter of the trunnion is given by

$$\Delta D = (12.363)\left(6.47 \times 10^{-6}\right)(-188)$$

$$= -0.01504"$$

So the trunnion is predicted to reduce in diameter by 0.01504". But, is this enough reduction in diameter? As per specifications, the trunnion needs to contract by

= trunnion outside diameter - hub inner diameter + diametric clearance

= 12.363 − 12.358 + 0.01

= 0.015"

So according to his calculations, immersing the steel trunnion in dry-ice/alcohol mixture gives the desired contraction of greater than 0.015" as the predicted contraction is 0.01504". But, when the steel trunnion was put in the hub, it got stuck. Why did this happen? Was our mathematical model adequate for this problem or did we create a mathematical error?

As shown in Figure 3 and Table 1, the thermal expansion coefficient of steel decreases with temperature and is not constant over the range of temperature the trunnion goes through. Hence, Equation (1) would overestimate the thermal contraction.

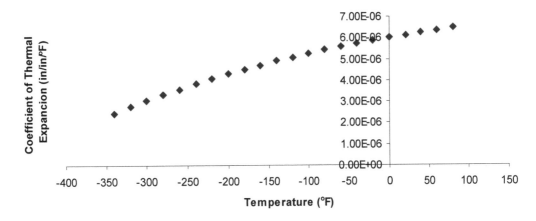

Figure 3 Varying thermal expansion coefficient as a function of temperature for cast steel.

The contraction in the diameter of the trunnion for which the thermal expansion coefficient varies as a function of temperature is given by

$$\Delta D = D \int_{T_{room}}^{T_{fluid}} \alpha \, dT \tag{2}$$

So one needs to curve fit the data to find the coefficient of thermal expansion as a function of temperature. This is done by regression where we best fit a curve through the data given in Table 1. In this case, we may fit a second order polynomial

$$\alpha = a_0 + a_1 \times T + a_2 \times T^2 \tag{3}$$

Table 1 Instantaneous thermal expansion coefficient as a function of temperature.

Temperature	Instantaneous Thermal Expansion
°F	μin/in/°F
80	6.47
60	6.36
40	6.24
20	6.12
0	6.00
-20	5.86
-40	5.72
-60	5.58
-80	5.43
-100	5.28
-120	5.09
-140	4.91
-160	4.72
-180	4.52
-200	4.30
-220	4.08
-240	3.83
-260	3.58
-280	3.33
-300	3.07
-320	2.76
-340	2.45

The values of the coefficients in the above Equation (3) will be found by polynomial regression (we will learn how to do this later in Chapter 06.04). At this point we are just going to give you these values and they are

$$\begin{bmatrix} a_0 \\ a_1 \\ a_2 \end{bmatrix} = \begin{bmatrix} 6.0150 \times 10^{-6} \\ 6.1946 \times 10^{-9} \\ -1.2278 \times 10^{-11} \end{bmatrix}$$

to give the polynomial regression model (Figure 4) as

$$\alpha = a_0 + a_1 T + a_2 T^2$$

$$= 6.0150 \times 10^{-6} + 6.1946 \times 10^{-9} T - 1.2278 \times 10^{-11} T^2$$

Knowing the values of a_0, a_1 nd a_2, we can then find the contraction in the trunnion diameter as

$$\Delta D = D \int_{T_{room}}^{T_{fluid}} (a_0 + a_1 T + a_2 T^2) dT$$

$$= D[a_0 (T_{fluid} - T_{room}) + a_1 \frac{(T_{fluid}^2 - T_{room}^2)}{2} + a_2 \frac{(T_{fluid}^3 - T_{room}^3)}{3}] \qquad (4)$$

which gives

$$\Delta D = 12.363 \left[\begin{array}{l} 6.0150 \times 10^{-6} \times (-108 - 80) + 6.1946 \times 10^{-9} \dfrac{\left((-108)^2 - (80)^2\right)}{2} \\ \\ -1.2278 \times 10^{-12} \dfrac{\left((-108)^3 - (80)^3\right)}{3} \end{array} \right]$$

$$= -0.013689''$$

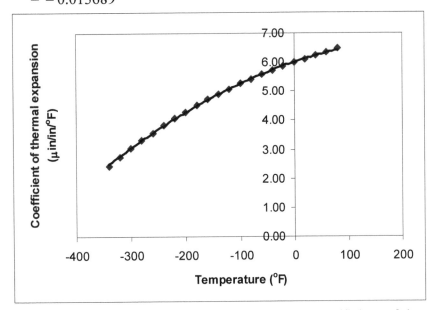

Figure 4 Second order polynomial regression model for coefficient of thermal expansion as a function of temperature.

What do we find here? The contraction in the trunnion is not enough to meet the required specification of 0.015".

So here are some questions that you may want to ask yourself?

1. What if the trunnion were immersed in liquid nitrogen (boiling temperature $= -321°F$)? Will that cause enough contraction in the trunnion?

2. Rather than regressing the thermal expansion coefficient data to a second order polynomial so that one can find the contraction in the trunnion OD, how would you use Trapezoidal rule of integration for unequal segments? What is the relative difference between the two results?

3. We chose a second order polynomial for regression. Would a different order polynomial be a better choice for regression? Is there an optimum order of polynomial you can find?

As mentioned at the beginning of this chapter, we generally see mathematical procedures that require the solution of nonlinear equations, differentiation, solution of simultaneous linear equations, interpolation, regression, integration, and differential equations. A physical example to illustrate the need for each of these mathematical procedures is given in the beginning of each chapter. You may want to look at them now to understand better why we need numerical methods in everyday life.

INTRODUCTION, APPROXIMATION AND ERRORS	
Topic	Introduction to Numerical Methods
Summary	Textbook notes of Introduction to Numerical Methods
Major	General Engineering
Authors	Autar Kaw
Date	April 29, 2010
Web Site	http://numericalmethods.eng.usf.edu

Multiple-Choice Test

Chapter 01.01
Introduction to Numerical Methods

1. Solving an engineering problem requires four steps. In order of sequence, the four steps are
   - (A) formulate, solve, interpret, implement
   - (B) solve, formulate, interpret, implement
   - (C) formulate, solve, implement, interpret
   - (D) formulate, implement, solve, interpret

2. One of the roots of the equation $x^3 - 3x^2 + x - 3 = 0$ is
   - (A) -1
   - (B) 1
   - (C) $\sqrt{3}$
   - (D) 3

3. The solution to the set of equations
   $$25a + b + c = 25$$
   $$64a + 8b + c = 71$$
   $$144a + 12b + c = 155$$
   most nearly is $(a, b, c) =$
   - (A) (1,1,1)
   - (B) (1,-1,1)
   - (C) (1,1,-1)
   - (D) does not have a unique solution.

4. The exact integral of
   $$\int_{0}^{\frac{\pi}{4}} 2\cos 2x\, dx$$
   is most nearly
   - (A) -1.000
   - (B) 1.000
   - (C) 0.000
   - (D) 2.000

01.01.1

5.   The value of $\dfrac{dy}{dx}(1.0)$, given $y = 2\sin(3x)$ most nearly is
     (A) -5.9399
     (B) -1.980
     (C) 0.31402
     (D) 5.9918

6.   The form of the exact solution of the ordinary differential equation
     $2\dfrac{dy}{dx} + 3y = 5e^{-x}$, $y(0) = 5$ is
     (A) $Ae^{-1.5x} + Be^{x}$
     (B) $Ae^{-1.5x} + Be^{-x}$
     (C) $Ae^{1.5x} + Be^{-x}$
     (D) $Ae^{-1.5x} + Bxe^{-x}$

     Complete solution

Problem Set

Chapter 01.01
Introduction to Numerical Methods

1. Give one example of an engineering problem where each of the following mathematical procedure is used. If possible, draw from your experience in other classes or from any professional experience you have gathered to date.
   a) Differentiation
   b) Nonlinear equations
   c) Simultaneous linear equations
   d) Regression
   e) Interpolation
   f) Integration
   g) Ordinary differential equations

2. Only using your nonprogrammable calculator, find the root of
   $$x^3 - 0.165x^2 + 3.993 \times 10^{-4} = 0$$
   by any method (show your work).

3. Solve the following system of simultaneous linear equations by any method
   $$25a + 5b + c = 106.8$$
   $$64a + 8b + c = 177.2$$
   $$144a + 12b + c = 279.2$$

4. You are given data for the upward velocity of a rocket as a function of time in the table below.

t	$v(t)$
s	m/s
10	305.31
20	701.53

   Find the velocity at $t = 16s$.

5. Integrate exactly
   $$\int_0^{\pi/2} \sin 2x \, dx$$

6. Find
   $$\frac{dy}{dx}(x = 1.4)$$
   given
   $$y = e^x + \sin(x)$$

01.01.1

7. Solve the following ordinary differential equation exactly

$$\frac{dy}{dx} + y = e^{-x}, y(0) = 5$$

Also find $y(0)$, $\frac{dy}{dx}(0)$, $y(2.5)$, $\frac{dy}{dx}(2.5)$

Chapter 01.02
Measuring Errors

After reading this chapter, you should be able to:
1. *find the true and relative true error,*
2. *find the approximate and relative approximate error,*
3. *relate the absolute relative approximate error to the number of significant digits at least correct in your answers, and*
4. *know the concept of significant digits.*

In any numerical analysis, errors will arise during the calculations. To be able to deal with the issue of errors, we need to
  (A) identify where the error is coming from, followed by
  (B) quantifying the error, and lastly
  (C) minimize the error as per our needs.
In this chapter, we will concentrate on item (B), that is, how to quantify errors.

Q: What is true error?
A: True error denoted by E_t is the difference between the true value (also called the exact value) and the approximate value.
  True Error = True value – Approximate value

Example 1
The derivative of a function $f(x)$ at a particular value of x can be approximately calculated by

$$f'(x) \approx \frac{f(x+h) - f(x)}{h}$$

of $f'(2)$ For $f(x) = 7e^{0.5x}$ and $h = 0.3$, find
  a) the approximate value of $f'(2)$
  b) the true value of $f'(2)$
  c) the true error for part (a)

Solution

a) $\qquad f'(x) \approx \dfrac{f(x+h) - f(x)}{h}$

For $x = 2$ and $h = 0.3$,

$$f'(2) \approx \frac{f(2+0.3) - f(2)}{0.3}$$

$$= \frac{f(2.3) - f(2)}{0.3}$$

$$= \frac{7e^{0.5(2.3)} - 7e^{0.5(2)}}{0.3}$$

$$= \frac{22.107 - 19.028}{0.3}$$

$$= 10.265$$

b) The exact value of $f'(2)$ can be calculated by using our knowledge of differential calculus.

$$f(x) = 7e^{0.5x}$$

$$f'(x) = 7 \times 0.5 \times e^{0.5x}$$

$$= 3.5e^{0.5x}$$

So the true value of $f'(2)$ is

$$f'(2) = 3.5e^{0.5(2)}$$

$$= 9.5140$$

c) True error is calculated as

$$E_t = \text{True value} - \text{Approximate value}$$

$$= 9.5140 - 10.265$$

$$= -0.75061$$

The magnitude of true error does not show how bad the error is. A true error of $E_t = -0.722$ may seem to be small, but if the function given in the Example 1 were $f(x) = 7 \times 10^{-6} e^{0.5x}$, the true error in calculating $f'(2)$ with $h = 0.3$, would be $E_t = -0.75061 \times 10^{-6}$. This value of true error is smaller, even when the two problems are similar in that they use the same value of the function argument, $x = 2$ and the step size, $h = 0.3$. This brings us to the definition of relative true error.

Q: What is relative true error?

A: Relative true error is denoted by $\in_t$ and is defined as the ratio between the true error and the true value.

$$\text{Relative True Error} = \frac{\text{True Error}}{\text{True Value}}$$

Example 2

The derivative of a function $f(x)$ at a particular value of x can be approximately calculated by

$$f'(x) \approx \frac{f(x+h) - f(x)}{h}$$

For $f(x) = 7e^{0.5x}$ and $h = 0.3$, find the relative true error at $x = 2$.

Solution

From Example 1,

$E_t =$ True value – Approximate value

$= 9.5140 - 10.265$

$= -0.75061$

Relative true error is calculated as

$$\in_t = \frac{\text{True Error}}{\text{True Value}}$$

$$= \frac{-0.75061}{9.5140}$$

$$= -0.078895$$

Relative true errors are also presented as percentages. For this example,

$\in_t = -0.0758895 \times 100\%$

$= -7.58895\%$

Absolute relative true errors may also need to be calculated. In such cases,

$\left|\in_t\right| = \left|-0.075888\right|$

$= 0.0758895$

$= 7.58895\%$

Q: What is approximate error?

A: In the previous section, we discussed how to calculate true errors. Such errors are calculated only if true values are known. An example where this would be useful is when one is checking if a program is in working order and you know some examples where the true error is known. But mostly we will not have the luxury of knowing true values as why would you want to find the approximate values if you know the true values. So when we are solving a problem numerically, we will only have access to approximate values. We need to know how to quantify error for such cases.

Approximate error is denoted by E_a and is defined as the difference between the present approximation and previous approximation.

Approximate Error $=$ Present Approximation – Previous Approximation

Example 3

The derivative of a function $f(x)$ at a particular value of x can be approximately calculated by

$$f'(x) \approx \frac{f(x+h) - f(x)}{h}$$

For $f(x) = 7e^{0.5x}$ and at $x = 2$, find the following

      a) $f'(2)$ using $h = 0.3$

      b) $f'(2)$ using $h = 0.15$

      c) approximate error for the value of $f'(2)$ for part (b)

Solution

a) The approximate expression for the derivative of a function is

$$f'(x) \approx \frac{f(x+h)-f(x)}{h}.$$

For $x=2$ and $h=0.3$,

$$f'(2) \approx \frac{f(2+0.3)-f(2)}{0.3}$$
$$= \frac{f(2.3)-f(2)}{0.3}$$
$$= \frac{7e^{0.5(2.3)}-7e^{0.5(2)}}{0.3}$$
$$= \frac{22.107-19.028}{0.3}$$
$$= 10.265$$

b) Repeat the procedure of part (a) with $h=0.15$,

$$f'(x) \approx \frac{f(x+h)-f(x)}{h}$$

For $x=2$ and $h=0.15$,

$$f'(2) \approx \frac{f(2+0.15)-f(2)}{0.15}$$
$$= \frac{f(2.15)-f(2)}{0.15}$$
$$= \frac{7e^{0.5(2.15)}-7e^{0.5(2)}}{0.15}$$
$$= \frac{20.50-19.028}{0.15}$$
$$= 9.8799$$

c) So the approximate error, E_a is

$$E_a = \text{Present Approximation} - \text{Previous Approximation}$$
$$= 9.8799 - 10.265$$
$$= -0.38474$$

The magnitude of approximate error does not show how bad the error is . An approximate error of $E_a = -0.38300$ may seem to be small; but for $f(x) = 7\times10^{-6}e^{0.5x}$, the approximate error in calculating $f'(2)$ with $h=0.15$ would be $E_a = -0.38474\times10^{-6}$. This value of approximate error is smaller, even when the two problems are similar in that they use the same value of the function argument, $x=2$, and $h=0.15$ and $h=0.3$. This brings us to the definition of relative approximate error.

Q: What is relative approximate error?
A: Relative approximate error is denoted by $\in_a$ and is defined as the ratio between the approximate error and the present approximation.

$$\text{Relative Approximate Error} = \frac{\text{Approximate Error}}{\text{Present Approximation}}$$

Example 4

The derivative of a function $f(x)$ at a particular value of x can be approximately calculated by

$$f'(x) \approx \frac{f(x+h) - f(x)}{h}$$

For $f(x) = 7e^{0.5x}$, find the relative approximate error in calculating $f'(2)$ using values from $h = 0.3$ and $h = 0.15$.

Solution

From Example 3, the approximate value of $f'(2) = 10.263$ using $h = 0.3$ and $f'(2) = 9.8800$ using $h = 0.15$.

$$E_a = \text{Present Approximation} - \text{Previous Approximation}$$
$$= 9.8799 - 10.265$$
$$= -0.38474$$

The relative approximate error is calculated as

$$\in_a = \frac{\text{Approximate Error}}{\text{Present Approximation}}$$
$$= \frac{-0.38474}{9.8799}$$
$$= -0.038942$$

Relative approximate errors are also presented as percentages. For this example,

$$\in_a = -0.038942 \times 100\%$$
$$= -3.8942\%$$

Absolute relative approximate errors may also need to be calculated. In this example

$$|\in_a| = |-0.038942|$$
$$= 0.038942 \text{ or } 3.8942\%$$

Q: While solving a mathematical model using numerical methods, how can we use relative approximate errors to minimize the error?

A: In a numerical method that uses iterative methods, a user can calculate relative approximate error $\in_a$ at the end of each iteration. The user may pre-specify a minimum acceptable tolerance called the pre-specified tolerance, $\in_s$. If the absolute relative approximate error $\in_a$ is less than or equal to the pre-specified tolerance $\in_s$, that is, $|\in_a| \leq \in_s$, then the acceptable error has been reached and no more iterations would be required.

Alternatively, one may pre-specify how many significant digits they would like to be correct in their answer. In that case, if one wants at least m significant digits to be correct in the answer, then you would need to have the absolute relative approximate error, $|\in_a| \leq 0.5 \times 10^{2-m} \%$.

Example 5

If one chooses 6 terms of the Maclaurin series for e^x to calculate $e^{0.7}$, how many significant digits can you trust in the solution? Find your answer without knowing or using the exact answer.

Solution

$$e^x = 1 + x + \frac{x^2}{2!} + \dots\dots\dots\dots$$

Using 6 terms, we get the current approximation as

$$e^{0.7} \cong 1 + 0.7 + \frac{0.7^2}{2!} + \frac{0.7^3}{3!} + \frac{0.7^4}{4!} + \frac{0.7^5}{5!}$$

$$= 2.0136$$

Using 5 terms, we get the previous approximation as

$$e^{0.7} \cong 1 + 0.7 + \frac{0.7^2}{2!} + \frac{0.7^3}{3!} + \frac{0.7^4}{4!}$$

$$= 2.0122$$

The percentage absolute relative approximate error is

$$\left| \in_a \right| = \left| \frac{2.0136 - 2.0122}{2.0136} \right| \times 100$$

$$= 0.069527\%$$

Since $\left| \in_a \right| \le 0.5 \times 10^{2-2}\%$, at least 2 significant digits are correct in the answer of

$$e^{0.7} \cong 2.0136$$

Q: But what do you mean by significant digits?

A: Significant digits are important in showing the truth one has in a reported number. For example, if someone asked me what the population of my county is, I would respond, "The population of the Hillsborough county area is 1 million". But if someone was going to give me a $100 for every citizen of the county, I would have to get an exact count. That count would have been 1,079,587 in year 2003. So you can see that in my statement that the population is 1 million, that there is only one significant digit, that is, 1, and in the statement that the population is 1,079,587, there are seven significant digits. So, how do we differentiate the number of digits correct in 1,000,000 and 1,079,587? Well for that, one may use scientific notation. For our data we show

$$1,000,000 = 1 \times 10^6$$

$$1,079,587 = 1.079587 \times 10^6$$

to signify the correct number of significant digits.

Example 5

Give some examples of showing the number of significant digits.

Solution

a) 0.0459 has three significant digits
b) 4.590 has four significant digits
c) 4008 has four significant digits
d) 4008.0 has five significant digits

e) 1.079×10^3 has four significant digits

f) 1.0790×10^3 has five significant digits

g) 1.07900×10^3 has six significant digits

INTRODUCTION, APPROXIMATION AND ERRORS	
Topic	Measuring Errors
Summary	Textbook notes on measuring errors
Major	General Engineering
Authors	Autar Kaw
Date	December 23, 2009
Web Site	http://numericalmethods.eng.usf.edu

Multiple-Choice Test

Chapter 01.02
Measuring Errors

1. True error is defined as
   (A) Present Approximation – Previous Approximation
   (B) True Value – Approximate Value
   (C) abs (True Value – Approximate Value)
   (D) abs (Present Approximation – Previous Approximation)

2. The expression for true error in calculating the derivative of $\sin(2x)$ at $x = \pi/4$ by using the approximate expression
   $$f'(x) \approx \frac{f(x+h) - f(x)}{h}$$
   is
   (A) $\dfrac{h - \cos(2h) - 1}{h}$
   (B) $\dfrac{h - \cos(h) - 1}{h}$
   (C) $\dfrac{1 - \cos(2h)}{h}$
   (D) $\dfrac{\sin(2h)}{h}$

3. The relative approximate error at the end of an iteration to find the root of an equation is 0.004%. The least number of significant digits we can trust in the solution is
   (A) 2
   (B) 3
   (C) 4
   (D) 5

4. The number 0.01850×10^3 has _____ significant digits
   (A) 3
   (B) 4
   (C) 5
   (D) 6

5.   The following gas stations were cited for irregular dispensation by the Department of Agriculture. Which one cheated you the most?

Station	Actual gasoline dispensed	Gasoline reading at pump
Ser	9.90	10.00
Cit	19.90	20.00
Hus	29.80	30.00
She	29.95	30.00

(A) Ser
(B) Cit
(C) Hus
(D) She

6.   The number of significant digits in the number 219900 is

(A) 4
(B) 5
(C) 6
(D) 4 or 5 or 6

Complete solution

Problem Set

Chapter 01.02
Measuring Error

1. The trigonometric function $\sin(x)$ can be calculated by using the following infinite series

$$\sin(x) = x - \frac{x^3}{3!} + \frac{x^5}{5!} - \frac{x^7}{7!} + \ldots$$

   a) What is the value of $\sin(2.17)$ by using the first three terms in the given series?
   b) What is the value of $\sin(2.17)$ by using the first four terms in the given series?
   c) Use your calculator for the true value of $\sin(2.17)$?
   d) What is the true error for answer in part (a)?
   e) What is the absolute true error for answer in part (a).
   f) What is the relative true error for answer in part (a).
   g) What is the absolute relative true error for answer in part (a).
   h) What is the approximate error for answer in part (b)?
   i) What is the absolute approximate error for answer in part (b).
   j) What is the relative approximate error for answer in part (b).
   k) What is the absolute relative approximate error for answer in part (b).
   l) Assume that you do not know the exact value of $\sin(2.17)$, how many significant digits are at least correct if you use four terms in the series?
   m) What should be the pre-specified relative error tolerance if at least 4 significant digits are required to be correct in calculating $\sin(2.17)$?

2. A Maclaurin series for a function is given by

$$f(x) = x - \frac{x^3}{3!} + \frac{x^5}{5!} + \ldots$$

   What is the absolute relative approximate error if three terms are used for calculating $f(1.2)$?

3. A Maclaurin series for a function is given by

$$f(x) = x - \frac{x^3}{3!} + \frac{x^5}{5!} + \ldots$$

   How many terms should be used in the series to consider that at least 2 significant digits are correct in your answer for $f(0.1)$?

01.02.1

4.   A gas station owned by Valdez gives you 9.90 gallons of gasoline when you actually paid for 9.95 gallons. Another gas station owned by Hessup gives you 19.80 gallons of gasoline when you actually paid for 19.85 gallons of gasoline. If you only had these two gas stations available in your town, which one would you go to next time you had to fill up your car? Use the concepts learned in measuring errors to justify your answer.

5.   The function e^x can be calculated by using the following infinite Maclaurin series

$$e^x = 1 + x + \frac{x^2}{2!} + \frac{x^3}{3!} + \frac{x^4}{4!} + \ ....$$

   a)   Use 5 terms to calculate the value of $e^{0.9}$?
   b)   How many significant digits in my calculation would be correct if I use 5 terms?
   c)   How do I know that I have used enough terms to calculate $e^{0.9}$, if I pre-specify a tolerance of 0.05%? What is the minimum number of terms I should use to achieve the pre-specified tolerance?
   d)   Where are the sources of error coming from in the above series?

6.   How many significant digits are correct in the following numbers
   a)   185000
   b)   0.0185
   c)   1.0185
   d) 185×10^3
   e) 1850×10^2
   f) 0.01850×10^5
   g) 0.0185×10^5
   h)   100.00
   i)   100.001

7.   What is the correct normalized scientific notation for 0.029411765 with 4 significant digits?

Chapter 01.03
Sources of Error

After reading this chapter, you should be able to:

1. *know that there are two inherent sources of error in numerical methods – round-off and truncation error,*
2. *recognize the sources of round-off and truncation error, and*
3. *know the difference between round-off and truncation error.*

Error in solving an engineering or science problem can arise due to several factors. First, the error may be in the modeling technique. A mathematical model may be based on using assumptions that are not acceptable. For example, one may assume that the drag force on a car is proportional to the velocity of the car, but actually it is proportional to the square of the velocity of the car. This itself can create huge errors in determining the performance of the car, no matter how accurate the numerical methods you may use are. Second, errors may arise from mistakes in programs themselves or in the measurement of physical quantities. But, in applications of numerical methods itself, the two errors we need to focus on are

1. Round off error
2. Truncation error.

Q: What is round off error?

A: A computer can only represent a number approximately. For example, a number like $\frac{1}{3}$ may be represented as 0.333333 on a PC. Then the round off error in this case is $\frac{1}{3} - 0.333333 = 0.000000\overline{3}$. Then there are other numbers that cannot be represented exactly. For example, π and $\sqrt{2}$ are numbers that need to be approximated in computer calculations.

Q: What problems can be created by round off errors?
A: Twenty-eight Americans were killed on February 25, 1991. An Iraqi Scud hit the Army barracks in Dhahran, Saudi Arabia. The patriot defense system had failed to track and intercept the Scud. What was the cause for this failure?
The Patriot defense system consists of an electronic detection device called the range gate. It calculates the area in the air space where it should look for a Scud. To find out where it

should aim next, it calculates the velocity of the Scud and the last time the radar detected the Scud. Time is saved in a register that has 24 bits length. Since the internal clock of the system is measured for every one-tenth of a second, 1/10 is expressed in a 24 bit-register as 0.00011001100110011001100. However, this is not an exact representation. In fact, it would need infinite numbers of bits to represent 1/10 exactly. So, the error in the representation in decimal format is

Figure 1 Patriot missile (Courtesy of the US Armed Forces, http://www.redstone.army.mil/history/archives/patriot/patriot.html)

$$\frac{1}{10} - (0 \times 2^{-1} + 0 \times 2^{-2} + 0 \times 2^{-3} + 1 \times 2^{-4} + \dots + 1 \times 2^{-22} + 0 \times 2^{-23} + 0 \times 2^{-24})$$

$$= 9.537 \times 10^{-8}$$

The battery was on for 100 consecutive hours, hence causing an inaccuracy of

$$= 9.537 \times 10^{-8} \frac{s}{0.1s} \times 100 \, hr \times \frac{3600s}{1hr}$$

$$= 0.3433s$$

The shift calculated in the range gate due to 0.3433s was calculated as 687m. For the Patriot missile defense system, the target is considered out of range if the shift was going to more than 137m.

Q: What is truncation error?
A: Truncation error is defined as the error caused by truncating a mathematical procedure. For example, the Maclaurin series for e^x is given as

$$e^x = 1 + x + \frac{x^2}{2!} + \frac{x^3}{3!} + \dots\dots\dots$$

This series has an infinite number of terms but when using this series to calculate e^x, only a finite number of terms can be used. For example, if one uses three terms to calculate e^x, then

$$e^x \approx 1 + x + \frac{x^2}{2!}.$$

the truncation error for such an approximation is

$$\text{Truncation error} = e^x - \left(1 + x + \frac{x^2}{2!}\right),$$

$$= \frac{x^3}{3!} + \frac{x^4}{4!} + \dots\dots\dots\dots$$

But, how can truncation error be controlled in this example? We can use the concept of relative approximate error to see how many terms need to be considered. Assume that one is calculating $e^{1.2}$ using the Maclaurin series, then

$$e^{1.2} = 1 + 1.2 + \frac{1.2^2}{2!} + \frac{1.2^3}{3!} + \dots\dots\dots\dots$$

Let us assume one wants the absolute relative approximate error to be less than 1%. In Table 1, we show the value of $e^{1.2}$, approximate error and absolute relative approximate error as a function of the number of terms, n.

n	$e^{1.2}$	E_a	$|\epsilon_a|\%$
1	1	-	-
2	2.2	1.2	54.546
3	2.92	0.72	24.658
4	3.208	0.288	8.9776
5	3.2944	0.0864	2.6226
6	3.3151	0.020736	0.62550

Using 6 terms of the series yields a $|\epsilon_a| < 1\%$.

Q: Can you give me other examples of truncation error?

A: In many textbooks, the Maclaurin series is used as an example to illustrate truncation error. This may lead you to believe that truncation errors are just chopping a part of the series. However, truncation error can take place in other mathematical procedures as well. For example to find the derivative of a function, we define

$$f'(x) = \lim_{x \to 0} \frac{f(x + \Delta x) - f(x)}{\Delta x}$$

But since we cannot use $\Delta x \to 0,$ we have to use a finite value of Δx, to give

$$f'(x) \approx \frac{f(x + \Delta x) - f(x)}{\Delta x}$$

So the truncation error is caused by choosing a finite value of Δx as opposed to a $\Delta x \to 0$.

For example, in finding $f'(3)$ for $f(x) = x^2$, we have the exact value calculated as follows.

$$f(x) = x^2$$

From the definition of the derivative of a function,

$$f'(x) = \lim_{\Delta x \to 0} \frac{f(x + \Delta x) - f(x)}{\Delta x}$$

$$= \lim_{\Delta x \to 0} \frac{(x + \Delta x)^2 - (x)^2}{\Delta x}$$

$$= \lim_{\Delta x \to 0} \frac{x^2 + 2x\Delta x + (\Delta x)^2 - x^2}{\Delta x}$$

$$= \lim_{\Delta x \to 0} (2x + \Delta x)$$

$$= 2x$$

This is the same expression you would have obtained by directly using the formula from your differential calculus class

$$\frac{d}{dx}(x^n) = nx^{n-1}$$

By this formula for

$$f(x) = x^2$$

$$f'(x) = 2x$$

The exact value of $f'(3)$ is

$$f'(3) = 2 \times 3$$

$$= 6$$

If we now choose $\Delta x = 0.2$, we get

$$f'(3) = \frac{f(3+0.2) - f(3)}{0.2}$$

$$= \frac{f(3.2) - f(3)}{0.2}$$

$$= \frac{3.2^2 - 3^2}{0.2}$$

$$= \frac{10.24 - 9}{0.2}$$

$$= \frac{1.24}{0.2}$$

$$= 6.2$$

We purposefully chose a simple function $f(x) = x^2$ with value of $x = 2$ and $\Delta x = 0.2$ because we wanted to have no round-off error in our calculations so that the truncation error can be isolated. The truncation error in this example is

$$6 - 6.2 = -0.2.$$

Can you reduce the truncate error by choosing a smaller Δx?

Another example of truncation error is the numerical integration of a function,

$$I = \int_a^b f(x)dx$$

Exact calculations require us to calculate the area under the curve by adding the area of the rectangles as shown in Figure 2. However, exact calculations requires an infinite number of such rectangles. Since we cannot choose an infinite number of rectangles, we will have truncation error.

For example, to find

$$\int_3^9 x^2 dx,$$

we have the exact value as

$$\int_{3}^{9} x^2 dx = \left[\frac{x^3}{3}\right]_{3}^{9}$$
$$= \left[\frac{9^3 - 3^3}{3}\right]$$
$$= 234$$

If we now choose to use two rectangles of equal width to approximate the area (see Figure 2) under the curve, the approximate value of the integral

$$\int_{3}^{9} x^2 dx = (x^2)\big|_{x=3}(6-3) + (x^2)\big|_{x=6}(9-6)$$
$$= (3^2)3 + (6^2)3$$
$$= 27 + 108$$
$$= 135$$

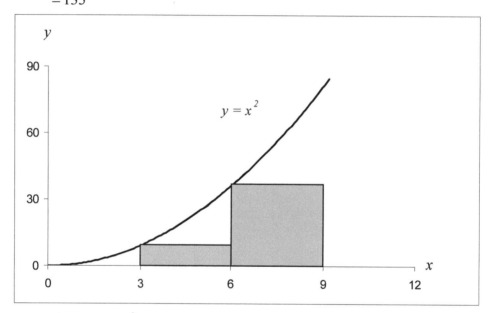

Figure 2 Plot of $y = x^2$ showing the approximate area under the curve from $x = 3$ to $x = 9$ using two rectangles.

Again, we purposefully chose a simple example because we wanted to have no round off error in our calculations. This makes the obtained error purely truncation. The truncation error is

234 − 135 = 99

Can you reduce the truncation error by choosing more rectangles as given in Figure 3? What is the truncation error?

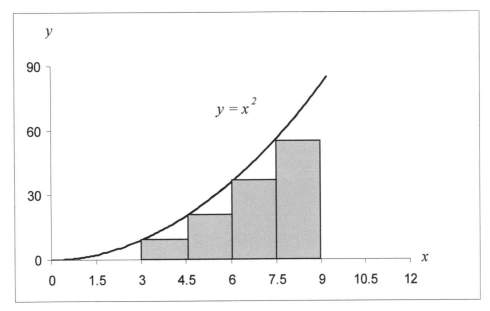

Figure 3 Plot of $y = x^2$ showing the approximate area under the curve from $x = 3$ to $x = 9$ using four rectangles.

References

"Patriot Missile Defense – Software Problem Led to System Failure at Dhahran, Saudi Arabia", GAO Report, General Accounting Office, Washington DC, February 4, 1992.

INTRODUCTION, APPROXIMATION AND ERRORS	
Topic	Sources of error
Summary	Textbook notes on sources of error
Major	General Engineering
Authors	Autar Kaw
Date	December 23, 2009
Web Site	http://numericalmethods.eng.usf.edu

Multiple-Choice Test

Chapter 01.03
Sources of Error

1. Truncation error is caused by approximating
   (A) irrational numbers
   (B) fractions
   (C) rational numbers
   (D) exact mathematical procedures

2. A computer that represents only 4 significant digits with chopping would calculate 66.666*33.333 as
   (A) 2220
   (B) 2221
   (C) 2221.17778
   (D) 2222

3. A computer that represents only 4 significant digits with rounding would calculate 66.666*33.333 as
   (A) 2220
   (B) 2221
   (C) 2221.17778
   (D) 2222

4. The truncation error in calculating $f'(2)$ for $f(x) = x^2$ by
   $$f'(x) \approx \frac{f(x+h) - f(x)}{h}$$
   with $h = 0.2$ is
   (A) -0.2
   (B) 0.2
   (C) 4.0
   (D) 4.2

5. The truncation error in finding $\int_{-3}^{9} x^3 dx$ using LRAM (left end point Riemann approximation) with equally portioned points $-3 < 0 < 3 < 6 < 9$ is
   (A) 648
   (B) 756
   (C) 972
   (D) 1620

6.   The number 1/10 is registered in a fixed 6 bit-register with all bits used for the fractional part. The difference gets accumulated every 1/10th of a second for one day. The magnitude of the accumulated difference is

        (A)   0.082

        (B)   135

        (C)   270

        (D)   5400

Complete solution

Problem Set

Chapter 01.03
Sources of Error

1. What is the round off error in representing 200/3 in a 6-significant digit computer that chops the last significant digit?

2. What is the round off error in representing 200/3 in a 6-significant digit computer that rounds off the last significant digit?

3. What is the truncation error in the calculation of the $f'(x)$ that uses the approximation

$$f'(x) \approx \frac{f(x + \Delta x) - f(x)}{\Delta x}$$

for

$$f(x) = x^3, \quad \Delta x = 0.4, \text{ and } x = 5.$$

4. What is the truncation error in the calculation of $\sin(\pi/2)$ if only first five terms of the Maclaurin series are used for the calculation? Ignore the round off error in your calculations.

$$\sin(x) = x - \frac{x^3}{3!} + \frac{x^5}{5!} - \frac{x^7}{7!} + \ldots \ldots$$

5.   The integral $\int_{3}^{9} x^2 dx$ can be calculated approximately by finding the area of the four

rectangles as shown in Figure 1.   What is the truncation error due to this approximation?

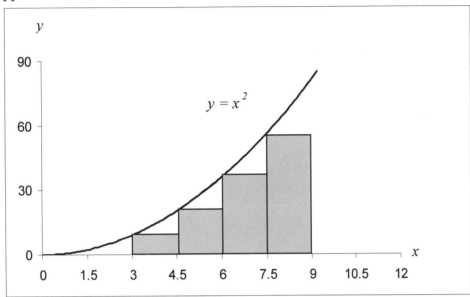

Figure 2 Plot of $y = x^2$ showing the approximate area under the curve from $x = 3$ to $x = 9$ using four rectangles.

6.   Below is the data given for thermal expansion coefficient of steel as a function of temperature.

Temperature	Instantaneous Thermal Expansion Coefficient
$^\circ F$	μ in/in$^\circ$F
80	6.47
60	6.36
40	6.24
20	6.12
0	6.00
-20	5.86
-40	5.72
-60	5.58
-80	5.43
-100	5.28
-120	5.09
-140	4.91
-160	4.72
-180	4.52
-200	4.30

-220	4.08
-240	3.83
-260	3.58
-280	3.33
-300	3.07
-320	2.76
-340	2.45

Regression is used to come up with a simple formula – a second order polynomial to relate the coefficient of thermal expansion coefficient of steel as a function of temperature. The formula given by MS Excel using default settings gives the formula as shown in Figure 3.

a) What is the value of the thermal expansion coefficient at $T = -300$, -200, -100, 0 and $100\,^\circ\mathrm{F}$? Compare these values with those given in the table above.

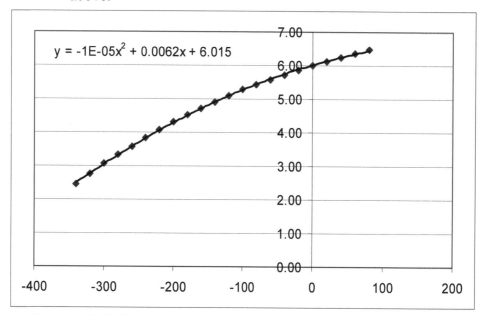

$$y = -1\mathrm{E}\text{-}05x^2 + 0.0062x + 6.015$$

Figure 3 default trend line given by excel

b) Now the default settings for the trend line (Figure 4) are changed to scientific format with four significant digits. What is the value of the thermal expansion coefficient at $T = -300$, -200, -100, 0 and $100\,^\circ\mathrm{F}$? Compare these values with those given in the table above. Do you get different answers in part (a) and part (b)? What do you attribute this difference to?

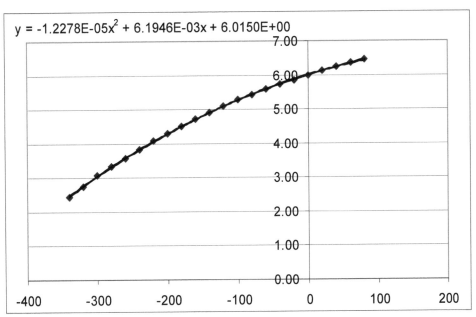

Figure 4 Trend line given by Excel using scientific format.

Chapter 01.04
Binary Representation of Numbers

After reading this chapter, you should be able to:

1. *convert a base-10 real number to its binary representation,*
2. *convert a binary number to an equivalent base-10 number.*

In everyday life, we use a number system with a base of 10. For example, look at the number 257.56. Each digit in 257.56 has a value of 0 through 9 and has a place value. It can be written as

$$257.76 = 2 \times 10^2 + 5 \times 10^1 + 7 \times 10^0 + 7 \times 10^{-1} + 6 \times 10^{-2}$$

In a binary system, we have a similar system where the base is made of only two digits 0 and 1. So it is a base 2 system. A number like (1011.0011) in base-2 represents the decimal number as

$$(1011.0011)_2 = \left((1 \times 2^3 + 0 \times 2^2 + 1 \times 2^1 + 1 \times 2^0) + (0 \times 2^{-1} + 0 \times 2^{-2} + 1 \times 2^{-3} + 1 \times 2^{-4})\right)_{10}$$
$$= 11.1875$$

in the decimal system.

To understand the binary system, we need to be able to convert binary numbers to decimal numbers and vice-versa.

We have already seen an example of how binary numbers are converted to decimal numbers. Let us see how we can convert a decimal number to a binary number. For example take the decimal number 11.1875. First, look at the integer part: 11.

1. Divide 11 by 2. This gives a quotient of 5 and a remainder of 1. Since the remainder is 1, $a_0 = 1$.
2. Divide the quotient 5 by 2. This gives a quotient of 2 and a remainder of 1. Since the remainder is 1, $a_1 = 1$.
3. Divide the quotient 2 by 2. This gives a quotient of 1 and a remainder of 0. Since the remainder is 0, $a_2 = 0$.
4. Divide the quotient 1 by 2. This gives a quotient of 0 and a remainder of 1. Since the remainder is , $a_3 = 1$.

Since the quotient now is 0, the process is stopped. The above steps are summarized in Table 1.

Table 1 Converting a base-10 integer to binary representation.

	Quotient	Remainder
11/2	5	$1 = a_0$
5/2	2	$1 = a_1$
2/2	1	$0 = a_2$
1/2	0	$1 = a_3$

Hence

$$(11)_{10} = (a_3 a_2 a_1 a_0)_2$$
$$= (1011)_2$$

For any integer, the algorithm for finding the binary equivalent is given in the flow chart on the next page.

Now let us look at the decimal part, that is, 0.1875.

1. Multiply 0.1875 by 2. This gives 0.375. The number before the decimal is 0 and the number after the decimal is 0.375. Since the number before the decimal is 0, $a_{-1} = 0$.

2. Multiply the number after the decimal, that is, 0.375 by 2. This gives 0.75. The number before the decimal is 0 and the number after the decimal is 0.75. Since the number before the decimal is 0, $a_{-2} = 0$.

3. Multiply the number after the decimal, that is, 0.75 by 2. This gives 1.5. The number before the decimal is 1 and the number after the decimal is 0.5. Since the number before the decimal is 1, $a_{-3} = 1$.

4. Multiply the number after the decimal, that is, 0.5 by 2. This gives 1.0. The number before the decimal is 1 and the number after the decimal is 0. Since the number before the decimal is 1, $a_{-4} = 1$.

Since the number after the decimal is 0, the conversion is complete. The above steps are summarized in Table 2.

Table 2. Converting a base-10 fraction to binary representation.

	Number	Number after decimal	Number before decimal
0.1875×2	0.375	0.375	$0 = a_{-1}$
0.375×2	0.75	0.75	$0 = a_{-2}$
0.75×2	1.5	0.5	$1 = a_{-3}$
0.5×2	1.0	0.0	$1 = a_{-4}$

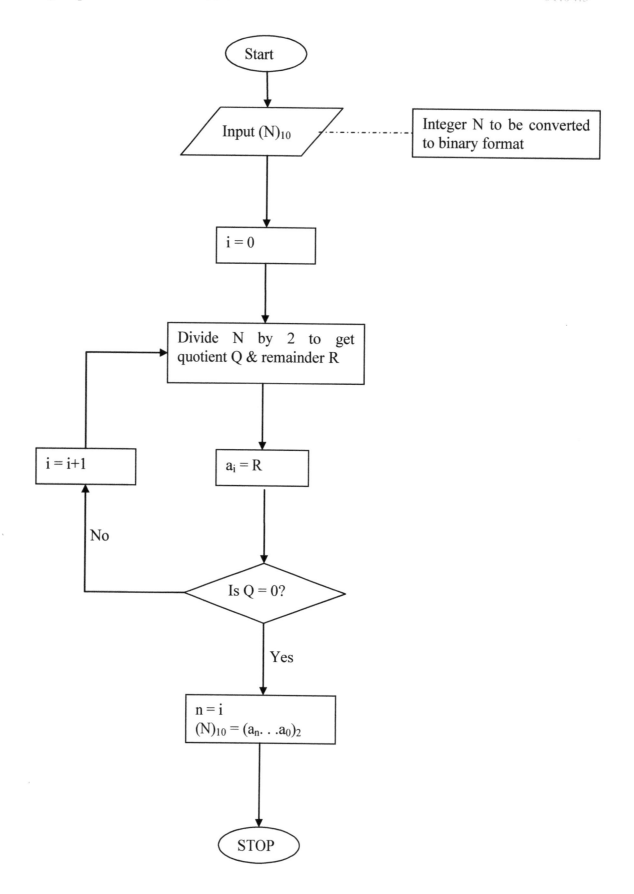

Hence

$$(0.1875)_{10} = (a_{-1}a_{-2}a_{-3}a_{-4})_2$$
$$= (0.0011)_2$$

The algorithm for any fraction is given in a flowchart on the next page.
Having calculated

$$(11)_{10} = (1011)_2$$

and

$$(0.1875)_{10} = (0.0011)_2,$$

we have

$$(11.1875)_{10} = (1011.0011)_2.$$

In the above example, when we were converting the fractional part of the number, we were left with 0 after the decimal number and used that as a place to stop. In many cases, we are never left with a 0 after the decimal number. For example, finding the binary equivalent of 0.3 is summarized in Table 3.

Table 3. Converting a base-10 fraction to approximate binary representation.

	Number	Number after decimal	Number before decimal
0.3×2	0.6	0.6	$0 = a_{-1}$
0.6×2	1.2	0.2	$1 = a_{-2}$
0.2×2	0.4	0.4	$0 = a_{-3}$
0.4×2	0.8	0.8	$0 = a_{-4}$
0.8×2	1.6	0.6	$1 = a_{-5}$

As you can see the process will never end. In this case, the number can only be approximated in binary format, that is,

$$(0.3)_{10} \approx (a_{-1}a_{-2}a_{-3}a_{-4}a_{-5})_2 = (0.01001)_2$$

Q: But what is the mathematics behinds this process of converting a decimal number to binary format?
A: Let z be the decimal number written as

$$z = x.y$$

where

x is the integer part and y is the fractional part.

We want to find the binary equivalent of x. So we can write

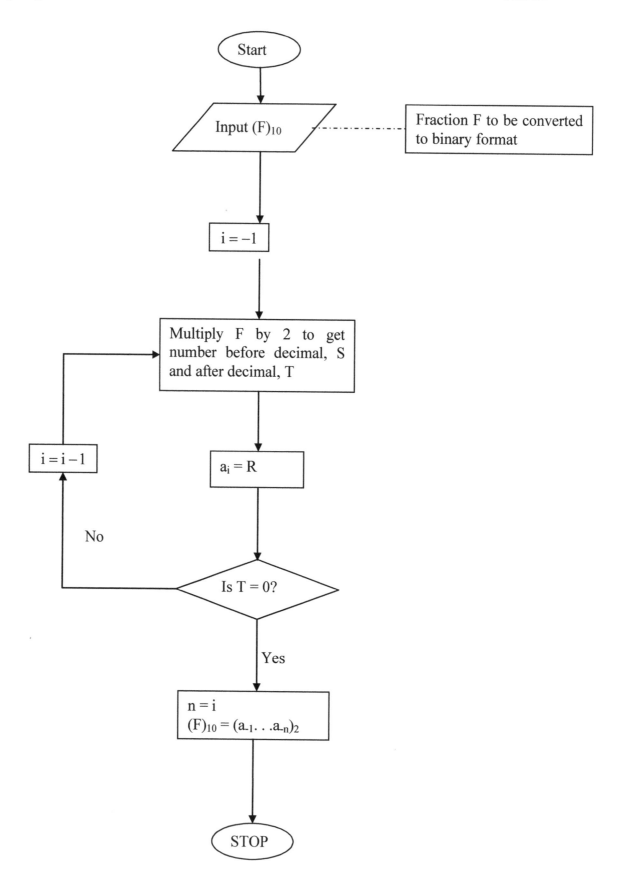

$$x = a_n 2^n + a_{n-1} 2^{n-1} + \ldots + a_0 2^0$$

If we can now find $a_0, \ldots, a_n$ in the above equation then

$$(x)_{10} = (a_n a_{n-1} \ldots a_0)_2$$

We now want to find the binary equivalent of y. So we can write

$$y = b_{-1} 2^{-1} + b_{-2} 2^{-2} + \ldots + b_{-m} 2^{-m}$$

If we can now find $b_{-1}, \ldots, b_{-m}$ in the above equation then

$$(y)_{10} = (b_{-1} b_{-2} \ldots b_{-m})_2$$

Let us look at this using the same example as before.

Example 1

Convert $(11.1875)_{10}$ to base 2.

Solution

To convert $(11)_{10}$ to base 2, what is the highest power of 2 that is part of 11. That power is 3, as $2^3 = 8$ to give

$$11 = 2^3 + 3$$

What is the highest power of 2 that is part of 3. That power is 1, as $2^1 = 2$ to give

$$3 = 2^1 + 1$$

So

$$11 = 2^3 + 3 = 2^3 + 2^1 + 1$$

What is the highest power of 2 that is part of 1. That power is 0, as $2^0 = 1$ to give

$$1 = 2^0$$

Hence

$$(11)_{10} = 2^3 + 2^1 + 1 = 2^3 + 2^1 + 2^0 = 1 \times 2^3 + 0 \times 2^2 + 1 \times 2^1 + 1 \times 2^0 = (1011)_2$$

To convert $(0.1875)_{10}$ to the base 2, we proceed as follows. What is the smallest negative power of 2 that is less than or equal to 0.1875. That power is -3 as $2^{-3} = 0.125$.
So

$$0.1875 = 2^{-3} + 0.0625$$

What is the next smallest negative power of 2 that is less than or equal to 0.0625. That power is -4 as $2^{-4} = 0.0625$.
So

$$0.1875 = 2^{-3} + 2^{-4}$$

Hence

$$(0.1875)_{10} = 2^{-3} + 0.0625 = 2^{-3} + 2^{-4} = 0 \times 2^{-1} + 0 \times 2^{-2} + 1 \times 2^{-3} + 1 \times 2^{-4} = (0.0011)_2$$

Since

$$(11)_{10} = (1011)_2$$

and

$$(0.1875)_{10} = (0.0011)_2$$

we get

$$(11.1875)_{10} = (1011.0011)_2$$

Can you show this algebraically for any general number?

Example 2

Convert $(13.875)_{10}$ to base 2.

Solution

For $(13)_{10}$, conversion to binary format is shown in Table 4.

Table 4. Conversion of base-10 integer to binary format.

	Quotient	Remainder
13/2	6	$1 = a_0$
6/2	3	$0 = a_1$
3/2	1	$1 = a_2$
1/2	0	$1 = a_3$

So

$$(13)_{10} = (1101)_2 .$$

Conversion of $(0.875)_{10}$ to binary format is shown in Table 5.

Table 5. Converting a base-10 fraction to binary representation.

	Number	Number after decimal	Number before decimal
0.875×2	1.75	0.75	$1 = a_{-1}$
0.75×2	1.5	0.5	$1 = a_{-2}$
0.5×2	1.0	0.0	$1 = a_{-3}$

So

$$(0.875)_{10} = (0.111)_2$$

Hence

$$(13.875)_{10} = (1101.111)_2$$

INTRODUCTION TO NUMERICAL METHODS	
Topic	Binary representation of number
Summary	Textbook notes on binary representation of numbers
Major	General Engineering
Authors	Autar Kaw
Date	April 29, 2010
Web Site	http://numericalmethods.eng.usf.edu

Multiple-Choice Test

Chapter 01.04
Binary Representation

1. $(25)_{10} = (?)_2$
   - (A) 100110
   - (B) 10011
   - (C) 11001
   - (D) 110010

2. $(1101)_2 = (?)_{10}$
   - (A) 3
   - (B) 13
   - (C) 15
   - (D) 26

3. $(25.375)_{10} = (?.?)_2$
   - (A) 100110.011
   - (B) 11001.011
   - (C) 10011.0011
   - (D) 10011.110

4. Representing $\sqrt{2}$ in a fixed point register with 2 bits for the integer part and 3 bits for the fractional part gives a round-off error of most nearly
   - (A) -0.085709
   - (B) 0.0392
   - (C) 0.1642
   - (D) 0.2892

5. An engineer working for the Department of Defense is writing a program that transfers non-negative real numbers to integer format. To avoid overflow problems, the maximum non-negative integer that can be represented in a 5-bit integer word is
   - (A) 16
   - (B) 31
   - (C) 63
   - (D) 64

6.   For a numerically controlled machine, integers need to be stored in a memory location. The minimum number of bits needed for an integer word to represent all integers between 0 and 1024 is

(A) 8
(B) 9
(C) 10
(D) 11

Complete solution

Problem Set

Chapter 01.04
Binary Representation

1. Convert the following
    a) $(19)_{10} = (?)_2$
    b) $(75)_{10} = (?)_2$

2. Convert the following
    a) $(110111)_2 = (?)_{10}$
    b) $(11001)_2 = (?)_{10}$

3. Convert the following
    a) $(0.375)_{10} = (?)_2$
    b) $(0.075)_{10} = (?)_2$

4. Convert the following
    a) $(0.110001)_2 = (0.?)_{10}$
    b) $(0.0111)_2 = (0.?)_{10}$

5. Convert the following
    a) $(19.375)_{10} = (?.?)_2$
    b) $(75.075)_{10} = (?.?)_2$

6. Convert the following
    a) $(110111.110001)_2 = (?.?)_{10}$
    b) $(11001.0111)_2 = (?.?)_{10}$

Chapter 01.05
Floating Point Representation

After reading this chapter, you should be able to:

1. *convert a base-10 number to a binary floating point representation,*
2. *convert a binary floating point number to its equivalent base-10 number,*
3. *understand the IEEE-754 specifications of a floating point representation in a typical computer,*
4. *calculate the machine epsilon of a representation.*

Consider an old time cash register that would ring any purchase between 0 and 999.99 units of money. Note that there are five (not six) working spaces in the cash register (the decimal number is shown just for clarification).

Q: How will the smallest number 0 be represented?
A: The number 0 will be represented as

0	0	0	.	0	0

Q: How will the largest number 999.99 be represented?
A: The number 999.99 will be represented as

9	9	9	.	9	9

Q: Now look at any typical number between 0 and 999.99, such as 256.78. How would it be represented?
A: The number 256.78 will be represented as

2	5	6	.	7	8

Q: What is the smallest change between consecutive numbers?
A: It is 0.01, like between the numbers 256.78 and 256.79.

Q: What amount would one pay for an item, if it costs 256.789?
A: The amount one would pay would be rounded off to 256.79 or chopped to 256.78. In either case, the maximum error in the payment would be less than 0.01.

Q: What magnitude of relative errors would occur in a transaction?
A: Relative error for representing small numbers is going to be high, while for large numbers the relative error is going to be small.

For example, for 256.786, rounding it off to 256.79 accounts for a round-off error of $256.786 - 256.79 = -0.004$. The relative error in this case is

$$\varepsilon_t = \frac{-0.004}{256.786} \times 100$$
$$= -0.001558\%.$$

For another number, 3.546, rounding it off to 3.55 accounts for the same round-off error of $3.546 - 3.55 = -0.004$. The relative error in this case is

$$\varepsilon_t = \frac{-0.004}{3.546} \times 100$$
$$= -0.11280\%.$$

Q: If I am interested in keeping relative errors of similar magnitude for the range of numbers, what alternatives do I have?

A: To keep the relative error of similar order for all numbers, one may use a floating-point representation of the number. For example, in floating-point representation, a number

256.78 is written as $+2.5678 \times 10^2$,

0.003678 is written as $+3.678 \times 10^{-3}$, and

-256.789 is written as -2.56789×10^2.

The general representation of a number in base-10 format is given as

$$sign \times mantissa \times 10^{exponent}$$

or for a number y,

$$y = \sigma \times m \times 10^e$$

Where

σ = sign of the number, +1 or -1

m = mantissa, $1 \le m < 10$

e = integer exponent (also called ficand)

Let us go back to the example where we have five spaces available for a number. Let us also limit ourselves to positive numbers with positive exponents for this example. If we use the same five spaces, then let us use four for the mantissa and the last one for the exponent. So the smallest number that can be represented is 1 but the largest number would be 9.999×10^9. By using the floating-point representation, what we lose in accuracy, we gain in the range of numbers that can be represented. For our example, the maximum number represented changed from 999.99 to 9.999×10^9.

What is the error in representing numbers in the scientific format? Take the previous example of 256.78. It would be represented as 2.568×10^2 and in the five spaces as

| 2 | 5 | 6 | 8 | 2 |

Another example, the number 576329.78 would be represented as 5.763×10^5 and in five spaces as

| 5 | 7 | 6 | 3 | 5 |

So, how much error is caused by such representation. In representing 256.78, the round off error created is $256.78 - 256.8 = -0.02$, and the relative error is

$$\varepsilon_t = \frac{-0.02}{256.78} \times 100 = -0.0077888\%,$$

In representing 576329.78, the round off error created is $576329.78 - 5.763 \times 10^5 = 29.78$, and the relative error is

$$\varepsilon_t = \frac{29.78}{576329.78} \times 100 = 0.0051672\%.$$

What you are seeing now is that although the errors are large for large numbers, but the relative errors are of the same order for both large and small numbers.

Q: How does this floating-point format relate to binary format?
A: A number y would be written as

$$y = \sigma \times m \times 2^e$$

Where

$\sigma =$ sign of number (negative or positive – use 0 for positive and 1 for negative),
$m =$ mantissa, $(1)_2 \le m < (10)_2$, that is, $(1)_{10} \le m < (2)_{10}$, and
$e =$ integer exponent.

Example 1

Represent $(54.75)_{10}$ in floating point binary format. Assuming that the number is written to a hypothetical word that is 9 bits long where the first bit is used for the sign of the number, the second bit for the sign of the exponent, the next four bits for the mantissa, and the next three bits for the exponent,

Solution

$$(54.75)_{10} = (110110.11)_2 = (1.1011011)_2 \times 2^{(5)_{10}}$$

The exponent 5 is equivalent in binary format as

$$(5)_{10} = (101)_2$$

Hence

$$(54.75)_{10} = (1.1011011)_2 \times 2^{(101)_2}$$

The sign of the number is positive, so the bit for the sign of the number will have zero in it.

$$\sigma = 0$$

The sign of the exponent is positive. So the bit for the sign of the exponent will have zero in it.

The mantissa

$$m = 1011$$

(There are only 4 places for the mantissa, and the leading 1 is not stored as it is always expected to be there), and

the exponent

$$e = 101.$$

we have the representation as

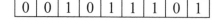

| 0 | 0 | 1 | 0 | 1 | 1 | 1 | 0 | 1 |

Example 2

What number does the below given floating point format

0	1	1	0	1	1	1	1	0

represent in base-10 format. Assume a hypothetical 9-bit word, where the first bit is used for the sign of the number, second bit for the sign of the exponent, next four bits for the mantissa and next three for the exponent.

Solution

Given

Bit Representation	Part of Floating point number
0	Sign of number
1	Sign of exponent
1011	Magnitude of mantissa
110	Magnitude of exponent

The first bit is 0, so the number is positive.
The second bit is 1, so the exponent is negative.
The next four bits, 1011, are the magnitude of the mantissa, so

$$m = (1.1011)_2 = \left(1 \times 2^0 + 1 \times 2^{-1} + 0 \times 2^{-2} + 1 \times 2^{-3} + 1 \times 2^{-4}\right)_{10} = (1.6875)_{10}$$

The last three bits, 110, are the magnitude of the exponent, so

$$e = (110)_2 = \left(1 \times 2^2 + 1 \times 2^1 + 0 \times 2^0\right)_{10} = (6)_{10}$$

The number in binary format then is

$$(1.1011)_2 \times 2^{-(110)_2}$$

The number in base-10 format is

$$= 1.6875 \times 2^{-6}$$
$$= 0.026367$$

Example 3

A machine stores floating-point numbers in a hypothetical 10-bit binary word. It employs the first bit for the sign of the number, the second one for the sign of the exponent, the next four for the exponent, and the last four for the magnitude of the mantissa.

    a) Find how 0.02832 will be represented in the floating-point 10-bit word.
    b) What is the decimal equivalent of the 10-bit word representation of part (a)?

Solution

a) For the number, we have the integer part as 0 and the fractional part as 0.02832
Let us first find the binary equivalent of the integer part

    Integer part $(0)_{10} = (0)_2$

Now we find the binary equivalent of the fractional part

    Fractional part: $.02832 \times 2$

                           0.05664×2

                           0.11328×2

                           0.22656×2

$$0.45312 \times 2$$
$$0.90624 \times 2$$
$$1.81248 \times 2$$
$$1.62496 \times 2$$
$$1.24992 \times 2$$
$$0.49984 \times 2$$
$$0.99968 \times 2$$
$$1.99936$$

Hence

$$(0.02832)_{10} \cong (0.00000111001)_2$$
$$= (1.11001)_2 \times 2^{-6}$$
$$\cong (1.1100)_2 \times 2^{-6}$$

The binary equivalent of exponent is found as follows

	Quotient	Remainder
6/2	3	$0 = a_0$
3/2	1	$1 = a_1$
1/2	0	$1 = a_2$

So

$$(6)_{10} = (110)_2$$

So

$$(0.02832)_{10} = (1.1100)_2 \times 2^{-(110)_2}$$
$$= (1.1100)_2 \times 2^{-(0110)_2}$$

Part of Floating point number	Bit Representation
Sign of number is positive	0
Sign of exponent is negative	1
Magnitude of the exponent	0110
Magnitude of mantissa	1100

The ten-bit representation bit by bit is

0	1	0	1	1	0	1	1	0	0

b) Converting the above floating point representation from part (a) to base 10 by following Example 2 gives

$$(1.1100)_2 \times 2^{-(0110)_2}$$
$$= \left(1 \times 2^0 + 1 \times 2^{-1} + 1 \times 2^{-2} + 0 \times 2^{-3} + 0 \times 2^{-4}\right) \times 2^{-\left(0 \times 2^3 + 1 \times 2^2 + 1 \times 2^1 + 0 \times 2^0\right)}$$
$$= (1.75)_{10} \times 2^{-(6)_{10}}$$
$$= 0.02734375$$

Q: How do you determine the accuracy of a floating-point representation of a number?

A: The machine epsilon, ϵ_{mach} is a measure of the accuracy of a floating point representation and is found by calculating the difference between 1 and the next number that can be represented. For example, assume a 10-bit hypothetical computer where the first bit is used for the sign of the number, the second bit for the sign of the exponent, the next four bits for the exponent and the next four for the mantissa.

We represent 1 as

0	0	0	0	0	0	0	0	0	0

and the next higher number that can be represented is

0	0	0	0	0	0	0	0	0	1

The difference between the two numbers is

$$(1.0001)_2 \times 2^{(0000)_2} - (1.0000)_2 \times 2^{(0000)_2}$$
$$= (0.0001)_2$$
$$= (1 \times 2^{-4})_{10}$$
$$= (0.0625)_{10}.$$

The machine epsilon is

$$\epsilon_{mach} = 0.0625.$$

The machine epsilon, ϵ_{mach} is also simply calculated as two to the negative power of the number of bits used for mantissa. As far as determining accuracy, machine epsilon, ϵ_{mach} is an upper bound of the magnitude of relative error that is created by the approximate representation of a number (See Example 4).

Example 4

A machine stores floating-point numbers in a hypothetical 10-bit binary word. It employs the first bit for the sign of the number, the second one for the sign of the exponent, the next four for the exponent, and the last four for the magnitude of the mantissa. Confirm that the magnitude of the relative true error that results from approximate representation of 0.02832 in the 10-bit format (as found in previous example) is less than the machine epsilon.

Solution

From Example 2, the ten-bit representation of 0.02832 bit-by-bit is

0	1	0	1	1	0	1	1	0	0

Again from Example 2, converting the above floating point representation to base-10 gives

$$(1.1100)_2 \times 2^{-(0110)_2}$$
$$= (1.75)_{10} \times 2^{-(6)_{10}}$$
$$= (0.02734375)_{10}$$

The absolute relative true error between the number 0.02832 and its approximate representation 0.02734375 is

$$|\varepsilon_t| = \left| \frac{0.02832 - 0.02734375}{0.02832} \right|$$
$$= 0.034472$$

which is less than the machine epsilon for a computer that uses 4 bits for mantissa, that is,

$$\varepsilon_{mach} = 2^{-4}$$
$$= 0.0625$$

Q: How are numbers actually represented in floating point in a real computer?

A: In an actual typical computer, a real number is stored as per the IEEE-754 (Institute of Electrical and Electronics Engineers) floating-point arithmetic format. To keep the discussion short and simple, let us point out the salient features of the single precision format.

- A single precision number uses 32 bits.
- A number y is represented as

$$y = \sigma \times \left(1.a_1 a_2 \cdots a_{23}\right) \cdot 2^e$$

where

σ = sign of the number (positive or negative)

a_i = entries of the mantissa, can be only 0 or 1, $i = 1,..,23$

e = the exponent

Note the 1 before the radix point.

- The first bit represents the sign of the number (0 for positive number and 1 for a negative number).
- The next eight bits represent the exponent. Note that there is no separate bit for the sign of the exponent. The sign of the exponent is taken care of by normalizing by adding 127 to the actual exponent. For example in the previous example, the exponent was 6. It would be stored as the binary equivalent of $127 + 6 = 133$. Why is 127 and not some other number added to the actual exponent? Because in eight bits the largest integer that can be represented is $(11111111)_2 = 255$, and halfway of 255 is 127. This allows negative and positive exponents to be represented equally. The normalized (also called biased) exponent has the range from 0 to 255, and hence the exponent e has the range of $-127 \le e \le 128$.
- If instead of using the biased exponent, let us suppose we still used eight bits for the exponent but used one bit for the sign of the exponent and seven bits for the exponent magnitude. In seven bits, the largest integer that can be represented is $(1111111)_2 = 127$ in which case the exponent e range would have been smaller, that is, $-127 \le e \le 127$. By biasing the exponent, the unnecessary representation of a negative zero and positive zero exponent (which are the same) is also avoided.
- Actually, the biased exponent range used in the IEEE-754 format is not 0 to 255, but 1 to 254. Hence, exponent e has the range of $-126 \le e \le 127$. So what are $e = -127$ and $e = 128$ used for? If $e = 128$ and all the mantissa entries are zeros, the number is $\pm\infty$ (the sign of infinity is governed by the sign bit), if $e = 128$ and the mantissa entries are not zero, the number being represented is Not a Number (NaN). Because of the leading 1 in the floating point representation, the number zero cannot be represented exactly. That is why the number zero (0) is represented by $e = -127$ and all the mantissa entries being zero.
- The next twenty-three bits are used for the mantissa.
- The largest number by magnitude that is represented by this format is

$$\left(1 \times 2^0 + 1 \times 2^{-1} + 1 \times 2^{-2} + \cdots + 1 \times 2^{-22} + 1 \times 2^{-23}\right) \times 2^{127} = 3.40 \times 10^{38}$$

The smallest number by magnitude that is represented, other than zero, is

$$\left(1 \times 2^0 + 0 \times 2^{-1} + 0 \times 2^{-2} + \cdots + 0 \times 2^{-22} + 0 \times 2^{-23}\right) \times 2^{-126} = 1.18 \times 10^{-38}$$

- Since 23 bits are used for the mantissa, the machine epsilon,

$$\in_{mach} = 2^{-23}$$
$$= 1.19 \times 10^{-7}.$$

Q: How are numbers represented in floating point in double precision in a computer?

A: In double precision IEEE-754 format, a real number is stored in 64 bits.
- The first bit is used for the sign,
- the next 11 bits are used for the exponent, and
- the rest of the bits, that is 52, are used for mantissa.

Can you find in double precision the
- range of the biased exponent,
- smallest number that can be represented,
- largest number that can be represented, and
- machine epsilon?

INTRODUCTION TO NUMERICAL METHODS	
Topic	Floating Point Representation
Summary	Textbook notes on floating point representation
Major	General Engineering
Authors	Autar Kaw
Date	December 23, 2009
Web Site	http://numericalmethods.eng.usf.edu

Multiple-Choice Test

Chapter 01.05
Floating Point Representation

1. A hypothetical computer stores real numbers in floating point format in 8-bit words. The first bit is used for the sign of the number, the second bit for the sign of the exponent, the next two bits for the magnitude of the exponent, and the next four bits for the magnitude of the mantissa. The number $e \cong 2.718$ in the 8-bit format is
    (A)   00010101
    (B)   00011010
    (C)   00010011
    (D)   00101010

2. A hypothetical computer stores real numbers in floating point format in 8-bit words. The first bit is used for the sign of the number, the second bit for the sign of the exponent, the next two bits for the magnitude of the exponent, and the next four bits for the magnitude of the mantissa. The number that $(10100111)_2$ represented in the above given 8-bit format is
    (A)   -5.75
    (B)   -2.875
    (C)   -1.75
    (D)   -0.359375

3. A hypothetical computer stores floating point numbers in 8-bit words. The first bit is used for the sign of the number, the second bit for the sign of the exponent, the next two bits for the magnitude of the exponent, and the next four bits for the magnitude of the mantissa. The machine epsilon is most nearly
    (A) 2^{-8}
    (B) 2^{-4}
    (C) 2^{-3}
    (D) 2^{-2}

4. A machine stores floating point numbers in 7-bit word. The first bit is used for the sign of the number, the next three for the biased exponent and the next three for the magnitude of the mantissa. The number $(0010110)_2$ represented in base-10 is
    (A)   0.375
    (B)   0.875
    (C)   1.5
    (D)   3.5

5.   A machine stores floating point numbers in 7-bit words. The first bit is stored for the sign of the number, the next three for the biased exponent and the next three for the magnitude of the mantissa. You are asked to represent 33.35 in the above word. The error you will get in this case would be
        (A)   underflow
        (B)   overflow
        (C)   NaN
        (D)   No error will be registered.

6.   A hypothetical computer stores floating point numbers in 9-bit words. The first bit is used for the sign of the number, the second bit for the sign of the exponent, the next three bits for the magnitude of the exponent, and the next four bits for the magnitude of the mantissa. Every second, the error between 0.1 and its binary representation in the 9-bit word is accumulated. The accumulated error after one day most nearly is
        (A)   0.002344
        (B)   20.25
        (C)   202.5
        (D)   8640

Complete solution

Problem Set

Chapter 01.05
Floating Point Representation

1. A hypothetical computer stores real numbers in floating point format in 8-bit words. The first bit is used for the sign of the number, the second bit for the sign of the exponent, the next two bits for the magnitude of the exponent, and the next four bits for the magnitude of the mantissa. Represent 3.1415 in the 8-bit format.

2. A hypothetical computer stores real numbers in floating point format in 8-bit words. The first bit is used for the sign of the number, the second bit for the sign of the exponent, the next two bits for the magnitude of the exponent, and the next four bits for the magnitude of the mantissa. What number does 10101111 represent in the above given 8-bit format?

3. A hypothetical computer stores real numbers in floating point format in 10-bit words. The first bit is used for the sign of the number, the second bit for the sign of the exponent, the next three bits for the magnitude of the exponent, and the next five bits for the magnitude of the mantissa. Represent -0.0456 in the 10-bit format.

4. A hypothetical computer stores real numbers in floating point format in 10-bit words. The first bit is used for the sign of the number, the second bit for the sign of the exponent, the next three bits for the magnitude of the exponent, and the next five bits for the magnitude of the mantissa. What number does 1011010011 represent in the above given 10-bit format?

5. A machine stores floating point numbers in 7-bit words. Employ first bit for the sign of the number, second one for the sign of the exponent, next two for the magnitude of the exponent, and the last three for the magnitude of the mantissa.
   a) By magnitude, what are the smallest negative and positive numbers in the system?
   b) By magnitude, what are the largest negative and positive numbers in the system?
   c) What is the machine epsilon?
   d) Represent e^1 in the 7-bit format.
   e) Represent 3.623 in the 7-bit format.
   f) What is the next higher number, x_2 after $x_1 = 0\ 1\ 1\ 0\ 1\ 1\ 0$ in the 7-bit format.
   g) Find $\left| \dfrac{x_2 - x_1}{x_1} \right|$ from part (f) and compare with the machine epsilon.

Chapter 01.06
Propagation of Errors

If a calculation is made with numbers that are not exact, then the calculation itself will have an error. How do the errors in each individual number propagate through the calculations. Let's look at the concept via some examples.

Example 1

Find the bounds for the propagation error in adding two numbers. For example if one is calculating $X + Y$ where
$$X = 1.5 \pm 0.05,$$
$$Y = 3.4 \pm 0.04 \ .$$

Solution

By looking at the numbers, the maximum possible value of X and Y are
$$X = 1.55 \text{ and } Y = 3.44$$
Hence
$$X + Y = 1.55 + 3.44 = 4.99$$
is the maximum value of $X + Y$.
The minimum possible value of X and Y are
$$X = 1.45 \text{ and } Y = 3.36.$$
Hence
$$X + Y = 1.45 + 3.36$$
$$= 4.81$$
is the minimum value of $X + Y$.
Hence
$$4.81 \leq X + Y \leq 4.99.$$

One can find similar intervals of the bound for the other arithmetic operations of $X - Y, X * Y,$ and X / Y. What if the evaluations we are making are function evaluations instead? How do we find the value of the propagation error in such cases.

If f is a function of several variables $X_1, X_2, X_3, \ldots, X_{n-1}, X_n$, then the maximum possible value of the error in f is

$$\Delta f \approx \left| \frac{\partial f}{\partial X_1} \Delta X_1 \right| + \left| \frac{\partial f}{\partial X_2} \Delta X_2 \right| + \ldots + \left| \frac{\partial f}{\partial X_{n-1}} \Delta X_{n-1} \right| + \left| \frac{\partial f}{\partial X_n} \Delta X_n \right|$$

Example 2

The strain in an axial member of a square cross-section is given by

$$\epsilon = \frac{F}{h^2 E}$$

where

F = axial force in the member, N
h = length or width of the cross-section, m
E = Young's modulus, Pa

Given

$F = 72 \pm 0.9$ N
$h = 4 \pm 0.1$ mm
$E = 70 \pm 1.5$ GPa

Find the maximum possible error in the measured strain.

Solution

$$\epsilon = \frac{72}{(4 \times 10^{-3})^2 (70 \times 10^9)}$$

$$= 64.286 \times 10^{-6}$$

$$= 64.286 \mu$$

$$\Delta \epsilon = \left| \frac{\partial \epsilon}{\partial F} \Delta F \right| + \left| \frac{\partial \epsilon}{\partial h} \Delta h \right| + \left| \frac{\partial \epsilon}{\partial E} \Delta E \right|$$

$$\frac{\partial \epsilon}{\partial F} = \frac{1}{h^2 E}$$

$$\frac{\partial \epsilon}{\partial h} = -\frac{2F}{h^3 E}$$

$$\frac{\partial \epsilon}{\partial E} = -\frac{F}{h^2 E^2}$$

$$\Delta E = \left| \frac{1}{h^2 E} \Delta F \right| + \left| \frac{2F}{h^3 E} \Delta h \right| + \left| \frac{F}{h^2 E^2} \Delta E \right|$$

$$= \left| \frac{1}{(4 \times 10^{-3})^2 (70 \times 10^9)} \times 0.9 \right| + \left| \frac{2 \times 72}{(4 \times 10^{-3})^3 (70 \times 10^9)} \times 0.0001 \right|$$

$$+ \left| \frac{72}{(4 \times 10^{-3})^2 (70 \times 10^9)^2} \times 1.5 \times 10^9 \right|$$

$$= 8.0357 \times 10^{-7} + 3.2143 \times 10^{-6} + 1.3776 \times 10^{-6}$$

$$= 5.3955 \times 10^{-6}$$

$$= 5.3955 \mu$$

Hence

$$\epsilon = (64.286 \mu \pm 5.3955 \mu)$$

implying that the axial strain, ϵ is between 58.8905μ and 69.6815μ

Example 3

Subtraction of numbers that are nearly equal can create unwanted inaccuracies. Using the formula for error propagation, show that this is true.

Solution

Let

$$z = x - y$$

Then

$$|\Delta z| = \left| \frac{\partial z}{\partial x} \Delta x \right| + \left| \frac{\partial z}{\partial y} \Delta y \right|$$

$$= |(1)\Delta x| + |(-1)\Delta y|$$

$$= |\Delta x| + |\Delta y|$$

So the absolute relative change is

$$\left| \frac{\Delta z}{z} \right| = \frac{|\Delta x| + |\Delta y|}{|x - y|}$$

As x and y become close to each other, the denominator becomes small and hence create large relative errors.

For example if

$$x = 2 \pm 0.001$$

$$y = 2.003 \pm 0.001$$

$$\left| \frac{\Delta z}{z} \right| = \frac{|0.001| + |0.001|}{|2 - 2.003|}$$

$$= 0.6667$$

$$= 66.67\%$$

INTRODUCTION TO NUMERICAL METHODS	
Topic	Propagation of Errors
Summary	Textbook notes on how errors propagate in arithmetic and function evaluations
Major	All Majors of Engineering
Authors	Autar Kaw
Last Revised	December 23, 2009
Web Site	http://numericalmethods.eng.usf.edu

Multiple-Choice Test

Chapter 01.06
Propagation of Errors

1. If $A = 3.56 \pm 0.05$ and $B = 3.25 \pm 0.04$, the values of $A + B$ are
   (A) $6.81 \le A + B \le 6.90$
   (B) $6.72 \le A + B \le 6.90$
   (C) $6.81 \le A + B \le 6.81$
   (D) $6.71 \le A + B \le 6.91$

2. A number A is correctly rounded to 3.18 from a given number B. Then $|A - B| \le C$, where C is
   (A) 0.005
   (B) 0.01
   (C) 0.18
   (D) 0.09999

3. Two numbers A and B are approximated as C and D, respectively. The relative error in $C \times D$ is given by

   (A) $\left| \left(\dfrac{A-C}{A} \right) \times \left(\dfrac{B-D}{B} \right) \right|$

   (B) $\left| \left(\dfrac{A-C}{A} \right) + \left(\dfrac{B-D}{B} \right) + \left(\dfrac{A-C}{A} \right) \times \left(\dfrac{B-D}{B} \right) \right|$

   (C) $\left| \left(\dfrac{A-C}{A} \right) + \left(\dfrac{B-D}{B} \right) - \left(\dfrac{A-C}{A} \right) \times \left(\dfrac{B-D}{B} \right) \right|$

   (D) $\left(\dfrac{A-C}{A} \right) - \left(\dfrac{B-D}{B} \right)$

4. The formula for normal strain in a longitudinal bar is given by $\epsilon = \dfrac{F}{AE}$ where

   F = normal force applied
   A = cross-sectional area of the bar
   E = Young's modulus

   If $F = 50 \pm 0.5 \, \text{N}$, $A = 0.2 \pm 0.002 \, \text{m}^2$, and $E = 210 \times 10^9 \pm 1 \times 10^9 \, \text{Pa}$, the maximum error in the measurement of strain is
   (A) 10^{-12}
   (B) 2.95×10^{-11}
   (C) 1.22×10^{-9}
   (D) 1.19×10^{-9}

5.   A wooden block is measured to be 60 mm by a ruler and the measurements are considered to be good to 1/4th of a millimeter. Then in the measurement of 60 mm, we have _____ significant digits.
        (A) 0
        (B) 1
        (C) 2
        (D) 3

6.   In the calculation of the volume of a cube of nominal size 5″, the uncertainty in the measurement of each side is 10%. The uncertainty in the measurement of the volume would be
        (A) 5.477%
        (B) 10.00%
        (C) 17.32%
        (D) 30.00%

Complete solution

Chapter 01.07
Taylor Theorem Revisited

After reading this chapter, you should be able to

1. *understand the basics of Taylor's theorem,*
2. *write transcendental and trigonometric functions as Taylor's polynomial,*
3. *use Taylor's theorem to find the values of a function at any point, given the values of the function and all its derivatives at a particular point,*
4. *calculate errors and error bounds of approximating a function by Taylor series, and*
5. *revisit the chapter whenever Taylor's theorem is used to derive or explain numerical methods for various mathematical procedures.*

The use of Taylor series exists in so many aspects of numerical methods that it is imperative to devote a separate chapter to its review and applications. For example, you must have come across expressions such as

$$\cos(x) = 1 - \frac{x^2}{2!} + \frac{x^4}{4!} - \frac{x^6}{6!} + \cdots \tag{1}$$

$$\sin(x) = x - \frac{x^3}{3!} + \frac{x^5}{5!} - \frac{x^7}{7!} + \cdots \tag{2}$$

$$e^x = 1 + x + \frac{x^2}{2!} + \frac{x^3}{3!} + \cdots \tag{3}$$

All the above expressions are actually a special case of Taylor series called the Maclaurin series. Why are these applications of Taylor's theorem important for numerical methods? Expressions such as given in Equations (1), (2) and (3) give you a way to find the approximate values of these functions by using the basic arithmetic operations of addition, subtraction, division, and multiplication.

Example 1

Find the value of $e^{0.25}$ using the first five terms of the Maclaurin series.
Solution

The first five terms of the Maclaurin series for e^x is

$$e^x \approx 1 + x + \frac{x^2}{2!} + \frac{x^3}{3!} + \frac{x^4}{4!}$$

$$e^{0.25} \approx 1 + 0.25 + \frac{0.25^2}{2!} + \frac{0.25^3}{3!} + \frac{0.25^4}{4!}$$

$$= 1.2840$$

The exact value of $e^{0.25}$ up to 5 significant digits is also 1.2840.

But the above discussion and example do not answer our question of what a Taylor series is. Here it is, for a function $f(x)$

$$f(x+h) = f(x) + f'(x)h + \frac{f''(x)}{2!}h^2 + \frac{f'''(x)}{3!}h^3 + \cdots \qquad (4)$$

provided all derivatives of $f(x)$ exist and are continuous between x and $x+h$.

What does this mean in plain English?

As Archimedes would have said (*without the fine print*), "*Give me the value of the function at a single point, and the value of all (first, second, and so on) its derivatives, and I can give you the value of the function at any other point*".

It is very important to note that the Taylor series is not asking for the expression of the function and its derivatives, just the value of the function and its derivatives at a single point.

Now the fine print: Yes, all the derivatives have to exist and be continuous between x (the point where you are) to the point, $x+h$ where you are wanting to calculate the function at. However, if you want to calculate the function approximately by using the nth order Taylor polynomial, then $1^{st}, 2^{nd}, \ldots, n^{th}$ derivatives need to exist and be continuous in the closed interval $[x, x+h]$, while the $(n+1)^{th}$ derivative needs to exist and be continuous in the open interval $(x, x+h)$.

Example 2

Take $f(x) = \sin(x)$, we all know the value of $\sin\left(\frac{\pi}{2}\right) = 1$. We also know the $f'(x) = \cos(x)$ and $\cos\left(\frac{\pi}{2}\right) = 0$. Similarly $f''(x) = -\sin(x)$ and $\sin\left(\frac{\pi}{2}\right) = 1$. In a way, we know the value of $\sin(x)$ and all its derivatives at $x = \frac{\pi}{2}$. We do not need to use any calculators, just plain differential calculus and trigonometry would do. Can you use Taylor series and this information to find the value of $\sin(2)$?

Solution

$$x = \frac{\pi}{2}$$

$$x + h = 2$$

$$h = 2 - x$$

$$= 2 - \frac{\pi}{2}$$

$$= 0.42920$$

So

$$f(x+h) = f(x) + f'(x)h + f''(x)\frac{h^2}{2!} + f'''(x)\frac{h^3}{3!} + f''''(x)\frac{h^4}{4!} + \cdots$$

$$x = \frac{\pi}{2}$$

$$h = 0.42920$$

$$f(x) = \sin(x), \ f\left(\frac{\pi}{2}\right) = \sin\left(\frac{\pi}{2}\right) = 1$$

$$f'(x) = \cos(x), \ f'\left(\frac{\pi}{2}\right) = 0$$

$$f''(x) = -\sin(x), \ f''\left(\frac{\pi}{2}\right) = -1$$

$$f'''(x) = -\cos(x), \ f'''\left(\frac{\pi}{2}\right) = 0$$

$$f''''(x) = \sin(x), \ f''''\left(\frac{\pi}{2}\right) = 1$$

Hence

$$f\left(\frac{\pi}{2}+h\right) = f\left(\frac{\pi}{2}\right) + f'\left(\frac{\pi}{2}\right)h + f''\left(\frac{\pi}{2}\right)\frac{h^2}{2!} + f'''\left(\frac{\pi}{2}\right)\frac{h^3}{3!} + f''''\left(\frac{\pi}{2}\right)\frac{h^4}{4!} + \cdots$$

$$f\left(\frac{\pi}{2}+0.42920\right) = 1 + 0(0.42920) - 1\frac{(0.42920)^2}{2!} + 0\frac{(0.42920)^3}{3!} + 1\frac{(0.42920)^4}{4!} + \cdots$$

$$= 1 + 0 - 0.092106 + 0 + 0.00141393 + \cdots$$

$$\cong 0.90931$$

The value of $\sin(2)$ I get from my calculator is 0.90930 which is very close to the value I just obtained. Now you can get a better value by using more terms of the series. In addition, you can now use the value calculated for $\sin(2)$ coupled with the value of $\cos(2)$ (which can be calculated by Taylor series just like this example or by using the $\sin^2 x + \cos^2 x \equiv 1$ identity) to find value of $\sin(x)$ at some other point. In this way, we can find the value of $\sin(x)$ for any value from $x = 0$ to 2π and then can use the periodicity of $\sin(x)$, that is $\sin(x) = \sin(x + 2n\pi), n = 1, 2, \ldots$ to calculate the value of $\sin(x)$ at any other point.

Example 3

Derive the Maclaurin series of $\sin(x) = x - \dfrac{x^3}{3!} + \dfrac{x^5}{5!} - \dfrac{x^7}{7!} + \cdots$

Solution

In the previous example, we wrote the Taylor series for $\sin(x)$ around the point $x = \dfrac{\pi}{2}$.

Maclaurin series is simply a Taylor series for the point $x = 0$.

$$f(x) = \sin(x), \ f(0) = 0$$

$$f'(x) = \cos(x), \, f'(0) = 1$$
$$f''(x) = -\sin(x), \, f''(0) = 0$$
$$f'''(x) = -\cos(x), \, f'''(0) = -1$$
$$f''''(x) = \sin(x), \, f''''(0) = 0$$
$$f'''''(x) = \cos(x), \, f'''''(0) = 1$$

Using the Taylor series now,

$$f(x+h) = f(x) + f'(x)h + f''(x)\frac{h^2}{2!} + f'''(x)\frac{h^3}{3!} + f''''(x)\frac{h^4}{4} + f'''''(x)\frac{h^5}{5} + \cdots$$

$$f(0+h) = f(0) + f'(0)h + f''(0)\frac{h^2}{2!} + f'''(0)\frac{h^3}{3!} + f''''(0)\frac{h^4}{4} + f'''''(0)\frac{h^5}{5} + \cdots$$

$$f(h) = f(0) + f'(0)h + f''(0)\frac{h^2}{2!} + f'''(0)\frac{h^3}{3!} + f''''(0)\frac{h^4}{4} + f'''''(0)\frac{h^5}{5} + \cdots$$

$$= 0 + 1(h) - 0\frac{h^2}{2!} - 1\frac{h^3}{3!} + 0\frac{h^4}{4} + 1\frac{h^5}{5} + \cdots$$

$$= h - \frac{h^3}{3!} + \frac{h^5}{5!} + \cdots$$

So

$$f(x) = x - \frac{x^3}{3!} + \frac{x^5}{5!} - \cdots$$

$$\sin(x) = x - \frac{x^3}{3!} + \frac{x^5}{5!} - \cdots$$

Example 4

Find the value of $f(6)$ given that $f(4) = 125$, $f'(4) = 74$, $f''(4) = 30$, $f'''(4) = 6$ and all other higher derivatives of $f(x)$ at $x = 4$ are zero.

Solution

$$f(x+h) = f(x) + f'(x)h + f''(x)\frac{h^2}{2!} + f'''(x)\frac{h^3}{3!} + \cdots$$
$$x = 4$$
$$h = 6 - 4$$
$$\quad = 2$$

Since fourth and higher derivatives of $f(x)$ are zero at $x = 4$.

$$f(4+2) = f(4) + f'(4)2 + f''(4)\frac{2^2}{2!} + f'''(4)\frac{2^3}{3!}$$

$$f(6) = 125 + 74(2) + 30\left(\frac{2^2}{2!}\right) + 6\left(\frac{2^3}{3!}\right)$$

$$= 125 + 148 + 60 + 8$$
$$= 341$$

Note that to find $f(6)$ exactly, we only needed the value of the function and all its derivatives at some other point, in this case, $x = 4$. We did not need the expression for the function and all its derivatives. Taylor series application would be redundant if we needed to know the expression for the function, as we could just substitute $x = 6$ in it to get the value of $f(6)$.

Actually the problem posed above was obtained from a known function $f(x) = x^3 + 3x^2 + 2x + 5$ where $f(4) = 125$, $f'(4) = 74$, $f''(4) = 30$, $f'''(4) = 6$, and all other higher derivatives are zero.

Error in Taylor Series

As you have noticed, the Taylor series has infinite terms. Only in special cases such as a finite polynomial does it have a finite number of terms. So whenever you are using a Taylor series to calculate the value of a function, it is being calculated approximately.

The Taylor polynomial of order n of a function $f(x)$ with $(n+1)$ continuous derivatives in the domain $[x, x+h]$ is given by

$$f(x+h) = f(x) + f'(x)h + f''(x)\frac{h^2}{2!} + \cdots + f^{(n)}(x)\frac{h^n}{n!} + R_n(x)$$

where the remainder is given by

$$R_n(x) = \frac{(x-h)^{n+1}}{(n+1)!}f^{(n+1)}(c).$$

where

$$x < c < x+h$$

that is, c is some point in the domain $(x, x+h)$.

Example 5

The Taylor series for e^x at point $x = 0$ is given by

$$e^x = 1 + x + \frac{x^2}{2!} + \frac{x^3}{3!} + \frac{x^4}{4!} + \frac{x^5}{5!} + \cdots$$

a) What is the truncation (true) error in the representation of e^1 if only four terms of the series are used?
b) Use the remainder theorem to find the bounds of the truncation error.
Solution

a) If only four terms of the series are used, then

$$e^x \approx 1 + x + \frac{x^2}{2!} + \frac{x^3}{3!}$$

$$e^1 \approx 1 + 1 + \frac{1^2}{2!} + \frac{1^3}{3!}$$

$$= 2.66667$$

The truncation (true) error would be the unused terms of the Taylor series, which then are

$$E_t = \frac{x^4}{4!} + \frac{x^5}{5!} + \cdots$$

$$= \frac{1^4}{4!} + \frac{1^5}{5!} + \cdots$$

$$\cong 0.0516152$$

b) But is there any way to know the bounds of this error other than calculating it directly? Yes,

$$f(x+h) = f(x) + f'(x)h + \cdots + f^{(n)}(x)\frac{h^n}{n!} + R_n(x)$$

where

$$R_n(x) = \frac{(x-h)^{n+1}}{(n+1)!} f^{(n+1)}(c), \; x < c < x+h, \text{ and}$$

c is some point in the domain $(x, x+h)$. So in this case, if we are using four terms of the Taylor series, the remainder is given by $(x=0, n=3)$

$$R_3(x) = \frac{(0-1)^{3+1}}{(3+1)!} f^{(3+1)}(c)$$

$$= \frac{1}{4!} f^{(4)}(c)$$

$$= \frac{e^c}{24}$$

Since

$$x < c < x+h$$
$$0 < c < 0+1$$
$$0 < c < 1$$

The error is bound between

$$\frac{e^0}{24} < R_3(1) < \frac{e^1}{24}$$

$$\frac{1}{24} < R_3(1) < \frac{e}{24}$$

$$0.041667 < R_3(1) < 0.113261$$

So the bound of the error is less than 0.113261 which does concur with the calculated error of 0.0516152.

Example 6

The Taylor series for e^x at point $x = 0$ is given by

$$e^x = 1 + x + \frac{x^2}{2!} + \frac{x^3}{3!} + \frac{x^4}{4!} + \frac{x^5}{5!} + \cdots$$

As you can see in the previous example that by taking more terms, the error bounds decrease and hence you have a better estimate of e^1. How many terms it would require to get an approximation of e^1 within a magnitude of true error of less than 10^{-6}?

Solution

Using $(n+1)$ terms of the Taylor series gives an error bound of

$$R_n(x) = \frac{(x-h)^{n+1}}{(n+1)!} f^{(n+1)}(c)$$

$$x = 0, h = 1, f(x) = e^x$$

$$R_n(0) = \frac{(0-1)^{n+1}}{(n+1)!} f^{(n+1)}(c)$$

$$= \frac{(-1)^{n+1}}{(n+1)!} e^c$$

Since

$$x < c < x + h$$
$$0 < c < 0 + 1$$
$$0 < c < 1$$
$$\frac{1}{(n+1)!} < |R_n(0)| < \frac{e}{(n+1)!}$$

So if we want to find out how many terms it would require to get an approximation of e^1 within a magnitude of true error of less than 10^{-6},

$$\frac{e}{(n+1)!} < 10^{-6}$$
$$(n+1)! > 10^6 e$$
$$(n+1)! > 10^6 \times 3 \qquad \text{(as we do not know the value of } e \text{ but it is less than 3)}.$$
$$n \geq 9$$

So 9 terms or more will get e^1 within an error of 10^{-6} in its value.

We can do calculations such as the ones given above only for simple functions. To do a similar analysis of how many terms of the series are needed for a specified accuracy for any general function, we can do that based on the concept of absolute relative approximate errors discussed in Chapter 01.02 as follows.

We use the concept of absolute relative approximate error (see Chapter 01.02 for details), which is calculated after each term in the series is added. The maximum value of m, for which the absolute relative approximate error is less than $0.5 \times 10^{2-m}\%$ is the least number of significant digits correct in the answer. It establishes the accuracy of the approximate value of a function without the knowledge of remainder of Taylor series or the true error.

INTRODUCTION TO NUMERICAL METHODS

Topic	Taylor Theorem Revisited
Summary	These are textbook notes on Taylor Series
Major	All engineering majors
Authors	Autar Kaw
Date	April 29, 2010
Web Site	http://numericalmethods.eng.usf.edu

Multiple-Choice Test

Chapter 01.07
Taylors Series Revisited

1. The coefficient of the x^5 term in the Maclaurin polynomial for $\sin(2x)$ is
   - (A) 0
   - (B) 0.0083333
   - (C) 0.016667
   - (D) 0.26667

2. Given $f(3) = 6$, $f'(3) = 8$, $f''(3) = 11$, and that all other higher order derivatives of $f(x)$ are zero at $x = 3$, and assuming the function and all its derivatives exist and are continuous between $x = 3$ and $x = 7$, the value of $f(7)$ is
   - (A) 38.000
   - (B) 79.500
   - (C) 126.00
   - (D) 331.50

3. Given that $y(x)$ is the solution to $\dfrac{dy}{dx} = y^3 + 2$, $y(0) = 3$ the value of $y(0.2)$ from a second order Taylor polynomial written around $x = 0$ is
   - (A) 4.400
   - (B) 8.800
   - (C) 24.46
   - (D) 29.00

4. The series $\displaystyle\sum_{n=0}^{\infty} (-1)^n \frac{x^{2n}}{(2n)!} 4^n$ is a Maclaurin series for the following function
   - (A) $\cos(x)$
   - (B) $\cos(2x)$
   - (C) $\sin(x)$
   - (D) $\sin(2x)$

5. The function

$$erf(x) = \frac{2}{\sqrt{\pi}} \int_0^x e^{-t^2} dt$$

is called the error function. It is used in the field of probability and cannot be calculated exactly for finite values of x. However, one can expand the integrand as a Taylor polynomial and conduct integration. The approximate value of $erf(2.0)$ using the first three terms of the Taylor series around $t = 0$ is

(A) -0.75225
(B) 0.99532
(C) 1.5330
(D) 2.8586

6. Using the remainder of Maclaurin polynomial of nth order for $f(x)$ defined as

$$R_n(x) = \frac{x^{n+1}}{(n+1)!} f^{(n+1)}(c), \quad n \geq 0, \ 0 \leq c \leq x$$

the least order of the Maclaurin polynomial required to get an absolute true error of at most 10^{-6} in the calculation of $\sin(0.1)$ is (do not use the exact value of $\sin(0.1)$ or $\cos(0.1)$ to find the answer, but the knowledge that $|\sin(x)| \leq 1$ and $|\cos(x)| \leq 1$).

(A) 3
(B) 5
(C) 7
(D) 9

Complete solution

Chapter 02.00A

Physical Problem for Differentiation
General Engineering

Problem Statement

A rocket is traveling vertically and expels fuel at a velocity of 2000 m/s at a consumption rate of 2100 kg/s. The initial mass of the rocket is 140,000 kg. If the rocket starts from rest, how can I calculate the acceleration of the rocket at 16 seconds?

Figure 1 A rocket launched into space[1]

[1] Source of rocket picture: NASA Langley Research Center, Office of Education, **edu.larc.nasa.gov/pstp/**

Solution

If

m_0 = initial mass of rocket at $t = 0$ (kg),

q = rate at which fuel is expelled (kg/s),

u = velocity at which the fuel is being expelled (m/s),

then since the fuel is expelled from the rocket, the mass of the rocket keeps decreasing with time. The mass of the rocket, m at anytime, t is

$$m = m_o - qt$$

The forces on the rocket at any time are found by applying Newton's second law of motion. Then

$$\sum F = ma$$
$$uq - mg = ma$$
$$uq - (m_o - qt)g = (m_o - qt)a$$

where

g = acceleration due to gravity $\left(\text{m/s}^2\right)$

$$a = \frac{uq}{m_o - qt} - g$$

$$\frac{dv}{dt} = \frac{uq}{m_o - qt} - g \qquad (1)$$

$$v = -u\log_e\left(m_0 - qt\right) - gt + C$$

Since the rocket starts from rest

$v = 0$ at $t = 0$

$$0 = -u\log_e\left(m_o\right) + C$$

$$C = u\log_e\left(m_o\right)$$

Hence

$$v = -u\log_e\left(m_o - qt\right) - gt + u\log_e\left(m_o\right)$$

$$\frac{dx}{dt} = u\log_e\left(\frac{m_o}{m_o - qt}\right) - gt \qquad (2)$$

$u = 2,000$ m/s

$m_o = 140,000$ kg

$q = 2100$ kg/s

$g = 9.8$ m/s^2

$t_0 = 0\,\text{s}$

$t_1 = 30\,\text{s}$

$$v = 2000\log_e\left(\frac{14\times10^4}{14\times10^4 - 2100t}\right) - 9.8t\,.$$

Can you numerically find the acceleration at $t = 16\,s$? You may say that we do not need numerical or analytical differentiation to calculate the acceleration, as equation (1) directly gives us the acceleration of the rocket at any time. True! We are just doing this as an exercise to illustrate numerical differentiation and we have a true expression of acceleration readily available for comparison with the numerical results.

Questions

1. Find the acceleration of the rocket at $t = 16\,s$.
2. Use different numerical differentiation techniques to find the acceleration at $t = 16\,s$. Compare these results with the exact answer.

DIFFERENTIATION	
Topic	Physical problem
Summary	A physical problem of find the acceleration of a rocket.
Major	General Engineering
Authors	Autar Kaw
Date	December 23, 2009
Web Site	http://numericalmethods.eng.usf.edu

Chapter 02.00B

Physical Problem for Differentiation
Chemical Engineering

At about 11:56 am on June 22, 1969 near the city of Cleveland in Ohio, an oil slick on the Cuyahoga River caught fire that burned for 24 minutes. This incident on a navigable river acted as a catalyst for congress to pass the Clean Water Act in 1972. The Federal Water Pollution Control Act prohibits the discharge of oil or oily waste substances or hazardous substances into or upon the navigable waters of the United States.

Interestingly, recreational boating is a growing activity in many waterways of the United States. Unfortunately, fuel leakages – however small – from so many boats can lead to formation of large oil slicks. The ideal would be for the recreational boats to use fuels that can evaporate as quickly as the fuels leak onto the surface of water.

Figure 1 Waves generated on a pond by a pebble

A new fuel for recreational boats being developed at the local university was tested at an area pond by a team of engineers. The interest is to document the environmental impact of the fuel – how quickly does the slick spreads? Table 1 shows the video camera record of the radius of the wave generated by a drop of the fuel that fell into the pond. To find the rate at which the contamination spreads requires numerical differentiation.

Table 1 Radius of wave generated as a function of time.

Time (s)	0	0.5	1.0	1.5	2.0	2.5	3.0	3.5	4.0	4.5	5.0
Radius(m)	0	0.236	0.667	1.225	1.886	2.635	3.464	4.365	5.333	6.364	7.454

QUESTIONS

1. Compute the rate at which the radius of the drop was changing at $t = 2$ and $t = 5$.
2. Estimate the rate at which the area of the contaminant was spreading across the pond at $t = 2$ and $t = 5$.

Topic	DIFFERENTIATION
Sub Topic	Physical Problem
Summary	Estimating the rate at which area of containment is spreading
Authors	Egwu Kalu
Last Revised	June 21, 2005
Web Site	http://numericalmethods.eng.usf.edu

Chapter 02.00D

Physical Problem for Differentiation
Computer Engineering

Human vision is an intriguing ability. The fact that we can effortlessly recognize objects, people, and read this document belies the complexity of the task that a significant portion of our brain is devoted to solving. You might be surprised to learn that this almost photographic perception of the world that we have is not what our eyes send to our brain. What we perceive is a reconstruction from the noisy, shaky output of elementary "things" or "features" detected in the retina. There is strong evidence that the first level of processing done in the retina involves detecting something called "edges" or positions of transitions from dark to bright or bright to dark points in the images. These points usually coincide with boundaries of things.

Figure 1 On left is an image, with the corresponding edge image shown on the right.

In Figure 1 above we see an example of an edge image. This process of "detecting" edges in an image is called edge detection and can be modeled as a differentiation process. In this module we will look into this differentiation process.

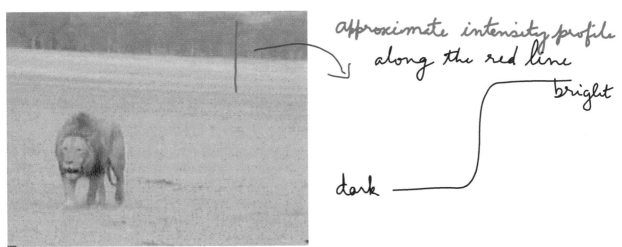

Figure 2 Edges corresponds to points in the image where there are intensity changes.
In the above Figure we see the profile of the intensity value along a line (shown in red) cutting an edge in the image. We represent small values to represent dark points in the image and large values to detect bright regions in the image. The value increases and saturates to the value of the bright region. The edges can be marked at point of the maximum change in intensity, or where the derivative is a maximum. We will study the behavior of this derivative for a class of models of the edges.

Example

One way to model the edge, which is denote by e^x, where x is the direction perpendicular to the edge, is using exponential functions.

$$e(x) = \begin{cases} 1 - e^{(-ax)} & \forall x \geq 0 \\ e^{(ax)} - 1 & \forall x \leq 0 \end{cases}$$

Plots of this function for various values of a are shown in the Figure 3 below. Ignore the fact that we have used negative values to represent intensity. We can always add a constant to shift the function "up", but the constant will not have any impact on the final derivative.

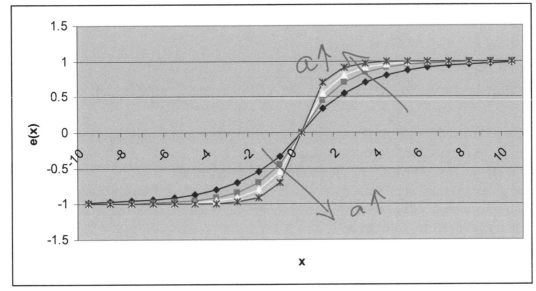

Figure 3 Plot of the exponential edge profile model for various values of the modeling parameter a.

.

The derivative of this profile model is given by

$$e(x) = \begin{cases} 1 - e^{(-ax)} & \forall x \geq 0 \\ e^{(ax)} - 1 & \forall x \leq 0 \end{cases}$$

(Note that at $x = 0$ both the derivatives have the same value of a; this shows that the function we used to model the edge profile is continuous in value and first derivative. This is just an aside fact that you might store in your brain for future use!)

What happens to the derivative as the underlying edge gets sharper? We see from Figure 4 that the value of the derivative gets larger and the peak gets sharper. Thus, strong edges, i.e. edges with sharp intensity transitions will results in stronger response.

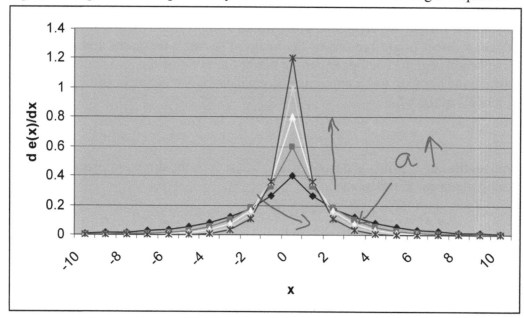

Figure 4 Plot of the derivative of the edge profile as the parameter a is increased.

QUESTIONS

1. What kind of "edge" is represented by the following edge profile model?
   $$e(x) = e^{(-ax^2)}$$
   Answer: Line edge: the edge will appear as a white line in a dark background. What happens to the width of this line as you change a.
2. Compute the first derivative of the above function given in #1.
3. Where, that is for what values of x, does this derivative reach a maximum or a minimum values? What happens to the distance between the maximum and minimum value locations as a is increased?
4. Where is the value of the derivative zero?

Topic	DIFFERENTIATION
Sub Topic	Physical Problem
Summary	To detect edges (boundaries) in images
Authors	Sudeep Sarkar
Date	December 7, 2008
Web Site	http://numericalmethods.eng.usf.edu

Chapter 02.00E

Physical Problem for Differentiation
Electrical Engineering

Electrical systems are used for a wide-array of applications in the commercial and industrial world. Many of them perform physical work using motors, compressors, solenoids, and similar components. In almost all cases, these devices employ electromagnetic principles and are thus inductive in nature. This presents an electrical load that result in a power factor lagging. Whenever the power factor of a load is not 1.0 (leading or lagging), it results in a discrepancy between the apparent power delivered to the load and the real power consumed by the load.

For most commercial and industrial power consumers, as opposed to residential, the electrical power utility bases its rate charge on the apparent power delivered. This often takes the form of a significant penalty for power factors much below 1.0 (e.g. 0.8). To help correct the power factor it is common to add capacitor banks in parallel with a load that can shift a lagging power factor toward 1.0. Under ideal circumstances, the capacitors could be connected and disconnected from the circuit at any time. Under practical conditions, however, this is not advisable.

The amount of energy in a capacitor is directly related to the voltage across the capacitor as shown in the familiar equation

$$E_c = \frac{1}{2}CV_c^2.$$

When a switch tries to disconnect the capacitor, the energy resists this disconnection, and the result is often sparking and gapping as the switch opens. This not only is a significant source of noise in the circuit, but it also results in damage to the switch that greatly reduces its effective service life. The solution to this problem is quite simple; just open the switch when the stored energy is zero. This, of course, occurs when the voltage across the capacitor is zero.

Unfortunately, it is not just a matter of monitoring the voltage and activating the switch when the voltage is zero. The normal frequency for AC power systems is 60 Hz (50 Hz in Europe). This means that there are 120 zero crossings per second and the typical mechanical switch is simply not fast enough to react "instantaneously" at the zero crossing. To deal with this a smart capacitor bank switch is needed. It monitors the voltage and using numerical methods anticipates the point of zero crossing and initiates the switch action enough in advance to have it occur as close to the zero crossing as possible.

This can be done using a first-order approximation of the Taylor Series as shown by the following equations as well as Figure 1.

$$f(t + \Delta t) \cong f(t) + f'(t)\Delta t = 0$$

$$\Delta t \cong -\frac{f(t)}{f'(t)}$$

If this formula looks a bit familiar, it is the same one used as the basis for Newton's Method as it is commonly used in root finding algorithms.

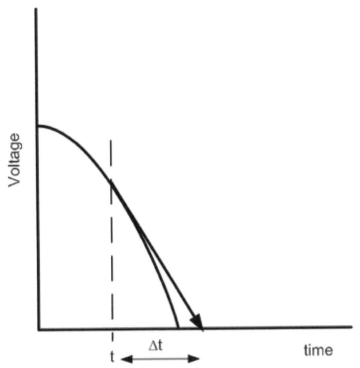

Figure 1 Illustration of Zero-Crossing Prediction Using First-Order Taylor Series

Suppose a system containing a capacitor bank has been constructed and the data of Table 1 was sampled during operation. Using a numerical differentiating algorithm determine the derivative at each point and use the Taylor Series approximation to determine the value of Δt which gives the future estimate of the zero crossing. Keep in mind that when Δt is determined to be negative then the voltage has already crossed the zero point and it will be necessary to wait for the next half cycle of the waveform.

Most numerical methods for taking a derivative (e.g. the Central Difference Method) rely on samples taken both before and after the period in question. In this problem that is not practical since our desire it to anticipate the future zero crossing at which the power should be turned off. Repeat your prior analysis using a differentiation algorithm that is one-sided, that is, one that only uses prior samples to determine the present value of the voltage's derivative.

Table 1 Voltage Samples

Time	Voltage	Time	Voltage
1	0.62161	13	-0.210796
2	0.362358	14	0.087499

3	0.070737	15	0.377978
4	-0.227202	16	0.634693
5	-0.504846	17	0.834713
6	-0.737394	18	0.96017
7	-0.904072	19	0.999859
8	-0.989992	20	0.950233
9	-0.98748	21	0.815725
10	-0.896758	22	0.608351
11	-0.725932	23	0.346635
12	-0.490261	24	0.053955

QUESTIONS

1. What effect does the order of your differentiation algorithm have on the ability to predict correctly the point of zero crossing? Is there an order at which there are diminishing returns on the ability to identify the point of zero crossing?

2. Using a higher-order approximation to the Taylor Series will also improve the prediction of the zero crossing, especially when it is a bit distant. Use a second-order model of the Taylor Series that requires both the first- and second-order derivative to determine Δt.

3. In a real AC system, there could easily be quite a large amount of noise on the sampled voltages. Are there any reasonable algorithms for minimizing the effects this noise has on the results?

4. The typical AC system in the United States uses a 60 Hz frequency (50 Hz in Europe). What is a reasonable sampling rate to use for the voltage sensor? How much does the required length for Δt impact your answer. Did you account for the problem of question (c) in your answer?

5. As in the data of Table 1, the samples have not been synchronized well with the cycles of the AC waveform (that is why you do not see 1 or -1 among the samples). Can you suggest a mechanism for bringing the samples in better synchronization with the cycles?

6. Most industrial smart-sensors for this application use a prediction and correction method to detect the zero crossing, that is, they predict the crossing and then see how close they are for a few cycles prior to the actual disconnecting action. How might such an algorithm be structured?

7. Would there be any advantage in using an interpolation or curve fitting algorithm (e.g. regression to a sinusoid) to better select the instant of true zero voltage?

8. In a system with multiple loads (e.g. a three-phase system), the best instant of shut off for one phase of the capacitor banks may not be the best for the others. Is there any way to determine the point of best compromise or is it simply better to shut each of them off at the zero crossing and tolerate the temporary imbalance to the three-phase system?

Topic	DIFFERENTIATION
Sub Topic	Physical Problem for Electrical Engineering for Differentiation
Summary	The vast majority of commercial and industrial loads are inductive in character. Many electrical consumers find it advantageous to use capacitor banks to adjust their power factor toward 1.0 to avoid extensive rate penalties from their power utility. As load conditions change, it becomes necessary to add or remove capacitors from the bank. The most opportune time to do this is when the voltage across the capacitor is zero to avoid arcing and damages to the switches. Since the switches are slower than the AC waveforms, it is necessary to use a derivative of the voltage to anticipate the zero crossing.
Authors	Henry Welch
Last Revised	June 21, 2005
Web Site	http://numericalmethods.eng.usf.edu

Chapter 02.00F

Physical Problem for Differentiation Industrial Engineering

The following is from http://www.firestone-tire-recall.com/pages/overview.html:

"The Firestone tire recall is perhaps the most deadly auto safety crisis in American history. US regulators on 16 October, 2000 have raised the death count to 119 (the death count has steadily risen from 62, later to 88 and 101 deaths reported on 9/20/2000). Experts believe there may be as many as 250 deaths and more than 3000 catastrophic injuries associated with the defective tires. Most of the deaths occur in accidents involving the Ford Explorer which tends to rollover when one of the tires blows out.

In May 2000, the National Highway Transportation Safety Administration issued a letter to Ford and Firestone requesting information about the high incidence of tire failure on Ford Explorer vehicles. During July, Ford obtained and analyzed the data on tire failure. The data revealed that 15" ATX and ATX II models and Wilderness AT tires had very high failure rates: the tread peels off. Many of the tires were made at a Decatur, Illinois plant. When the tires fail, the vehicle often rolls over and kills the occupants.

Ford Officials estimate the defect rate is 241 tires per million for 15 inch ATX and ATX II tires. By contrast Ford says there are no defects in 16 inch tires per million and only 2.3 incidents per million on other tires.

On August 9th, both companies decided on the recall. Ford and Firestone disagreed as to how to break the news. Bridgestone/Firestone officials wanted to read a statement at a joint briefing without answering any questions. Ford strongly disagreed with this strategy and warned of disaster if they refused questions. Ultimately questions were asked, many of them remain unanswered."

In our daily lives, we depend on a lot of different products. Their inability to perform may cause us inconveniences and sometimes more dire consequences as in the Firestone tire recall case. Therefore, companies are required to carefully study, document and control the reliability of their products before they are released to the market.

02.00F.1

Reliability Function

Reliability function is frequently used to describe the probability of an item operating under certain conditions for a certain amount of time without failure. The reliability function is a function of time, in that every reliability value has an associated time value. In other words, one must specify a time value with the desired reliability value, that is, 95% reliability at 100 hours.

Mathematically, the reliability function $R(t)$ is the probability that a system will be successfully operating without failure in the interval from $t = 0$ to t,

$$R(t) = P(T > t), t \geq 0$$

$$= \int_{t}^{\infty} f(s)ds$$

where T is a random variable representing the failure time or time-to-failure and $f(t)$ is the time to failure distribution function. More often than not, the time to failure distribution function is denoted by exponential, Weibull, normal or lognormal distribution based on the characteristics of the underlying product or the system. However, for complex practical systems the above distributions may not provide an accurate fit for the time to failure distribution function.

Also of interest is the failure distribution function $F(t)$ which describes the probability of an item failing before a certain period of time. As you may guess, the failure distribution function and the reliability function are related to each other by

$$F(t) + R(t) = 1$$

where

$$F(t) = \int_{0, -\infty}^{t} f(s)ds$$

Failure Rate Function

The failure rate function, or hazard function, is also very important in reliability analysis because it specifies the rate of the system aging. The failure rate function $h(t)$ is defined as:

$$h(t) = \lim_{\Delta t \to 0} \frac{R(t) - R(t + \Delta t)}{\Delta t R(t)}$$

$$= \frac{f(t)}{R(t)}$$

The importance of the failure rate function is that it indicates the changing rate in the aging behavior over the life of a population of components. For example, if the time to failure distribution function follows an exponential distribution with parameter λ, then the failure rate function is

$$h(t) = \frac{f(t)}{R(t)}$$

$$= \frac{\lambda e^{-\lambda t}}{e^{-\lambda t}}$$

$$= \lambda$$

This means that the failure rate function of the exponential distribution is a constant. In this case, the system does not have any aging property. This assumption is usually valid for software systems. However, for hardware systems, the failure rate could have other shapes. More information regarding reliability analysis can be found in [1].

A series systems, shown in Figure 1, is defined as n independent components arranged in series. The reliability of the system at time t, $R_s(t)$, is the probability that all components survive to time t, or in other words,

$$R_s(t) = R_1(t)R_2(t)....R_n(t) = \prod_{i=1}^{n} R_i(t)$$

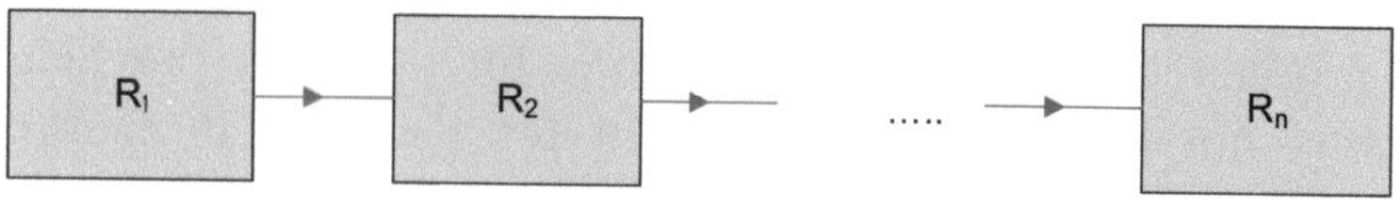

R₁ → R₂ → ..... → Rₙ

Figure 1 Block diagram of a series system

Problem Statement

The following example relies on the research published in [2]. Low power portable direct methanol fuel cell (DMFC) systems provide higher energy density and longer operational life compared with Li-ion batteries widely used in portable electronic devices such as cellular phones, laptops, etc.

DMFC systems consist of three main subsystems, namely the fuel cell stack, fuel tank and the Balance of Plant which are assumed to be independently connected to each other in series as shown in Figure 2. These systems are still an immature technology and there is no publicly available reliable failure data for DMFC components.

Figure 2 Block diagram of a DFMC system

Consider the following reliability data in Table 1 for the DMFC system.

Table 1. Reliability of DFMC system

t (hrs)	0	1	10	100	1000	2000	3000	4000	5000
$R(t)$	1	0.9999	0.9998	0.9980	0.9802	0.9609	0.9419	0.9233	0.9050

QUESTIONS

1. Calculate the value of the failure rate function, $h(t)$ at $t = 10$ hours.
2. Calculate the value of the failure rate function, $h(t)$ at $t = 2000$ hours.
3. Calculate the value of the failure rate function, $h(t)$ at $t = 4000$ hours.
4. Compare the results you have in questions 1-3. What can be said about the failure rate function and the time to failure distribution function $F(t)$ of the DMFC system based on the data provided?
5. You are told that the estimated failure rate for the fuel tank and the fuel cell stack are constant with values 5.42×10^{-8} and 7.78×10^{-6}. Can you calculate an estimate the failure rate for the Balance of Plant?
6. If you are told that the time to failure distribution function of the DFMC system is exponential with parameter $\lambda = 1.21 \times 10^{-5}$, calculate the accuracy of your answers to questions 1-3.

References

[1] E. A. Elsayed (1996), Reliability Engineering, Addison-Wesley.

[2] N.S. Sisworahardjo, M.S.Alam and G. Aydinli, "Reliability and availability of low power portable direct methanol fuel cells", Journal of Power Sources, 177, 2008, p.412-418.

Topic	Differentiation
Sub Topic	Physical Problem for Industrial Engineering
Summary	Reliability of manufactured parts over time
Author	Ali Yalcin
Date	Nov 10th, 2008
Web Site	http://numericalmethods.eng.usf.edu

Chapter 02.00G

Physical Problem for Differentiation Mechanical Engineering

Problem Statement

To make the fulcrum (Figure 1) of a bascule bridge, a long hollow steel shaft called the trunnion is shrink fit into a steel hub.

Figure 1 Trunnion-Hub-Girder (THG) assembly.

This is done by first immersing the trunnion in a cold medium such as dry-ice/alcohol mixture. After the trunnion reaches a steady state temperature of the cold medium, the trunnion outer diameter contracts, is taken out and slid though the hole of the hub (Figure 2).

When the trunnion heats up, it expands and creates an interference fit with the hub. In 1995, on one of the bridges in Florida, this assembly procedure did not work as designed. Before the trunnion could be inserted fully into the hub, the trunnion got stuck. So a new trunnion and hub had to be ordered worth $50,000. Coupled with construction delays, the total loss ran into more than hundred thousand dollars.

Why did the trunnion get stuck? This was because the trunnion had not contracted enough to slide through the hole.

Now the same designer is working on making the fulcrum for another bascule bridge. Can you help him so that he does not make the same mistake?

For this new bridge, he needs to fit a hollow trunnion of outside diameter 12.363" in a hub of inner diameter 12.358". His plan is to put the trunnion in dry ice/alcohol mixture (temperature of dry ice/alcohol mixture is $-108°F$) to contract the trunnion so that it can be slid through the hole of the hub. To slide the trunnion without sticking, he has also specified a diametral clearance of at least 0.01". Assume the room temperature is $80°F$, is immersing it in dry-ice/alcohol mixture a correct decision?

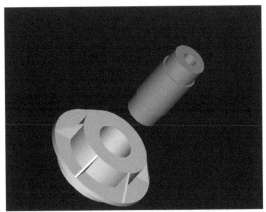 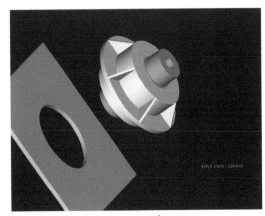

Figure 2 Trunnion slid through the hub after contracting

Solution

Looking at the records of the designer for the previous bridge where the trunnion got stuck in the hub, it was found that he used the thermal expansion coefficient at room temperature to calculate the contraction in the trunnion diameter. In that case the reduction, ΔD in the outer diameter of the trunnion is

$$\Delta D = D\alpha\Delta T \tag{1}$$

where

D = outer diameter of the trunnion,
α = coefficient of thermal expansion coefficient at room temperature,
ΔT = change in temperature,

Given

$D = 12.363"$
$\alpha = 6.817 \times 10^{-6}$ in/in/°F at $80°F$
$$\Delta T = T_{fluid} - T_{room}$$
$$= -108 - 80$$
$$= -188°F$$

where

T_{fluid} = temperature of dry-ice/alcohol mixture

T_{room} = room temperature

The reduction in the trunnion outer diameter is given by

$$\Delta D = 12.363 \times \left(6.47 \times 10^{-6}\right)\left(-188\right)$$
$$= -0.01504"$$

So the trunnion is predicted to reduce in diameter by 0.01504". But, is this enough reduction in diameter? As per the specifications, he needs the trunnion to contract by

= trunnion outside diameter - hub inner diameter + diametral clearance
= 12.363"−12.358"+0.01"
= 0.015"

So according to his calculations, it is enough to put the steel trunnion in dry-ice/alcohol mixture to get the desired contraction of 0.015" as he is predicting a contraction of 0.01504".

But as shown in the Figure 3, the thermal expansion coefficient of steel decreases with decrease in temperature and is not constant over the range of temperature the trunnion goes through. Hence the above formula (Equation 1) would overestimate the thermal contraction. This is the mistake he made in the calculations for the earlier bridge.

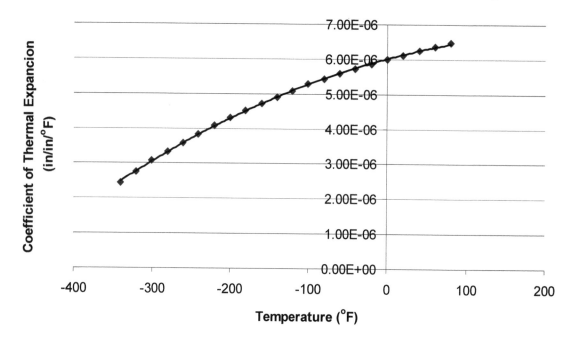

Figure 3 Varying thermal expansion coefficient as a function of temperature for cast steel. To find contraction of a steel cylinder immersed in a bath of liquid nitrogen, one needs to know the thermal expansion coefficient data as a function of temperature. This data is given for steel in Table 1.

Table 1 Instantaneous thermal expansion coefficient as a function of temperature

Temperature, T ($°F$)	Coefficient of thermal expansion, (μin/in/$°F$)
80	6.47
40	6.24
-40	5.72
-120	5.09
-200	4.30
-280	3.33
-340	2.45

An exercise to appreciate the way the thermal expansion coefficient changes with respect to the temperature, we can look into the slope of the thermal expansion coefficient with respect to temperature at low and high temperatures.

QUESTIONS

1. Using the data from Table 1, is the rate of change of coefficient of thermal expansion with respect to temperature more at $T = 80°F$ than at $T = -340°F$? Use any numerical differentiation technique.

2. The data given in the Table 1 can be regressed to $\alpha = a_0 + a_1 T + a_2 T^2$ to get $\alpha = 6.0217 \times 10^{-6} + 6.2782 \times 10^{-9} T - 1.2218 \times 10^{-11} T^2$. Compare the results with problem 1 if you use the regression curve to find the rate of change of coefficient of thermal expansion with respect to temperature at $T = 80°F$ and at $T = -340°F$.

DIFFERENTIATION	
Topic	Differentiation
Summary	A physical problem of finding how the thermal expansion coefficient varies with respect to the temperature is modeled. To find the variation, the problem would be modeled as a numerical differentiation problem.
Major	Mechanical Engineering
Authors	Autar Kaw
Date	February 16, 2010
Web Site	http://numericalmethods.eng.usf.edu

Multiple-Choice Test

Chapter 02.01
A Primer on Differentiation

1. The definition of the first derivative of a function $f(x)$ is

    (A) $f'(x) = \dfrac{f(x + \Delta x) + f(x)}{\Delta x}$

    (B) $f'(x) = \dfrac{f(x + \Delta x) - f(x)}{\Delta x}$

    (C) $f'(x) = \lim\limits_{\Delta x \to 0} \dfrac{f(x + \Delta x) + f(x)}{\Delta x}$

    (D) $f'(x) = \lim\limits_{\Delta x \to 0} \dfrac{f(x + \Delta x) - f(x)}{\Delta x}$

2. Given $y = 5e^{3x} + \sin x$, $\dfrac{dy}{dx}$ is

    (A) $5e^{3x} + \cos x$

    (B) $15e^{3x} + \cos x$

    (C) $15e^{3x} - \cos x$

    (D) $2.666e^{3x} - \cos x$

3. Given $y = \sin 2x$, $\dfrac{dy}{dx}$ at $x = 3$ is most nearly

    (A) 0.9600

    (B) 0.9945

    (C) 1.920

    (D) 1.989

4. Given $y = x^3 \ln x$, $\dfrac{dy}{dx}$ is

    (A) $3x^2 \ln x$

    (B) $3x^2 \ln x + x^2$

    (C) x^2

    (D) $3x$

5. The velocity of a body as a function of time is given as $v(t) = 5e^{-2t} + 4$, where t is in seconds, and v is in m/s. The acceleration in m/s^2 at $t = 0.6$ s is

(A) -3.012
(B) 5.506
(C) 4.147
(D) -10.00

6. If $x^2 + 2xy = y^2$, then $\dfrac{dy}{dx}$ is

(A) $\dfrac{x+y}{y-x}$

(B) $2x + 2y$

(C) $\dfrac{x+1}{y}$

(D) $-x$

Complete Solution

Problem Set

Chapter 02.01
Background on Differentiation

1. Find the slope of the secant line for
$$y = 4x^2 + 6x - 7$$
if the secant is drawn between points at $x = 3$ and $x = 5$.

2. Find the slope of the tangent line to
$$y = 4x^2 + 6x - 7$$
at $x = 3$.

3. Find the derivative of
$$y = 4x^2 + 6x - 7$$
at $x = 3$.

4. Find the derivative of
$$y = \frac{1}{5x - 3}$$
at $x = 2$.

5. Find the derivative of
$$y = \frac{2x - 6}{5x - 9}$$
at $x = 4$.

6. Find the derivative of
$$y = (2x - 6)(5x - 9)$$
at $x = 4$.

7. Find y'' at $x = 2$, given
$$y = 4x^2 + 6x - 7$$

8. Find y'' at $x = 4$, given
$$y = \frac{2x - 6}{5x - 9}.$$

02.01.1

9.   Show that

$$\left|\frac{y''}{(1+(y')^2)^{3/2}}\right| = \frac{1}{r}$$

if

$$x^2 + y^2 = r^2.$$

10.   Given

$$x^2 y + x y^2 + y^2 = 5,$$

find y' and y''.

11.   For

$$f(x) = x^2 + 3x,$$

find the critical points, and the minimum and maximum value in the domain $[-5, 1]$.

12.   Find the optimum angle θ for maximizing the cross-section of the gutter given in the figure below. The total length of the sheet from which the gutter is made is 9", where $BC = 3"$.

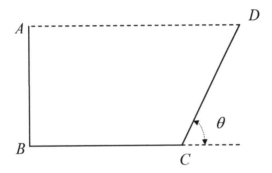

13.   A rectangle is inscribed in a semi-circle of radius 2 m. If the area of the rectangle is to be maximized, find the dimensions of the rectangle.

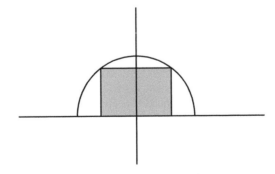

Chapter 02.02
Differentiation of Continuous Functions

After reading this chapter, you should be able to:

1. *derive formulas for approximating the first derivative of a function,*
2. *derive formulas for approximating derivatives from Taylor series,*
3. *derive finite difference approximations for higher order derivatives, and*
4. *use the developed formulas in examples to find derivatives of a function.*

The derivative of a function at x is defined as

$$f'(x) = \lim_{\Delta x \to 0} \frac{f(x + \Delta x) - f(x)}{\Delta x}$$

To be able to find a derivative numerically, one could make Δx finite to give,

$$f'(x) \approx \frac{f(x + \Delta x) - f(x)}{\Delta x}.$$

Knowing the value of x at which you want to find the derivative of $f(x)$, we choose a value of Δx to find the value of $f'(x)$. To estimate the value of $f'(x)$, three such approximations are suggested as follows.

Forward Difference Approximation of the First Derivative

From differential calculus, we know

$$f'(x) = \lim_{\Delta x \to 0} \frac{f(x + \Delta x) - f(x)}{\Delta x}$$

For a finite Δx,

$$f'(x) \approx \frac{f(x + \Delta x) - f(x)}{\Delta x}$$

The above is the forward divided difference approximation of the first derivative. It is called forward because you are taking a point ahead of x. To find the value of $f'(x)$ at $x = x_i$, we may choose another point Δx ahead as $x = x_{i+1}$. This gives

$$f'(x_i) \approx \frac{f(x_{i+1}) - f(x_i)}{\Delta x}$$

02.01.1

$$= \frac{f(x_{i+1}) - f(x_i)}{x_{i+1} - x_i}$$

where

$$\Delta x = x_{i+1} - x_i$$

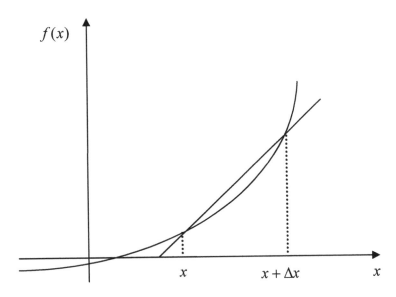

Figure 1 Graphical representation of forward difference approximation of first derivative.

Example 1

The velocity of a rocket is given by

$$v(t) = 2000 \ln\left[\frac{14 \times 10^4}{14 \times 10^4 - 2100t}\right] - 9.8t, \ 0 \le t \le 30$$

where v is given in m/s and t is given in seconds. At $t = 16\,\text{s}$,

a) use the forward difference approximation of the first derivative of $v(t)$ to calculate the acceleration. Use a step size of $\Delta t = 2\,\text{s}$.
b) find the exact value of the acceleration of the rocket.
c) calculate the absolute relative true error for part (b).

Solution

(a) $a(t_i) \approx \dfrac{v(t_{i+1}) - v(t_i)}{\Delta t}$

$t_i = 16$

$\Delta t = 2$

$t_{i+1} = t_i + \Delta t$

$\quad = 16 + 2$

$\quad = 18$

$$a(16) \approx \frac{v(18) - v(16)}{2}$$

$$v(18) = 2000 \ln\left[\frac{14 \times 10^4}{14 \times 10^4 - 2100(18)}\right] - 9.8(18)$$

$$= 453.02 \text{ m/s}$$

$$v(16) = 2000 \ln\left[\frac{14 \times 10^4}{14 \times 10^4 - 2100(16)}\right] - 9.8(16)$$

$$= 392.07 \text{ m/s}$$

Hence

$$a(16) \approx \frac{v(18) - v(16)}{2}$$

$$= \frac{453.02 - 392.07}{2}$$

$$= 30.474 \text{ m/s}^2$$

(b) The exact value of $a(16)$ can be calculated by differentiating

$$v(t) = 2000 \ln\left[\frac{14 \times 10^4}{14 \times 10^4 - 2100t}\right] - 9.8t$$

as

$$a(t) = \frac{d}{dt}[v(t)]$$

Knowing that

$$\frac{d}{dt}[\ln(t)] = \frac{1}{t} \text{ and } \frac{d}{dt}\left[\frac{1}{t}\right] = -\frac{1}{t^2}$$

$$a(t) = 2000 \left(\frac{14 \times 10^4 - 2100t}{14 \times 10^4}\right) \frac{d}{dt}\left(\frac{14 \times 10^4}{14 \times 10^4 - 2100t}\right) - 9.8$$

$$= 2000 \left(\frac{14 \times 10^4 - 2100t}{14 \times 10^4}\right)(-1)\left(\frac{14 \times 10^4}{(14 \times 10^4 - 2100t)^2}\right)(-2100) - 9.8$$

$$= \frac{-4040 - 29.4t}{-200 + 3t}$$

$$a(16) = \frac{-4040 - 29.4(16)}{-200 + 3(16)}$$

$$= 29.674 \text{ m/s}^2$$

(c) The absolute relative true error is

$$|\epsilon_t| = \left|\frac{\text{True Value} - \text{Approximate Value}}{\text{True Value}}\right| \times 100$$

$$= \left| \frac{29.674 - 30.474}{29.674} \right| \times 100$$
$$= 2.6967\%$$

Backward Difference Approximation of the First Derivative

We know

$$f'(x) = \lim_{\Delta x \to 0} \frac{f(x + \Delta x) - f(x)}{\Delta x}$$

For a finite Δx,

$$f'(x) \approx \frac{f(x + \Delta x) - f(x)}{\Delta x}$$

If Δx is chosen as a negative number,

$$f'(x) \approx \frac{f(x + \Delta x) - f(x)}{\Delta x}$$
$$= \frac{f(x) - f(x - \Delta x)}{\Delta x}$$

This is a backward difference approximation as you are taking a point backward from x. To find the value of $f'(x)$ at $x = x_i$, we may choose another point Δx behind as $x = x_{i-1}$. This gives

$$f'(x_i) \approx \frac{f(x_i) - f(x_{i-1})}{\Delta x}$$
$$= \frac{f(x_i) - f(x_{i-1})}{x_i - x_{i-1}}$$

where

$$\Delta x = x_i - x_{i-1}$$

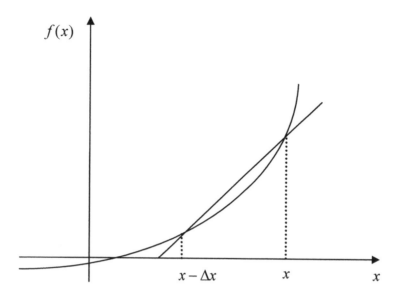

Figure 2 Graphical representation of backward difference approximation of first derivative.

Example 2

The velocity of a rocket is given by

$$v(t) = 2000\ln\left[\frac{14 \times 10^4}{14 \times 10^4 - 2100t}\right] - 9.8t, 0 \le t \le 30$$

(a) Use the backward difference approximation of the first derivative of $v(t)$ to calculate the acceleration at $t = 16\,\text{s}$. Use a step size of $\Delta t = 2\,\text{s}$.

(b) Find the absolute relative true error for part (a).

Solution

$$a(t) \approx \frac{v(t_i) - v(t_{i-1})}{\Delta t}$$

$$t_i = 16$$

$$\Delta t = 2$$

$$\begin{aligned} t_{i-1} &= t_i - \Delta t \\ &= 16 - 2 \\ &= 14 \end{aligned}$$

$$a(16) \approx \frac{v(16) - v(14)}{2}$$

$$\begin{aligned} v(16) &= 2000\ln\left[\frac{14 \times 10^4}{14 \times 10^4 - 2100(16)}\right] - 9.8(16) \\ &= 392.07\,\text{m/s} \end{aligned}$$

$$v(14) = 2000\ln\left[\frac{14 \times 10^4}{14 \times 10^4 - 2100(14)}\right] - 9.8(14)$$

$$= 334.24 \, \text{m/s}$$

$$a(16) \approx \frac{v(16) - v(14)}{2}$$

$$= \frac{392.07 - 334.24}{2}$$

$$= 28.915 \, \text{m/s}^2$$

(b) The exact value of the acceleration at $t = 16 \, \text{s}$ from Example 1 is

$$a(16) = 29.674 \, \text{m/s}^2$$

The absolute relative true error for the answer in part (a) is

$$\left| \epsilon_t \right| = \left| \frac{29.674 - 28.915}{29.674} \right| \times 100$$

$$= 2.5584\%$$

Forward Difference Approximation from Taylor Series

Taylor's theorem says that if you know the value of a function $f(x)$ at a point x_i and all its derivatives at that point, provided the derivatives are continuous between x_i and x_{i+1}, then

$$f(x_{i+1}) = f(x_i) + f'(x_i)(x_{i+1} - x_i) + \frac{f''(x_i)}{2!}(x_{i+1} - x_i)^2 + \ldots$$

Substituting for convenience $\Delta x = x_{i+1} - x_i$

$$f(x_{i+1}) = f(x_i) + f'(x_i)\Delta x + \frac{f''(x_i)}{2!}(\Delta x)^2 + \ldots$$

$$f'(x_i) = \frac{f(x_{i+1}) - f(x_i)}{\Delta x} - \frac{f''(x_i)}{2!}(\Delta x) + \ldots$$

$$f'(x_i) = \frac{f(x_{i+1}) - f(x_i)}{\Delta x} + O(\Delta x)$$

The $O(\Delta x)$ term shows that the error in the approximation is of the order of Δx.

Can you now derive from the Taylor series the formula for the backward divided difference approximation of the first derivative?

As you can see, both forward and backward divided difference approximations of the first derivative are accurate on the order of $O(\Delta x)$. Can we get better approximations? Yes, another method to approximate the first derivative is called the **central difference approximation of the first derivative.**

From the Taylor series

$$f(x_{i+1}) = f(x_i) + f'(x_i)\Delta x + \frac{f''(x_i)}{2!}(\Delta x)^2 + \frac{f'''(x_i)}{3!}(\Delta x)^3 + \ldots \tag{1}$$

and

$$f(x_{i-1}) = f(x_i) - f'(x_i)\Delta x + \frac{f''(x_i)}{2!}(\Delta x)^2 - \frac{f'''(x_i)}{3!}(\Delta x)^3 + \ldots \tag{2}$$

Subtracting Equation (2) from Equation (1)

$$f(x_{i+1}) - f(x_{i-1}) = f'(x_i)(2\Delta x) + \frac{2f'''(x_i)}{3!}(\Delta x)^3 + \ldots$$

$$f'(x_i) = \frac{f(x_{i+1}) - f(x_{i-1})}{2\Delta x} - \frac{f'''(x_i)}{3!}(\Delta x)^2 + \ldots$$

$$= \frac{f(x_{i+1}) - f(x_{i-1})}{2\Delta x} + O(\Delta x)^2$$

hence showing that we have obtained a more accurate formula as the error is of the order of $O(\Delta x)^2$.

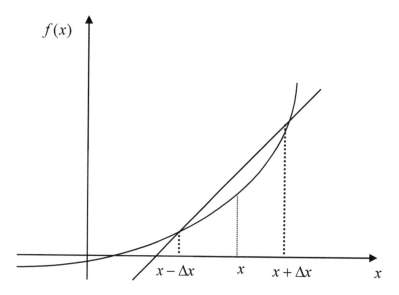

Figure 3 Graphical representation of central difference approximation of first derivative.

Example 3

The velocity of a rocket is given by

$$v(t) = 2000 \ln\left[\frac{14 \times 10^4}{14 \times 10^4 - 2100t}\right] - 9.8t, \, 0 \le t \le 30.$$

(a) Use the central difference approximation of the first derivative of $v(t)$ to calculate the acceleration at $t = 16\,\text{s}$. Use a step size of $\Delta t = 2\,\text{s}$.
(b) Find the absolute relative true error for part (a).
Solution

$$a(t_i) \approx \frac{v(t_{i+1}) - v(t_{i-1})}{2\Delta t}$$

$$t_i = 16$$

$$\Delta t = 2$$

$$t_{i+1} = t_i + \Delta t$$
$$= 16 + 2$$
$$= 18$$
$$t_{i-1} = t_i - \Delta t$$
$$= 16 - 2$$
$$= 14$$
$$a(16) \approx \frac{v(18) - v(14)}{2(2)}$$
$$= \frac{v(18) - v(14)}{4}$$

$$v(18) = 2000 \ln\left[\frac{14 \times 10^4}{14 \times 10^4 - 2100(18)}\right] - 9.8(18)$$
$$= 453.02 \, \text{m/s}$$

$$v(14) = 2000 \ln\left[\frac{14 \times 10^4}{14 \times 10^4 - 2100(14)}\right] - 9.8(14)$$
$$= 334.24 \, \text{m/s}$$

$$a(16) \approx \frac{v(18) - v(14)}{4}$$
$$= \frac{453.02 - 334.24}{4}$$
$$= 29.694 \, \text{m/s}^2$$

(b) The exact value of the acceleration at $t = 16 \, \text{s}$ from Example 1 is
$$a(16) = 29.674 \, \text{m/s}^2$$

The absolute relative true error for the answer in part (a) is
$$|\epsilon_t| = \left|\frac{29.674 - 29.694}{29.674}\right| \times 100$$
$$= 0.069157\%$$

The results from the three difference approximations are given in Table 1.

Table 1 Summary of $a(16)$ using different difference approximations

Type of difference approximation	$a(16)$ (m/s^2)	$|\epsilon_t|\%$
Forward	30.475	2.6967
Backward	28.915	2.5584
Central	29.695	0.069157

Clearly, the central difference scheme is giving more accurate results because the order of accuracy is proportional to the square of the step size. In real life, one would not know the exact value of the derivative – so how would one know how accurately they have found the value of the derivative? A simple way would be to start with a step size and keep on halving the step size until the absolute relative approximate error is within a pre-specified tolerance.

Take the example of finding $v'(t)$ for

$$v(t) = 2000 \ln\left[\frac{14 \times 10^4}{14 \times 10^4 - 2100t}\right] - 9.8t$$

at $t = 16$ using the backward difference scheme. Given in Table 2 are the values obtained using the backward difference approximation method and the corresponding absolute relative approximate errors.

Table 2 First derivative approximations and relative errors for different Δt values of backward difference scheme.

Δt	$v'(t)$	$|\epsilon_a|\%$
2	28.915	
1	29.289	1.2792
0.5	29.480	0.64787
0.25	29.577	0.32604
0.125	29.625	0.16355

From the above table, one can see that the absolute relative approximate error decreases as the step size is reduced. At $\Delta t = 0.125$, the absolute relative approximate error is 0.16355%, meaning that at least 2 significant digits are correct in the answer.

Finite Difference Approximation of Higher Derivatives

One can also use the Taylor series to approximate a higher order derivative. For example, to approximate $f''(x)$, the Taylor series is

$$f(x_{i+2}) = f(x_i) + f'(x_i)(2\Delta x) + \frac{f''(x_i)}{2!}(2\Delta x)^2 + \frac{f'''(x_i)}{3!}(2\Delta x)^3 + \ldots \quad (3)$$

where

$$x_{i+2} = x_i + 2\Delta x$$

$$f(x_{i+1}) = f(x_i) + f'(x_i)(\Delta x) + \frac{f''(x_i)}{2!}(\Delta x)^2 + \frac{f'''(x_i)}{3!}(\Delta x)^3 \ldots \quad (4)$$

where

$$x_{i-1} = x_i - \Delta x$$

Subtracting 2 times Equation (4) from Equation (3) gives

$$f(x_{i+2}) - 2f(x_{i+1}) = -f(x_i) + f''(x_i)(\Delta x)^2 + f'''(x_i)(\Delta x)^3 \ldots$$

$$f''(x_i) = \frac{f(x_{i+2}) - 2f(x_{i+1}) + f(x_i)}{(\Delta x)^2} - f'''(x_i)(\Delta x) + \dots$$

$$f''(x_i) \approx \frac{f(x_{i+2}) - 2f(x_{i+1}) + f(x_i)}{(\Delta x)^2} + O(\Delta x) \qquad (5)$$

Example 4

The velocity of a rocket is given by

$$v(t) = 2000\ln\left[\frac{14 \times 10^4}{14 \times 10^4 - 2100t}\right] - 9.8t, 0 \le t \le 30$$

Use the forward difference approximation of the second derivative of $v(t)$ to calculate the jerk at $t = 16\,\text{s}$. Use a step size of $\Delta t = 2\,\text{s}$.

Solution

$$j(t_i) \approx \frac{v(t_{i+2}) - 2v(t_{i+1}) + v(t_i)}{(\Delta t)^2}$$

$$t_i = 16$$

$$\Delta t = 2$$

$$t_{i+1} = t_i + \Delta t$$
$$= 16 + 2$$
$$= 18$$

$$t_{i+2} = t_i + 2(\Delta t)$$
$$= 16 + 2(2)$$
$$= 20$$

$$j(16) \approx \frac{v(20) - 2v(18) + v(16)}{(2)^2}$$

$$v(20) = 2000\ln\left[\frac{14 \times 10^4}{14 \times 10^4 - 2100(20)}\right] - 9.8(20)$$
$$= 517.35\,\text{m/s}$$

$$v(18) = 2000\ln\left[\frac{14 \times 10^4}{14 \times 10^4 - 2100(18)}\right] - 9.8(18)$$
$$= 453.02\,\text{m/s}$$

$$v(16) = 2000\ln\left[\frac{14 \times 10^4}{14 \times 10^4 - 2100(16)}\right] - 9.8(16)$$
$$= 392.07\,\text{m/s}$$

$$j(16) \approx \frac{517.35 - 2(453.02) + 392.07}{4}$$
$$= 0.84515\,\text{m/s}^3$$

The exact value of $j(16)$ can be calculated by differentiating

$$v(t) = 2000 \ln\left[\frac{14 \times 10^4}{14 \times 10^4 - 2100t}\right] - 9.8t$$

twice as

$$a(t) = \frac{d}{dt}[v(t)] \text{ and}$$

$$j(t) = \frac{d}{dt}[a(t)]$$

Knowing that

$$\frac{d}{dt}[\ln(t)] = \frac{1}{t} \text{ and}$$

$$\frac{d}{dt}\left[\frac{1}{t}\right] = -\frac{1}{t^2}$$

$$a(t) = 2000\left(\frac{14 \times 10^4 - 2100t}{14 \times 10^4}\right)\frac{d}{dt}\left(\frac{14 \times 10^4}{14 \times 10^4 - 2100t}\right) - 9.8$$

$$= 2000\left(\frac{14 \times 10^4 - 2100t}{14 \times 10^4}\right)(-1)\left(\frac{14 \times 10^4}{\left(14 \times 10^4 - 2100t\right)^2}\right)(-2100) - 9.8$$

$$= \frac{-4040 - 29.4t}{-200 + 3t}$$

Similarly it can be shown that

$$j(t) = \frac{d}{dt}[a(t)]$$

$$= \frac{18000}{(-200 + 3t)^2}$$

$$j(16) = \frac{18000}{[-200 + 3(16)]^2}$$

$$= 0.77909 \, \text{m/s}^3$$

The absolute relative true error is

$$|\epsilon_t| = \left|\frac{0.77909 - 0.84515}{0.77909}\right| \times 100$$

$$= 8.4797\%$$

The formula given by Equation (5) is a forward difference approximation of the second derivative and has an error of the order of $O(\Delta x)$. Can we get a formula that has a better accuracy? Yes, we can derive the central difference approximation of the second derivative. The Taylor series is

$$f(x_{i+1}) = f(x_i) + f'(x_i)\Delta x + \frac{f''(x_i)}{2!}(\Delta x)^2 + \frac{f'''(x_i)}{3!}(\Delta x)^3 + \frac{f''''(x_i)}{4!}(\Delta x)^4 + \ldots \quad (6)$$

where

$$x_{i+1} = x_i + \Delta x$$

$$f(x_{i-1}) = f(x_i) - f'(x_i)\Delta x + \frac{f''(x_i)}{2!}(\Delta x)^2 - \frac{f'''(x_i)}{3!}(\Delta x)^3 + \frac{f''''(x_i)}{4!}(\Delta x)^4 - \ldots \quad (7)$$

where

$$x_{i-1} = x_i - \Delta x$$

Adding Equations (6) and (7), gives

$$f(x_{i+1}) + f(x_{i-1}) = 2f(x_i) + f''(x_i)(\Delta x)^2 + f'''(x_i)\frac{(\Delta x)^4}{12} + \ldots$$

$$f''(x_i) = \frac{f(x_{i+1}) - 2f(x_i) + f(x_{i-1})}{(\Delta x)^2} - \frac{f'''(x_i)(\Delta x)^2}{12} + \ldots$$

$$= \frac{f(x_{i+1}) - 2f(x_i) + f(x_{i-1})}{(\Delta x)^2} + O(\Delta x)^2$$

Example 5

The velocity of a rocket is given by

$$v(t) = 2000\ln\left[\frac{14 \times 10^4}{14 \times 10^4 - 2100t}\right] - 9.8t, \quad 0 \le t \le 30,$$

(a) Use the central difference approximation of the second derivative of $v(t)$ to calculate the jerk at $t = 16\,\text{s}$. Use a step size of $\Delta t = 2\,\text{s}$.

Solution

$$a(t_i) \approx \frac{v(t_{i+1}) - 2v(t_i) + v(t_{i-1})}{(\Delta t)^2}$$

$$t_i = 16$$
$$\Delta t = 2$$
$$t_{i+1} = t_i + \Delta t$$
$$\quad = 16 + 2$$
$$\quad = 18$$
$$t_{i+2} = t_i - \Delta t$$
$$\quad = 16 - 2$$
$$\quad = 14$$

$$j(16) \approx \frac{v(18) - 2v(16) + v(14)}{(2)^2}$$

$$v(18) = 2000\ln\left[\frac{14 \times 10^4}{14 \times 10^4 - 2100(18)}\right] - 9.8(18)$$

$$= 453.02 \, \text{m/s}$$

$$v(16) = 2000 \ln\left[\frac{14 \times 10^4}{14 \times 10^4 - 2100(16)}\right] - 9.8(16)$$

$$= 392.07 \, \text{m/s}$$

$$v(14) = 2000 \ln\left[\frac{14 \times 10^4}{14 \times 10^4 - 2100(14)}\right] - 9.8(14)$$

$$= 334.24 \, \text{m/s}$$

$$j(16) \approx \frac{v(18) - 2v(16) + v(14)}{(2)^2}$$

$$= \frac{453.02 - 2(392.07) + 334.24}{4}$$

$$= 0.77969 \, \text{m/s}^3$$

The absolute relative true error is

$$|\epsilon_t| = \left|\frac{0.77908 - 0.77969}{0.77908}\right| \times 100$$

$$= 0.077992\%$$

DIFFERENTIATION	
Topic	Differentiation of Continuous functions
Summary	These are textbook notes of differentiation of continuous functions
Major	General Engineering
Authors	Autar Kaw, Luke Snyder
Date	December 23, 2009
Web Site	http://numericalmethods.eng.usf.edu

Multiple-Choice Test

Chapter 02.02
Differentiation of Continuous Functions

1. The definition of the first derivative of a function $f(x)$ is

   (A) $f'(x) = \dfrac{f(x+\Delta x) + f(x)}{\Delta x}$

   (B) $f'(x) = \dfrac{f(x+\Delta x) - f(x)}{\Delta x}$

   (C) $f'(x) = \lim\limits_{\Delta x \to 0} \dfrac{f(x+\Delta x) + f(x)}{\Delta x}$

   (D) $f'(x) = \lim\limits_{\Delta x \to 0} \dfrac{f(x+\Delta x) - f(x)}{\Delta x}$

2. The exact derivative of $f(x) = x^3$ at $x = 5$ is most nearly
   - (A) 25.00
   - (B) 75.00
   - (C) 106.25
   - (D) 125.00

3. Using the forwarded divided difference approximation with a step size of 0.2, the derivative of $f(x) = 5e^{2.3x}$ at $x = 1.25$ is
   - (A) 163.4
   - (B) 203.8
   - (C) 211.1
   - (D) 258.8

4. A student finds the numerical value of $\dfrac{d}{dx}(e^x) = 20.220$ at $x = 3$ using a step size of 0.2. Which of the following methods did the student use to conduct the differentiation?
   - (A) Backward divided difference
   - (B) Calculus, that is, exact
   - (C) Central divided difference
   - (D) Forward divided difference

5. Using the backward divided difference approximation, $\frac{d}{dx}(e^x) = 4.3715$ at $x = 1.5$ for a step size of 0.05. If you keep halving the step size to find $\frac{d}{dx}(e^x)$ at $x = 1.5$ before two significant digits can be considered to be at least correct in your answer, the step size would be (you cannot use the exact value to determine the answer)

    (A) 0.05/2
    (B) 0.05/4
    (C) 0.05/8
    (D) 0.05/16

6. The heat transfer rate q over a surface is given by

    $$q = -kA\frac{dT}{dy}$$

    where

    k = thermal conductivity $\left(\dfrac{J}{s \cdot m \cdot K}\right)$

    A = surface area (m^2)
    T = temperature (K)
    y = distance normal to the surface (m)

    Given

    $k = 0.025\dfrac{J}{s \cdot m \cdot K}$

    $A = 3\,m^2$

    the temperature T over the surface varies as

    $$T = -1493y^3 + 2200y^2 - 1076y + 500$$

    The heat transfer rate q at the surface most nearly is

    (A) -1076 W
    (B) 37.5 W
    (C) 80.7 W
    (D) 500 W

Complete Solution

Problem Set

Chapter 02.02
Differentiation of Continuous Functions

1. Find the exact value of $\frac{dy}{dx}(x=5)$, given

    $y = e^x + \sin(x)$.

2. Given the function $f(x) = \sin(2x)$ and using a step size of $h = 0.1$, find
    a) $f'(\pi/3)$ using forward divided difference scheme. Also, find the absolute relative true error.
    b) $f'(\pi/3)$ using backward divided difference scheme. Also, find the absolute relative true error.
    c) $f'(\pi/3)$ using central divided difference scheme. Also, find the absolute relative true error.

3. Using forward divided difference scheme, find the first derivative of the function $f(x) = \sin(2x)$ at $x = \pi/3$ correct within 3 significant digits. Start with a step size of $h = 0.01$ and keep halving it till you find the answer.

4. The velocity of a body is given by
    $$v(t) = 20ln(120 - 4t), \quad 0 < t < 10$$
    where t is in seconds and v is in m/s.
    a) What is the exact acceleration at $t = 2$ seconds?
    b) What is the acceleration at $t = 2$ seconds using any divided difference scheme of numerical differentiation with a step size of 0.25 seconds?
    c) Use any numerical scheme to find jerk (rate of change of acceleration) at $t = 2$ seconds using a step size of 0.25 seconds?

5. Using forward divided difference, the first derivative of a function $f(x)$ is found at $x = 0.8$. With a step size of 0.2, $f'(0.8) \approx 0.95375$, while with a step size of 0.1, $f'(0.8) \approx 0.96851$. Find a better estimate of $f'(x)$ with the above information knowing that the order of accuracy of the forward divided difference scheme is O(step size).

6. The error in using central divided difference scheme to find the first derivative of the function is of $O(h^2)$, where h is the step size. If the true error in finding $f'(\alpha)$ with a step size $h = 0.5$ is 1.6, estimate the true error in finding $f'(\alpha)$ with a step size of $h = 0.125$.

7.   The voltage of a variable power source is given by

$$v(t) = 3\frac{dc}{dt} + 5c,$$

where c is the current in amperes, time is in seconds, and v is the voltage in volts. Find the voltage in volts at $t = 6$ seconds if $c = 5\cos(2t)$.

Chapter 02.03
Differentiation of Discrete Functions

After reading this chapter, you should be able to:

1. *find approximate values of the first derivative of functions that are given at discrete data points, and*
2. *use Lagrange polynomial interpolation to find derivatives of discrete functions.*

To find the derivatives of functions that are given at discrete points, several methods are available. Although these methods are mainly used when the data is spaced unequally, they can be used for data that is spaced equally as well.

Forward Difference Approximation of the First Derivative

We know

$$f'(x) = \lim_{\Delta x \to 0} \frac{f(x + \Delta x) - f(x)}{\Delta x}$$

For a finite Δx,

$$f'(x) \approx \frac{f(x + \Delta x) - f(x)}{\Delta x}$$

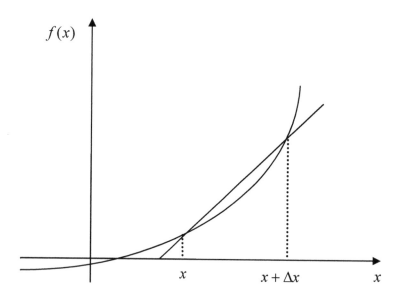

Figure 1 Graphical representation of forward difference approximation of first derivative.

So given $n+1$ data points $(x_0, y_0), (x_1, y_1), (x_2, y_2), \ldots, (x_n, y_n)$, the value of $f'(x)$ for $x_i \le x \le x_{i+1}$, $i = 0, \ldots, n-1$, is given by

$$f'(x_i) \approx \frac{f(x_{i+1}) - f(x_i)}{x_{i+1} - x_i}$$

Example 1

The upward velocity of a rocket is given as a function of time in Table 1.

Table 1 Velocity as a function of time.

t (s)	$v(t)$ (m/s)
0	0
10	227.04
15	362.78
20	517.35
22.5	602.97
30	901.67

Using forward divided difference, find the acceleration of the rocket at $t = 16$ s.
Solution

To find the acceleration at $t = 16$ s, we need to choose the two values of velocity closest to $t = 16$ s, that also bracket $t = 16$ s to evaluate it. The two points are $t = 15$ s and $t = 20$ s

$$a(t_i) \approx \frac{v(t_{i+1}) - v(t_i)}{\Delta t}$$

$$t_i = 15$$

$$t_{i+1} = 20$$

$$\Delta t = t_{i+1} - t_i$$

$$= 20 - 15$$

$$= 5$$

$$a(16) \approx \frac{v(20) - v(15)}{5}$$

$$= \frac{517.35 - 362.78}{5}$$

$$= 30.914 \, \text{m/s}^2$$

Direct Fit Polynomials

In this method, given $n+1$ data points $(x_0, y_0), (x_1, y_1), (x_2, y_2), \ldots, (x_n, y_n)$, one can fit a nth order polynomial given by

$$P_n(x) = a_0 + a_1 x + \ldots\ldots + a_{n-1} x^{n-1} + a_n x^n$$

To find the first derivative,

$$P_n'(x) = \frac{dP_n(x)}{dx} = a_1 + 2a_2 x + \ldots\ldots + (n-1)a_{n-1} x^{n-2} + n a_n x^{n-1}$$

Similarly, other derivatives can also be found.

Example 2

The upward velocity of a rocket is given as a function of time in Table 2.

Table 2 Velocity as a function of time.

t (s)	$v(t)$ (m/s)
0	0
10	227.04
15	362.78
20	517.35
22.5	602.97
30	901.67

Using a third order polynomial interpolant for velocity, find the acceleration of the rocket at $t = 16 \, \text{s}$.

Solution

For the third order polynomial (also called cubic interpolation), we choose the velocity given by

$$v(t) = a_0 + a_1 t + a_2 t^2 + a_3 t^3$$

Since we want to find the velocity at $t = 16\,\text{s}$, and we are using a third order polynomial, we need to choose the four points closest to $t = 16$ and that also bracket $t = 16$ to evaluate it. The four points are $t_0 = 10, t_1 = 15,\ t_2 = 20$ and $t_3 = 22.5$.

$$t_0 = 10,\ \ v(t_0) = 227.04$$
$$t_1 = 15,\ \ v(t_1) = 362.78$$
$$t_2 = 20,\ \ v(t_2) = 517.35$$
$$t_3 = 22.5,\ \ v(t_3) = 602.97$$

such that

$$v(10) = 227.04 = a_0 + a_1(10) + a_2(10)^2 + a_3(10)^3$$
$$v(15) = 362.78 = a_0 + a_1(15) + a_2(15)^2 + a_3(15)^3$$
$$v(20) = 517.35 = a_0 + a_1(20) + a_2(20)^2 + a_3(20)^3$$
$$v(22.5) = 602.97 = a_0 + a_1(22.5) + a_2(22.5)^2 + a_3(22.5)^3$$

Writing the four equations in matrix form, we have

$$
\begin{bmatrix}
1 & 10 & 100 & 1000 \\
1 & 15 & 225 & 3375 \\
1 & 20 & 400 & 8000 \\
1 & 22.5 & 506.25 & 11391
\end{bmatrix}
\begin{bmatrix}
a_0 \\ a_1 \\ a_2 \\ a_3
\end{bmatrix}
=
\begin{bmatrix}
227.04 \\ 362.78 \\ 517.35 \\ 602.97
\end{bmatrix}
$$

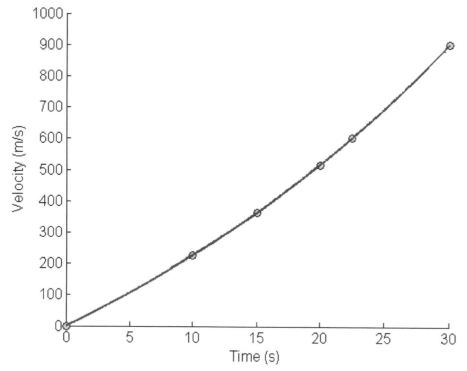

Figure 2 Graph of upward velocity of the rocket vs. time.

Solving the above four equations gives

$$a_0 = -4.3810$$
$$a_1 = 21.289$$
$$a_2 = 0.13065$$
$$a_3 = 0.0054606$$

Hence

$$v(t) = a_0 + a_1 t + a_2 t^2 + a_3 t^3$$
$$= -4.3810 + 21.289t + 0.13065t^2 + 0.0054606t^3, \quad 10 \le t \le 22.5$$

The acceleration at $t = 16$ is given by

$$a(16) = \frac{d}{dt} v(t) \Big|_{t=16}$$

Given that $v(t) = -4.3810 + 21.289t + 0.13065t^2 + 0.0054606t^3, \quad 10 \le t \le 22.5$,

$$a(t) = \frac{d}{dt} v(t)$$
$$= \frac{d}{dt}\left(-4.3810 + 21.289t + 0.13065t^2 + 0.0054606t^3\right)$$
$$= 21.289 + 0.26130t + 0.016382t^2, \quad 10 \le t \le 22.5$$
$$a(16) = 21.289 + 0.26130(16) + 0.016382(16)^2$$
$$= 29.664 \text{ m/s}^2$$

Lagrange Polynomial

In this method, given $(x_0, y_0), \ldots, (x_n, y_n)$, one can fit a nth order Lagrangian polynomial given by

$$f_n(x) = \sum_{i=0}^{n} L_i(x) f(x_i)$$

where n in $f_n(x)$ stands for the nth order polynomial that approximates the function $y = f(x)$ and

$$L_i(x) = \prod_{\substack{j=0 \\ j \ne i}}^{n} \frac{x - x_j}{x_i - x_j}$$

$L_i(x)$ is a weighting function that includes a product of $n-1$ terms with terms of $j = i$ omitted.

Then to find the first derivative, one can differentiate $f_n(x)$ once, and so on for other derivatives.

For example, the second order Lagrange polynomial passing through $(x_0, y_0), (x_1, y_1)$, and (x_2, y_2) is

$$f_2(x) = \frac{(x-x_1)(x-x_2)}{(x_0-x_1)(x_0-x_2)}f(x_0) + \frac{(x-x_0)(x-x_2)}{(x_1-x_0)(x_1-x_2)}f(x_1) + \frac{(x-x_0)(x-x_1)}{(x_2-x_0)(x_2-x_1)}f(x_2)$$

Differentiating the above equation gives

$$f_2'(x) = \frac{2x-(x_1+x_2)}{(x_0-x_1)(x_0-x_2)}f(x_0) + \frac{2x-(x_0+x_2)}{(x_1-x_0)(x_1-x_2)}f(x_1) + \frac{2x-(x_0+x_1)}{(x_2-x_0)(x_2-x_1)}f(x_2)$$

Differentiating again would give the second derivative as

$$f_2''(x) = \frac{2}{(x_0-x_1)(x_0-x_2)}f(x_0) + \frac{2}{(x_1-x_0)(x_1-x_2)}f(x_1) + \frac{2}{(x_2-x_0)(x_2-x_1)}f(x_2)$$

Example 3

The upward velocity of a rocket is given as a function of time in Table 3.

Table 3 Velocity as a function of time.

t (s)	$v(t)$ (m/s)
0	0
10	227.04
15	362.78
20	517.35
22.5	602.97
30	901.67

Determine the value of the acceleration at $t = 16\,\text{s}$ using second order Lagrangian polynomial interpolation for velocity.

Solution

$$v(t) = \left(\frac{t-t_1}{t_0-t_1}\right)\left(\frac{t-t_2}{t_0-t_2}\right)v(t_0) + \left(\frac{t-t_0}{t_1-t_0}\right)\left(\frac{t-t_2}{t_1-t_2}\right)v(t_1) + \left(\frac{t-t_0}{t_2-t_0}\right)\left(\frac{t-t_1}{t_2-t_1}\right)v(t_2)$$

$$a(t) = \frac{2t-(t_1+t_2)}{(t_0-t_1)(t_0-t_2)}v(t_0) + \frac{2t-(t_0+t_2)}{(t_1-t_0)(t_1-t_2)}v(t_1) + \frac{2t-(t_0+t_1)}{(t_2-t_0)(t_2-t_1)}v(t_2)$$

$$a(16) = \frac{2(16)-(15+20)}{(10-15)(10-20)}(227.04) + \frac{2(16)-(10+20)}{(15-10)(15-20)}(362.78)$$
$$+ \frac{2(16)-(10+15)}{(20-10)(20-15)}(517.35)$$
$$= -0.06(227.04) - 0.08(362.78) + 0.14(517.35)$$
$$= 29.784\,\text{m/s}^2$$

DIFFERENTIATION	
Topic	Differentiation of Discrete Functions
Summary	These are textbook notes differentiation of discrete functions
Major	General Engineering
Authors	Autar Kaw, Luke Snyder
Date	December 23, 2009
Web Site	http://numericalmethods.eng.usf.edu

Multiple-Choice Test

Chapter 02.03
Differentiation of Discrete Functions

1. The definition of the first derivative of a function $f(x)$ is

    (A) $f'(x) = \dfrac{f(x+\Delta x) + f(x)}{\Delta x}$

    (B) $f'(x) = \dfrac{f(x+\Delta x) - f(x)}{\Delta x}$

    (C) $f'(x) = \lim\limits_{\Delta x \to 0} \dfrac{f(x+\Delta x) + f(x)}{\Delta x}$

    (D) $f'(x) = \lim\limits_{\Delta x \to 0} \dfrac{f(x+\Delta x) - f(x)}{\Delta x}$

2. Using the forward divided difference approximation with a step size of 0.2, the derivative of the function at $x = 2$ is given as

x	1.8	2.0	2.2	2.4	2.6
$f(x)$	6.0496	7.3890	9.0250	11.023	13.464

    (A) 6.697
    (B) 7.389
    (C) 7.438
    (D) 8.180

3. A student finds the numerical value of $f'(x) = 20.220$ at $x = 3$ using a step size of 0.2. Which of the following methods did the student use to conduct the differentiation if $f(x)$ is given in the table below?

x	2.6	2.8	3.0	3.2	3.4	3.6
$f(x)$	$e^{2.6}$	$e^{2.8}$	e^{3}	$e^{3.2}$	$e^{3.4}$	$e^{3.6}$

    (A) Backward divided difference
    (B) Calculus, that is, exact
    (C) Central divided difference
    (D) Forward divided difference

4.   The upward velocity of a body is given as a function of time as

t, s	10	15	20	22
v, m/s	22	36	57	10

To find the acceleration at $t = 17$ s, a scientist finds a second order polynomial approximation for the velocity, and then differentiates it to find the acceleration. The estimate of the acceleration in m/s^2 at $t = 17$ s is most nearly

   (A)   4.060
   (B)   4.200
   (C)   8.157
   (D)   8.498

5.   The velocity of a rocket is given as a function of time as

t, s	0	0.5	1.2	1.5	1.8
v, m/s	0	213	223	275	300

Allowed to use the forward divided difference, backward divided difference or central divided difference approximation of the first derivative, your best estimate for the acceleration $\left(a = \dfrac{dv}{dt} \right)$ of the rocket in m/s^2 at $t = 1.5$ seconds is

   (A)   83.33
   (B)   128.33
   (C)   173.33
   (D)   183.33

6.   In a circuit with an inductor of inductance L, a resistor with resistance R, and a variable voltage source $E(t)$,

$$E(t) = L\frac{di}{dt} + Ri$$

The current, i, is measured at several values of time as

Time, t (secs)	1.00	1.01	1.03	1.1
Current, i (amperes)	3.10	3.12	3.18	3.24

If $L = 0.98$ henries and $R = 0.142$ ohms, the most accurate expression for $E(1.00)$ is

   (A) $0.98\left(\dfrac{3.24 - 3.10}{0.1} \right) + (0.142)(3.10)$

   (B) 0.142×3.10

   (C) $0.98\left(\dfrac{3.12 - 3.10}{0.01} \right) + (0.142)(3.10)$

   (D) $0.98\left(\dfrac{3.12 - 3.10}{0.01} \right)$

Complete Solution

Problem Set

Chapter 02.03
Differentiation of Discrete Functions

1. Given below is the value of a function at discrete values of x

x	0	0.4	0.9	1.8	2.5
$f(x)$	20	75	121	126	171

Estimate $f'(0.9)$ using

a) Forward divided difference scheme,
b) Backward divided difference scheme, and
c) Central divided difference scheme.

2. The upward velocity of a rocket is given as a function of time in the table below

t, s	0	10	15	20	22.5	30
$v(t)$, m/s	0	227.04	362.78	517.35	602.97	901.67

Use the first, second and third order polynomial direct method interpolation to find the acceleration at $t = 9.5$ s. What is the true error if I told you that the data given in the table was derived from the formula

$$v(t) = 2000\ln\left[\frac{14 \times 10^4}{14 \times 10^4 - 2100t}\right] - 9.8t, \quad 0 \le t \le 30$$

3. The upward velocity of a rocket is given as a function of time in the table below.

t, s	0	10	15	20	22.5	30
$v(t)$, m/s	0	227.04	362.78	517.35	602.97	901.67

From data given, use the first, second and third order Lagrangian method interpolation to find the acceleration at $t = 9.5$s. What is the true error, if I told you that the data given in the table was derived from the formula

$$v(t) = 2000\ln\left[\frac{14 \times 10^4}{14 \times 10^4 - 2100t}\right] - 9.8t, \quad 0 \le t \le 30$$

4. An aircraft position during an emergency landing exercise on a runway was timed as follows

t, s	0	0.4	1.00	1.75	2.5
x, m	20	71	110	161	178

What is your best estimate for the velocity of the aircraft at $t = 1.75$ s?

5. An aircraft position during an emergency landing exercise on a runway was timed as follows

t, s	0	0.4	1.00	1.75	2.5
x, m	20	71	110	161	178

Estimate the acceleration of the jet fighter at $t = 1.75$ s by any method.

6. The location of a futuristic car is given as a function of time

t, s	0	0.5	1.2	1.5	1.8
x, m	0	213	223	275	300

What is your best estimate for the momentum $M = mv$ (m =mass, v =velocity) of the car at $t = 1.5$ seconds? Assume the mass of the car is 2006 kg.

Chapter 03.00A

Physical Problem for Nonlinear Equations
General Engineering

Problem Statement

You are working for 'DOWN THE TOILET COMPANY' that makes floats for ABC commodes. The ball has a specific gravity of 0.6 and has a radius of 5.5 cm. You are asked to find the depth to which the ball will get submerged when floating in water (see Figure 1).

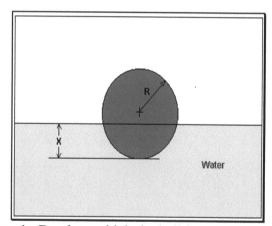

Figure 1   Depth to which the ball is submerged in water

Solution

According to Newton's third law of motion, every action has an equal and opposite reaction. In this case, the weight of the ball is balanced by the buoyancy force (Figure 2).

Weight of ball = Buoyancy force   (1)

The weight of the ball is given by

Weight of ball = (Volume of ball) × (Density of ball) × (Acceleration due to gravity)

$$= \left(\frac{4}{3}\pi R^3\right)(\rho_b)(g) \tag{2}$$

where

R = radius of ball (m),

ρ = density of ball (kg/m^3),

g = acceleration due to gravity (m/s^2).

The buoyancy force[1] is given by

Buoyancy force = Weight of water displaced

= (Volume of ball under water) (Density of water)

(Acceleration due to gravity)

$$= \pi x^2 \left(R - \frac{x}{3} \right) \rho_w g \qquad (3)$$

where

x = depth to which ball is submerged,

ρ_w = density of water.

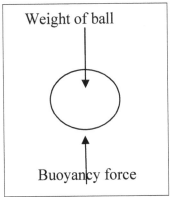

Figure 2 Free Body Diagram showing the forces acting on the ball immersed in water

Now substituting Equations (2) and (3) in Equation (1),

$$\frac{4}{3}\pi R^3 \rho_b g = \pi x^2 \left(R - \frac{x}{3} \right) \rho_w g$$

$$4R^3 \rho_b = 3x^2 (R - \frac{x}{3}) \rho_w$$

$$4R^3 \rho_b - 3x^2 R \rho_w + x^3 \rho_w = 0$$

$$4R^3 \frac{\rho_b}{\rho_w} - 3x^2 R + x^3 = 0$$

$$4R^3 \gamma_b - 3x^2 R + x^3 = 0 \qquad (4)$$

where

the specific gravity of the ball, γ_b is given by

$$\gamma_b = \frac{\rho_b}{\rho_w} \qquad (5)$$

Given

$R = 5.5\,\text{cm} = 0.055\,\text{m}$,

$\gamma_b = 0.6$, and

substituting in Equation (4), we get

---

[1] The derivation of the volume of the ball submerged under water is given in the appendix.

$$4(0.055)^3(0.6) - 3x^2(0.055) + x^3 = 0$$
$$3.993 \times 10^{-4} - 0.165x^2 + x^3 = 0 \tag{6}$$

The above equation is a nonlinear equation. Solving it would give us the value of 'x', that is, the depth to which the ball is submerged under water.

Appendix A

Derivation of the formula for the volume of a ball submerged under water.
How do you find that the volume of the ball submerged under water as given by

$$V = \frac{\pi h^2(3r - h)}{3} \tag{7}$$

where

r = radius of the ball,
h = height of the ball to which the ball is submerged.

From calculus,

$$V = \int_{r-h}^{r} A\,dx \tag{8}$$

where A is the cross-sectioned area at a distance x from the center of the sphere. The lower limit of integration is $x = r - h$ as that is where the water line is

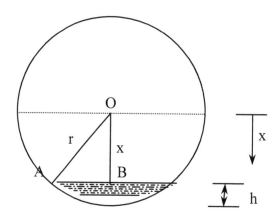

Figure 3   Deriving the equation for volume of ball under water

and the upper limit is r as that is the bottom of the sphere. So, what is the A at any location x.
From Figure 3, for a location x,

$OB = x$,
$OA = r$,

then

$$AB = \sqrt{OA^2 - OB^2}$$
$$= \sqrt{r^2 - x^2}. \tag{9}$$

and AB is the radius of the area at x. So at location B is

$$A = \pi(AB)^2 = \pi\left(r^2 - x^2\right) \tag{10}$$

so

$$V = \int_{r-h}^{r} \pi\left(r^2 - x^2\right)dx$$

$$= \pi\left(r^2 x - \frac{x^3}{3}\right)_{r-h}^{r}$$

$$= \pi\left[\left(r^2 r - \frac{r^3}{3}\right) - \left(r^2(r-h) - \frac{(r-h)^3}{3}\right)\right]$$

$$= \frac{\pi h^2(3r - h)}{3}. \tag{11}$$

NONLINEAR EQUATIONS

Topic	Physical problem for nonlinear equations for general engineering
Summary	A physical problem of finding the depth to which a ball would float in water is modeled as a nonlinear equation.
Major	General Engineering
Authors	Autar Kaw
Date	December 23, 2009
Web Site	http://numericalmethods.eng.usf.edu

[1] The derivation of the volume of the ball submerged under water is given in the appendix.

Chapter 03.00B

Physical Problem for Nonlinear Equations
Chemical Engineering

Problem Statement

Years ago, a businessperson called me and wanted to know how he could find how much oil was left in his storage tank. His tank was spherical and was 6 feet in diameter. Well, I suggested him to get a 8ft steel ruler and use it as a dipstick (Figure 1). Knowing the height

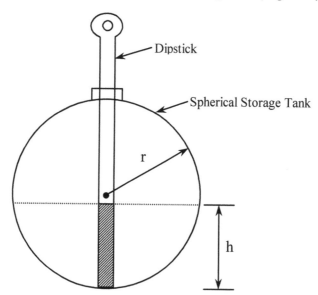

Figure 1 Oil in a spherical storage tank.

to which the dip-stick would become wet with oil, one would know the height h of the oil in the tank. The volume V of oil left in the tank then is

$$V = \frac{\pi h^2 (3r - h)}{3} \tag{1}$$

where, r is the radius of the tank. But, he did not stop there. He wanted me to design a steel ruler for him so that he would directly get the reading from the dipstick. How would I design such a dipstick?

Solution

The problem is inverse of what he wanted originally. To design a dipstick, I would have to mark the height corresponding to a volume. To do that I would need to solve the equation

$$V = \frac{\pi h^2 (3r - h)}{3}$$

for the height for a given volume and radius. For example, where would you mark the scale for $4 ft^3$ of oil?

$$4 = \frac{\pi h^2 (3 \times 3 - h)}{3}$$

$$h^3 - 9h^2 + \frac{12}{\pi} = 0$$

$$f(h) = h^3 - 9h^2 + 3.8197 = 0$$

Therefore, this nonlinear equation needs to be solved. To mark the scale for other volumes, you will need to substitute the value for the volume and solve for h. Continue to do this for different preset volumes to develop the scale.

Appendix A: Derivation of the formula for the volume of the oil based on radius of the tank and the height of oil in the tank.

How do you find that the volume of oil is given by

$$V = \frac{\pi h^2 (3r - h)}{3}$$

From calculus,

$$V = \int_{r-h}^{r} A\, dx$$

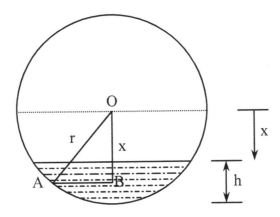

Figure 2   Deriving the equation for volume of oil in the tank.

where A is the cross-sectioned area at the location x, from the center of the sphere. The lower limit of integration is $x = r - h$ as that is where the oil line is and the upper limit is r as that is the bottom of the sphere. So, what is A at any location x?

From Figure 2, for a location x

$$OB = x$$
$$OA = r$$

then

$$AB = \sqrt{OA^2 - OB^2}$$
$$= \sqrt{r^2 - x^2}$$

and AB is the radius of the area at x. So the area at location x is

$$A = \pi(AB)^2$$
$$= \pi\left(r^2 - x^2\right)$$

so

$$V = \int_{r-h}^{r} \pi\left(r^2 - x^2\right)dx$$

$$= \pi\left(r^2 x - \frac{x^3}{3}\right)\bigg|_{r-h}^{r}$$

$$= \pi\left[\left(r^2 r - \frac{r^3}{3}\right) - \left(r^2(r-h) - \frac{(r-h)^3}{3}\right)\right]$$

$$= \frac{\pi h^2 (3r - h)}{3}.$$

NONLINEAR EQUATIONS	
Topic	Nonlinear equations
Summary	A physical problem of designing a scale to find the volume of oil in a spherical tank.
Major	Chemical Engineering
Authors	Autar Kaw
Date	December 23, 2009
Web Site	http://numericalmethods.eng.usf.edu

Chapter 03.00C

Physical Problem for Nonlinear Equations
Civil Engineering

Problem

My spouse asked me to build a bookshelf (Figure 1) for her books. Her books range from $8\frac{1}{2}$" in to 11" in height, and would take 29" of space along the length. She asked me how much would the bookshelf sag, as she does not like sagging bookshelves we had during graduate student days. After all, our tolerance to sagging does sag after graduation! So, as a true engineer, before going to the local building store, I modeled the problem to find the maximum deflection of the bookshelf. I assumed a shelf of thickness $3/8$" and width 12". The Young's modulus of a typical wood shelf material is 3.667 Msi.

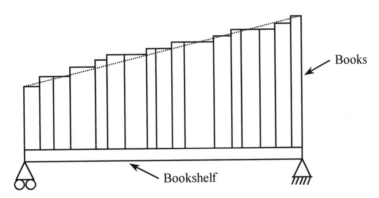

Figure 1 Distributions of books on the bookshelf.

Solution

I assume the following

- 100 pages of $8\frac{1}{2}$"×11" book paper weighs 1 lb (on its website www.usps.gov, United States Post Office suggests 6 letter size pages weigh about 1 ounce, so 100 pages would be approximately a pound).

- 400 pages take up the space of 1" in thickness (I actually measured several textbooks and found an average.)

- the books decrease linearly in height from 11" from the right end to $8\frac{1}{2}$" on the left, and the book width is $8\frac{1}{2}$" for all books,

The total weight W of the books is found as follows. If all the books were of dimensions $11"\times 8\frac{1}{2}"$, the weight of the books would be

$$W = 29\,\text{in} \times 400\frac{\text{pages}}{\text{in}} \times \frac{1\,\text{lb}}{100\,\text{pages}}$$

$$= 116\,lb$$

But since the books decrease in height from 11" to $8\frac{1}{2}"$, while the width of the books is assumed to be constant at $8\frac{1}{2}"$, the actual total weight of the books is calculated as

$$W = \frac{\frac{1}{2}\left(11 + 8\frac{1}{2}\right)29}{(11)(29)} \times 116$$

$$\approx 103\,lb$$

Now assuming that the weight 'W' is distributed linearly from the left end to the right as a distribution q (Figure 2),

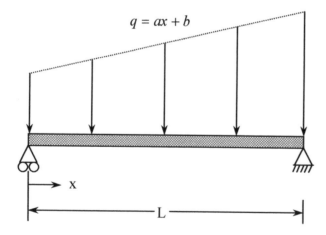

Figure 2   Approximate weight distribution of books.

Then the total weight W over the length L

$$W = \int_{0}^{L} q\,dx$$

$$= \int_{0}^{L} (ax + b)\,dx$$

$$= a\frac{L^2}{2} + bL \tag{1}$$

Also, the weight distribution can be assumed to be in the same ratio as the height of the books at the two ends, then

$$\frac{q(x=0)}{q(x=L)} = \frac{8.5}{11}$$

$$\frac{a(0)+b}{aL+b} = \frac{8.5}{11}$$

$$\frac{b}{aL+b} = \frac{8.5}{11} \tag{2}$$

Substituting

$$W = 103\,\text{lb},$$
$$L = 29'',$$

in Equations (1) and (2), we get

$$a\frac{29^2}{2} + b(29) = 103$$

$$\frac{b}{a(29)+b} = \frac{8.5}{11}$$

or

$$420.5a + 29b = 103$$
$$-246.5a + 3b = 0$$

The above set of equations gives the solution as

$$a = 0.031403$$
$$b = 3.0964$$

So the weight distribution is given by

$$q = 0.031403x + 3.0964, \quad 0 \le x \le 29.$$

Now let us find the deflection in the beam. The deflection y as a function of x along the length of the beam is given by

$$\frac{d^2 y}{dx^2} = \frac{M}{EI}$$

where

$$M = \text{Bending moment (lb.in)}$$
$$E = \text{Young's modulus (psi)}$$
$$I = \text{Second moment of area (in}^4)$$

To find the bending moment, we need to first find the reaction force at the support. Let R_1 and R_2 be the reactions at the left and right support, respectively (Figure 3). Then from the sum of forces in the vertical direction,

$$R_1 + R_2 = W$$

and the moment at the left support is zero as it is simply supported

$$R_2 L - \int_0^L (ax+b)x\,dx = 0$$

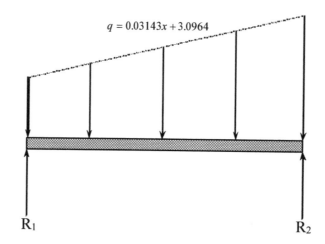

$q = 0.03143x + 3.0964$

R₁

R₂

Figure 3   Reaction at the end of shelf supports.

$$R_2 L - a\frac{L^3}{3} - \frac{bL^2}{2} = 0$$

Substituting

$W = 103$,
$a = 0.031403$,
$b = 3.0964$,
$L = 29$,

the equilibrium equations are

$$R_1 + R_2 = 103$$

$$R_2(29) - (0.031403)\frac{29^3}{3} - 3.0964\frac{29^2}{2} = 0$$

gives

$$R_1 = 49.300\, lb$$

$$R_2 = 53.701\, lb$$

The bending moment at any cross-section at a distance of x from the left end is then given by summing the moments at a cross-section of distance x from the left end as (Figure 4)

$$M(x) - R_1 x + \int_0^L (ax' + b)(x - x')dx' = 0$$

$$M(x) = R_1 x \int_0^L (ax' + b)(x - x')dx'$$

$$= R_1 x - \frac{1}{6}ax^3 - \frac{1}{2}bx^2$$

Substituting value of R_1, a and b,

$$R_1 = 49.299$$

$$a = 0.031403$$

$$b = 3.0964$$

the bending moment equation is given by

$$M(x) = 49.299x - \frac{1}{6}(0.031403)x^3 - \frac{1}{2}(3.0964)x^2$$
$$M(x) = 49.299x - 0.0052339x^3 - 1.5482x^2$$

So

$$EI\frac{d^2v}{dx^2} = M(x)$$
$$\frac{d^2v}{dx^2} = \frac{M(x)}{EI}$$

$$E = 3.667\,Msi$$
$$I = \frac{1}{12}ht^3$$

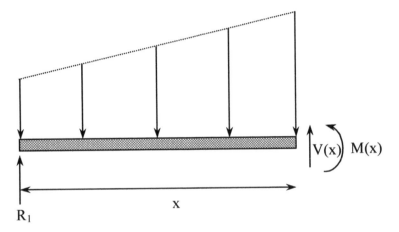

Figure 4   Free body diagram to find bending moment at a cross-section.

where
   h = width of shelf
   t = thickness of shelf
$$I = \frac{1}{12} \times 12 \times \left(\frac{3}{8}\right)^3$$
$$= 0.052734\,in$$

Hence

$$\frac{d^2v}{dx^2} = \frac{M(x)}{EI}$$
$$= \frac{49.29x - 0.0052339x^3 - 1.5428x^2}{3.6667 \times 10^6 \times 0.052734}$$
$$= 0.25496 \times 10^{-3}x - 0.27068 \times 10^{-7}x^3 - 0.80067 \times 10^{-5}x^2$$

Integrating with respect to x gives

$$\frac{dv}{dx} = 0.25496 \times 10^{-3} x^2 - 0.67670 \times 10^{-8} x^4 - 0.26689 \times 10^{-5} x^3 + c_1$$

Integrating once again with respect to x gives

$$v(x) = 0.42493 \times 10^{-4} x^3 - 0.13534 \times 10^{-8} x^5 - 0.66723 \times 10^{-6} x^4 + c_1 x + c_2$$

Now the boundary conditions at $x = 0$ and $x = \text{L}$ are that the displacement is zero at the ends,

$$v(0) = 0$$
$$v(L) = 0$$

So from

$$v(0) = 0$$

we get

$$c_2 = 0, \text{ and}$$

from

$$v(L) = 0,$$

we get

$$0 = 0.42493 \times 10^{-3} L^3 - 0.13534 \times 10^{-8} L^5 - 0.66723 \times 10^{-6} L^4 + c_1 L$$

Substituting $\text{L} = 29''$

$$0 = 0.42493 \times 10^{-3} (29)^3 - 0.13534 \times 10^{-8} (29)^5 - 0.66723 \times 10^{-6} (29)^4 + c_1 (29)$$
$$c_1 = -0.018506$$

Hence the vertical deflection in the beam is given by

$$v(x) = 0.42493 \times 10^{-4} x^3 - 0.13534 \times 10^{-8} x^5 - 0.66723 \times 10^{-6} x^4 - 0.018506x$$

But to find where the deflection would be maximum, we need to take the first derivative of the deflection to find where

$$\frac{dv}{dx} = 0,$$

that is

$$\frac{d}{dx}(0.42493 \times 10^{-4} x^3 - 0.13534 \times 10^{-8} x^5 - 0.66723 \times 10^{-6} x^4 - 0.018506x) = 0$$

$$f(x) = 0.12748 \times 10^{-3} x^2 - 0.67670 \times 10^{-8} x^4 - 0.26689 \times 10^{-5} x^3 - 0.018506 = 0$$

Now here is a nonlinear equation that needs to solved to find where the maximum deflection occurs. Then substituting the obtained value of x in $v(x)$ would give us the maximum sagging in the beam.

Topic	NONLINEAR EQUATIONS
Sub Topic	Physical Problem
Summary	A physical problem of finding the maximum sagging in a bookshelf.
Authors	Autar Kaw
Date	December 23, 2009
Web Site	http://numericalmethods.eng.usf.edu

Chapter 03.00D

Physical Problem for Nonlinear Equations
Computer Engineering

Problem Statement

Many super computers do not have a unit to divide numbers. But why? Well, a divide operation in modern computers can take 20 to 25 clock cycles, and that is five times what it takes for multiplication [1]. Instead, a divide unit, based on numerically solving a nonlinear equation, is developed. This allows for a faster divide operation. This is how it works. If you want to find the value of b/a where b and a are real numbers, one can look at

$$\frac{b}{a} = b * \frac{1}{a} = b * c$$

where

$$c = \frac{1}{a}$$

So, if one is able to find c, we only need to multiply b and c to find b/a. So how do we find c without the divide unit.
Equation

$$c = \frac{1}{a}$$

can be written as an equation

$$f(c) = ac - 1 = 0$$

If one is able to find the root of this equation without using a division, then we have the value of $1/a$.

Although we do not explain the numerical methods of solving nonlinear equations in this section of the notes, it becomes necessary to do so in this example. The Newton-Raphson method of solving a nonlinear equation is used in finding $1/a$. The Newton Raphson method of solving an equation $f(c) = 0$ is given by the iterative formula

$$c_{i+1} = c_i - \frac{f(c_i)}{f'(c_i)},$$

where

c_{i+1} is the new approximation of of the root of $f(c) = 0$ and

c_i is the previous approximation of the root of $f(c) = 0$.

What is the appropriate function to use to find the inverse of a?

a) Using

$$f(c) = ac - 1 = 0$$

gives

$$f'(c) = a$$

and the Newton-Raphson method formula gives

$$c_{i+1} = c_i - \frac{ac_i - 1}{a}$$

$$c_{i+1} = \frac{1}{a}$$

This is of no use as it involves division.

b) Using

$$f(c) = a - \frac{1}{c} = 0$$

gives

$$f'(c) = \frac{1}{c^2}$$

$$c_{i+1} = c_i - \frac{a - \dfrac{1}{c_i}}{\dfrac{1}{c_i^2}}$$

$$= c_i - c_i^2 \left(a - \frac{1}{c_i} \right)$$

$$c_{i+1} = c_i(2 - c_i a)$$

This one is the acceptable iterative formula to find the inverse of a as it does not involve division.

Starting with an initial guess for the inverse of a, one can find newer approximations by using the above iterative formula. Each iteration requires two multiplications and one subtraction. However, the number of iterations required to find the inverse of a very much depends on the initial approximation. More accurate is the starting approximation, less number of iterations are required to find the inverse of a. Since the convergence of Newton Raphson method is quadratic, it may take up to six iterations to get an accurate reciprocal in double precision. By using look-up tables for the initial approximation, the number of iterations required can be reduced to two [2]. Also, the operation of $(2 - c_i a)$ may be carried in a fused multiply-subtract unit to further reduce the clock cycles needed for the computation.

References

1. Oberman, S.F., Flynn, M.J., "Division Algorithms and Implementations", IEEE Transactions on Computers, Vol. 46, No. 8, 1997.
2. Wong, D., Flynn, M.J., "Fat Division using accurate quotient approximations to reduce the number of iteratoimns", IEEE Transactions on Computers, Vol. 41, No. 8, 981-995, 1992.

Appendix A: Example of using Newton–Raphson method to find the inverse of a number.

Let us find $\dfrac{1}{2.5}$

The Newton –Raphson method formula is given by

$$c_{i+1} = c_i\left(2 - 2.5c_i\right)$$

Starting with estimate of inverse as $c_0 = 0.5$,

$$c_1 = 0.5\left[2 - 2.5(0.5)\right]$$
$$= 0.375$$

$$c_2 = 0.375\left[2 - 2.5(0.375)\right]$$
$$= 0.3984$$

$$c_3 = 0.3984\left[2 - 2.5(0.3984)\right]$$
$$= 0.3999$$

$$c_4 = 0.3999\left[2 - 2.5(0.3999)\right]$$
$$= 0.4000$$

It took four iterations to find the inverse of 2.5 correct up to 4 significant digits.

Topic	NONLINEAR EQUATION
Sub Topic	Physical Problem
Summary	For efficient design of the Cray supercomputer, it does not have a divide unit. It uses solution of a nonlinear equation to find the inverse of a number.
Authors	Autar Kaw
Last Revised	December 23, 2009
Web Site	http://numericalmethods.eng.usf.edu

Chapter 03.00E

Physical Problem for Nonlinear Equations
Electrical Engineering

Summary

Thermistors are temperature measuring devices based on that resistance of materials changes with temperature. To find whether the resistor is calibrated properly, one needs to solve a problem of a nonlinear equation.

Thermistors are temperature-measuring devices based on the principle that the thermistor material exhibits a change in electrical resistance with a change in temperature. By measuring the resistance of the thermistor material, one can then determine the temperature.

Thermistors are generally a piece of semiconductor (Figure 1) made from metal oxides such as those of manganese, nickel, cobalt, etc. These pieces may be made into a bead, disk, wafer, etc depending on the application.

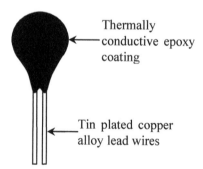

Thermally conductive epoxy coating

Tin plated copper alloy lead wires

Figure 1. Sketch of a thermistor.

There are two types of thermistors – negative temperature coefficient (NTC) and positive temperature coefficient (PTC) thermistors. For NTCs, the resistance decreases with temperature, while for PTCs, the temperature increases with temperature. It is the NTCs that are generally used for temperature measurement.

Why would we want to use thermistors for measuring temperature as opposed to other choices such as thermocouples? It is because thermistors have

- high sensitivity giving more accuracy,

- a fast response to temperature changes for accuracy and quicker measurements, and
- relatively high resistance for decreasing the errors caused by the resistance of lead wires themselves.

But thermistors have a nonlinear output and are valued for a limited range. So, when a thermistor is manufactured, the manufacturer supplies a resistance vs. temperature curve. The curve generally used that gives an accurate representation is given by Steinhart and Hart equation

$$\frac{1}{T} = a_0 + a_1 \ln(R) + a_3 \{\ln(R)\}^3 \tag{1}$$

where

T is temperature in Kelvin, and

R is resistance in ohms.

a_0, a_1, a_3 are constants of the calibration curve.

As an example, for an actual thermistor – Part No 10K3A made by Betatherm sensors, the values of the three coefficients are given as

$$a_0 = 1.129241 \times 10^{-4}$$

$$a_1 = 2.341077 \times 10^{-4}$$

$$a_3 = 8.775468 \times 10^{-8}$$

and are found by measuring the resistance of the thermistor at three reference points (namely $0^0 C, 25^0 C$ and $70^0 C$ in this case) and using equation (1) to set up three simultaneous linear equations to find the three constants a_0, a_1, a_3. The resulting Steinhart-Hart equation for the 10K3A Betatherm thermistor is

$$\frac{1}{T} = 1.129241 \times 10^{-3} + 2.341077 \times 10^{-4} \ln(R) + 8.775468 \times 10^{-8} \{\ln(R)\}^3 \tag{2}$$

where note that T is in Kelvin and R is in ohms.

Using a digital system to measure temperature, an analog system is used to measure the thermistor resistances and convert that to a temperature reading. You want to confirm that the Resistance vs. Temperature data compares well with the published R/T data for the range for which the thermistor will be used. For example for the above thermistor, error of no more than $\pm 0.01^0 C$ is acceptable. What is the range of the resistance then you can consider to be within this acceptable limit at $19^0 C$? To find this we need to solve the equation for a temperature of $19 \pm 0.01 = 18.99^0 C$ to $19.01^0 C$ range. These equations are

$$\frac{1}{19.01 + 273.15} = 1.129241 \times 10^{-3} + 2.341077 \times 10^{-4} \ln(R) + 8.775468 \times 10^{-8} \{\ln(R)\}^3$$

$$3.42278 \times 10^{-3} = 1.129241 \times 10^{-3} + 2.341077 \times 10^{-4} \ln(R) + 8.775468 \times 10^{-8} \{\ln(R)\}^3 \tag{3}$$

and

$$\frac{1}{18.99 + 273.15} = 1.129241 \times 10^{-3} + 2.341077 \times 10^{-4} \ln(R) + 8.775468 \times 10^{-8} \{\ln(R)\}^3$$

$$3.42301 \times 10^{-3} = 1.129241 \times 10^{-3} + 2.341077 \times 10^{-4} \ln(R) + 8.775468 \times 10^{-8} \{\ln(R)\}^3 \tag{4}$$

Equations (3) and (4) are independent nonlinear equations that need to be solved for R.

References

1. Betatherm sensors, http://www.betatherm.com
2. Valvanao, J., "Measuring Temeparture Using Thermistors", Curcuit Cellar Online, August 2000, http://www.circuitcellar.com/online
3. Lavenuta, G., "Negative Temperature Coefficient Thermistors: Part 1: Characteristics, Materials, and Configurations", http://www.globalspec.com/cornerstone/ref/negtemp.html
4. Potter, D., "Measuring Temperature with Thermistors – a Tutorial", National Instruments Application Note 065, http://www.seas.upenn.edu/courses/belab/ReferenceFiles/Thermisters/an065.pdf
5. Steinhart, J.S. and Hart, S.R., 1968. "Calibration Curves for Thermistors," Deep Sea Research 15:497.
6. Sapoff, M. et al. 1982. "The Exactness of Fit of Resistance-Temperature Data of Thermistors with Third-Degree Polynomials," Temperature, Its Measurement and Control in Science and Industry, Vol. 5, James F. Schooley, ed., American Institute of Physics, New York, NY:875.
7. Siwek, W.R., et al. 1992. "A Precision Temperature Standard Based on the Exactness of Fit of Thermistor Resistance-Temperature Data Using Third Degree Polynomials," Temperature, Its Measurement and Control in Science and Industry, Vol. 6, James F. Schooley, ed., American Institute of Physics, New York, NY:491-496.

Questions

Answer the following questions
1. Note that if we substitute $x = \ln(R)$, the equation becomes a cubic equation in x. The cubic equation will have three roots. Could some of these roots be complex? If so how many?
2. Solving the cubic equation exactly would require major effort. However using numerical techniques, we can solve this equation and any other equation of the form $f(x) = 0$. Solve the above equation by all the methods you have learned assuming you want at least 3 significant digits to be correct in your answer.
3. How can you use the knowledge of the physics of the problem to develop initial guess(es) for the numerical methods?
4. If more than one root of the above equation is real, how do you choose the valid root? Or, are all the possible real roots physically acceptable?

Topic	NONLINEAR EQUATION
Sub Topic	Physical Problem
Summary	
Authors	Autar Kaw
Last Revised	December 23, 2009
Web Site	http://numericalmethods.eng.usf.edu

Chapter 03.00F

Physical Problem for Nonlinear Equations
Industrial Engineering

Problem Statement

You have been recently employed by a start-up computer assembly company called the "MOM AND POP COMPUTER SHOP". As a recent graduate with a bachelor's degree in industrial engineering, you have been asked by the president, to determine the minimum number of computers that the shop will have to sell to make a profit during the first year in business.

Solution

First, it is important to determine the first costs or capital costs, CC, associated with starting the business. The capital costs include such items as:
- computer assembly and diagnostic equipment,
- office furniture,
- workbenches, and
- initial inventory purchase, to name a few.

It is assumed that the capital costs, CC, associated with the business are

$CC = \$20,000$

Second, it is important to determine the repeated costs or operating costs, OC, associated with operating the business for the first year. Operating costs differ from capital costs mainly in that operating costs must be paid repeatedly (every year in this instance), in contrast to capital costs, which involve a one-time payment. Operating costs can be broken down into three major classifications:

1. indirect costs or fixed costs, FC
2. direct or variable costs, VC, and
3. semivariable or regulated costs, RC,

where

$OC = FC + VC + RC$

Fixed costs include items that are not generally a function of the production level, such as:
- building lease,
- real estate taxes,
- utilities (DSL or cable modem, basic electric and local phone),

- insurance, and
- marketing, to name a few.

These fixed costs could, however, increase say if the production level reaches a point when a larger building is needed or when more phone lines needs to be installed. It is assumed that the fixed costs, FC, associated with the business are

$$FC = \$15,000$$

Variable costs include items that are a direct function, often linear, of the production level, such as:

- materials (computer components),
- utilities (production electric and long distance phone),
- labor (also includes supervision and payroll charges),
- maintenance, and
- distribution (packaging and shipping), to name a few.

It is assumed that the variable costs, VC, associated with the business are

$$VC = \$625n$$

where n is the number of computers produced. Regulated costs include items that are also a direct function, though often non-linear, of the production level, such as:

- labor (also includes supervision and payroll charges),

For instance, if production levels reach a certain level, another employee may need to be hired. It is assumed that the regulated costs, RC, associated with the business are

$$RC = \$30n^{1.5}$$

Combining the fixed, variable and regulated costs gives the operating cost, that is,

$$CC = FC + VC + RC$$

$$CC = \$15,000 + \$500n + 30n^{1.5}$$

And the total cost, TC, to operate the business for the first year is the capital costs plus the operating costs, that is

$$TC = CC + OC$$

$$TC = \$20,000 + \$15,000 + \$625n + \$30n^{1.5}$$

$$TC - \$35,000 + \$625n + \$30n^{1.5}$$

All of the costs (capital, fixed, variable, regulated, operating, and total) are shown below in Figure 1.

Next, it is important to determine the total sales, TS, associated with operating the business for the first year. Total sales can be broken down into two major classifications:

1. product sales, PS, and
2. discounted sales, DS,

where

$$TS = PS - DS$$

If they sell n computers, their product sales, PS, are

$$PS = \$15000n$$

This represents the $1500 selling price for each computer. It is assumed that the discounted sales, DS, are

$$DS = \$10n^{1.5}$$

which represents a discount as the number of computers sold increases. The total sales is then given by

$$TS = PS - DS$$
$$TS = \$1500n - \$10n^{1.5}$$

All of the sales (product, discounted, and total) revenue are shown below in Figure 2.

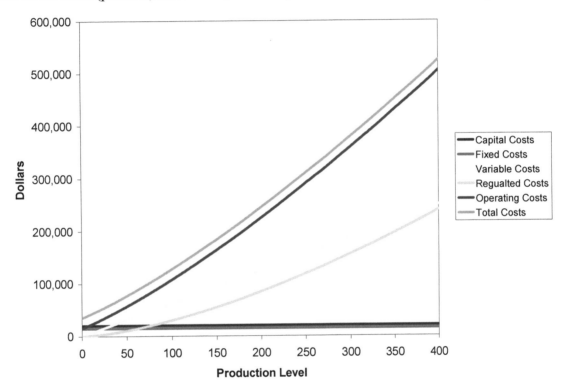

Figure 1 Capital, Fixed, Variable, Regulated, Operating, And Total Costs

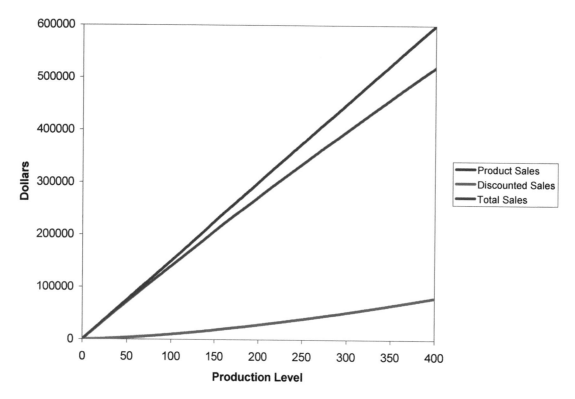

Figure 2 Product, Discounted, And Total Sales

All of the costs and sales revenue are shown next in Figure 3.

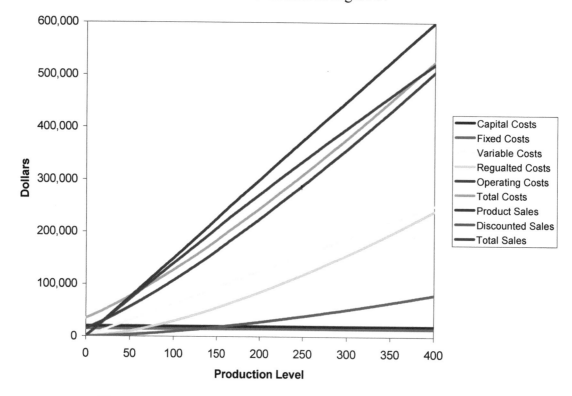

Figure 3 All of the Costs and Sales Revenue

At the break-even point there is no profit, so the capital cost plus the product cost equals the product sales (see Figure 4).

$$TC = TS$$
$$\$35,000 + \$625n + \$30n^{1.5} = \$1500n - \$10n^{1.5}$$

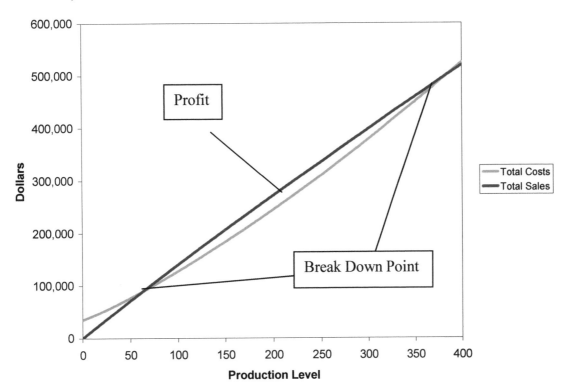

Figure 4 Break-Even Point and Profit Margin

Simplifying the previous equation yields the following nonlinear equation that needs to solved.

$$\$35,000 - \$875n + \$40n^{1.5} = 0$$

The value of n is the minimum number of computers that the shop will have to sell to make a profit. This is called the *break-even point*.

Questions
1. Will some of the roots be complex for the above nonlinear equation?
2. Using numerical techniques, we can solve this equation and any other equation of the form $f(x) = 0$. Solve the above equation by all the methods you have learned assuming you want at least 3 significant digits to be correct in your answer.
3. How can you use the knowledge of the problem to develop initial guess(es) for the numerical methods?

4. Determine the production level that produces the most profit.
5. Determine the second break-even point, after which a loss is realized.
6. Reformulate the problem to determine the break-even point for the second year in business assuming that no capital costs are incurred.

Topic	NONLINEAR EQUATIONS
Sub Topic	Physical Problem
Summary	A physical problem of determining how many computers a business would have to sell to turn a profit. To find this number of computers to be sold, the physical model is a nonlinear equation.
Authors	Glen Besterfield
Date	August 15, 2002
Web Site	http://numericalmethods.eng.usf.edu

Chapter 03.00G

Physical Problem for Nonlinear Equations
Mechanical Engineering

Problem Statement

To make the fulcrum (Figure 1) of a bascule bridge, a long hollow steel shaft called the trunnion is shrink fit into a steel hub. The resulting steel trunnion-hub assembly is then shrink fit into the girder of the bridge.

Figure 1 Trunnion-Hub-Girder (THG) assembly.

This is done by first immersing the trunnion in a cold medium such as dry-ice/alcohol mixture. After the trunnion reaches the steady state temperature of the cold medium, the trunnion outer diameter contracts. The trunnion is taken out of the medium and slid though the hole of the hub (Figure 2).

When the trunnion heats up, it expands and creates an interference fit with the hub. In 1995, on one of the bridges in Florida, this assembly procedure did not work as designed. Before the trunnion could be inserted fully into the hub, the trunnion got stuck. So a new trunnion and hub had to be ordered at a cost of $50,000. Coupled with construction delays, the total loss was more than hundred thousand dollars.

Why did the trunnion get stuck? This was because the trunnion had not contracted enough to slide through the hole.

Now the same designer is working on making the fulcrum for another bascule bridge. Can you help him/her so that he does not make the same mistake?

For this new bridge, he needs to fit a hollow trunnion of outside diameter 12.363" in a hub of inner diameter 12.358". His plan is to put the trunnion in dry ice/alcohol mixture (temperature of the fluid - dry ice/alcohol mixture is $-108°F$) to contract the trunnion so that it can be slided through the hole of the hub. To slide the trunnion without sticking, he has also specified a diametrical clearance of at least 0.01" between the trunnion and the hub. Assuming the room temperature is $80°F$, is immersing it in dry-ice/alcohol mixture a correct decision? What temperature does he need to cool the trunnion to so that he gets the desired contraction?

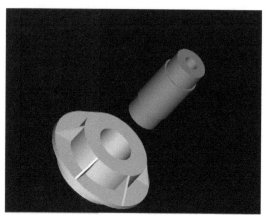

Figure 2 Trunnion slided through the hub after contracting

Solution

Looking at the designer's record for the previous bridge (where the trunnion got stuck in the hub), it was found that he/she used the thermal expansion coefficient at room temperature to calculate the contraction in the trunnion diameter. In that case the reduction, ΔD in the outer diameter of the trunnion is

$$\Delta D = D\alpha\Delta T \qquad (1)$$

where

$D =$ outer diameter of the trunnion,

$\alpha =$ coefficient of thermal expansion coefficient at room temperature, and

$\Delta T =$ change in temperature,

Given

$D = 12.363"$

$\alpha = 6.817 \times 10^{-6} \, \text{in/in/}°F$ at $80°F$

$\Delta T = T_{fluid} - T_{room}$

$\quad = -108 - 80$

$\quad = -188°F$

where

$T_{fluid} =$ temperature of dry-ice/alcohol mixture

$T_{room} =$ room temperature

the reduction in the trunnion outer diameter is given by

$$\Delta D = (12.363)(6.47 \times 10^{-6})(-188)$$

$$= -0.01504"$$

So the trunnion is predicted to reduce in diameter by 0.01504". But, is this enough reduction in diameter? As per specifications, he needs the trunnion to contract by

= trunnion outside diameter - hub inner diameter + diametral clearance

$$= 12.363" - 12.358" + 0.01"$$

$$= 0.015"$$

So according to his calculations, immersing the steel trunnion in dry-ice/alcohol mixture gives the desired contraction of 0.015" as he is predicting a contraction of 0.01504".

But as shown in Figure 3, the thermal expansion coefficient of steel decreases with temperature and is not constant over the range of temperature the trunnion goes through. Hence the above formula (Equation 1) would overestimate the thermal contraction. This is the mistake he made in the calculations for the earlier bridge.

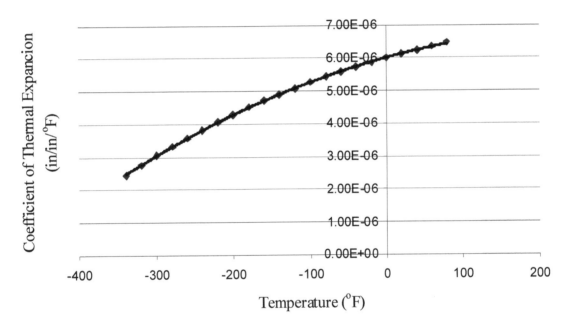

Figure 3   Varying thermal expansion coefficient as a function of temperature for cast steel.

The contraction in the diameter for the trunnion for which the thermal expansion coefficient varies as a function of temperature is given by

$$\Delta D = D \int_{T_{room}}^{T_{fluid}} \alpha \, dT \qquad (2)$$

Note that Equation (2) reduces to Equation (1) if the coefficient of thermal expansion is assumed to be constant. In Figure 3, the thermal expansion coefficient of a typical cast steel is approximated by a second order polynomial[1] 1as

$$\alpha = -1.2278 \times 10^{-11} T^2 + 6.1946 \times 10^{-9} T + 6.0150 \times 10^{-6}$$

Since the desired contraction is at least $0.015''$, that is, $\Delta D = -0.015''$,

$$-0.015 = 12.363 \int_{80}^{T_{fluid}} \left(-1.2278 \times 10^{-11} T^2 + 6.1946 \times 10^{-9} T + 6.015 \times 10^{-6}\right) dT$$

$$-0.015 = 12.363 \left[-1.2278 \times 10^{-11} \frac{T^3}{3} + 6.1946 \times 10^{-9} \frac{T^2}{2} + 6.015 \times 10^{-6} T \right]_{80}^{T_{fluid}}$$

$$-0.015 = 12.363 (-0.40927 \times 10^{-11} T_{fluid}^3 + 0.30973 \times 10^{-8} T_{fluid}^2 + 0.60150 \times 10^{-5} T_{fluid}$$

$$- 0.49893 \times 10^{-3})$$

$$f(T_f) = -0.50598 \times 10^{-10} T_f^3 + 0.38292 \times 10^{-7} T_f^2 + 0.74363 \times 10^{-4} T_f + 0.88318 \times 10^{-2} = 0$$

One can solve this nonlinear equation to find the minimum fluid temperature needed to cool down the trunnion and get the desired contraction. Is cooling in dry-ice/alcohol mixture still your recommendation? You will be surprised that it would not be the correct decision to make.

Topic	NONLINEAR EQUATIONS
Sub Topic	Physical Problem
Summary	A physical problem of finding how much cooling a shaft needs to be shrink fit into a hollow hub. The temperature to which the cooling needs to be done is modeled as a nonlinear equation.
Authors	Autar Kaw
Date	December 7, 2008
Web Site	http://numericalmethods.eng.usf.edu

---

[1] The second order polynomial is derived using regression analysis which is another mathematical procedure where numerical methods are employed. Regression analysis approximates discrete data such as the thermal expansion coefficient vs. temperature data as a continuous function. This is an excellent example of where one has to use numerical methods of more than one procedure to solve a real life problem.

Chapter 03.01
Solution of Quadratic Equations

After reading this chapter, you should be able to:

1. *find the solutions of quadratic equations,*
2. *derive the formula for the solution of quadratic equations,*
3. *solve simple physical problems involving quadratic equations.*

What are quadratic equations and how do we solve them?

A quadratic equation has the form

$$ax^2 + bx + c = 0, \text{ where } a \neq 0$$

The solution to the above quadratic equation is given by

$$x = \frac{-b \pm \sqrt{b^2 - 4ac}}{2a}$$

So the equation has two roots, and depending on the value of the discriminant, $b^2 - 4ac$, the equation may have real, complex or repeated roots.

If $b^2 - 4ac < 0$, the roots are complex.

If $b^2 - 4ac > 0$, the roots are real.

If $b^2 - 4ac = 0$, the roots are real and repeated.

Example 1

Derive the solution to $ax^2 + bx + c = 0$.
Solution

$$ax^2 + bx + c = 0$$

Dividing both sides by a, $(a \neq 0)$, we get

$$x^2 + \frac{b}{a}x + \frac{c}{a} = 0$$

Note if $a = 0$, the solution to

$$ax^2 + bx + c = 0$$

is

$$x = -\frac{c}{b}$$

Rewrite

$$x^2 + \frac{b}{a}x + \frac{c}{a} = 0$$

as

$$\left(x + \frac{b}{2a}\right)^2 - \frac{b^2}{4a^2} + \frac{c}{a} = 0$$

$$\left(x + \frac{b}{2a}\right)^2 = \frac{b^2}{4a^2} - \frac{c}{a}$$

$$= \frac{b^2 - 4ac}{4a^2}$$

$$x + \frac{b}{2a} = \pm\sqrt{\frac{b^2 - 4ac}{4a^2}}$$

$$= \pm\frac{\sqrt{b^2 - 4ac}}{2a}$$

$$x = -\frac{b}{2a} \pm \frac{\sqrt{b^2 - 4ac}}{2a}$$

$$= \frac{-b \pm \sqrt{b^2 - 4ac}}{2a}$$

Example 2

A ball is thrown down at 50 mph from the top of a building. The building is 420 feet tall. Derive the equation that would let you find the time the ball takes to reach the ground.
Solution

The distance s covered by the ball is given by

$$s = ut + \frac{1}{2}gt^2$$

where

u = initial velocity (ft/s)
g = acceleration due to gravity (ft/s^2)
t = time (s)

Given

$$u = 50\frac{\text{miles}}{\text{hour}} \times \frac{1\,\text{hour}}{3600\,\text{s}} \times \frac{5280\ \text{ft}}{1\,\text{mile}}$$

$$= 73.33\frac{\text{ft}}{\text{s}}$$

$$g = 32.2\frac{\text{ft}}{\text{s}^2}$$

$$s = 420\,\text{ft}$$

we have

$$420 = 73.33t + \frac{1}{2}(32.2)t^2$$

$$16.1t^2 + 73.33t - 420 = 0$$

The above equation is a quadratic equation, the solution of which would give the time it would take the ball to reach the ground. The solution of the quadratic equation is

$$t = \frac{-73.33 \pm \sqrt{73.33^2 - 4 \times 16.1 \times (-420)}}{2(16.1)}$$

$$= 3.315, -7.870$$

Since $t > 0$, the valid value of time t is 3.315 s.

NONLINEAR EQUATIONS	
Topic	Solution of quadratic equations
Summary	Textbook notes on solving quadratic equations
Major	General Engineering
Authors	Autar Kaw
Date	December 23, 2009
Web Site	http://numericalmethods.eng.usf.edu

Multiple-Choice Test

Chapter 03.01
Background Nonlinear Equations

1. The value of x that satisfies $f(x) = 0$ is called the
   - (A) root of an equation $f(x) = 0$
   - (B) root of a function $f(x)$
   - (C) zero of an equation $f(x) = 0$
   - (D) none of the above

2. A quadratic equation has _____ root(s).
   - (A) one
   - (B) two
   - (C) three
   - (D) four

3. For a certain cubic equation, at least one of the roots is known to be a complex root. How many total complex roots does the cubic equation have?
   - (A) one
   - (B) two
   - (C) three
   - (D) cannot be determined

4. An equation such as $\tan x = x$ has _____ root(s).
   - (A) zero
   - (B) one
   - (C) two
   - (D) infinite

5. A polynomial of order n has _____ zeros.
   - (A) $n-1$
   - (B) n
   - (C) $n+1$
   - (D) $n+2$

6. The velocity of a body is given by $v(t) = 5e^{-t} + 4$, where t is in seconds and v is in m/s. The velocity of the body is 6 m/s at $t =$ _____ seconds.
   - (A) 0.1823
   - (B) 0.3979
   - (C) 0.9163
   - (D) 1.609

Complete Solution

Problem Set

Chapter 03.01
Background of Nonlinear Equations

1. Find the roots of the equation $2x^2 + 5x + 3 = 0$.

2. Find the roots of the equation $2x^2 + 4x + 4 = 0$.

3. Using any method, estimate the first non-negative root of the equation $\tan(x) = x$. Plot the function, $\tan(x)$ and x to help you to find an approximate answer.

4. You are working for 'DOWN THE TOILET COMPANY' that makes floats for ABC commodes. The ball has a specific gravity of 0.6 and has a radius of 5.5 cm. You are asked to find the depth to which the ball will get submerged when floating in water.

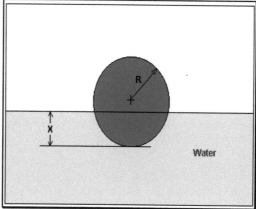

The equation that gives the depth x (unit of x is m) to which the ball is submerged under water is given by
$$x^3 - 0.165x^2 + 3.993 \times 10^{-4} = 0$$
Note that the cubic equation will have three roots. Can some of these roots be complex. If so how many complex roots can it have? If more than one root of the above equation is real, how do you choose the acceptable root? Or are all the real roots physically acceptable?

5. A ball is thrown down at 50 mph from the top of a building. The building is 420 feet tall. The time in seconds the ball would take to reach the ground is given by

$$16.1t^2 + 73.33t - 420 = 0, t \geq 0$$

   a) How many roots does the quadratic equation have?
   b) Which of the two roots is a valid answer?
   c) How much time would the ball take to reach the ground if it was just let go rather than thrown?
   d) If the quadratic equation gave you complex roots, what would be your conclusion?

6. A straight steel ruler that is 12" long at the initial temperature of $80°F$ contracts in length when dipped in a cold liquid. It is allowed to reach steady state. If the reduction in the length at steady state is found to be 0.001", find the nonlinear equation (you do not have to solve it) that will allow you to find the temperature of the liquid. The reduction in the length, ΔL is given by

$$\Delta L = L \int_{T_{initial}}^{T_{liquid}} \alpha \, dT$$

where

   L = initial length of the ruler,
   $\alpha = -1.2 \times 10^{-11} T^2 + 6.2 \times 10^{-9} T + 6 \times 10^{-6}$ (units of α are in/in/°F, and units of temperature are °F)
   T_{liquid} = temperature of the liquid,
   $T_{initial}$ = initial temperature of the steel ruler.

Chapter 03.03
Bisection Method of Solving a Nonlinear Equation

After reading this chapter, you should be able to:

1. *follow the algorithm of the bisection method of solving a nonlinear equation,*
2. *use the bisection method to solve examples of finding roots of a nonlinear equation, and*
3. *enumerate the advantages and disadvantages of the bisection method.*

What is the bisection method and what is it based on?

One of the first numerical methods developed to find the root of a nonlinear equation $f(x) = 0$ was the bisection method (also called *binary-search* method). The method is based on the following theorem.

Theorem

An equation $f(x) = 0$, where $f(x)$ is a real continuous function, has at least one root between x_ℓ and x_u if $f(x_\ell)f(x_u) < 0$ (See Figure 1).

Note that if $f(x_\ell)f(x_u) > 0$, there may or may not be any root between x_ℓ and x_u (Figures 2 and 3). If $f(x_\ell)f(x_u) < 0$, then there may be more than one root between x_ℓ and x_u (Figure 4). So the theorem only guarantees one root between x_ℓ and x_u.

Bisection method

Since the method is based on finding the root between two points, the method falls under the category of bracketing methods.

Since the root is bracketed between two points, x_ℓ and x_u, one can find the mid-point, x_m between x_ℓ and x_u. This gives us two new intervals

1. x_ℓ and x_m, and
2. x_m and x_u.

03.03.1

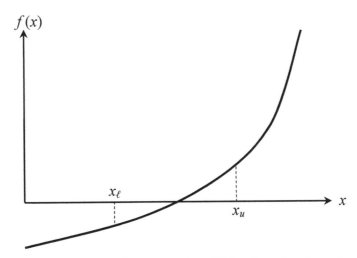

Figure 1 At least one root exists between the two points if the function is real, continuous, and changes sign.

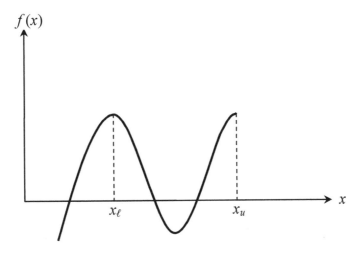

Figure 2 If the function $f(x)$ does not change sign between the two points, roots of the equation $f(x) = 0$ may still exist between the two points.

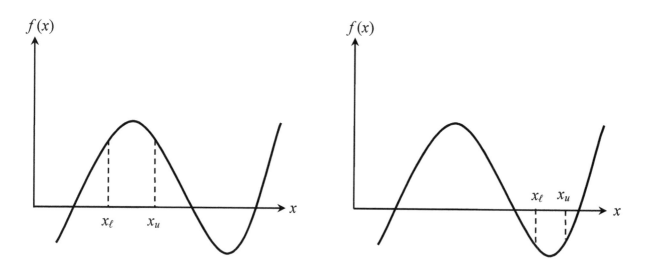

Figure 3 If the function $f(x)$ does not change sign between two points, there may not be any roots for the equation $f(x) = 0$ between the two points.

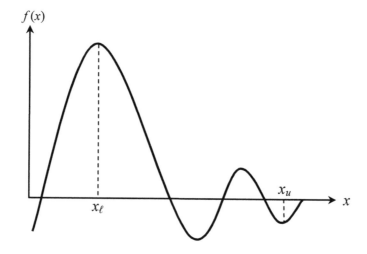

Figure 4 If the function $f(x)$ changes sign between the two points, more than one root for the equation $f(x) = 0$ may exist between the two points.

Is the root now between x_ℓ and x_m or between x_m and x_u? Well, one can find the sign of $f(x_\ell)f(x_m)$, and if $f(x_\ell)f(x_m) < 0$ then the new bracket is between x_ℓ and x_m, otherwise, it is between x_m and x_u. So, you can see that you are literally halving the interval. As one repeats this process, the width of the interval $[x_\ell, x_u]$ becomes smaller and smaller, and you can zero in to the root of the equation $f(x) = 0$. The algorithm for the bisection method is given as follows.

Algorithm for the bisection method

The steps to apply the bisection method to find the root of the equation $f(x) = 0$ are

1. Choose x_ℓ and x_u as two guesses for the root such that $f(x_\ell)f(x_u) < 0$, or in other words, $f(x)$ changes sign between x_ℓ and x_u.

2. Estimate the root, x_m, of the equation $f(x) = 0$ as the mid-point between x_ℓ and x_u as

$$x_m = \frac{x_\ell + x_u}{2}$$

3. Now check the following
   a) If $f(x_\ell)f(x_m) < 0$, then the root lies between x_ℓ and x_m; then $x_\ell = x_\ell$ and $x_u = x_m$.
   b) If $f(x_\ell)f(x_m) > 0$, then the root lies between x_m and x_u; then $x_\ell = x_m$ and $x_u = x_u$.
   c) If $f(x_\ell)f(x_m) = 0$; then the root is x_m. Stop the algorithm if this is true.

4. Find the new estimate of the root

$$x_m = \frac{x_\ell + x_u}{2}$$

Find the absolute relative approximate error as

$$\left|\epsilon_a\right| = \left|\frac{x_m^{new} - x_m^{old}}{x_m^{new}}\right| \times 100$$

where

x_m^{new} = estimated root from present iteration

x_m^{old} = estimated root from previous iteration

5. Compare the absolute relative approximate error $\left|\epsilon_a\right|$ with the pre-specified relative error tolerance ϵ_s. If $\left|\epsilon_a\right| > \epsilon_s$, then go to Step 3, else stop the algorithm. Note one should also check whether the number of iterations is more than the maximum number of iterations allowed. If so, one needs to terminate the algorithm and notify the user about it.

Example 1

You are working for 'DOWN THE TOILET COMPANY' that makes floats for ABC commodes. The floating ball has a specific gravity of 0.6 and has a radius of 5.5 cm. You are asked to find the depth to which the ball is submerged when floating in water.

The equation that gives the depth x to which the ball is submerged under water is given by

$$x^3 - 0.165x^2 + 3.993 \times 10^{-4} = 0$$

Use the bisection method of finding roots of equations to find the depth x to which the ball is submerged under water. Conduct three iterations to estimate the root of the above equation. Find the absolute relative approximate error at the end of each iteration, and the number of significant digits at least correct at the end of each iteration.

Solution

From the physics of the problem, the ball would be submerged between $x = 0$ and $x = 2R$, where

R = radius of the ball,

that is

$0 \leq x \leq 2R$
$0 \leq x \leq 2(0.055)$
$0 \leq x \leq 0.11$

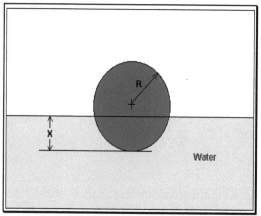

Figure 5 Floating ball problem.

Lets us assume

$x_\ell = 0, \, x_u = 0.11$

Check if the function changes sign between x_ℓ and x_u.

$f(x_\ell) = f(0) = (0)^3 - 0.165(0)^2 + 3.993 \times 10^{-4} = 3.993 \times 10^{-4}$

$f(x_u) = f(0.11) = (0.11)^3 - 0.165(0.11)^2 + 3.993 \times 10^{-4} = -2.662 \times 10^{-4}$

Hence

$f(x_\ell)f(x_u) = f(0)f(0.11) = (3.993 \times 10^{-4})(-2.662 \times 10^{-4}) < 0$

So there is at least one root between x_ℓ and x_u, that is between 0 and 0.11.

Iteration 1
The estimate of the root is

$x_m = \dfrac{x_\ell + x_u}{2}$

$= \dfrac{0 + 0.11}{2}$

$= 0.055$

$f(x_m) = f(0.055) = (0.055)^3 - 0.165(0.055)^2 + 3.993 \times 10^{-4} = 6.655 \times 10^{-5}$

$f(x_\ell)f(x_u) = f(0)f(0.055) = (3.993 \times 10^{-4})(6.655 \times 10^{-4}) > 0$

Hence the root is bracketed between x_m and x_u, that is, between 0.055 and 0.11. So, the lower and upper limit of the new bracket is

$$x_\ell = 0.055, \, x_u = 0.11$$

At this point, the absolute relative approximate error $|\epsilon_a|$ cannot be calculated as we do not have a previous approximation.

Iteration 2

The estimate of the root is

$$x_m = \frac{x_\ell + x_u}{2}$$
$$= \frac{0.055 + 0.11}{2}$$
$$= 0.0825$$

$$f(x_m) = f(0.0825) = (0.0825)^3 - 0.165(0.0825)^2 + 3.993 \times 10^{-4} = -1.622 \times 10^{-4}$$
$$f(x_\ell)f(x_m) = f(0.055)f(0.0825) = \left(6.655 \times 10^{-5}\right) \times \left(-1.622 \times 10^{-4}\right) < 0$$

Hence, the root is bracketed between x_ℓ and x_m, that is, between 0.055 and 0.0825. So the lower and upper limit of the new bracket is

$$x_\ell = 0.055, \, x_u = 0.0825$$

The absolute relative approximate error $|\epsilon_a|$ at the end of Iteration 2 is

$$|\epsilon_a| = \left| \frac{x_m^{new} - x_m^{old}}{x_m^{new}} \right| \times 100$$
$$= \left| \frac{0.0825 - 0.055}{0.0825} \right| \times 100$$
$$= 33.33\%$$

None of the significant digits are at least correct in the estimated root of $x_m = 0.0825$ because the absolute relative approximate error is greater than 5%.

Iteration 3

$$x_m = \frac{x_\ell + x_u}{2}$$
$$= \frac{0.055 + 0.0825}{2}$$
$$= 0.06875$$

$$f(x_m) = f(0.06875) = (0.06875)^3 - 0.165(0.06875)^2 + 3.993 \times 10^{-4} = -5.563 \times 10^{-5}$$
$$f(x_\ell)f(x_m) = f(0.055)f(0.06875) = (6.655 \times 10^5) \times (-5.563 \times 10^{-5}) < 0$$

Hence, the root is bracketed between x_ℓ and x_m, that is, between 0.055 and 0.06875. So the lower and upper limit of the new bracket is

$$x_\ell = 0.055, \, x_u = 0.06875$$

The absolute relative approximate error $|\epsilon_a|$ at the ends of Iteration 3 is

$$|\in_a| = \left| \frac{x_m^{new} - x_m^{old}}{x_m^{new}} \right| \times 100$$

$$= \left| \frac{0.06875 - 0.0825}{0.06875} \right| \times 100$$

$$= 20\%$$

Still none of the significant digits are at least correct in the estimated root of the equation as the absolute relative approximate error is greater than 5%.

Seven more iterations were conducted and these iterations are shown in Table 1.

Table 1 Root of $f(x) = 0$ as function of number of iterations for bisection method.

Iteration	x_ℓ	x_u	x_m	$|\in_a|\%$	$f(x_m)$
1	0.00000	0.11	0.055	----------	6.655×10^{-5}
2	0.055	0.11	0.0825	33.33	-1.622×10^{-4}
3	0.055	0.0825	0.06875	20.00	-5.563×10^{-5}
4	0.055	0.06875	0.06188	11.11	4.484×10^{-6}
5	0.06188	0.06875	0.06531	5.263	-2.593×10^{-5}
6	0.06188	0.06531	0.06359	2.702	-1.0804×10^{-5}
7	0.06188	0.06359	0.06273	1.370	-3.176×10^{-6}
8	0.06188	0.06273	0.0623	0.6897	6.497×10^{-7}
9	0.0623	0.06273	0.06252	0.3436	-1.265×10^{-6}
10	0.0623	0.06252	0.06241	0.1721	-3.0768×10^{-7}

At the end of 10th iteration,

$$|\in_a| = 0.1721\%$$

Hence the number of significant digits at least correct is given by the largest value of m for which

$$|\in_a| \le 0.5 \times 10^{2-m}$$

$$0.1721 \le 0.5 \times 10^{2-m}$$

$$0.3442 \le 10^{2-m}$$

$$\log(0.3442) \le 2 - m$$

$$m \le 2 - \log(0.3442) = 2.463$$

So

$$m = 2$$

The number of significant digits at least correct in the estimated root of 0.06241 at the end of the 10th iteration is 2.

Advantages of bisection method

a) The bisection method is always convergent. Since the method brackets the root, the method is guaranteed to converge.

b) As iterations are conducted, the interval gets halved. So one can guarantee the error in the solution of the equation.

Drawbacks of bisection method

a) The convergence of the bisection method is slow as it is simply based on halving the interval.

b) If one of the initial guesses is closer to the root, it will take larger number of iterations to reach the root.

c) If a function $f(x)$ is such that it just touches the x-axis (Figure 6) such as

$$f(x) = x^2 = 0$$

it will be unable to find the lower guess, x_ℓ, and upper guess, x_u, such that

$$f(x_\ell)f(x_u) < 0$$

d) For functions $f(x)$ where there is a singularity[1] and it reverses sign at the singularity, the bisection method may converge on the singularity (Figure 7). An example includes

$$f(x) = \frac{1}{x}$$

where $x_\ell = -2$, $x_u = 3$ are valid initial guesses which satisfy

$$f(x_\ell)f(x_u) < 0$$

However, the function is not continuous and the theorem that a root exists is also not applicable.

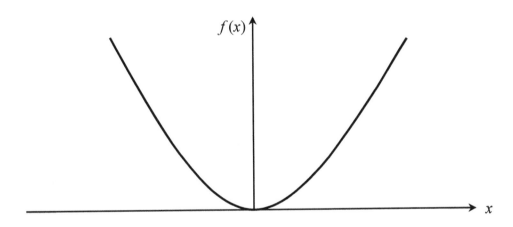

Figure 6 The equation $f(x) = x^2 = 0$ has a single root at $x = 0$ that cannot be bracketed.

---

[1] A singularity in a function is defined as a point where the function becomes infinite. For example, for a function such as $1/x$, the point of singularity is $x = 0$ as it becomes infinite.

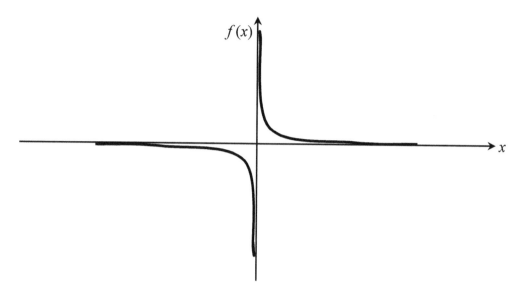

Figure 7 The equation $f(x) = \dfrac{1}{x} = 0$ has no root but changes sign.

NONLINEAR EQUATIONS	
Topic	Bisection method of solving a nonlinear equation
Summary	These are textbook notes of bisection method of finding roots of nonlinear equation, including convergence and pitfalls.
Major	General Engineering
Authors	Autar Kaw
Date	December 23, 2009
Web Site	http://numericalmethods.eng.usf.edu

Multiple-Choice Test

Chapter 03.03
Bisection Method

1. The bisection method of finding roots of nonlinear equations falls under the category of a (an) _____ method.
   - (A) open
   - (B) bracketing
   - (C) random
   - (D) graphical

2. If $f(x)$ is a real continuous function in $[a,b]$, and $f(a)f(b) < 0$, then for $f(x) = 0$, there is (are) _____ in the domain $[a,b]$.
   - (A) one root
   - (B) an undeterminable number of roots
   - (C) no root
   - (D) at least one root

3. Assuming an initial bracket of $[1,5]$, the second (at the end of 2 iterations) iterative value of the root of $te^{-t} - 0.3 = 0$ using the bisection method is
   - (A) 0
   - (B) 1.5
   - (C) 2
   - (D) 3

4. To find the root of $f(x) = 0$, a scientist is using the bisection method. At the beginning of an iteration, the lower and upper guesses of the root are x_l and x_u. At the end of the iteration, the absolute relative approximate error in the estimated value of the root would be
   - (A) $\left| \dfrac{x_u}{x_u + x_\ell} \right|$
   - (B) $\left| \dfrac{x_\ell}{x_u + x_\ell} \right|$
   - (C) $\left| \dfrac{x_u - x_\ell}{x_u + x_\ell} \right|$
   - (D) $\left| \dfrac{x_u + x_\ell}{x_u - x_\ell} \right|$

03.03.1

5. For an equation like $x^2 = 0$, a root exists at $x = 0$. The bisection method cannot be adopted to solve this equation in spite of the root existing at $x = 0$ because the function $f(x) = x^2$
    (A) is a polynomial
    (B) has repeated roots at $x = 0$
    (C) is always non-negative
    (D) has a slope equal to zero at $x = 0$

6. The ideal gas law is given by
    $$pv = RT$$
    where p is the pressure, v is the specific volume, R is the universal gas constant, and T is the absolute temperature. This equation is only accurate for a limited range of pressure and temperature. Vander Waals came up with an equation that was accurate for larger ranges of pressure and temperature given by
    $$\left(p + \frac{a}{v^2}\right)(v - b) = RT$$
    Where a and b are empirical constants dependent on a particular gas. Given the value of $R = 0.08$, $a = 3.592$, $b = 0.04267$, $p = 10$ and $T = 300$ (assume all units are consistent), one is going to find the specific volume, v, for the above values. Without finding the solution from the Vander Waals equation, what would be a good initial guess for v?
    (A) 0
    (B) 1.2
    (C) 2.4
    (D) 3.6

Complete Solution

Problem Set

Chapter 03.03
Bisection Method of Nonlinear Equations

1. Find the estimate of the root of $x^2 - 4 = 0$ by using the bisection method. Use initial guesses of 1.7 and 2.4. Conduct three iterations, and calculate the approximate error, true error, absolute relative approximate error, and absolute relative true error at the end of each iteration.

2. You are working for DOWN THE TOILET COMPANY that makes floats for ABC commodes. The ball has a specific gravity of 0.6 and has a radius of 5.5 cm. You are asked to find the depth to which the ball will get submerged when floating in water.

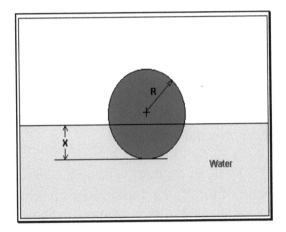

The equation that gives the depth x (unit of x is m) to which the ball is submerged under water is given by
$$x^3 - 0.165x^2 + 3.993 \times 10^{-4} = 0$$
Solving it exactly would require some effort. However using numerical techniques such as bisection method, we can solve this equation and any other equation of the form $f(x) = 0$. Solve the above equation by bisection method and do the following. Use initial guesses as $x = 0$ and $x = 0.11$.
   a) Conduct three iterations.
   b) Calculate the absolute relative approximate error at the end of each step.
   c) Find the number of significant digits at least correct at the end of each iteration.
   d) How can you use the knowledge of the physics of the problem to develop initial guesses for the bisection method?

3. The velocity of a body is given by the following equation
$$v(t) = te^{-t} + \frac{1}{t}$$
where

        t is given in seconds and v is given in m/s.

Find the time when the velocity of the body will be 0.35 m/s. Use bisection method and conduct three iterations. Use initial bracketing guess of [1,8]. Show all steps in calculating the estimated root, absolute relative approximate error and the velocity of the body for each iteration. Also, tabulate your answers as iteration number, estimated root, absolute relative approximate error, and velocity of the body.

4. Enumerate the drawbacks of the bisection method of solving nonlinear equations.

5. The velocity of a body is given by
$$v = 5e^{-t} + 4 + \sin(t),$$
where

        v is given in m/s,
        t is given in s.

Derive the nonlinear equation that you will need to solve to find when the acceleration of the body would be $1.54\,\text{m/s}^2$. Find the solution of the equation by using three iterations of the bisection method.

6. To solve the equation $f(x) = 0$, an engineer is using the bisection method. He starts with an initial valid bracket of [2, 7]. Find the maximum possible absolute true error in his estimate of the root at the end of two iterations? Show your reasoning clearly for your answer.

7. Estimate the next guess for the root of $x^2 - 16 = 0$ by using a modified bisection method as explained below. The initial bracket of [1,8] is found as a valid bracket. In case of bisection method, root estimated at the end of first iteration is the midpoint between 1 and 8. Instead in the modified bisection method, the root estimated at the end of the first iteration would be the point where the straight line drawn from the function at $x = 1$ to the function at $x = 8$ crosses the x-axis. What is this estimate of the root?

Chapter 03.04
Newton-Raphson Method of Solving a Nonlinear Equation

After reading this chapter, you should be able to:

1. *derive the Newton-Raphson method formula,*
2. *develop the algorithm of the Newton-Raphson method,*
3. *use the Newton-Raphson method to solve a nonlinear equation, and*
4. *discuss the drawbacks of the Newton-Raphson method.*

Introduction

Methods such as the bisection method and the false position method of finding roots of a nonlinear equation $f(x) = 0$ require bracketing of the root by two guesses. Such methods are called *bracketing methods*. These methods are always convergent since they are based on reducing the interval between the two guesses so as to zero in on the root of the equation.

In the Newton-Raphson method, the root is not bracketed. In fact, only one initial guess of the root is needed to get the iterative process started to find the root of an equation. The method hence falls in the category of *open methods*. Convergence in open methods is not guaranteed but if the method does converge, it does so much faster than the bracketing methods.

Derivation

The Newton-Raphson method is based on the principle that if the initial guess of the root of $f(x) = 0$ is at x_i, then if one draws the tangent to the curve at $f(x_i)$, the point x_{i+1} where the tangent crosses the x-axis is an improved estimate of the root (Figure 1).

Using the definition of the slope of a function, at $x = x_i$

$$f'(x_i) = \tan\theta$$
$$= \frac{f(x_i) - 0}{x_i - x_{i+1}},$$

which gives

$$x_{i+1} = x_i - \frac{f(x_i)}{f'(x_i)} \qquad (1)$$

Equation (1) is called the Newton-Raphson formula for solving nonlinear equations of the form $f(x)=0$. So starting with an initial guess, x_i, one can find the next guess, x_{i+1}, by using Equation (1). One can repeat this process until one finds the root within a desirable tolerance.

Algorithm

The steps of the Newton-Raphson method to find the root of an equation $f(x)=0$ are
1. Evaluate $f'(x)$ symbolically
2. Use an initial guess of the root, x_i, to estimate the new value of the root, x_{i+1}, as

$$x_{i+1} = x_i - \frac{f(x_i)}{f'(x_i)}$$

3. Find the absolute relative approximate error $|\epsilon_a|$ as

$$|\epsilon_a| = \left| \frac{x_{i+1} - x_i}{x_{i+1}} \right| \times 100$$

4. Compare the absolute relative approximate error with the pre-specified relative error tolerance, ϵ_s. If $|\epsilon_a| > \epsilon_s$, then go to Step 2, else stop the algorithm. Also, check if the number of iterations has exceeded the maximum number of iterations allowed. If so, one needs to terminate the algorithm and notify the user.

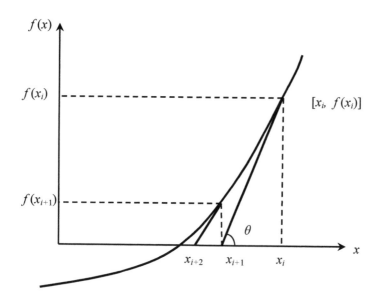

Figure 1 Geometrical illustration of the Newton-Raphson method.

Example 1

You are working for 'DOWN THE TOILET COMPANY' that makes floats for ABC commodes. The floating ball has a specific gravity of 0.6 and has a radius of 5.5 cm. You are asked to find the depth to which the ball is submerged when floating in water.

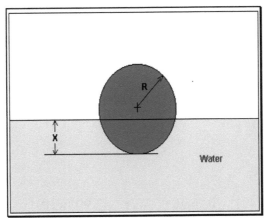

Figure 2   Floating ball problem.

The equation that gives the depth x in meters to which the ball is submerged under water is given by
$$x^3 - 0.165x^2 + 3.993 \times 10^{-4} = 0$$
Use the Newton-Raphson method of finding roots of equations to find
- a)   the depth x to which the ball is submerged under water. Conduct three iterations to estimate the root of the above equation.
- b)   the absolute relative approximate error at the end of each iteration, and
- c)   the number of significant digits at least correct at the end of each iteration.

Solution

$$f(x) = x^3 - 0.165x^2 + 3.993 \times 10^{-4}$$
$$f'(x) = 3x^2 - 0.33x$$

Let us assume the initial guess of the root of $f(x) = 0$ is $x_0 = 0.05$ m. This is a reasonable guess (discuss why $x = 0$ and $x = 0.11$ m are not good choices) as the extreme values of the depth x would be 0 and the diameter (0.11 m) of the ball.

Iteration 1
The estimate of the root is
$$x_1 = x_0 - \frac{f(x_0)}{f'(x_0)}$$
$$= 0.05 - \frac{(0.05)^3 - 0.165(0.05)^2 + 3.993 \times 10^{-4}}{3(0.05)^2 - 0.33(0.05)}$$
$$= 0.05 - \frac{1.118 \times 10^{-4}}{-9 \times 10^{-3}}$$
$$= 0.05 - (-0.01242)$$
$$= 0.06242$$

The absolute relative approximate error $\left|\epsilon_a\right|$ at the end of Iteration 1 is

$$\left|\epsilon_a\right| = \left|\frac{x_1 - x_0}{x_1}\right| \times 100$$

$$= \left|\frac{0.06242 - 0.05}{0.06242}\right| \times 100$$

$$= 19.90\%$$

The number of significant digits at least correct is 0, as you need an absolute relative approximate error of 5% or less for at least one significant digit to be correct in your result.

Iteration 2

The estimate of the root is

$$x_2 = x_1 - \frac{f(x_1)}{f'(x_1)}$$

$$= 0.06242 - \frac{(0.06242)^3 - 0.165(0.06242)^2 + 3.993 \times 10^{-4}}{3(0.06242)^2 - 0.33(0.06242)}$$

$$= 0.06242 - \frac{-3.97781 \times 10^{-7}}{-8.90973 \times 10^{-3}}$$

$$= 0.06242 - (4.4646 \times 10^{-5})$$

$$= 0.06238$$

The absolute relative approximate error $\left|\epsilon_a\right|$ at the end of Iteration 2 is

$$\left|\epsilon_a\right| = \left|\frac{x_2 - x_1}{x_2}\right| \times 100$$

$$= \left|\frac{0.06238 - 0.06242}{0.06238}\right| \times 100$$

$$= 0.0716\%$$

The maximum value of m for which $\left|\epsilon_a\right| \leq 0.5 \times 10^{2-m}$ is 2.844. Hence, the number of significant digits at least correct in the answer is 2.

Iteration 3

The estimate of the root is

$$x_3 = x_2 - \frac{f(x_2)}{f'(x_2)}$$

$$= 0.06238 - \frac{(0.06238)^3 - 0.165(0.06238)^2 + 3.993 \times 10^{-4}}{3(0.06238)^2 - 0.33(0.06238)}$$

$$= 0.06238 - \frac{4.44 \times 10^{-11}}{-8.91171 \times 10^{-3}}$$

$$= 0.06238 - (-4.9822 \times 10^{-9})$$

$$= 0.06238$$

The absolute relative approximate error $\left|\epsilon_a\right|$ at the end of Iteration 3 is

$$|\epsilon_a| = \left| \frac{0.06238 - 0.06238}{0.06238} \right| \times 100$$

$$= 0$$

The number of significant digits at least correct is 4, as only 4 significant digits are carried through in all the calculations.

Drawbacks of the Newton-Raphson Method

1. Divergence at inflection points

If the selection of the initial guess or an iterated value of the root turns out to be close to the inflection point (see the definition in the appendix of this chapter) of the function $f(x)$ in the equation $f(x) = 0$, Newton-Raphson method may start diverging away from the root. It may then start converging back to the root. For example, to find the root of the equation

$$f(x) = (x-1)^3 + 0.512 = 0$$

the Newton-Raphson method reduces to

$$x_{i+1} = x_i - \frac{(x_i^3 - 1)^3 + 0.512}{3(x_i - 1)^2}$$

Starting with an initial guess of $x_0 = 5.0$, Table 1 shows the iterated values of the root of the equation. As you can observe, the root starts to diverge at Iteration 6 because the previous estimate of 0.92589 is close to the inflection point of $x = 1$ (the value of $f'(x)$ is zero at the inflection point). Eventually, after 12 more iterations the root converges to the exact value of $x = 0.2$.

Table 1   Divergence near inflection point.

Iteration Number	x_i
0	5.0000
1	3.6560
2	2.7465
3	2.1084
4	1.6000
5	0.92589
6	−30.119
7	−19.746
8	−12.831
9	−8.2217
10	−5.1498
11	−3.1044
12	−1.7464
13	−0.85356
14	−0.28538
15	0.039784
16	0.17475
17	0.19924
18	0.2

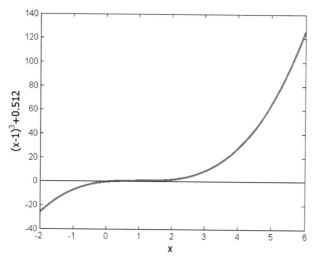

Figure 3 Divergence at inflection point for $f(x) = (x-1)^3 = 0$.

2. Division by zero

For the equation

$$f(x) = x^3 - 0.03x^2 + 2.4 \times 10^{-6} = 0$$

the Newton-Raphson method reduces to

$$x_{i+1} = x_i - \frac{x_i^3 - 0.03x_i^2 + 2.4 \times 10^{-6}}{3x_i^2 - 0.06x_i}$$

For $x_0 = 0$ or $x_0 = 0.02$, division by zero occurs (Figure 4). For an initial guess close to 0.02 such as $x_0 = 0.01999$, one may avoid division by zero, but then the denominator in the formula is a small number. For this case, as given in Table 2, even after 9 iterations, the Newton-Raphson method does not converge.

Table 2 Division by near zero in Newton-Raphson method.

Iteration Number	x_i	$f(x_i)$	$\lvert \in_a \rvert \%$
0	0.019990	-1.60000×10^{-6}	——
1	-2.6480	18.778	100.75
2	-1.7620	-5.5638	50.282
3	-1.1714	-1.6485	50.422
4	-0.77765	-0.48842	50.632
5	-0.51518	-0.14470	50.946
6	-0.34025	-0.042862	51.413
7	-0.22369	-0.012692	52.107
8	-0.14608	-0.0037553	53.127
9	-0.094490	-0.0011091	54.602

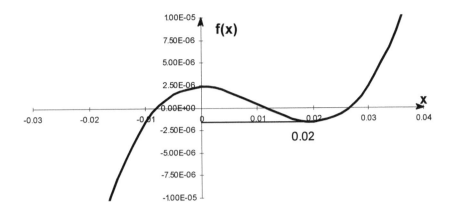

Figure 4   Pitfall of division by zero or a near zero number.

3. Oscillations near local maximum and minimum

Results obtained from the Newton-Raphson method may oscillate about the local maximum or minimum without converging on a root but converging on the local maximum or minimum. Eventually, it may lead to division by a number close to zero and may diverge. For example, for

$$f(x) = x^2 + 2 = 0$$

the equation has no real roots (Figure 5 and Table 3).

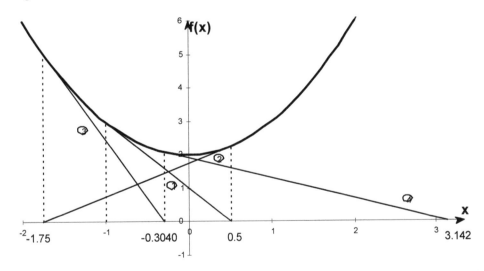

Figure 5   Oscillations around local minima for $f(x) = x^2 + 2$.

Table 3   Oscillations near local maxima and minima in Newton-Raphson method.

Iteration Number	x_i	$f(x_i)$	$|\epsilon_a|\%$
0	−1.0000	3.00	———
1	0.5	2.25	300.00
2	−1.75	5.063	128.571
3	−0.30357	2.092	476.47
4	3.1423	11.874	109.66
5	1.2529	3.570	150.80
6	−0.17166	2.029	829.88
7	5.7395	34.942	102.99
8	2.6955	9.266	112.93
9	0.97678	2.954	175.96

4. Root jumping

In some case where the function $f(x)$ is oscillating and has a number of roots, one may choose an initial guess close to a root. However, the guesses may jump and converge to some other root. For example for solving the equation $\sin x = 0$ if you choose $x_0 = 2.4\pi = (7.539822)$ as an initial guess, it converges to the root of $x = 0$ as shown in Table 4 and Figure 6. However, one may have chosen this as an initial guess to converge to $x = 2\pi = 6.2831853$.

Table 4   Root jumping in Newton-Raphson method.

Iteration Number	x_i	$f(x_i)$	$|\epsilon_a|\%$
0	7.539822	0.951	———
1	4.462	−0.969	68.973
2	0.5499	0.5226	711.44
3	−0.06307	−0.06303	971.91
4	8.376×10^{-4}	8.375×10^{-5}	7.54×10^4
5	-1.95861×10^{-13}	-1.95861×10^{-13}	4.28×10^{10}

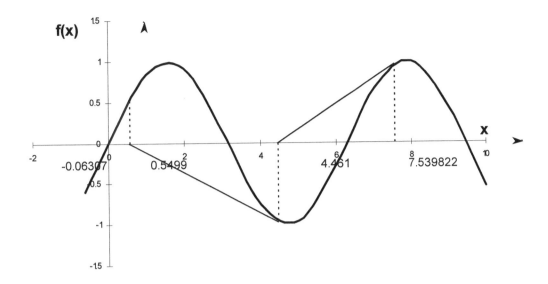

Figure 6 Root jumping from intended location of root for $f(x) = \sin x = 0$.

Appendix A. What is an inflection point?

For a function $f(x)$, the point where the concavity changes from up-to-down or down-to-up is called its inflection point. For example, for the function $f(x) = (x-1)^3$, the concavity changes at $x = 1$ (see Figure 3), and hence $(1,0)$ is an inflection point.

An inflection points MAY exist at a point where $f''(x) = 0$ and where $f''(x)$ does not exist. The reason we say that it MAY exist is because if $f''(x) = 0$, it only makes it a possible inflection point. For example, for $f(x) = x^4 - 16$, $f''(0) = 0$, but the concavity does not change at $x = 0$. Hence the point $(0, -16)$ is not an inflection point of $f(x) = x^4 - 16$.

For $f(x) = (x-1)^3$, $f''(x)$ changes sign at $x = 1$ ($f''(x) < 0$ for $x < 1$, and $f''(x) > 0$ for $x > 1$), and thus brings up the *Inflection Point Theorem* for a function $f(x)$ that states the following.

"If $f'(c)$ exists and $f''(c)$ changes sign at $x = c$, then the point $(c, f(c))$ is an inflection point of the graph of f."

Appendix B. Derivation of Newton-Raphson method from Taylor series

Newton-Raphson method can also be derived from Taylor series. For a general function $f(x)$, the Taylor series is

$$f(x_{i+1}) = f(x_i) + f'(x_i)(x_{i+1} - x_i) + \frac{f''(x_i)}{2!}(x_{i+1} - x_i)^2 + \cdots$$

As an approximation, taking only the first two terms of the right hand side,

$$f(x_{i+1}) \approx f(x_i) + f'(x_i)(x_{i+1} - x_i)$$

and we are seeking a point where $f(x) = 0$, that is, if we assume

$$f(x_{i+1}) = 0,$$

$$0 \approx f(x_i) + f'(x_i)(x_{i+1} - x_i)$$

which gives

$$x_{i+1} = x_i - \frac{f(x_i)}{f'(x_i)}$$

This is the same Newton-Raphson method formula series as derived previously using the geometric method.

NONLINEAR EQUATIONS	
Topic	Newton-Raphson Method of Solving Nonlinear Equations
Summary	Text book notes of Newton-Raphson method of finding roots of nonlinear equation, including convergence and pitfalls.
Major	General Engineering
Authors	Autar Kaw
Date	December 23, 2009
Web Site	http://numericalmethods.eng.usf.edu

Multiple-Choice Test

Chapter 03.04
Newton-Raphson Method

1. The Newton-Raphson method of finding roots of nonlinear equations falls under the category of _____ methods.
   - (A) bracketing
   - (B) open
   - (C) random
   - (D) graphical

2. The Newton-Raphson method formula for finding the square root of a real number R from the equation $x^2 - R = 0$ is,

   (A) $x_{i+1} = \dfrac{x_i}{2}$

   (B) $x_{i+1} = \dfrac{3x_i}{2}$

   (C) $x_{i+1} = \dfrac{1}{2}\left(x_i + \dfrac{R}{x_i}\right)$

   (D) $x_{i+1} = \dfrac{1}{2}\left(3x_i - \dfrac{R}{x_i}\right)$

3. The next iterative value of the root of $x^2 - 4 = 0$ using the Newton-Raphson method, if the initial guess is 3, is
   - (A) 1.5
   - (B) 2.067
   - (C) 2.167
   - (D) 3.000

4. The root of the equation $f(x) = 0$ is found by using the Newton-Raphson method. The initial estimate of the root is $x_0 = 3$, $f(3) = 5$. The angle the line tangent to the function $f(x)$ makes at $x = 3$ is $57°$ with respect to the x-axis. The next estimate of the root, x_1 most nearly is
   - (A) −3.2470
   - (B) −0.2470
   - (C) 3.2470
   - (D) 6.2470

5.   The root of $x^3 = 4$ is found by using the Newton-Raphson method. The successive iterative values of the root are given in the table below.

Iteration Number	Value of Root
0	2.0000
1	1.6667
2	1.5911
3	1.5874
4	1.5874

The iteration number at which I would first trust at least two significant digits in the answer is

      (A) 1
      (B) 2
      (C) 3
      (D) 4

6.   The ideal gas law is given by
$$pv = RT$$
where p is the pressure, v is the specific volume, R is the universal gas constant, and T is the absolute temperature. This equation is only accurate for a limited range of pressure and temperature. Vander Waals came up with an equation that was accurate for larger ranges of pressure and temperature given by
$$\left(p + \frac{a}{v^2} \right)(v - b) = RT$$
where a and b are empirical constants dependent on a particular gas. Given the value of $R = 0.08$, $a = 3.592$, $b = 0.04267$, $p = 10$ and $T = 300$ (assume all units are consistent), one is going to find the specific volume, v, for the above values. Without finding the solution from the Vander Waals equation, what would be a good initial guess for v?

      (A) 0
      (B) 1.2
      (C) 2.4
      (D) 3.6

Complete Solution

Problem Set

Chapter 03.04
Newton-Raphson Method of Nonlinear Equations

1. Find the estimate of the root of $x^2 - 4 = 0$ by using Newton-Raphson method, if the initial guess of the root is 3. Conduct three iterations. Also, calculate the approximate error, true error, absolute relative approximate error, and absolute relative true error at the end of each iteration.

2. The velocity of a body is given by $v(t) = 5e^{-t} + 6$, where v is in m/s and t is in seconds.
    a) Use the Newton Raphson method to find the time when the velocity will be 7.0 m/s. Use only two iterations and take $t = 2$ seconds as the initial guess.
    b) What is the relative true error at the end of the second iteration for part (a)?

3. You are working for DOWN THE TOILET COMPANY that makes floats for ABC commodes. The ball has a specific gravity of 0.6 and has a radius of 5.5 cm. You are asked to find the depth to which the ball will get submerged when floating in water.

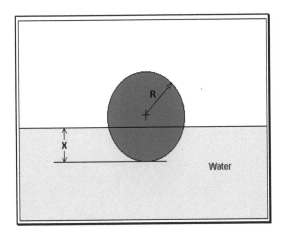

    The equation that gives the depth x (unit of x is m) to which the ball is submerged under water is given by
    $$x^3 - 0.165x^2 + 3.993 \times 10^{-4} = 0$$
    Solving it exactly would require some effort. However, using numerical techniques such as Newton-Raphson method, we can solve this equation and any other equation of the form $f(x) = 0$. Solve the above equation by Newton-Raphson method and do the following.
    a) Conduct three iterations. Use an initial guess $x = 0.055\text{m}$.
    b) Calculate the absolute relative approximate error at the end of each step.

    c) Find the number of significant digits at least correct at the end of each iteration.

    d) How could you have used the knowledge of the physics of the problem to develop initial guess for the Newton-Raphson method?

4.   The root of the equation $f(x) = 0$ is found by using the Newton-Raphson method. If the initial estimate of the root is assumed to be $x_0 = 3$, given $f(3) = 5$, and the angle the tangent makes to the function $f(x)$ at $x = 3$ is $57°$, what is the next estimate of the root, x_1?

5.   The root of the equation $f(x) = 0$ is found by using Newton-Raphson method. The initial estimate of the root is assumed to be $x_0 = 5.0$, and the angle the tangent makes with the x-axis to the function $f(x)$ at $x_0 = 5.0$ is $89.236°$. If the next estimate of the root is, $x_1 = 3.693$, what is the value of the function $f(x)$ at $x = 5$?

6.   Find the Newton-Raphson method formula for finding the square root of a real number R from the equation $x^2 - R = 0$. Find the square root of 50.41 by using the formula. Assume 50.41 as the initial guess. How many iterations does it take to get at least 3 significant digits correct in your answer? Do not calculate the true value to answer the question.

Chapter 03.05
Secant Method of Solving Nonlinear Equations

After reading this chapter, you should be able to:

1. *derive the secant method to solve for the roots of a nonlinear equation,*
2. *use the secant method to numerically solve a nonlinear equation.*

What is the secant method and why would I want to use it instead of the Newton-Raphson method?

The Newton-Raphson method of solving a nonlinear equation $f(x) = 0$ is given by the iterative formula

$$x_{i+1} = x_i - \frac{f(x_i)}{f'(x_i)} \tag{1}$$

One of the drawbacks of the Newton-Raphson method is that you have to evaluate the derivative of the function. With availability of symbolic manipulators such as Maple, MathCAD, MATHEMATICA and MATLAB, this process has become more convenient. However, it still can be a laborious process, and even intractable if the function is derived as part of a numerical scheme. To overcome these drawbacks, the derivative of the function, $f(x)$ is approximated as

$$f'(x_i) = \frac{f(x_i) - f(x_{i-1})}{x_i - x_{i-1}} \tag{2}$$

Substituting Equation (2) in Equation (1) gives

$$x_{i+1} = x_i - \frac{f(x_i)(x_i - x_{i-1})}{f(x_i) - f(x_{i-1})} \tag{3}$$

The above equation is called the secant method. This method now requires two initial guesses, but unlike the bisection method, the two initial guesses do not need to bracket the root of the equation. The secant method is an open method and may or may not converge. However, when secant method converges, it will typically converge faster than the bisection method. However, since the derivative is approximated as given by Equation (2), it typically converges slower than the Newton-Raphson method.

The secant method can also be derived from geometry, as shown in Figure 1. Taking two initial guesses, x_{i-1} and x_i, one draws a straight line between $f(x_i)$ and $f(x_{i-1})$ passing through the x-axis at x_{i+1}. ABE and DCE are similar triangles.

Hence

$$\frac{AB}{AE} = \frac{DC}{DE}$$

$$\frac{f(x_i)}{x_i - x_{i+1}} = \frac{f(x_{i-1})}{x_{i-1} - x_{i+1}}$$

On rearranging, the secant method is given as

$$x_{i+1} = x_i - \frac{f(x_i)(x_i - x_{i-1})}{f(x_i) - f(x_{i-1})}$$

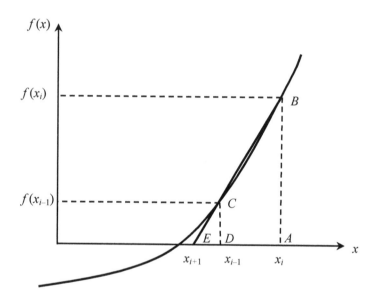

Figure 1 Geometrical representation of the secant method.

Example 1

You are working for 'DOWN THE TOILET COMPANY' that makes floats (Figure 2) for ABC commodes. The floating ball has a specific gravity of 0.6 and a radius of 5.5 cm. You are asked to find the depth to which the ball is submerged when floating in water.

The equation that gives the depth x to which the ball is submerged under water is given by

$$x^3 - 0.165x^2 + 3.993 \times 10^{-4} = 0$$

Use the secant method of finding roots of equations to find the depth x to which the ball is submerged under water. Conduct three iterations to estimate the root of the above equation. Find the absolute relative approximate error and the number of significant digits at least correct at the end of each iteration.

Solution

$$f(x) = x^3 - 0.165x^2 + 3.993 \times 10^{-4}$$

Let us assume the initial guesses of the root of $f(x) = 0$ as $x_{-1} = 0.02$ and $x_0 = 0.05$.

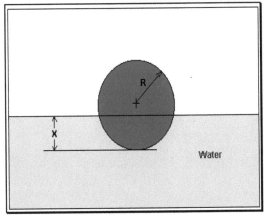

Figure 2 Floating ball problem.

Iteration 1

The estimate of the root is

$$
\begin{aligned}
x_1 &= x_0 - \frac{f(x_0)(x_0 - x_{-1})}{f(x_0) - f(x_{-1})} \\
&= x_0 - \frac{\left(x_0^3 - 0.165x_0^2 + 3.993 \times 10^{-4}\right) \times (x_0 - x_{-1})}{\left(x_0^3 - 0.165x_0^2 + 3.993 \times 10^{-4}\right) - \left(x_{-1}^3 - 0.165x_{-1}^2 + 3.993 \times 10^{-4}\right)} \\
&= 0.05 - \frac{\left[0.05^3 - 0.165(0.05)^2 + 3.993 \times 10^{-4}\right] \times [0.05 - 0.02]}{\left[0.05^3 - 0.165(0.05)^2 + 3.993 \times 10^{-4}\right] - \left[0.02^3 - 0.165(0.02)^2 + 3.993 \times 10^{-4}\right]} \\
&= 0.06461
\end{aligned}
$$

The absolute relative approximate error $|\epsilon_a|$ at the end of Iteration 1 is

$$
\begin{aligned}
|\epsilon_a| &= \left| \frac{x_1 - x_0}{x_1} \right| \times 100 \\
&= \left| \frac{0.06461 - 0.05}{0.06461} \right| \times 100 \\
&= 22.62\%
\end{aligned}
$$

The number of significant digits at least correct is 0, as you need an absolute relative approximate error of 5% or less for one significant digit to be correct in your result.

Iteration 2

$$
\begin{aligned}
x_2 &= x_1 - \frac{f(x_1)(x_1 - x_0)}{f(x_1) - f(x_0)} \\
&= x_1 - \frac{\left(x_1^3 - 0.165x_1^2 + 3.993 \times 10^{-4}\right) \times (x_1 - x_0)}{\left(x_1^3 - 0.165x_1^2 + 3.993 \times 10^{-4}\right) - \left(x_0^3 - 0.165x_0^2 + 3.993 \times 10^{-4}\right)}
\end{aligned}
$$

$$= 0.06461 - \frac{\left[0.06461^3 - 0.165(0.06461)^2 + 3.993 \times 10^{-4}\right] \times (0.06461 - 0.05)}{\left[0.06461^3 - 0.165(0.06461)^2 + 3.993 \times 10^{-4}\right] - \left[0.05^3 - 0.165(0.05)^2 + 3.993 \times 10^{-4}\right]}$$

$$= 0.06241$$

The absolute relative approximate error $\left|\in_a\right|$ at the end of Iteration 2 is

$$\left|\in_a\right| = \left|\frac{x_2 - x_1}{x_2}\right| \times 100$$

$$= \left|\frac{0.06241 - 0.06461}{0.06241}\right| \times 100$$

$$= 3.525\%$$

The number of significant digits at least correct is 1, as you need an absolute relative approximate error of 5% or less.

Iteration 3

$$x_3 = x_2 - \frac{f(x_2)(x_2 - x_1)}{f(x_2) - f(x_1)}$$

$$= x_2 - \frac{\left(x_2^3 - 0.165x_2^2 + 3.993 \times 10^{-4}\right) \times (x_2 - x_1)}{\left(x_2^3 - 0.165x_2^2 + 3.993 \times 10^{-4}\right) - \left(x_1^3 - 0.165x_1^2 + 3.993 \times 10^{-4}\right)}$$

$$= 0.06241 - \frac{\left[0.06241^3 - 0.165(0.06241)^2 + 3.993 \times 10^{-4}\right] \times (0.06241 - 0.06461)}{\left[0.06241^3 - 0.165(0.06241)^2 + 3.993 \times 10^{-4}\right] - \left[0.06461^3 - 0.165(0.06461)^2 + 3.993 \times 10^{-4}\right]}$$

$$= 0.06238$$

The absolute relative approximate error $\left|\in_a\right|$ at the end of Iteration 3 is

$$\left|\in_a\right| = \left|\frac{x_3 - x_2}{x_3}\right| \times 100$$

$$= \left|\frac{0.06238 - 0.06241}{0.06238}\right| \times 100$$

$$= 0.0595\%$$

The number of significant digits at least correct is 2, as you need an absolute relative approximate error of 0.5% or less. Table 1 shows the secant method calculations for the results from the above problem.

Table 1 Secant method results as a function of iterations.

Iteration Number, i	x_{i-1}	x_i	x_{i+1}	$\left|\in_a\right|\%$	$f(x_{i+1})$
1	0.02	0.05	0.06461	22.62	-1.9812×10^{-5}
2	0.05	0.06461	0.06241	3.525	-3.2852×10^{-7}
3	0.06461	0.06241	0.06238	0.0595	2.0252×10^{-9}
4	0.06241	0.06238	0.06238	-3.64×10^{-4}	-1.8576×10^{-13}

NONLINEAR EQUATIONS	
Topic	Secant Method for Solving Nonlinear Equations.
Summary	These are textbook notes of secant method of finding roots of nonlinear equations. Derivations and examples are included.
Major	General Engineering
Authors	Autar Kaw
Date	December 23, 2009
Web Site	http://numericalmethods.eng.usf.edu

Multiple-Choice Test

Secant Method
Chapter 03.05

1. The secant method of finding roots of nonlinear equations falls under the category of _____ methods.
   - (A) bracketing
   - (B) graphical
   - (C) open
   - (D) random

2. The secant method formula for finding the square root of a real number R from the equation $x^2 - R = 0$ is
   - (A) $\dfrac{x_i x_{i-1} + R}{x_i + x_{i-1}}$
   - (B) $\dfrac{x_i x_{i-1}}{x_i + x_{i-1}}$
   - (C) $\dfrac{1}{2}\left(x_i + \dfrac{R}{x_i}\right)$
   - (D) $\dfrac{2x_i^2 + x_i x_{i-1} - R}{x_i + x_{i-1}}$

3. The next iterative value of the root of $x^2 - 4 = 0$ using secant method, if the initial guesses are 3 and 4, is
   - (A) 2.2857
   - (B) 2.5000
   - (C) 5.5000
   - (D) 5.7143

4. The root of the equation $f(x) = 0$ is found by using the secant method. Given one of the initial estimates is $x_0 = 3$, $f(3) = 5$, and the angle the secant line makes with the x-axis is $57°$, the next estimate of the root, x_1, is
   - (A) -3.2470
   - (B) -0.24704
   - (C) 3.247
   - (D) 6.2470

5.   For finding the root of $\sin x = 0$ by the secant method, the following choice of initial guesses would not be appropriate.

(A) $\dfrac{\pi}{4}$ and $\dfrac{\pi}{2}$

(B) $\dfrac{\pi}{4}$ and $\dfrac{3\pi}{4}$

(C) $-\dfrac{\pi}{2}$ and $\dfrac{\pi}{2}$

(D) $\dfrac{\pi}{3}$ and $\dfrac{\pi}{2}$

6.   When drugs are given orally to a patient, the drug concentration c in the blood stream at time t is given by a formula

$$c = Kte^{-at}$$

where K is dependent on parameters such as the dose administered while a is dependent on the absorption and elimination rates of the drug. If $K = 2$ and $a = 0.25$, and t is in seconds and c is in mg/ml, the time at which the maximum concentration is reached is given by the solution of the equation

(A) $2te^{-0.25t} = 0$

(B) $2e^{-0.25t} - 2te^{-0.25t} = 0$

(C) $2e^{-0.25t} - 0.5te^{-0.25t} = 0$

(D) $2te^{-0.25t} = 2$

Complete Solution

Problem Set

Chapter 03.05
Secant Method of Nonlinear Equations

1. Find the estimate of the root of $x^2 - 4 = 0$ by using secant method, if initial guesses of the roots are 3 and 5. Conduct three iterations. Also, calculate the approximate error, true error, absolute relative approximate error, and absolute relative true error at the end of each iteration.

2. The velocity of a body is given by $v(t) = 5e^{-t} + 6$, where v is in m/s and t is in seconds.
    a) Use secant method to find when the velocity will be 7.0 m/s. Use only two iterations and take $t = 2$ and $t = 3.5$ seconds as the initial guesses.
    b) What is the relative true error at the end of the second iteration for part (a)?

3. You are working for DOWN THE TOILET COMPANY that makes floats for ABC commodes. The ball has a specific gravity of 0.6 and has a radius of 5.5 cm. You are asked to find the depth to which the ball will get submerged when floating in water.

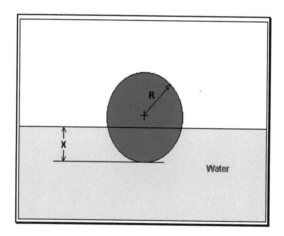

The equation that gives the depth x (unit of x is in m) to which the ball is submerged under water is given by
$$x^3 - 0.165x^2 + 3.993 \times 10^{-4} = 0$$
Solving it exactly would require some effort. However using numerical techniques such as secant method, we can solve this equation and any other equation of the form $f(x) = 0$. Solve the above equation by secant method and do the following.
    a) Conduct three iterations. Use initial guesses of 0.055 and 0.0825.
    b) Calculate the absolute relative approximate error at the end of each step.
    c) Find the number of significant digits that are at least correct at the end of each iteration.

03.05.1

d) How could you have used the knowledge of the physics of the problem to develop initial guesses for the secant method?

4. The root of the equation $f(x) = 0$ is found by using secant method. The initial guesses for the root are assumed to be $x_0 = 3$ and $x_1 = 2$. Given $f(3) = 28$ and $f(2) = 4$, what is the
    a) angle the secant makes with the x-axis,
    b) next estimate of the root, x_2.

5. The root of the equation $f(x) = 0$ is found by using secant method. If the initial estimates of the root are $x_0 = 5.0$ and $x_1 = 2.0$, and the angle the secant makes with the x-axis between $x_0 = 5.0$ and $x_1 = 2.0$ is $88.75°$. If the next estimate of the root is $x_2 = 1.9130$, what is the value of the function $f(x)$ at $x = 2$?

6. Find the secant method formula for finding the square root of a real number R from the equation $x^2 - R = 0$. Use the formula to find the square root of 50.41. Assume 50.41 and 25.205 as the initial guesses. How many iterations does it take to get at least 3 significant digits correct in your answer? Do not calculate the true value to answer the question.

Chapter 04.00A

Physical Problem for Simultaneous Linear Equations
General Engineering

Problem Statement

The upward velocity of a rocket is given at three different times in the following table

Time, t	Velocity, v
s	m/s
5	106.8
8	177.2
12	279.2

The velocity data is approximated by a polynomial as

Figure 1 A rocket launched into space[1]

$$v(t) = at^2 + bt + c, \quad 5 \le t \le 12.$$

Set up the equations in matrix form to find the coefficients a, b, c of the velocity profile.

Solution

The polynomial is going through three data points (t_1, v_1), (t_2, v_2), and (t_3, v_3) where from the above table

$$t_1 = 5, v_1 = 106.8$$
$$t_2 = 8, v_2 = 177.2$$
$$t_3 = 12, v_3 = 279.2$$

Requiring that $v(t) = at^2 + bt + c$ passes through the three data points gives

$$v(t_1) = v_1 = at_1^2 + bt_1 + c$$
$$v(t_2) = v_2 = at_2^2 + bt_2 + c$$
$$v(t_3) = v_3 = at_3^2 + bt_3 + c$$

Substituting the data (t_1, v_1), (t_2, v_2), (t_3, v_3) gives

$$a(5^2) + b(5) + c = 106.8$$
$$a(8^2) + b(8) + c = 177.2$$
$$a(12^2) + b(12) + c = 279.2$$

or

$$25a + 5b + c = 106.8$$
$$64a + 8b + c = 177.2$$
$$144a + 12b + c = 279.2$$

This set of equations can be rewritten in the matrix form as

$$\begin{bmatrix} 25a + & 5b + & c \\ 64a + & 8b + & c \\ 144a + & 12b + & c \end{bmatrix} = \begin{bmatrix} 106.8 \\ 177.2 \\ 279.2 \end{bmatrix}$$

The above equation can be written as a linear combination as follows

$$a\begin{bmatrix} 25 \\ 64 \\ 144 \end{bmatrix} + b\begin{bmatrix} 5 \\ 8 \\ 12 \end{bmatrix} + c\begin{bmatrix} 1 \\ 1 \\ 1 \end{bmatrix} = \begin{bmatrix} 106.8 \\ 177.2 \\ 279.2 \end{bmatrix}$$

---

[1] Source of rocket picture: NASA Langley Research Center, Office of Education, **edu.larc.nasa.gov/pstp/**

and further using matrix multiplications gives

$$\begin{bmatrix} 25 & 5 & 1 \\ 64 & 8 & 1 \\ 144 & 12 & 1 \end{bmatrix} \begin{bmatrix} a \\ b \\ c \end{bmatrix} = \begin{bmatrix} 106.8 \\ 177.2 \\ 279.2 \end{bmatrix}$$

The solution of the above three simultaneous linear equations will give the value of a, b, c.

QUESTIONS

1. Solve for the values of a, b, c.
2. Verify if you get back the value of the velocity data at t=5s.
3. Estimate the velocity of the rocket at t=7.5s?
4. Estimate the acceleration of the rocket at t=7.5 s?
5. Estimate the distance covered by the rocket between t=5.5 s and 8.9 s.
6. If the following data is given for the velocity of the rocket as a function of time, and you are asked to use a quadratic polynomial to approximate the velocity profile to find the velocity at t=16 s, what data points would you choose and why?

t	v(t)
s	m/s
0	0
10	227.04
15	362.78
20	517.35
22.5	602.97
30	901.67

SIMULTANEOUS LINEAR EQUATIONS

Topic	Simultaneous Linear Equations
Summary	Velocity profile of a rocket.
Major	General Engineering
Authors	Autar Kaw
Date	March 8, 2010
Web Site	http://numericalmethods.eng.usf.edu

Chapter 04.00B

Physical Problem for Simultaneous Linear Equations
Chemical Engineering

Problem Statement: Liquid-liquid extraction depends on the ability of some metal ions to form metal complexes with organic acids. The method is used to separate, concentrate, and purify metals and organic compounds. Liquid-liquid extraction was the technique used to produce weapon grade uranium during the arms race (cold war) era. The technique is also used to recover noble metals used in catalytic processes such as oil refining etc.

In liquid-liquid extraction, the metal ion in the aqueous phase is recovered by mixing the aqueous phase with an organic phase. The metal ion forms a complex with the organic phase and floats on top of the aqueous phase. The organic phase can be decanted and separated from the aqueous phase and the complexed metal ion recovered in a useful form using an acid (nitric acid for nitrates, sulfuric acid for sulfates etc).

A liquid-liquid extraction process conducted in the Electrochemical Materials Laboratory involved the extraction of nickel from the aqueous phase into an organic phase. A typical experimental data from the laboratory is given in Table 1.

Table 1 Aqueous and organic phase concentration of nickel.

Ni aqueous phase (g/l)	2	2.5	3	3.5	4
Ni organic phase (g/l)	8.57	10	12	14	15.66

Estimate the amount of nickel in organic phase when 2.3 g/l is in the aqueous phase. Use quadratic interpolation.

Solution

The polynomial is going through three data points (a_1, g_1), (a_2, g_2), and (a_3, g_3) where from the above table

$$a_1 = 2, g_1 = 8.57$$
$$a_2 = 2.5, g_2 = 10$$
$$a_3 = 3, g_3 = 12$$

Requiring that $g = x_1 a^2 + x_2 a + x_3$ passes through the three data points gives

$$g(a_1) = g_1 = x_1 a_1^2 + x_2 a_1 + x_3$$

$$g(a_2) = g_2 = x_1 a_2^2 + x_2 a_2 + x_3$$
$$g(a_3) = g_3 = x_1 a_3^2 + x_2 a_3 + x_3$$

Substituting the data $(a_1, g_1), (a_2, g_2), (a_3, g_3)$

$$x_1(2)^2 + x_2(2) + x_3 = 8.57$$
$$x_1(2.5)^2 + x_2(2.5) + x_3 = 10$$
$$x_1(3)^2 + x_2(3) + x_3 = 12$$

gives

$$4x_1 + 2x_2 + x_3 = 8.57$$
$$6.25x_1 + 2.5x_2 + x_3 = 10$$
$$9x_1 + 3x_2 + x_3 = 12$$

This set of equations can be rewritten in the matrix form as

$$\begin{bmatrix} 4x_1 + & 2x_2 + & x_3 \\ 6.25x_1 + & 2.5x_2 + & x_3 \\ 9x_1 + & 3x_2 + & x_3 \end{bmatrix} = \begin{bmatrix} 8.57 \\ 10 \\ 12 \end{bmatrix}$$

The above equations can be written as a linear combination as follows

$$x_1 \begin{bmatrix} 4 \\ 6.25 \\ 9 \end{bmatrix} + x_2 \begin{bmatrix} 2 \\ 2.5 \\ 3 \end{bmatrix} + x_3 \begin{bmatrix} 1 \\ 1 \\ 1 \end{bmatrix} = \begin{bmatrix} 8.57 \\ 10 \\ 12 \end{bmatrix}$$

and further using matrix multiplication gives

$$\begin{bmatrix} 4 & 2 & 1 \\ 6.25 & 25 & 1 \\ 9 & 3 & 1 \end{bmatrix} \begin{bmatrix} x_1 \\ x_2 \\ x_3 \end{bmatrix} = \begin{bmatrix} 8.57 \\ 10 \\ 12 \end{bmatrix}$$

The solution of the above simultaneous linear equations will give the value of x_1, x_2, x_3.

QUESTIONS:

1. Verify if you get back the value of the Ni organic phase when the Ni aqueous phase is 2.5 g/l.
2. Estimate the value of the Ni organic phase when the Ni aqueous phase is 2.78 g/l
3. Estimate the error between linear interpolation and quadratic interpolation values obtained for nickel in organic phase when 2.78 g/l is in the aqueous phase.

SIMULTANEOUS LINEAR EQUATIONS	
Topic	Simultaneous Linear Equations
Summary	Estimating Nickel in Organic Phase
Major	Chemical Engineering
Authors	Egwu Eric Kalu
Date	December 23, 2009
Web Site	http://numericalmethods.eng.usf.edu

Chapter 04.00C

Physical Problem for Simultaneous Linear Equations
Civil Engineering

Problem Statement: A pressure vessel can only be subjected to an amount of internal pressure that is limited by the strength of material used. For example, take a pressure vessel of internal radius of $a = 5"$ and outer radius, $b = 8"$, made of ASTM 36 steel (yield strength of ASTM 36 steel is 36 ksi). How much internal pressure can this pressure vessel take before it is considered to have failed?

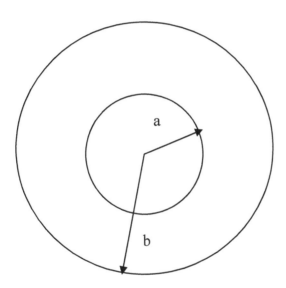

Figure 1 A single cylinder pressure vessel with internal radius, a and outer radius, b.

The hoop and radial stress in a cylindrical pressure vessel is given by [1]

$$\sigma_r = \frac{a^2 p_i}{b^2 - a^2}\left(1 - \frac{b^2}{r^2}\right) \tag{1}$$

$$\sigma_\theta = \frac{a^2 p_i}{b^2 - a^2}\left(1 + \frac{b^2}{r^2}\right) \tag{2}$$

The maximum normal stress anywhere in the cylinder is the hoop stress at the inner radius, a

$$\sigma_\theta|_{max} = p_i\left(\frac{b^2 + a^2}{b^2 - a^2}\right) \tag{3}$$

Assuming a factor of safety of 2, while the yield strength is given as 36 ksi,

$$\frac{36 \times 10^3}{2} = p_i\left(\frac{8^2 + 5^2}{8^2 - 5^2}\right)$$

$$p_i = 7.887 \, \text{ksi}$$

You can see from Equation (3) that even for $b \gg a$, the maximum internal pressure one can apply is only $p_i = 18 \, \text{ksi}$. Therefore, what can an engineer do to maximize the internal pressure, while keeping the material and radial dimensions the same? He or she can use a compounded cylinder. One can create a compounded cylinder by shrink fitting one cylinder into another, and hence creating pre-existing favorable stresses to allow more internal pressure. Let us see how that would work?

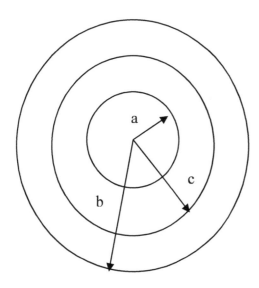

Figure 2 A compounded cylinder pressure vessel with internal radius, a, outer radius, b, and interface at $r = c$.

Let us make the compounded cylinder of two cylinders (Figure 2). Cylinder 1 has an internal radius of $a = 5"$, and outer radius $c = 6.5"$, while Cylinder 2 has an internal radius of $c = 6.5"$ and outer radius, $b = 8"$. Assume that that radial interference, $\delta = 0.007"$ occurs at the interface of a compounded cylinder at $r = c = 6.5"$. How does one find then the pressure that can be applied to the compounded cylinder of internal radius, $a = 5"$ and outer radius, $b = 8"$?

For a cylinder 1, the radial displacement, u_1 is given by

$$u_1 = c_1 r + \frac{c_2}{r} \tag{4}$$

the radial stress, σ_r^1 and hoop stress, σ_θ^1 by

$$\sigma_r^1 = \frac{E}{1-v^2}\left[c_1(1+v) - c_2\left(\frac{1-v}{r^2}\right)\right] \tag{5}$$

$$\sigma_\theta^1 = \frac{E}{1-v^2}\left[c_1(1+v) + c_2\left(\frac{1-v}{r^2}\right)\right] \tag{6}$$

where

$E=$ Young's modulus of steel,
$v=$ Poisson's ratio of steel.

For cylinder 2, the radial displacements, u_2 is given by

$$u_2 = c_3 r + \frac{c_4}{r} \tag{7}$$

the radial stress, σ_r^2 and hoop stress, σ_θ^2 by

$$\sigma_r^2 = \frac{E}{1-v^2}\left[c_3(1+v) - c_4\left(\frac{1-v}{r^2}\right)\right] \tag{8}$$

$$\sigma_\theta^2 = \frac{E}{1-v^2}\left[c_3(1+v) + c_4\left(\frac{1-v}{r^2}\right)\right] \tag{9}$$

So if one is able to find the four constants, c_1, c_2, c_3 and c_4, one can find the stresses in the compounded cylinder to be able to find what internal pressure can be applied. So how do we find the four unknown constants?

The boundary and interface conditions are
The radial stress at the inner radius, $r = a$ is the applied internal pressure

$$\sigma_r^1(r=a) = -p_i \tag{10}$$

The radial stress is continuous at the interface, $r = c$

$$\sigma_r^1(r=c) = \sigma_r^2(r=c) \tag{11}$$

The radial displacement at the interface, $r = c$ has a jump of the radial interference, δ

$$u_2(r=c) - u_1(r=c) = \delta \tag{12}$$

The radial stress at the outer radius, $r = c$ is

$$\sigma_r^2(r=b) = 0 \tag{13}$$

This will set up four equations and four unknowns, if we know what internal pressure we are applying. Assume, we are applying the same pressure as the single cylinder can take, that is, $p_i = 7.887\,\text{ksi}$ and let us see later what stresses it creates in the compounded cylinder.

Assuming $E = 30 \times 10^6 \text{psi}$, $v = 0.3$, Equations (10) through (13) become

$$\frac{30 \times 10^6}{1-0.3^2}\left[c_1(1+0.3) - c_2\left(\frac{1-0.3}{5^2}\right)\right] = -7.887 \times 10^3$$

$$\frac{30 \times 10^6}{1-0.3^2}\left[c_1(1+0.3) - c_2\left(\frac{1-0.3}{6.5^2}\right)\right] = \frac{30 \times 10^6}{1-0.3^2}\left[c_3(1+0.3) - c_4\left(\frac{1-0.3}{6.5^2}\right)\right]$$

$$c_3(6.5) + \frac{c_4}{6.5} - c_1(6.5) - \frac{c_2}{6.5} = 0.007$$

$$\frac{30 \times 10^6}{1 - 0.3^2}\left[c_3(1 + 0.3) - c_4\left(\frac{1 - 0.3}{8^2}\right)\right] = 0$$

Writing the above equations in matrix form, we get

$$\begin{bmatrix} 4.2857 \times 10^7 & -9.2307 \times 10^5 & 0 & 0 \\ 4.2857 \times 10^7 & -5.4619 \times 10^5 & -4.2857 \times 10^7 & 5.4619 \times 10^5 \\ -6.5 & -0.15384 & 6.5 & 0.15384 \\ 0 & 0 & 4.2857 \times 10^7 & -3.6057 \times 10^5 \end{bmatrix}\begin{bmatrix} c_1 \\ c_2 \\ c_3 \\ c_4 \end{bmatrix} = \begin{bmatrix} -7.887 \times 10^3 \\ 0 \\ 0.007 \\ 0 \end{bmatrix}$$

$$(14)$$

Solving these four simultaneous linear equations, we can find the four constants.

REFERENCES

1. A.C. Ugural, S.K. Fenster, Advanced strength and applied elasticity, Third Edition, Prentice Hall, New York, 1995.
2. J.E. Shigley, C.R. Mischke, Chapter 19 - Limits and fits, Standard handbook of machine design, McGraw-Hill, New York, 1986.

QUESTIONS

1. Find the unknown constants of Equation (14) using different numerical methods.
2. Knowing that the critical points in the compounded cylinder are $r = a, c-, c+, \text{and } b$, find the maximum hoop stress in the compounded cylinder. What is its value compared to the maximum hoop stress allowable of 18 ksi?
3. Find the maximum internal pressure you can apply to the compounded cylinder? Compare it with the maximum possible internal pressure for a single cylinder of same dimensions.
4. The radial interference at the interface is created by making the inner cylinder 1 to have a larger outer radius than the inner radius of cylinder 2. Standard interference fits dictate the limits of these dimensions. If a cylinder 2 is fit into cylinder 1, there is an upper and lower limit by which the nominal diameter of each cylinder varies at the interface. This limit L in thousands of an inch, is given by [2]

   $$L = CD^{1/3}$$

   where D (nominal diameter) is in inches and the coefficient C, based on the type of fit, is given in Table 1 below.

Cylinder	Limit	Class of fit	
		FN2	FN3
1	Lower	0.000	0.000
	Upper	0.907	0.907
2	Lower	2.717	3.739
	Upper	3.288	4.310

Assuming FN2 fit at the interface, find the maximum internal pressure you would recommend.

SIMULATENAOUS LINEAR EQUATIONS	
Topic	Simultaneous Linear Equations
Summary	Compounded cylinder capability vs single cylinder capability to handle internal pressures
Major	Civil Engineering
Authors	Autar Kaw
Date	December 23, 2009
Web Site	http://numericalmethods.eng.usf.edu

Chapter 04.00D

Physical Problem for Computer Engineering Simultaneous Linear Equations

Problem Statement

Human vision has the remarkable ability to infer 3D shapes from 2D images. When we look at 2D photographs or TV we do not see them as 2D shapes, rather as 3D entities with surfaces and volumes. Perception research has unraveled many of the cues that are used by us. The intriguing question is can we replicate some of these abilities on a computer? To this end, in this assignment we are going to look at one way to engineer a solution to the 3D shape from 2D images problem. Apart from the pure fun of solving a new problem, there are many practical applications of this technology such as in automated inspection of machine parts, inference of obstructing surfaces for robot navigation, and even in robot assisted surgery.

Image is a collection of gray level values at set of predetermined sites known as pixels, arranged in an array. These gray level values are also known as image intensities. The registered intensity at an image pixel is dependent on a number of factors such as the lighting conditions, surface orientation and surface material properties. The nature of lighting and its placement can drastically affect the appearance of a scene. Can we infer shape of the underlying surface given images as in the images below in Figure 1.

Figure 1 Images of a surface taken with three different light directions. Can you guess the shape of the underlying surface?

Physics of the Problem

To be able to reconstruct the shape of the underlying surface, we have to first understand the image formation process. The simplest image formation model assumes that the camera is far away from the scene so that we have assume that the image is a scaled version of the world. The simplest light model consists of a point light that is far away. This is not an unrealistic assumption. A good example of such a light source is the sun. We also assume that the surface is essentially matte that reflects lights uniformly in all directions, unlike specular (or mirror-like surfaces). These kinds of surfaces are called Lambertian surfaces; examples include walls, and carpet.

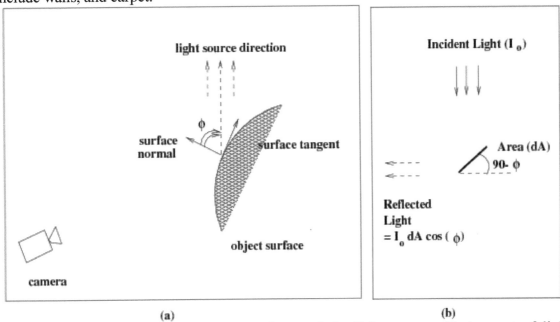

(a)   (b)

Figure 2 Relationship between the surface and the light source. (b) Amount of light reflected by an elemental area (dA) is proportional to the cosine of the angle between the light source direction and the surface normal

The image brightness of a Lambertian surface is dependent on the local surface orientation with respect to the light source. Since the point light source is far away we will assume that the incident light is locally uniform and comes from a single direction, i.e, the light rays are parallel to each other. This situation is illustrated in Figure 2. Let the incident light intensity be denoted by I_0. Also let the angle between the light source and local surface orientation be denoted by ϕ. Then the registered image intensity, $I(u,v)$, of that point is given by

$$I(u,v) = I_0 \rho \cos(\phi) = I_0 \rho (n_x s_x + n_y s_y + n_z s_z)$$

where the surface normal, n, and the light source direction, s, are given by:

$$n = \begin{bmatrix} n_x \\ n_y \\ n_z \end{bmatrix}, s = \begin{bmatrix} s_x \\ s_y \\ s_z \end{bmatrix}$$

and ρ is a number capturing the surface reflection property at the location (x,y), and It is referred to as the surface albedo. Black surfaces tend to have low albedo and white surfaces tend to high albedo. Note that the registered intensity in the image does not depend on the camera location because a Lambertian surface reflects light equally in all directions. This would not be true for specular surfaces and the corresponding image formation equation would involve the viewing direction.

The variation in image intensity is essentially dependent on the local surface orientation. If the surface normal and the light source directions are aligned then we have the maximum intensity and the observed intensity of the lowest when the angle between the light source and the local surface orientation is 90^0. Thus, given the knowledge of light source and the local surface albedo, it should be possible to infer the local surface orientation from the local image intensity variations. This is what we explore next.

Solution

The mapping of surface orientation to image intensity is many to one. Thus, it is not possible to infer the surface orientation from just one intensity image in the absence of any other knowledge. We need multiple samples per point in the scene. How many samples do we need? The vector specifying the surface normal has three components, which implies that we need three. So, we engineer a setup to infer surface orientation from image intensities. Instead of just one image of a scene, let us take three images of the same scene, without moving either the camera or the scene, but with three different light sources, turned on one at a time. These three different light sources are placed at different locations in space. Let the three light source directions, relative to the camera, be specified by the vectors

$$s^1 = \begin{bmatrix} s^1_x \\ s^1_y \\ s^1_z \end{bmatrix}, s^2 = \begin{bmatrix} s^2_x \\ s^2_y \\ s^2_z \end{bmatrix}, s^3 = \begin{bmatrix} s^3_x \\ s^3_y \\ s^3_z \end{bmatrix}$$

Corresponding pixels in the three images would have three different intensities I_1, I_2, and I_3 for three light source directions. Let the surface normal corresponding to the pixel under consideration be denoted by

$$n = \begin{bmatrix} n_x \\ n_y \\ n_z \end{bmatrix}$$

Assuming Lambertian surfaces, the three intensities can be related to the surface normal and the light source directions

$$I_i = I_0\rho(n_x s^i_x + n_y s^i_y + n_z s^i_z), \forall i = 1,2,3$$

In these three equations, the known variables are the intensities, I_1, I_2, I_3, and the light source directions, s_1, s_2, s_3. The unknowns are the incident intensity, I_3, surface albedo, ρ, and the surface normal, n. These unknowns can be bundled into three unknown variables, $m_x = I_0\rho n_x$, $m_y = I_0\rho n_y$, and $m_z = I_0\rho n_z$. We will recover the surface normal by normalizing the recovered m vector, using the fact that the magnitude of the normal is one. The normalizing constant will give us the product $I_0\rho$. Thus, for each point in the image, we have three simultaneous equations in three unknowns.

$$\begin{bmatrix} I_1 \\ I_2 \\ I_3 \end{bmatrix} = \begin{bmatrix} s_x^1 & s_y^1 & s_z^1 \\ s_x^2 & s_y^2 & s_z^2 \\ s_x^3 & s_y^3 & s_z^3 \end{bmatrix} \begin{bmatrix} m_x \\ m_y \\ m_z \end{bmatrix}$$

Worked Out Example

Consider the middle of the sphere in Figure 1. We know that the surface normal points towards the camera (i.e. towards the viewer). Assume a 3D coordinate system centered at the camera with x-direction along the horizontal direction, y-direction along the vertical direction, and z-direction is away from the camera into the scene. Then the actual surface normal of the middle of the sphere is given by [0, 0, -1] – the negative denotes that it point in the direction opposite the z-axis. Let us see how close our estimate is to the actual value.

The intensity of the middle of the sphere in the three views, $I_1 = 247$, $I_2 = 248$, and $I_3 = 239$, respectively. The light directions for the three images are along [5, 0, -20], [0, 5, -20], and [-5, -5, -20], respectively. Normalizing the three vectors we get the normal directions towards the lights and construct the 3 by 3 matrix

$$\begin{bmatrix} s_x^1 & s_y^1 & s_z^1 \\ s_x^2 & s_y^2 & s_z^2 \\ s_x^3 & s_y^3 & s_z^3 \end{bmatrix} = \begin{bmatrix} 0.2425 & 0 & -0.9701 \\ 0 & 0.2425 & -0.9701 \\ -0.2357 & -0.2357 & -0.9428 \end{bmatrix}$$

Solving the corresponding 3 simultaneous equations, we arrive the following solution for the m-vector:

$$\begin{bmatrix} m_x \\ m_y \\ m_z \end{bmatrix} = \begin{bmatrix} 0.0976 \\ 4.2207 \\ -254.5774 \end{bmatrix}$$

Normalizing this vector we get the surface normal

$$\begin{bmatrix} n_x \\ n_y \\ n_z \end{bmatrix} = \begin{bmatrix} 0.0004 \\ 0.0166 \\ -0.9999 \end{bmatrix}$$

The corresponding normalizing constant is 254.6124, which is the product of the intensity of the illumination and the surface (albedo) reflectance factor $(I_0\rho)$. Compare the estimate of the surface normal to the actual one. The difference is quantization effects – in images we can represent intensities as a finite sized integer – 8-bit integers in our case.

We can repeat the above computations for each point in the scene to arrive at estimates of the corresponding surface normals. Figure 3(a) is a visualization of the surface normals thus estimated as a vector field. In Figure 3(b), we see the product $I_0\rho$ visualized as image intensities. As expected, it is the same at all points on the sphere. In another problem module, how do we recover the underlying surface from these surface normals?

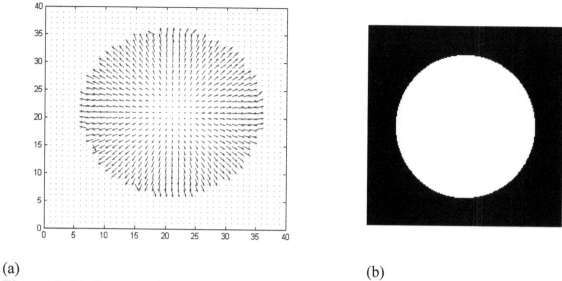

(a)   (b)

Figure 3 (a) Recovered surface normal at each point on the sphere. Just the first two components of the vectors are shown as a arrows. (b) Recovered product $I_0\rho$ for all points

QUESTIONS

1. What can you infer about the surface normal for the brightest point in the image? What about the darkest point in the scene?
2. What assumptions do you have to make to make the above inferences?

SIMULTANEOUS LINEAR EQUATIONS	
Topic	Physical Problem
Summary	To infer the surface shape from images
Major	Computer Engineering
Authors	Sudeep Sarkar
Last Revised	July 22, 2005
Web Site	http://numericalmethods.eng.usf.edu

Chapter 04.00E

Physical Problem for Electrical Engineering Simultaneous Linear Equations

Problem Statement

Three-phase AC systems are the norm for most industrial applications. AC power in the form of voltage and current it delivered from the power company using three-phase distribution systems and many larger loads are three-phase loads in the form of motors, compressors, or similar. Sources and loads can be configured in either wye (where sources or loads are connected from line to neutral/ground) or delta (where sources or loads are connected from line to line) configurations and mixing between the types is common. Figure 1 shows the general wiring of a wye-wye three-phase system modeling all of the impedances typically found in such a system.

During the typical analysis undertaken in most circuits textbooks, it is assumed that the system is entirely balanced. This means that all the source, line, and load impedances are equivalent, that is,

$$Z_a = Z_b = Z_c$$
$$Z_{aA} = Z_{bB} = Z_{cC}$$
$$Z_{AN} = Z_{bN} = Z_{CN}$$

Under this assumption, the circuit is then typically reduced to a single-phase equivalent circuit model and the resultant circuit is solved with a single loop equation. What happens, however, when the system is unbalanced? Typically because the three load impedances Z_{AN}, Z_{BN} and Z_{CN} are not equal, which results in different currents through each load, is often measured in terms of the percentage difference between the load currents.

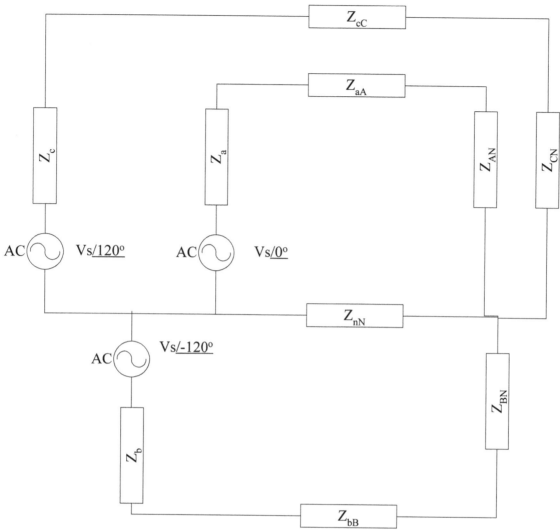

Figure 1 A Three-Phase Wye-Wye System with Positive Phase Sequence

Creating an imbalance in a three-phase system is not all that difficult. Consider a small business operating in an isolated leg of the power grid so that localized aspects of a load are not "balanced" by other neighboring loads. Let's assume that the primary load for this system is a 45 kVA set of three-phase motors at 0.8 power factor lagging and, further, that the electrician that did the wiring for the lighting mistakenly connected two banks of lights to the A phase, one to the B phase and none to the C phase creating an imbalance in the system. Each of these lighting loads is 1500 W. The load for this system is shown in Figure 2.

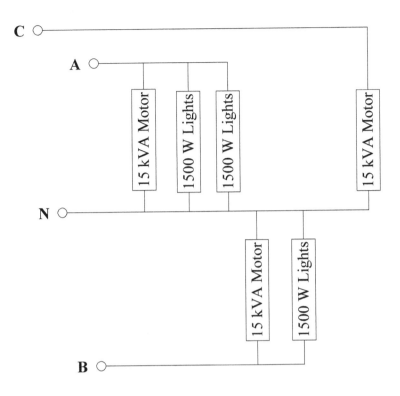

Figure 2 Model of the System Load

The impedance of each of the loads can be determined by examining the power consumed in each phase of the system

$$A:3000+15000/-36.87° = 3000+12000 - j9000 = 15000 - j9000 = 17.49/-30.96° kVA$$

$$B:1500+15000/-36.87° = 1500+12000 - j9000 = 13500 - j9000 = 16.22/-33.69° kVA$$

$$C:15.00/-36.87° kVA$$

Converting these to impedances using the formula $S = \dfrac{|V|^2}{Z}$ with $V = 120V$ yields:

$$Z_{AN} = 0.8233/30.96°\Omega = R_A + jX_A = 0.7060 + j0.4236\Omega$$
$$Z_{BN} = 0.8878/33.39°\Omega = R_B + jX_B = 0.7387 + j0.4925\Omega$$
$$Z_{CN} = 0.9600/36.87°\Omega = R_C + jX_C = 0.7680 + j0.5760\Omega$$

For the rest of this analysis we will assume that each phase of the system has an equivalent source and line impedance of $R_s + jX_s = 0.0300 + j0.0200\Omega$ and that the ground return wire has an impedance of $R_n + jZ_n = 0.0100 + j0.0080\Omega$. This yields the equivalent circuit of Figure 3.

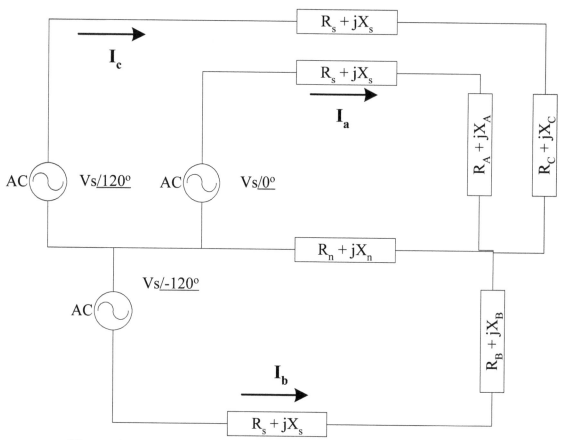

Figure 3 Equivalent Circuit Model for the Working Problem

The circuit can be analyzed using three loop equations using the currents I_a, I_b, and I_c shown in Figure 3. For loop A this yields the complex equation:

Loop A:

$$-V_s\underline{0^\circ} + I_a\left(R_s + jX_s + R_A + jX_A\right) + \left(I_a + I_b + I_c\right)\left(R_n + jX_n\right) = 0$$

with loops B and C yielding similar results. Assuming that our simultaneous equation solver is not capable of handling complex numbers we can turn the loop A equation into two separate non-complex equations addressing both the real and imaginary parts. Using $I_a = I_{ar} + jI_{ai}$ and collecting terms yields:

Real A:

$$I_{ar}\left(R_s + R_A + R_n\right) - I_{ai}\left(X_s + X_A + X_n\right) + I_{br}R_n - I_{bi}X_n + I_{cr}R_n - I_{ci}X_n = 120 \tag{1}$$

Imaginary A:

$$I_{ar}\left(X_s + X_A + X_n\right) + I_{ai}\left(R_s + R_A + R_n\right) + I_{br}X_n + I_{bi}R_n + I_{cr}X_n + I_{ci}R_n = 0 \tag{2}$$

Applying the same analysis to the B and C loops yields the remaining equations for the system.

Real B:

$$I_{ar}R_n - I_{ai}X_n + I_{br}\left(R_s + R_B + R_n\right) - I_{bi}\left(X_s + X_B + X_n\right) + I_{cr}R_n - I_{ci}X_n = -60 \tag{3}$$

Imaginary B:

$$I_{ar}X_n + I_{ai}R_n + I_{br}\left(X_s + X_B + X_n\right) + I_{bi}\left(R_s + R_B + R_n\right) + I_{cr}X_n + I_{ci}R_n = -103.9 \tag{4}$$

Real C:

$$I_{ar}R_n - I_{ai}X_n + I_{br}R_n - I_{bi}X_n + I_{cr}(R_s + R_C + R_n) - I_{ci}(X_s + X_C + X_n) = -60 \qquad (5)$$

Imaginary C:

$$I_{ar}X_n + I_{ai}R_n + I_{br}X_n + I_{bi}R_n + I_{cr}(X_s + X_C + X_n) + I_{ci}(R_s + R_C + R_n) = 103.9 \qquad (6)$$

This yields a system of six linear equations and six unknowns $(I_{ar}, I_{ai}, I_{br}, I_{bi}, I_{cr}, \text{and } I_{ci})$ that can be solved by any conventional means. This is shown in matrix form in Figure 4.

$$\begin{bmatrix} 0.7460 & -0.4516 & 0.0100 & -0.0080 & 0.0100 & -0.0080 \\ 0.4516 & 0.7460 & 0.0080 & 0.0100 & 0.0080 & 0.0100 \\ 0.0100 & -0.0080 & 0.7787 & -0.5205 & 0.0100 & -0.0080 \\ 0.0080 & 0.0100 & 0.5205 & 0.7787 & 0.0080 & 0.0100 \\ 0.0100 & -0.0080 & 0.0100 & -0.0080 & 0.8080 & -0.6040 \\ 0.0080 & 0.0100 & 0.0080 & 0.0100 & 0.6040 & 0.8080 \end{bmatrix} \begin{bmatrix} I_{ar} \\ I_{ai} \\ I_{br} \\ I_{bi} \\ I_{cr} \\ I_{ci} \end{bmatrix} = \begin{bmatrix} 120.0 \\ 0.000 \\ -60.00 \\ -103.9 \\ -60.00 \\ 103.9 \end{bmatrix} \qquad (7)$$

Figure 4 Complete System of Equations

Once the currents are known it is a simple procedure to determine the voltages across the three motor terminals $(V_{AN}, V_{BN}, \text{and } V_{CN})$ using Ohm's Law.

$$V_{AN} = (I_{ar} + jI_{ai})(R_A + jX_A)$$
$$V_{BN} = (I_{br} + jI_{bi})(R_B + jX_B)$$
$$V_{CN} = (I_{cr} + jI_{ci})(R_C + jX_C)$$

To better evaluate the imbalance, the percentage difference in currents through the actual load elements is more often considered. The best way to think of this as three people pulling and pushing together. If they do not pull and push in balance, things can become unstable. In the case of a three-phase motor, this can result in significant wobble with corresponding wear in the bearings and other parts. To determine the current through each load is again computed using Ohm's Law.

$$I_{Aload} = \frac{V_{AN}}{Z_{3\phi}}, I_{Bload} = \frac{V_{BN}}{Z_{3\phi}} I_{Cload} = \frac{V_{CN}}{Z_{3\phi}}$$

$$Z_{3\phi} = 0.7680 + j0.5760 \Omega$$

where $Z_{3\phi}$ was computed earlier as Z_C. Do not forget that the lighting loads are separate.

QUESTIONS

1. What would be the ramifications of solving the problem directly using the three complex linear equations? Could we do it using an approach like Gauss-Jordan Elimination? What about some of the other numerical methods used to solve simultaneous linear equations?

2. This problem is only interesting if the ground return leg Z_{nN} is non-zero. Otherwise, we have three loop equations that are completely independent of each other and can be solved directly. Why is that the case?

3. A much more interesting and practical problem occurs when the motor load is a Delta configuration. Since it does not have the ground return line in the middle it results in additional loop equations. Sketch the equivalent circuit for a system with a Wye source and a mix of Delta and Wye loads. Write the set of equations that result from this system. Solve them.

SIMULTANEOUS LINEAR EQUATIONS	
Topic	Simultaneous Linear Equations
Summary	Three phase loads in AC systems
Major	Electrical Engineering
Authors	Henry Welch
Date	June 30, 2005
Web Site	http://numericalmethods.eng.usf.edu

Chapter 04.00F

Physical Problem for Industrial Engineering Simultaneous Linear Equations

Problem Statement

A company that manufactures small toys recently received a contract from a fast-food company, to manufacture three toys, at a low cost, to be added to kid's lunches. The company has to manufacture toys for boys (toy B), girls (toy G) and a generic version (toy U). Furthermore, based on the demand and demographics, the fast food company has specified that 5% more girl's toys than boy's toys should be produced, and that there is no constraint is specified on the number of generic toys. The components of each toy (B, G, and U) must be injection molded out of plastic (Process 1) and then assembled (Process 2). After the toys have been designed, it is determined that the following production times will be needed on each toy:

- Toy B will require 2 minutes for injection molding 6 toys and 1 minute for assembling all 6 toys.
- Toy G will require 2 minutes for injection molding 12 toys and 8 minutes for assembling all 12 toys.
- Toy U will require 4 minutes for injection molding 6 toys and 2 minutes for assembling all 6 toys.

Note that because of daily scheduled maintenance of the injection molding machine, it can only run for a maximum of 756 out of 1440 minutes a day, whereas the assembly line works 3 shifts a day with scheduled breaks for a maximum of 1260 out of 1440 minutes per day. An industrial engineer working for the toy company is asked to determine the production schedule that maximizes, on a daily basis, the use of both the injection molding machine and the assembly line.

Background The variables need to solve the problem are listed in Table 1

04.00F.1

Table 1. Variables for these different toys.

Variable	Toy B	Toy G	Toy U
Time (minutes) required in Process 1 per toy	B_1	G_1	U_1
Time (minutes) required in Process 2 per toy	B_2	G_2	U_2
Total manufactured per day	X_B	X_G	X_U

The total time required to produce toys in process 1 (injection molding) has to be equal to the maximum minutes per day that process 1 can run, that is,

$$B_1 X_B + G_1 X_G + U_1 X_U = M_1$$

where M_1 is the maximum minutes that process 1 can run per day. Similarly, for process 2 (assembly),

$$B_2 X_B + G_2 X_G + U_2 X_U = M_2$$

where M_2 is the maximum minutes that process 2 can run per day. Finally, the constraint of 5% more girl's toys than boy's toys is expressed as

$$1.05 X_B = X_G \qquad \text{or}$$

$$1.05 X_B - X_G = 0$$

The previous three simultaneous linear equations can be expressed in matrix form as follows

$$\begin{bmatrix} B_1 & G_1 & U_1 \\ B_2 & G_2 & U_2 \\ 1.05 & -1 & 0 \end{bmatrix} \begin{Bmatrix} X_B \\ X_G \\ X_U \end{Bmatrix} = \begin{Bmatrix} M_1 \\ M_2 \\ 0 \end{Bmatrix}$$

Solution

The input variables to the preceding simultaneous linear equations are

$$B_1 = \frac{2}{6} = \frac{1}{3} \text{ toy per minute}$$

$$B_2 = \frac{1}{6} \text{ toy per minute}$$

$$G_1 = \frac{2}{12} = \frac{1}{6} \text{ toy per minute}$$

$$G_2 = \frac{8}{12} = \frac{2}{3} \text{ toy per minute}$$

$$U_1 = \frac{4}{6} = \frac{2}{3} \text{ toy per minute}$$

$$U_2 = \frac{2}{6} = \frac{1}{3} \text{ toy per minute}$$

$$M_1 = 756 \text{ minutes per day}$$

$$M_2 = 1260 \text{ minutes per day}$$

Substituting onto the matrix representation of the simultaneous linear equations yields

$$\frac{1}{6}\begin{bmatrix} 2 & 1 & 4 \\ 1 & 4 & 2 \\ 6.3 & -6 & 0 \end{bmatrix}\begin{Bmatrix} X_B \\ X_G \\ X_U \end{Bmatrix} = \begin{Bmatrix} 756 \\ 1260 \\ 0 \end{Bmatrix}$$

One needs to solve these simultaneous linear equations to find the number of boys, girl and unisex toys for maximizing the manufacturing facility yield.

SIMULTANEOUS LINEAR EQUATIONS	
Topic	Simultaneous Linear Equations
Summary	Maximizing assembly line yield.
Major	Industrial Engineering
Authors	Glen Besterfield
Date	December 23, 2009
Web Site	http://numericalmethods.eng.usf.edu

Chapter 04.00G

Physical Problem for Simultaneous Linear Equations
Mechanical Engineering

Problem Statement

To make the fulcrum (Figure 1) of a bascule bridge, a long hollow steel shaft called the trunnion is shrink fit into a steel hub. The resulting steel trunnion-hub assembly is then shrink fit into the girder of the bridge.

Trunnion

Hub

Girder

Figure 1 Trunnion-Hub-Girder (THG) assembly.

This is done by first immersing the trunnion in a cold medium such as dry-ice/alcohol mixture. After the trunnion reaches the steady state temperature of the cold medium, the trunnion outer diameter contracts. The trunnion is taken out of the medium and slid though the hole of the hub (Figure 2).

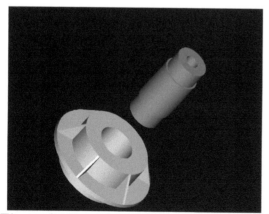

Figure 2 Trunnion slid through the hub after contracting

When the trunnion heats up, it expands and creates an interference fit with the hub. In 1995, on one of the bridges in Florida, this assembly procedure did not work as designed. Before the trunnion could be inserted fully into the hub, the trunnion got stuck. Luckily the trunnion was taken out before it got stuck permanently. Otherwise, a new trunnion and hub would needed to be ordered at a cost of $50,000. Coupled with construction delays, the total loss could have been more than hundred thousand dollars.

Why did the trunnion get stuck? This was because the trunnion had not contracted enough to slide through the hole. Can you find out why?

A hollow trunnion of outside diameter 12.363" is to be fitted in a hub of inner diameter 12.358". The trunnion was put in dry ice/alcohol mixture (temperature of the fluid - dry ice/alcohol mixture is $-108°F$) to contract the trunnion so that it can be slided through the hole of the hub. To slide the trunnion without sticking, a diametrical clearance of at least 0.01" is required between the trunnion and the hub. Assuming the room temperature is $80°F$, is immersing it in dry-ice/alcohol mixture a correct decision?

Solution

To calculate the contraction in the diameter of the trunnion, thermal expansion coefficient at room temperature is used. In that case the reduction, ΔD in the outer diameter of the trunnion is

$$\Delta D = D\alpha\Delta T \tag{1}$$

where

D = outer diameter of the trunnion,

α = coefficient of thermal expansion coefficient at room temperature, and

ΔT = change in temperature,

Given

$D = 12.363"$

$\alpha = 6.817 \times 10^{-6}$ in/in/°F at 80°F

$\Delta T = T_{fluid} - T_{room}$

$= -108 - 80$

$= -188°F$

where

T_{fluid} = temperature of dry-ice/alcohol mixture

T_{room} = room temperature

the reduction in the trunnion outer diameter is given by

$$\Delta D = (12.363)(6.47 \times 10^{-6})(-188)$$

$$= -0.01504"$$

So the trunnion is predicted to reduce in diameter by 0.01504". But, is this enough reduction in diameter? As per specifications, he needs the trunnion to contract by

= trunnion outside diameter - hub inner diameter + diametral clearance

= 12.363"−12.358"+0.01"

= 0.015"

So according to his calculations, immersing the steel trunnion in dry-ice/alcohol mixture gives the desired contraction of 0.015" as we predict a contraction of 0.01504".

But as shown in Figure 3, the thermal expansion coefficient of steel decreases with temperature and is not constant over the range of temperature the trunnion goes through. Hence, Equation 1 would overestimate the thermal contraction.

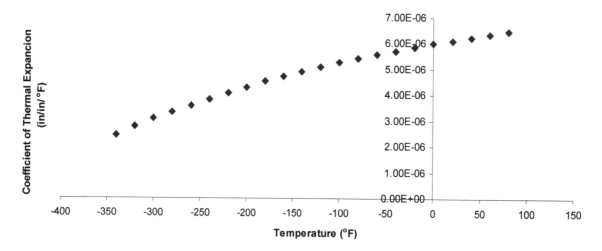

Figure 3 Varying thermal expansion coefficient as a function of temperature for cast steel.

The contraction in the diameter for the trunnion for which the thermal expansion coefficient varies as a function of temperature is given by

$$\Delta D = D \int_{T_{room}}^{T_{fluid}} \alpha \, dT \qquad (2)$$

So one needs to find the curve to find the coefficient of thermal expansion as a function of temperature. This is done by regression where we best fit a curve through the data given in Table 1.

Table 1 Instantaneous thermal expansion coefficient as a function of temperature.

Temperature	Instantaneous Thermal Expansion Coefficient
°F	μin/in/°F
80	6.47
60	6.36
40	6.24
20	6.12
0	6.00
-20	5.86
-40	5.72
-60	5.58
-80	5.43
-100	5.28
-120	5.09
-140	4.91
-160	4.72
-180	4.52

-200	4.30
-220	4.08
-240	3.83
-260	3.58
-280	3.33
-300	3.07
-320	2.76
-340	2.45

Assuming that the coefficient of thermal expansion is related to temperature by a second order polynomial,

$$\alpha = a_0 + a_1 T + a_2 T^2 \tag{3}$$

Given the data points (α_1, T_1), (α_2, T_2), ..., (α_n, T_n) as in Figure 3 and Table 1, the sum of the square of the residuals (sum of the square of the differences between the observed and predicted values) is

$$S_r = \sum_{i=1}^{n} \left(\alpha_i - \{a_0 + a_1 T_i + a_2 T_i^2\} \right)^2$$

$$= \sum_{i=1}^{n} \left(\alpha_i - a_0 - a_1 T_i - a_2 T_i^2 \right)^2 \tag{4}$$

To minimize the value of the sum of the square of the residuals, we take the derivative with respect to each of the three unknown coefficients to give

$$\frac{\partial S_r}{\partial a_0} = \sum_{i=1}^{n} 2\left(\alpha_i - a_0 - a_1 T_i - a_2 T_i^2 \right)(-1)$$

$$= 2\left[-\sum_{i=1}^{n} \alpha_i + n a_0 + a_1 \sum_{i=1}^{n} T_i + a_2 \sum_{i=1}^{n} T_i^2 \right]$$

$$\frac{\partial S_r}{\partial a_1} = \sum_{i=1}^{n} 2\left(\alpha_i - a_0 - a_1 T_i - a_2 T_i^2 \right)(-T_i)$$

$$= 2\left[-\sum_{i=1}^{n} \alpha_i T_i + a_0 \sum_{i=1}^{n} T_i + a_1 \sum_{i=1}^{n} T_i^2 + a_2 \sum_{i=1}^{n} T_i^3 \right]$$

$$\frac{\partial S_r}{\partial a_2} = \sum_{i=1}^{n} 2\left(\alpha_i - a_0 - a_1 T_i - a_2 T_i^2 \right)(-T_i^2)$$

$$= 2\left[-\sum_{i=1}^{n} \alpha_i T_i^2 + a_0 \sum_{i=1}^{n} T_i^2 + a_1 \sum_{i=1}^{n} T_i^3 + a_2 \sum_{i=1}^{n} T_i^4 \right] \tag{5}$$

Setting three partial derivatives in Equation (5) equal to zero gives,

$$n a_0 + a_1 \sum_{i=1}^{n} T_i + a_2 \sum_{i=1}^{n} T_i^2 = \sum_{i=1}^{n} \alpha_i$$

$$a_0 \sum_{i=1}^{n} T_i + a_1 \sum_{i=1}^{n} T_i^2 + a_2 \sum_{i=1}^{n} T_i^3 = \sum_{i=1}^{n} \alpha_i T_i$$

$$a_0 \sum_{i=1}^{n} T_i^2 + a_1 \sum_{i=1}^{n} T_i^3 + a_2 \sum_{i=1}^{n} T_i^4 = \sum_{i=1}^{n} \alpha_i T_i^2 \tag{6}$$

The set of equations given by equations(6a), (6b), and (6c) are simultaneous linear equations. The number of data points in the Figure (3) is 24 as given in Table 1. Hence

$$n = 24$$

$$\sum_{i=1}^{24} T_i = -2860$$

$$\sum_{i=1}^{24} T_i^2 = 7.26 \times 10^5$$

$$\sum_{i=1}^{24} T_i^3 = -1.86472 \times 10^8$$

$$\sum_{i=1}^{24} T_i^4 = 5.24357 \times 10^{10}$$

$$\sum_{i=1}^{24} \alpha_i = 1.057 \times 10^{-4}$$

$$\sum_{i=1}^{24} \alpha_i T_i = -1.04162 \times 10^{-2}$$

$$\sum_{i=1}^{24} \alpha_i T_i^2 = 2.56799$$

$$24a_0 - 2860a_1 + 7.26 \times 10^5 a_2 = 1.057 \times 10^{-4}$$
$$-2860a_0 + 7.26 \times 10^5 a_1 - 1.8647 \times 10^8 a_2 = -1.04162 \times 10^{-2}$$
$$7.26 \times 10^5 a_0 - 1.86472 \times 10^8 a_1 + 5.24357 \times 10^{10} a_2 = 2.56799$$

In matrix form, the three simultaneous linear equations can be written as

$$\begin{bmatrix} 24 & -2860 & 7.26 \times 10^5 \\ -2860 & 7.26 \times 10^5 & -1.86472 \times 10^8 \\ 7.26 \times 10^5 & -1.86472 \times 10^8 & 5.24357 \times 10^{10} \end{bmatrix} \begin{bmatrix} a_0 \\ a_1 \\ a_2 \end{bmatrix} = \begin{bmatrix} 1.057 \times 10^{-4} \\ -1.04162 \times 10^{-2} \\ 2.56799 \end{bmatrix}$$

QUESTIONS

1. Can you now find the contraction in the trunnion outer diameter?
2. Is the magnitude of contraction more than 0.015" as required?
3. If that is not the case, what if the trunnion were immersed in liquid nitrogen (boiling temperature$=-321°F$)? Will that give enough contraction in the trunnion?
4. Redo problem#1 using a third order polynomial as the regression model. How much different is the estimate of contraction using the third order polynomial?
5. Find the optimum polynomial order to use for the regression model.
6. Find the effect of the number of significant digits used in solving the set of the equations for problem#4 as you must have noticed the large range in the order of the numbers in the coefficient matrix.

SIMULTANEOUS LINEAR EQUATIONS

Topic	Simultaneous linear equations
Summary	Contraction in a trunnion
Major	Mechanical Engineering
Authors	Autar Kaw
Date	December 23, 2009
Web Site	http://numericalmethods.eng.usf.edu

Chapter 04.01
Introduction to Matrix Algebra

After reading this chapter, you should be able to

1. *know what a matrix is,*
2. *identify special types of matrices,*
3. *know when two matrices are equal,*
4. *add, subtract and multiply matrices,*
5. *rules of binary matrix operations,*
6. *find transpose of a matrix,*
7. *find inverse of a matrix and its application to solving simultaneous linear equations.*

What is a matrix?

Matrices are everywhere. If you have used a spreadsheet such as Excel or written a table, you have used a matrix. Matrices make presentation of numbers clearer and make calculations easier to program. Look at the matrix below about the sale of tires in a Blowoutr'us store – given by quarter and make of tires.

	Quarter 1	Quarter 2	Quarter 3	Quarter 4
Tirestone	25	20	3	2
Michigan	5	10	15	25
Copper	6	16	7	27

If one wants to know how many *Copper* tires were sold in *Quarter 4*, we go along the row *Copper* and column *Quarter 4* and find that it is 27.

So what is a matrix?

A matrix is a rectangular array of elements. The elements can be symbolic expressions or numbers. Matrix [A] is denoted by

$$[A] = \begin{bmatrix} a_{11} & a_{12} & .... & a_{1n} \\ a_{21} & a_{22} & .... & a_{2n} \\ \vdots & & & \vdots \\ a_{m1} & a_{m2} & .... & a_{mn} \end{bmatrix}$$

Row i of [A] has n elements and is $\begin{bmatrix} a_{i1} & a_{i2} .... a_{in} \end{bmatrix}$ and

04.01.1

Column j of [A] has m elements and is $\begin{bmatrix} a_{1j} \\ a_{2j} \\ \vdots \\ a_{mj} \end{bmatrix}$

Each matrix has rows and columns and this defines the size of the matrix. If a matrix [A] has m rows and n columns, the size of the matrix is denoted by $m \times n$. The matrix [A] may also be denoted by $[A]_{m \times n}$ to show that $[A]$ is a matrix with m rows and n columns.

Each entry in the matrix is called the entry or element of the matrix and is denoted by a_{ij} where i is the row number and j is the column number of the element.
The matrix for the tire sales example could be denoted by the matrix [A] as

$$[A] = \begin{bmatrix} 25 & 20 & 3 & 2 \\ 5 & 10 & 15 & 25 \\ 6 & 16 & 7 & 27 \end{bmatrix}$$

There are 3 rows and 4 columns, so the size of the matrix is 3×4. In the above $[A]$ matrix, $a_{34} = 27$.

What are the special types of matrices?

Vector: A vector is a matrix that has only one row or one column. There are two types of vectors – row vectors and column vectors.
Row vector: If a matrix has one row, it is called a row vector
$$[B] = [b_1 \ b_2 \ \ldots \ldots b_m]$$
and m is the dimension of the row vector.

Example 1

Give an example of a row vector.
Solution

$[B] = [25 \ 20 \ 3 \ 2 \ 0]$ is an example of a row vector of dimension 5.

Column vector: If a matrix has one column, it is called a column vector

$$[C] = \begin{bmatrix} c_1 \\ \vdots \\ \vdots \\ c_n \end{bmatrix}$$

and n is the dimension of the vector.

Example 2

Give an example of a column vector.

Solution

$$[C] = \begin{bmatrix} 25 \\ 5 \\ 6 \end{bmatrix}$$

is an example of a column vector of dimension 3.

Square matrix: If the number of rows (m) of a matrix is equal to the number of columns (n) of the matrix, ($m = n$), it is called a square matrix. The entries $a_{11}, a_{22}, \ldots a_{nn}$ are called the diagonal elements of a square matrix. Sometimes the diagonal of the matrix is also called the principal or main of the matrix.

Example 3

Give an example of a square matrix.
Solution

$$[A] = \begin{bmatrix} 25 & 20 & 3 \\ 5 & 10 & 15 \\ 6 & 15 & 7 \end{bmatrix}$$

is a square matrix as it has same number of rows and columns, that is, three.
The diagonal elements of [A] are $a_{11} = 25, a_{22} = 10, a_{33} = 7$.

Upper triangular matrix: A $m \times n$ matrix for which $a_{ij} = 0, i > j$ is called an upper triangular matrix. That is, all the elements below the diagonal entries are zero.

Example 4

Give an example of an upper triangular matrix.
Solution

$$[A] = \begin{bmatrix} 10 & -7 & 0 \\ 0 & -0.001 & 6 \\ 0 & 0 & 15005 \end{bmatrix}$$

is an upper triangular matrix.

Lower triangular matrix: A $m \times n$ matrix for which $a_{ij} = 0, j > i$ is called a lower triangular matrix. That is, all the elements above the diagonal entries are zero.

Example 5

Give an example of a lower triangular matrix.

Solution

$$[A] = \begin{bmatrix} 1 & 0 & 0 \\ 0.3 & 1 & 0 \\ 0.6 & 2.5 & 1 \end{bmatrix}$$

is a lower triangular matrix.

Diagonal matrix: A square matrix with all non-diagonal elements equal to zero is called a diagonal matrix, that is, only the diagonal entries of the square matrix can be non-zero, $(a_{ij} = 0, i \neq j)$.

Example 6

Give examples of a diagonal matrix.
Solution

$$[A] = \begin{bmatrix} 3 & 0 & 0 \\ 0 & 2.1 & 0 \\ 0 & 0 & 5 \end{bmatrix}$$

is a diagonal matrix.
Any or all the diagonal entries of a diagonal matrix can be zero.
For example

$$[A] = \begin{bmatrix} 3 & 0 & 0 \\ 0 & 2.1 & 0 \\ 0 & 0 & 0 \end{bmatrix}$$

is also a diagonal matrix.

Identity matrix: A diagonal matrix with all diagonal elements equal to one is called an identity matrix, ($a_{ij} = 0, i \neq j$; and $a_{ii} = 1$ for all i).

Example 7

Give an example of an identity matrix.
Solution

$$[A] = \begin{bmatrix} 1 & 0 & 0 & 0 \\ 0 & 1 & 0 & 0 \\ 0 & 0 & 1 & 0 \\ 0 & 0 & 0 & 1 \end{bmatrix}$$

is an identity matrix.

Zero matrix: A matrix whose all entries are zero is called a zero matrix, ($a_{ij} = 0$ for all i and j).

Example 8

Give examples of a zero matrix.
Solution

$$[A] = \begin{bmatrix} 0 & 0 & 0 \\ 0 & 0 & 0 \\ 0 & 0 & 0 \end{bmatrix}$$

$$[B] = \begin{bmatrix} 0 & 0 & 0 \\ 0 & 0 & 0 \end{bmatrix}$$

$$[C] = \begin{bmatrix} 0 & 0 & 0 & 0 \\ 0 & 0 & 0 & 0 \\ 0 & 0 & 0 & 0 \end{bmatrix}$$

$$[D] = \begin{bmatrix} 0 & 0 & 0 \end{bmatrix}$$

are all examples of a zero matrix.

Tridiagonal matrices: A tridiagonal matrix is a square matrix in which all elements not on the major diagonal, the diagonal above the major diagonal and the diagonal below the major diagonal are zero.

Example 9

Give an example of a tridiagonal matrix.
Solution

$$[A] = \begin{bmatrix} 2 & 4 & 0 & 0 \\ 2 & 3 & 9 & 0 \\ 0 & 0 & 5 & 2 \\ 0 & 0 & 3 & 6 \end{bmatrix}$$

is a tridiagonal matrix.

When are two matrices considered to be equal?

Two matrices [A] and [B] are equal if the size of [A] and [B] is the same (number of rows and columns are same for [A] and [B]) and $a_{ij} = b_{ij}$ for all i and j.

Example 10

What would make

$$[A] = \begin{bmatrix} 2 & 3 \\ 6 & 7 \end{bmatrix} \text{ to be equal to}$$

$$[B] = \begin{bmatrix} b_{11} & 3 \\ 6 & b_{22} \end{bmatrix},$$

Solution

The two matrices $[A]$ and $[B]$ would be equal if
$b_{11} = 2,\ b_{22} = 7.$

How do you add two matrices?

Two matrices [A] and [B] can be added only if they are the same size, then the addition is shown as

$$[C] = [A] + [B]$$

where

$$c_{ij} = a_{ij} + b_{ij}$$

Example 11

Add two matrices

$$[A] = \begin{bmatrix} 5 & 2 & 3 \\ 1 & 2 & 7 \end{bmatrix}$$

$$[B] = \begin{bmatrix} 6 & 7 & -2 \\ 3 & 5 & 19 \end{bmatrix}$$

Solution

$$[C] = [A] + [B]$$

$$= \begin{bmatrix} 5 & 2 & 3 \\ 1 & 2 & 7 \end{bmatrix} + \begin{bmatrix} 6 & 7 & -2 \\ 3 & 5 & 19 \end{bmatrix}$$

$$= \begin{bmatrix} 5+6 & 2+7 & 3-2 \\ 1+3 & 2+5 & 7+19 \end{bmatrix}$$

$$= \begin{bmatrix} 11 & 9 & 1 \\ 4 & 7 & 26 \end{bmatrix}$$

Example 12

Blowout r'us store has two locations A and B, and their sales of tires are given by make (in rows) and quarters (in columns) as shown below.

$$[A] = \begin{bmatrix} 25 & 20 & 3 & 2 \\ 5 & 10 & 15 & 25 \\ 6 & 16 & 7 & 27 \end{bmatrix}$$

$$[B] = \begin{bmatrix} 20 & 5 & 4 & 0 \\ 3 & 6 & 15 & 21 \\ 4 & 1 & 7 & 20 \end{bmatrix}$$

where the rows represent sale of Tirestone, Michigan and Copper tires and the columns represent the quarter number - 1, 2, 3, 4. What are the total sales of the two locations by make and quarter?

Solution

$$[C] = [A] + [B]$$

$$= \begin{bmatrix} 25 & 20 & 3 & 2 \\ 5 & 10 & 15 & 25 \\ 6 & 16 & 7 & 27 \end{bmatrix} + \begin{bmatrix} 20 & 5 & 4 & 0 \\ 3 & 6 & 15 & 21 \\ 4 & 1 & 7 & 20 \end{bmatrix}$$

$$= \begin{bmatrix} (25+20) & (20+5) & (3+4) & (2+0) \\ (5+3) & (10+6) & (15+15) & (25+21) \\ (6+4) & (16+1) & (7+7) & (27+20) \end{bmatrix}$$

$$= \begin{bmatrix} 45 & 25 & 7 & 2 \\ 8 & 16 & 30 & 46 \\ 10 & 17 & 14 & 47 \end{bmatrix}$$

So if one wants to know the total number of Copper tires sold in quarter 4 in the two locations, we would look at Row 3 – Column 4 to give

$$c_{34} = 47.$$

How do you subtract two matrices?

Two matrices [A] and [B] can be subtracted only if they are the same size and the subtraction is given by

$$[D] = [A] - [B]$$

where

$$d_{ij} = a_{ij} - b_{ij}$$

Example 13

Subtract matrix [B] from matrix [A].

$$[A] = \begin{bmatrix} 5 & 2 & 3 \\ 1 & 2 & 7 \end{bmatrix}$$

$$[B] = \begin{bmatrix} 6 & 7 & -2 \\ 3 & 5 & 19 \end{bmatrix}$$

Solution

$$[C] = [A] - [B]$$

$$= \begin{bmatrix} 5 & 2 & 3 \\ 1 & 2 & 7 \end{bmatrix} - \begin{bmatrix} 6 & 7 & -2 \\ 3 & 5 & 19 \end{bmatrix}$$

$$= \begin{bmatrix} 5-6 & 2-7 & 3-(-2) \\ 1-3 & 2-5 & 7-19 \end{bmatrix}$$

$$= \begin{bmatrix} -1 & -5 & 5 \\ -2 & -3 & -12 \end{bmatrix}$$

Example 14

Blowout r'us store has two locations A and B and their sales of tires are given by make (in rows) and quarters (in columns) as shown below.

$$[A] = \begin{bmatrix} 25 & 20 & 3 & 2 \\ 5 & 10 & 15 & 25 \\ 6 & 16 & 7 & 27 \end{bmatrix}$$

$$[B] = \begin{bmatrix} 20 & 5 & 4 & 0 \\ 3 & 6 & 15 & 21 \\ 4 & 1 & 7 & 20 \end{bmatrix}$$

where the rows represent sale of Tirestone, Michigan and Copper tires and the columns represent the quarter number- 1, 2, 3, 4. How many more tires did store A sell than store B of each brand in each quarter?

Solution

$$[D] = [A] - [B]$$

$$= \begin{bmatrix} 25 & 20 & 3 & 2 \\ 5 & 10 & 15 & 25 \\ 6 & 16 & 7 & 27 \end{bmatrix} - \begin{bmatrix} 20 & 5 & 4 & 0 \\ 3 & 6 & 15 & 21 \\ 4 & 1 & 7 & 20 \end{bmatrix}$$

$$= \begin{bmatrix} 25-20 & 20-5 & 3-4 & 2-0 \\ 5-3 & 10-6 & 15-15 & 25-21 \\ 6-4 & 16-1 & 7-7 & 27-20 \end{bmatrix}$$

$$= \begin{bmatrix} 5 & 15 & -1 & 2 \\ 2 & 4 & 0 & 4 \\ 2 & 15 & 0 & 7 \end{bmatrix}$$

So if you want to know how many more Copper Tires were sold in quarter 4 in Store A than Store B, $d_{34} = 7$. Note that $d_{13} = -1$ implying that store A sold 1 less Michigan tire than Store B in quarter 3.

How do I multiply two matrices?

Two matrices [A] and [B] can be multiplied only if the number of columns of [A] is equal to the number of rows of [B] to give

$$[C]_{m \times n} = [A]_{m \times p} [B]_{p \times n}$$

If [A] is a $m \times p$ matrix and [B] is a $p \times n$ matrix, the resulting matrix [C] is a $m \times n$ matrix.

So how does one calculate the elements of [C] matrix?

$$c_{ij} = \sum_{k=1}^{p} a_{ik} b_{kj}$$

$$= a_{i1}b_{1j} + a_{i2}b_{2j} + \ldots + a_{ip}b_{pj}$$

for each $i = 1, 2, \ldots, m$, and $j = 1, 2, \ldots, n$.

To put it in simpler terms, the i_{th} row and j_{th} column of the [C] matrix in [C] = [A][B] is calculated by multiplying the i_{th} row of [A] by the j_{th} column of [B], that is,

$$c_{ij} = [a_{i1} \ a_{i2} \ ...... a_{ip}] \begin{bmatrix} b_{1j} \\ b_{2j} \\ \vdots \\ \vdots \\ b_{pj} \end{bmatrix}$$

$$= a_{i1} b_{1j} + a_{i2} b_{2j} + ... + a_{ip} b_{pj}.$$

$$= \sum_{k=1}^{p} a_{ik} b_{kj}$$

Example 15

Given

$$[A] = \begin{bmatrix} 5 & 2 & 3 \\ 1 & 2 & 7 \end{bmatrix}$$

$$[B] = \begin{bmatrix} 3 & -2 \\ 5 & -8 \\ 9 & -10 \end{bmatrix}$$

find

$$[C] = [A][B]$$

Solution

c_{12} can be found by multiplying the first row of [A] by the second column of [B],

$$c_{12} = [5 \quad 2 \quad 3] \begin{bmatrix} -2 \\ -8 \\ -10 \end{bmatrix}$$

$$= (5)(-2) + (2)(-8) + (3)(-10)$$

$$= -56$$

Similarly, one can find the other elements of [C] to give

$$[C] = \begin{bmatrix} 52 & -56 \\ 76 & -88 \end{bmatrix}$$

Example 16

Blowout r'us store location A and the sales of tires are given by make (in rows) and quarters (in columns) as shown below

$$[A] = \begin{bmatrix} 25 & 20 & 3 & 2 \\ 5 & 10 & 15 & 25 \\ 6 & 16 & 7 & 27 \end{bmatrix}$$

where the rows represent sale of Tirestone, Michigan and Copper tires and the columns represent the quarter number - 1, 2, 3, 4. Find the per quarter sales of store A if following are the prices of each tire.

Tirestone = $33.25

Michigan = $40.19

Copper = $25.03

Solution

The answer is given by multiplying the price matrix by the quantity sales of store A. The price matrix is $[33.25 \quad 40.19 \quad 25.03]$, then the per quarter sales of store A would be given by

$$[C] = [33.25 \quad 40.19 \quad 25.03] \begin{bmatrix} 25 & 20 & 3 & 2 \\ 5 & 10 & 15 & 25 \\ 6 & 16 & 7 & 27 \end{bmatrix}$$

$$c_{ij} = \sum_{k=1}^{3} a_{ik} b_{kj}$$

$$c_{11} = \sum_{k=1}^{3} a_{1k} b_{k1}$$
$$= a_{11}b_{11} + a_{12}b_{21} + a_{13}b_{31}$$
$$= (33.25)(25) + (40.19)(5) + (25.03)(6)$$
$$= \$1182.38$$

Similarly
$$c_{12} = \$1467.38,$$
$$c_{13} = \$877.81,$$
$$c_{14} = \$1747.06.$$

So each quarter sales of store A in dollars are given by the four columns of the row vector
$$[C] = [1182.38 \quad 1467.38 \quad 877.81 \quad 1747.06]$$

Remember since we are multiplying a 1×3 matrix by a 3×4 matrix, the resulting matrix is a 1×4 matrix.

What is a scalar product of a constant and a matrix?

If $[A]$ is a $n \times n$ matrix and k is a real number, then the scalar product of k and $[A]$ is another matrix [B], where $b_{ij} = k a_{ij}$.

Example 17

Let $[A] = \begin{bmatrix} 2.1 & 3 & 2 \\ 5 & 1 & 6 \end{bmatrix}$. Find 2 [A]

Solution

$$[A] = \begin{bmatrix} 2.1 & 3 & 2 \\ 5 & 1 & 6 \end{bmatrix}$$

Then

$$2[A] = 2 \begin{bmatrix} 2.1 & 3 & 2 \\ 5 & 1 & 6 \end{bmatrix}$$

$$= \begin{bmatrix} (2)(2.1) & (2)(3) & (2)(2) \\ (2)(5) & (2)(1) & (2)(6) \end{bmatrix}$$

$$= \begin{bmatrix} 4.2 & 6 & 4 \\ 10 & 2 & 12 \end{bmatrix}$$

What is a linear combination of matrices?

If $[A_1], [A_2], \ldots\ldots\ldots, [A_p]$ are matrices of the same size and $k_1, k_2, \ldots\ldots, k_p$ are scalars, then

$$k_1[A_1] + k_2[A_2] + \ldots\ldots + k_p[A_p]$$

is called a linear combination of $[A_1], [A_2]\cdots\cdots, [A_p]$.

Example 18

If

$$[A_1] = \begin{bmatrix} 5 & 6 & 2 \\ 3 & 2 & 1 \end{bmatrix}, [A_2] = \begin{bmatrix} 2.1 & 3 & 2 \\ 5 & 1 & 6 \end{bmatrix}, [A_3] = \begin{bmatrix} 0 & 2.2 & 2 \\ 3 & 3.5 & 6 \end{bmatrix}$$

then find

$$[A_1] + 2[A_2] - 0.5[A_3]$$

Solution

$$= \begin{bmatrix} 5 & 6 & 2 \\ 3 & 2 & 1 \end{bmatrix} + 2 \begin{bmatrix} 2.1 & 3 & 2 \\ 5 & 1 & 6 \end{bmatrix} - 0.5 \begin{bmatrix} 0 & 2.2 & 2 \\ 3 & 3.5 & 6 \end{bmatrix}$$

$$= \begin{bmatrix} 5 & 6 & 2 \\ 3 & 2 & 1 \end{bmatrix} + \begin{bmatrix} 4.2 & 6 & 4 \\ 10 & 2 & 12 \end{bmatrix} - \begin{bmatrix} 0 & 1.1 & 1 \\ 1.5 & 1.75 & 3 \end{bmatrix}$$

$$= \begin{bmatrix} 9.2 & 10.9 & 5 \\ 11.5 & 2.25 & 10 \end{bmatrix}$$

What are some of the rules of binary matrix operations?

Commutative law of addition

If [A] and [B] are *mxn* matrices, then

$$[A]+[B]=[B]+[A]$$

Associate law of addition

If [A], [B] and [C] all are mxn matrices, then
$$[A]+([B]+[C])=([A]+[B])+[C]$$

Associate law of multiplication

If [A], [B] and [C] are mxn, nxp and pxr size matrices, respectively, then
$$[A]([B][C])=([A][B])[C]$$
and the resulting matrix size on both sides is mxr.

Distributive law

If [A] and [B] are mxn size matrices, and [C] and [D] are nxp size matrices
$$[A]([C]+[D])=[A][C]+[A][D]$$
$$([A]+[B])[C]=[A][C]+[B][C]$$
and the resulting matrix size on both sides is mxp.

Example 19

Illustrate the associative law of multiplication of matrices using

$$[A]=\begin{bmatrix} 1 & 2 \\ 3 & 5 \\ 0 & 2 \end{bmatrix}, \quad [B]=\begin{bmatrix} 2 & 5 \\ 9 & 6 \end{bmatrix}, \quad [C]=\begin{bmatrix} 2 & 1 \\ 3 & 5 \end{bmatrix}$$

Solution

$$[B][C]=\begin{bmatrix} 2 & 5 \\ 9 & 6 \end{bmatrix}\begin{bmatrix} 2 & 1 \\ 3 & 5 \end{bmatrix}=\begin{bmatrix} 19 & 27 \\ 36 & 39 \end{bmatrix}$$

$$[A][B][C]=\begin{bmatrix} 1 & 2 \\ 3 & 5 \\ 0 & 2 \end{bmatrix}\begin{bmatrix} 19 & 27 \\ 36 & 39 \end{bmatrix}=\begin{bmatrix} 91 & 105 \\ 237 & 276 \\ 72 & 78 \end{bmatrix}$$

$$[A][B]=\begin{bmatrix} 1 & 2 \\ 3 & 5 \\ 0 & 2 \end{bmatrix}\begin{bmatrix} 2 & 5 \\ 9 & 6 \end{bmatrix}=\begin{bmatrix} 20 & 17 \\ 51 & 45 \\ 18 & 12 \end{bmatrix}$$

$$[A][B][C]=\begin{bmatrix} 20 & 17 \\ 51 & 45 \\ 18 & 12 \end{bmatrix}\begin{bmatrix} 2 & 1 \\ 3 & 5 \end{bmatrix}=\begin{bmatrix} 91 & 105 \\ 237 & 276 \\ 72 & 78 \end{bmatrix}$$

The above illustrates the associate law of multiplication of matrices.

Is [A][B]=[B][A]?

First both operations $[A][B]$ and $[B][A]$ are only possible if $[A]$ and $[B]$ are square matrices of same size. Why? If $[A][B]$ exists, number of columns of $[A]$ has to be same as the number of rows of $[B]$ and if $[B][A]$ exists, number of columns of $[B]$ has to be same as the number of rows of $[A]$.

Even then in general $[A][B] \neq [B][A]$.

Example 20

Illustrate if $[A][B]=[B][A]$ for the following matrices

$$[A] = \begin{bmatrix} 6 & 3 \\ 2 & 5 \end{bmatrix}, \quad [B] = \begin{bmatrix} -3 & 2 \\ 1 & 5 \end{bmatrix}$$

Solution

$$[A][B] = \begin{bmatrix} 6 & 3 \\ 2 & 5 \end{bmatrix} \begin{bmatrix} -3 & 2 \\ 1 & 5 \end{bmatrix}$$

$$= \begin{bmatrix} -15 & 27 \\ -1 & 29 \end{bmatrix}$$

$$[B][A] = \begin{bmatrix} -3 & 2 \\ 1 & 5 \end{bmatrix} \begin{bmatrix} 6 & 3 \\ 2 & 5 \end{bmatrix}$$

$$= \begin{bmatrix} -14 & 1 \\ 16 & 28 \end{bmatrix}$$

$$[A][B] \neq [B][A]$$

Transpose of a matrix: Let [A] be a $m \times n$ matrix. Then [B] is the transpose of the [A] if $b_{ji} = a_{ij}$ for all i and j. That is, the ith row and the jth column element of [A] is the jth row and i^{th} column element of [B]. Note, [B] would be a $n \times m$ matrix. The transpose of [A] is denoted by $[A]^t$.

Example 21

Find the transpose of

$$[A] = \begin{bmatrix} 25 & 20 & 3 & 2 \\ 5 & 10 & 15 & 25 \\ 6 & 16 & 7 & 27 \end{bmatrix}$$

Solution

The transpose of [A] is

$$[A]^T = \begin{bmatrix} 25 & 5 & 6 \\ 20 & 10 & 16 \\ 3 & 15 & 7 \\ 2 & 25 & 27 \end{bmatrix}$$

Note, the transpose of a row vector is a column vector and the transpose of a column vector is a row vector.

Also, note that the transpose of a transpose of a matrix is the matrix itself, that is,

$$\left([A]^T\right)^T = [A]. \quad \text{Also,} \quad ([A]+[B])^T = [A]^T + [B]^T; (c[A])^T = c[A]^T \ .$$

Symmetric matrix: A square matrix $[A]$ with real elements where $a_{ij} = a_{ji}$ for $i = 1,\ldots\ldots,n$ and $j = 1,\ldots\ldots,n$ is called a symmetric matrix. This is same as, if $[A] = [A]^T$, then $[A]$ is a symmetric matrix.

Example 22

Give an example of a symmetric matrix.
Solution

$$[A] = \begin{bmatrix} 21.2 & 3.2 & 6 \\ 3.2 & 21.5 & 8 \\ 6 & 8 & 9.3 \end{bmatrix}$$

is a symmetric matrix as $a_{12} = a_{21} = 3.2$; $a_{13} = a_{31} = 6$ and $a_{23} = a_{32} = 8$.

Matrix algebra is used for solving system of equations. Can you illustrate this concept?

Matrix algebra is used to solve a system of simultaneous linear equations. In fact, for many mathematical procedures such as solution of set of nonlinear equations, interpolation, integration, and differential equations, the solutions reduce to a set of simultaneous linear equations. Let us illustrate with an example for interpolation.

Example 23

The upward velocity of a rocket is given at three different times on the following table

Time, t	Velocity, v
s	m/s
5	106.8
8	177.2
12	279.2

The velocity data is approximated by a polynomial as

$$v(t) = at^2 + bt + c, \quad 5 \leq t \leq 12.$$

Set up the equations in matrix form to find the coefficients a, b, c of the velocity profile.

Solution

The polynomial is going through three data points $(t_1, v_1), (t_2, v_2),$ and (t_3, v_3) where from the above table

$$t_1 = 5, v_1 = 106.8$$
$$t_2 = 8, v_2 = 177.2$$
$$t_3 = 12, v_3 = 279.2$$

Requiring that $v(t) = at^2 + bt + c$ passes through the three data points gives

$$v(t_1) = v_1 = at_1^2 + bt_1 + c$$
$$v(t_2) = v_2 = at_2^2 + bt_2 + c$$
$$v(t_3) = v_3 = at_3^2 + bt_3 + c$$

Substituting the data $(t_1, v_1), (t_2, v_2), (t_3, v_3)$ gives

$$a(5^2) + b(5) + c = 106.8$$
$$a(8^2) + b(8) + c = 177.2$$
$$a(12^2) + b(12) + c = 279.2$$

or

$$25a + 5b + c = 106.8$$
$$64a + 8b + c = 177.2$$
$$144a + 12b + c = 279.2$$

This set of equations can be rewritten in the matrix form as

$$\begin{bmatrix} 25a + & 5b + & c \\ 64a + & 8b + & c \\ 144a + & 12b + & c \end{bmatrix} = \begin{bmatrix} 106.8 \\ 177.2 \\ 279.2 \end{bmatrix}$$

The above equation can be written as a linear combination as follows

$$a\begin{bmatrix} 25 \\ 64 \\ 144 \end{bmatrix} + b\begin{bmatrix} 5 \\ 8 \\ 12 \end{bmatrix} + c\begin{bmatrix} 1 \\ 1 \\ 1 \end{bmatrix} = \begin{bmatrix} 106.8 \\ 177.2 \\ 279.2 \end{bmatrix}$$

and further using matrix multiplications gives

$$\begin{bmatrix} 25 & 5 & 1 \\ 64 & 8 & 1 \\ 144 & 12 & 1 \end{bmatrix}\begin{bmatrix} a \\ b \\ c \end{bmatrix} = \begin{bmatrix} 106.8 \\ 177.2 \\ 279.2 \end{bmatrix}$$

The above is an illustration of why matrix algebra is needed. The complete solution to the set of equations is given later in this chapter.

For a general set of m linear equations and n unknowns,

$$a_{11}x_1 + a_{22}x_2 + \cdots\cdots + a_{1n}x_n = c_1$$

$$a_{21}x_1 + a_{22}x_2 + \cdots\cdots + a_{2n}x_n = c_2$$

$$\cdots\cdots\cdots\cdots\cdots\cdots\cdots\cdots\cdots\cdots\cdots\cdots$$

$$\cdots\cdots\cdots\cdots\cdots\cdots\cdots\cdots\cdots\cdots\cdots\cdots$$

$$a_{m1}x_1 + a_{m2}x_2 + \cdots\cdots + a_{mn}x_n = c_m$$

can be rewritten in the matrix form as

$$
\begin{bmatrix}
a_{11} & a_{12} & . & . & a_{1n} \\
a_{21} & a_{22} & . & . & a_{2n} \\
\vdots & & & & \vdots \\
\vdots & & & & \vdots \\
a_{m1} & a_{m2} & . & . & a_{mn}
\end{bmatrix}
\begin{bmatrix}
x_1 \\
x_2 \\
. \\
. \\
x_n
\end{bmatrix}
=
\begin{bmatrix}
c_1 \\
c_2 \\
. \\
. \\
c_m
\end{bmatrix}
$$

Denoting the matrices by $[A]$, $[X]$, and $[C]$, the system of equation is $[A]$ $[X]=[C]$, where $[A]$ is called the coefficient matrix, $[C]$ is called the right hand side vector and $[X]$ is called the solution vector.

Sometimes $[A]$ $[X]=[C]$ systems of equations is written in the augmented form. That is

$$
[A \vdots C] =
\begin{bmatrix}
a_{11} & a_{12} & \cdots & a_{1n} & \vdots\, c_1 \\
a_{21} & a_{22} & \cdots & a_{2n} & \vdots\, c_2 \\
\vdots & & & \vdots & \vdots \\
\vdots & & & \vdots & \vdots \\
a_{m1} & a_{m2} & \cdots & a_{mn} & \vdots\, c_n
\end{bmatrix}
$$

Can you divide two matrices?

If [A] [B] = [C] is defined, it might seem intuitive that $[A]=\dfrac{[C]}{[B]}$, but matrix division is not defined. However an inverse of a matrix can be defined for certain types of square matrices. The inverse of a square matrix [A], if existing, is denoted by $[A]^{-1}$ such that $[A][A]^{-1} = [I] = [A]^{-1}[A]$.

In other words, let [A] be a square matrix. If [B] is another square matrix of same size such that [B][A] = [I], then [B] is the inverse of [A]. [A] is then called to be invertible or nonsingular. If $[A]^{-1}$ does not exist, [A] is called to be noninvertible or singular.

If [A] and [B] are two *nxn* matrices such that [B] [A] = [I], then these statements are also true

    a) [B] is the inverse of [A]
    b) [A] is the inverse of [B]
    c) [A] and [B] are both invertible
    d) [A] [B]=[I].
    e) [A] and [B] are both nonsingular
    f) all columns of [A] or [B]are linearly independent
    g) all rows of [A] or [B] are linearly independent.

Example 24

Show if

$$[B] = \begin{bmatrix} 3 & 2 \\ 5 & 3 \end{bmatrix} \text{ is the inverse of } [A] = \begin{bmatrix} -3 & 2 \\ 5 & -3 \end{bmatrix}$$

Solution

$$[B][A] = \begin{bmatrix} 3 & 2 \\ 5 & 3 \end{bmatrix}\begin{bmatrix} -3 & 2 \\ 5 & -3 \end{bmatrix}$$

$$= \begin{bmatrix} 1 & 0 \\ 0 & 1 \end{bmatrix}$$

$$= [I]$$

Since $[B][A] = [I]$, $[B]$ is the inverse of $[A]$ and $[A]$ is the inverse of $[B]$. But we can also show that

$$[A][B] = \begin{bmatrix} -3 & 2 \\ 5 & -3 \end{bmatrix}\begin{bmatrix} 3 & 2 \\ 5 & 3 \end{bmatrix}$$

$$= \begin{bmatrix} 1 & 0 \\ 0 & 1 \end{bmatrix} = [I]$$

to show that $[A]$ is the inverse of $[B]$.

Can I use the concept of the inverse of a matrix to find the solution of a set of equations $[A][X] = [C]$?

Yes, if the number of equations is same as the number of unknowns, the coefficient matrix $[A]$ is a square matrix.

Given

$$[A][X] = [C]$$

Then, if $[A]^{-1}$ exists, multiplying both sides by $[A]^{-1}$.

$$[A]^{-1}[A][X] = [A]^{-1}[C]$$

$$[I][X] = [A]^{-1}[C]$$

$$[X] = [A]^{-1}[C]$$

This implies that if we are able to find $[A]^{-1}$, the solution vector of $[A][X] = [C]$ is simply a multiplication of $[A]^{-1}$ and the right hand side vector, $[C]$.

How do I find the inverse of a matrix?

If $[A]$ is a $n \times n$ matrix, then $[A]^{-1}$ is a $n \times n$ matrix and according to the definition of inverse of a matrix

$$[A][A]^{-1} = [I].$$

Denoting

$$[A] = \begin{bmatrix} a_{11} & a_{12} & \cdot & \cdot & a_{1n} \\ a_{21} & a_{22} & \cdot & \cdot & a_{2n} \\ \cdot & \cdot & \cdot & \cdot & \cdot \\ \cdot & \cdot & \cdot & \cdot & \cdot \\ a_{n1} & a_{n2} & \cdot & \cdot & a_{nn} \end{bmatrix}$$

$$[A]^{-1} = \begin{bmatrix} a'_{11} & a'_{12} & \cdot & \cdot & a'_{1n} \\ a'_{21} & a'_{22} & \cdot & \cdot & a'_{2n} \\ \cdot & \cdot & \cdot & \cdot & \cdot \\ \cdot & \cdot & \cdot & \cdot & \cdot \\ a'_{n1} & a'_{n2} & \cdot & \cdot & a'_{nn} \end{bmatrix}$$

$$[I] = \begin{bmatrix} 1 & 0 & \cdot & \cdot & \cdot & 0 \\ 0 & 1 & & & & 0 \\ 0 & & \cdot & & & \cdot \\ \cdot & & & 1 & & \cdot \\ \cdot & & & & \cdot & \cdot \\ 0 & \cdot & \cdot & \cdot & \cdot & 1 \end{bmatrix}$$

Using the definition of matrix multiplication, the first column of the $[A]^{-1}$ matrix can then be found by solving

$$\begin{bmatrix} a_{11} & a_{12} & \cdot & \cdot & a_{1n} \\ a_{21} & a_{22} & \cdot & \cdot & a_{2n} \\ \cdot & \cdot & \cdot & \cdot & \cdot \\ \cdot & \cdot & \cdot & \cdot & \cdot \\ a_{n1} & a_{n2} & \cdot & \cdot & a_{nn} \end{bmatrix} \begin{bmatrix} a'_{11} \\ a'_{21} \\ \cdot \\ \cdot \\ a'_{n1} \end{bmatrix} = \begin{bmatrix} 1 \\ 0 \\ \cdot \\ \cdot \\ 0 \end{bmatrix}$$

Similarly, one can find the other columns of the $[A]^{-1}$ matrix by changing the right hand side accordingly.

Example 25

The upward velocity of the rocket is given by

Time, t	Velocity, v
s	m/s
5	106.8
8	177.2
12	279.2

In an earlier example, we wanted to approximate the velocity profile by

$$v(t) = at^2 + bt + c, \quad 5 \le 8 \le 12$$

We found that the coefficients a, b, c are given by

$$\begin{bmatrix} 25 & 5 & 1 \\ 64 & 8 & 1 \\ 144 & 12 & 1 \end{bmatrix}\begin{bmatrix} a \\ b \\ c \end{bmatrix} = \begin{bmatrix} 106.8 \\ 177.2 \\ 279.2 \end{bmatrix}$$

First find the inverse of

$$[A] = \begin{bmatrix} 25 & 5 & 1 \\ 64 & 8 & 1 \\ 144 & 12 & 1 \end{bmatrix}$$

and then use the definition of inverse to find the coefficients a, b, c.

Solution

If $[A]^{-1} = \begin{bmatrix} a'_{11} & a'_{12} & a'_{13} \\ a'_{21} & a'_{22} & a'_{23} \\ a'_{31} & a'_{32} & a'_{33} \end{bmatrix}$

is the inverse of [A],
Then

$$\begin{bmatrix} 25 & 5 & 1 \\ 64 & 8 & 1 \\ 144 & 12 & 1 \end{bmatrix}\begin{bmatrix} a'_{11} & a'_{12} & a'_{13} \\ a'_{21} & a'_{22} & a'_{23} \\ a'_{31} & a'_{32} & a'_{33} \end{bmatrix} = \begin{bmatrix} 1 & 0 & 0 \\ 0 & 1 & 0 \\ 0 & 0 & 1 \end{bmatrix}$$

gives three sets of equations

$$\begin{bmatrix} 25 & 5 & 1 \\ 64 & 8 & 1 \\ 144 & 12 & 1 \end{bmatrix}\begin{bmatrix} a'_{11} \\ a'_{21} \\ a'_{31} \end{bmatrix} = \begin{bmatrix} 1 \\ 0 \\ 0 \end{bmatrix}$$

$$\begin{bmatrix} 25 & 5 & 1 \\ 64 & 8 & 1 \\ 144 & 12 & 1 \end{bmatrix}\begin{bmatrix} a'_{12} \\ a'_{22} \\ a'_{32} \end{bmatrix} = \begin{bmatrix} 0 \\ 1 \\ 0 \end{bmatrix}$$

$$\begin{bmatrix} 25 & 5 & 1 \\ 64 & 8 & 1 \\ 144 & 12 & 1 \end{bmatrix}\begin{bmatrix} a'_{13} \\ a'_{23} \\ a'_{33} \end{bmatrix} = \begin{bmatrix} 0 \\ 0 \\ 1 \end{bmatrix}$$

Solving the above three sets of equations separately gives

$$\begin{bmatrix} a'_{11} \\ a'_{21} \\ a'_{31} \end{bmatrix} = \begin{bmatrix} 0.04762 \\ -0.9524 \\ 4.571 \end{bmatrix}$$

$$\begin{bmatrix} a'_{12} \\ a'_{22} \\ a'_{32} \end{bmatrix} = \begin{bmatrix} -0.08333 \\ 1.417 \\ -5.000 \end{bmatrix}$$

$$\begin{bmatrix} a'_{13} \\ a'_{23} \\ a'_{33} \end{bmatrix} = \begin{bmatrix} 0.03571 \\ -0.4643 \\ 1.429 \end{bmatrix}$$

Hence

$$[A]^{-1} = \begin{bmatrix} 0.04762 & -0.08333 & 0.03571 \\ -0.9524 & 1.417 & -0.4643 \\ 4.571 & -5.000 & 1.429 \end{bmatrix}$$

Now

$$[A][X] = [C]$$

where

$$[X] = \begin{bmatrix} a \\ b \\ c \end{bmatrix}$$

$$[C] = \begin{bmatrix} 106.8 \\ 177.2 \\ 279.2 \end{bmatrix}$$

Using the definition of $[A]^{-1}$,

$$[A]^{-1}[A][X] = [A]^{-1}[C]$$
$$[X] = [A]^{-1}[C]$$
$$= \begin{bmatrix} 0.04762 & -0.08333 & 0.03571 \\ -0.9524 & 1.417 & -0.4643 \\ 4.571 & -5.000 & 1.429 \end{bmatrix} \begin{bmatrix} 106.8 \\ 177.2 \\ 279.2 \end{bmatrix}$$

$$\begin{bmatrix} a \\ b \\ c \end{bmatrix} = \begin{bmatrix} 0.2900 \\ 19.70 \\ 1.050 \end{bmatrix}$$

So

$$v(t) = at^2 + bt + c, 5 \le t \le 12$$
$$= 0.2900t^2 + 19.70t + 1.050, 5 \le t \le 12$$

If the inverse of a square matrix [A] exists, is it unique?

Yes, the inverse of a square matrix is unique, if it exists. The proof is as follows. Assume that the inverse of [A] is [B] and if this inverse is not unique, then let another inverse of [A] exist called [C].

[B] is inverse of [A], then

$$[B][A] = [I]$$

Multiply both sides by [C],

[B][A][C] = [I][C]

[B][A][C] = [C]

Since [C] is inverse of [A], [A][C] = [I]

[B][I] = [C]

[B] = [C]

This shows that [B] and [C] are the same. So inverse of [A] is unique.

INTRODUCTION TO MATRIX ALGEBRA	
Topic	Introduction to Matrix Algebra
Summary	Know what a matrix is; Identify special types of matrices; When two matrices are equal; Add, subtract and multiply matrices; Learn rules of binary operations on matrices; Know what unary operations mean; Find the transpose of a square matrix and it relationship to symmetric matrices; Setup simultaneous linear equations in matrix form and vice-versa; Understand the concept of inverse of a matrix.
Major	General Engineering
Authors	Autar Kaw
Date	March 23, 2010
Web Site	http://numericalmethods.eng.usf.edu

Multiple-Choice Test

Chapter 04.01
Background Simultaneous Linear Equations

1. Given $[A] = \begin{bmatrix} 6 & 2 & 3 & 9 \\ 0 & 1 & 2 & 3 \\ 0 & 0 & 4 & 5 \\ 0 & 0 & 0 & 6 \end{bmatrix}$ then $[A]$ is a (an) _____ matrix.

    (A) diagonal
    (B) identity
    (C) lower triangular
    (D) upper triangular

2. A square matrix $[A]$ is lower triangular if

    (A) $a_{ij} = 0, j > i$

    (B) $a_{ij} = 0, i > j$

    (C) $a_{ij} \neq 0, i > j$

    (D) $a_{ij} \neq 0, j > i$

3. Given
    $$[A] = \begin{bmatrix} 12.3 & -12.3 & 20.3 \\ 11.3 & -10.3 & -11.3 \\ 10.3 & -11.3 & -12.3 \end{bmatrix}, \quad [B] = \begin{bmatrix} 2 & 4 \\ -5 & 6 \\ 11 & -20 \end{bmatrix}$$

    then if
    $$[C] = [A][B], \text{ then}$$
    $c_{31} = $ _____

    (A) -58.2
    (B) -37.6
    (C) 219.4
    (D) 259.4

4.   The following system of equations has _____ solution(s).
$$x + y = 2$$
$$6x + 6y = 12$$
(A) infinite
(B) no
(C) two
(D) unique

5.   Consider there are only two computer companies in a country. The companies are named Dude and Imac. Each year, Dude keeps 1/5th of its customers, while the rest switch to Imac. Each year, Imac keeps 1/3rd of its customers, while the rest switch to Dude. If in 2003, Dude had 1/6th of the market and Imac had 5/6th of the market, what will be the share of Dude computers when the market becomes stable?
(A) 37/90
(B) 5/11
(C) 6/11
(D) 53/90

6.   Three kids - Jim, Corey and David receive an inheritance of $2,253,453. The money is put in three trusts but is not divided equally to begin with. Corey's trust is three times that of David's because Corey made an A in Dr. Kaw's class. Each trust is put in an interest generating investment. The three trusts of Jim, Corey and David pays an interest of 6%, 8%, 11%, respectively. The total interest of all the three trusts combined at the end of the first year is $190,740.57. The equations to find the trust money of Jim (J), Corey (C) and David (D) in a matrix form is

(A) $\begin{bmatrix} 1 & 1 & 1 \\ 0 & 3 & -1 \\ 0.06 & 0.08 & 0.11 \end{bmatrix} \begin{bmatrix} J \\ C \\ D \end{bmatrix} = \begin{bmatrix} 2,253,453 \\ 0 \\ 190,740.57 \end{bmatrix}$

(B) $\begin{bmatrix} 1 & 1 & 1 \\ 0 & 1 & -3 \\ 0.06 & 0.08 & 0.11 \end{bmatrix} \begin{bmatrix} J \\ C \\ D \end{bmatrix} = \begin{bmatrix} 2,253,453 \\ 0 \\ 190,740.57 \end{bmatrix}$

(C) $\begin{bmatrix} 1 & 1 & 1 \\ 0 & 1 & -3 \\ 6 & 8 & 11 \end{bmatrix} \begin{bmatrix} J \\ C \\ D \end{bmatrix} = \begin{bmatrix} 2,253,453 \\ 0 \\ 190,740.57 \end{bmatrix}$

(D) $\begin{bmatrix} 1 & 1 & 1 \\ 0 & 3 & -1 \\ 6 & 8 & 11 \end{bmatrix} \begin{bmatrix} J \\ C \\ D \end{bmatrix} = \begin{bmatrix} 2,253,453 \\ 0 \\ 19,074,057 \end{bmatrix}$

Complete Solution

Problem Set

Chapter 04.01
Background on Simultaneous Linear Equations

1. Write an example of a row vector of dimension 4.

2. Write an example of a column vector of dimension 4.

3. Write an example of a square matrix of order 4×4.

4. Write an example of a tri-diagonal matrix of order 4×4.

5. Write an example of a identity matrix of order 5×5.

6. Write an example of a upper triangular matrix of order 4×4.

7. Write an example of a lower triangular matrix of order 4×4.

8. Which of these matrices are strictly diagonally dominant?

    a) $[A] = \begin{bmatrix} 15 & 6 & 7 \\ 2 & -4 & 2 \\ 3 & 2 & 6 \end{bmatrix}$

    b) $[A] = \begin{bmatrix} 5 & 6 & 7 \\ 2 & -4 & 2 \\ 3 & 2 & -5 \end{bmatrix}$

    c) $[A] = \begin{bmatrix} 5 & 3 & 2 \\ 6 & -8 & 2 \\ 7 & -5 & 12 \end{bmatrix}$

9. For the following matrices

$$[A] = \begin{bmatrix} 3 & 0 \\ -1 & 2 \\ 1 & 1 \end{bmatrix}, [B] = \begin{bmatrix} 4 & -1 \\ 0 & 2 \end{bmatrix}, [C] = \begin{bmatrix} 5 & 2 \\ 3 & 5 \\ 6 & 7 \end{bmatrix},$$

find where possible
   a) 4[A]+5[C]
   b) [A][B]
   c) [A]-2[C]

10. Food orders are taken from two engineering departments for a takeout. The order is tabulated below.
    Food order:

$$\begin{array}{c} \\ Mechanical \\ Civil \end{array} \begin{array}{ccc} \overset{Chicken}{\underset{Sandwich}{}} & Fries & Drink \\ \begin{bmatrix} 25 & 35 & 25 \\ 21 & 20 & 21 \end{bmatrix} \end{array}$$

However they have a choice of buying this food from three different restaurants. Their prices for the three food items are tabulated below

Price Matrix:

$$\begin{array}{c} \\ Chicken\ Sandwich \\ Fries \\ Drink \end{array} \begin{array}{ccc} McFat & Burcholestrol & \overset{Kentucky}{\underset{Sodium}{}} \\ \begin{bmatrix} 2.42 & 2.38 & 2.46 \\ 0.93 & 0.90 & 0.89 \\ 0.95 & 1.03 & 1.13 \end{bmatrix} \end{array}$$

Show how much each department will pay for their order at each restaurant. Which restaurant would be more economical to order from for each department?

11. Given

$$[A] = \begin{bmatrix} 12.3 & -12.3 & 10.3 \\ 11.3 & -10.3 & -11.3 \\ 10.3 & -11.3 & -12.3 \end{bmatrix},$$

$$[B] = \begin{bmatrix} 2 & 4 \\ -5 & 6 \\ 11 & -20 \end{bmatrix}.$$

Find [C] if [C] = [A] [B] .

12. The set of equations
$$\begin{bmatrix} 1 & 2 & 5 \\ 7 & 3 & 9 \\ 8 & 5 & 14 \end{bmatrix} \begin{bmatrix} x_1 \\ x_2 \\ x_3 \end{bmatrix} = \begin{bmatrix} 8 \\ 19 \\ 27 \end{bmatrix}$$
has unique, no, or infinite solutions. Which is it?

13. For what values of a will the following simultaneous linear equations

$$x_1 + x_2 + x_3 = 4$$

$$x_3 = 2$$

$$\left(a^2 - 4\right)x_1 + x_3 = a - 2$$

have
   a) Unique solution
   b) No solution
   c) Infinite solutions

14. Find if
$$[A] = \begin{bmatrix} 5 & -2.5 \\ -2 & 3 \end{bmatrix}$$
and
$$[B] = \begin{bmatrix} 0.3 & 0.25 \\ 0.2 & 0.5 \end{bmatrix}$$
are inverse of each other.

15. Find if
$$[A] = \begin{bmatrix} 5 & 2.5 \\ 2 & 3 \end{bmatrix}$$
and
$$[B] = \begin{bmatrix} 0.3 & -0.25 \\ 0.2 & 0.5 \end{bmatrix}$$
are inverse of each other.

16. Three kids - Jim, Corey and David receive an inheritance of $2,253,453. The money is put in three trusts but is not divided equally to begin with. Corey gets three times what David gets because Corey made an "A" in Dr. Kaw's class. Each trust is put in an interest generating investment. The three trusts of Jim, Corey and David pays an interest of 6%, 8%, 11%, respectively. The combined interest gained in all the three trusts at the end of the first year is $190,740.57. How much money was invested in each trust? Set the following as equations in a matrix form. Identify the unknowns. Do not solve for the unknowns.

17. By any scientific method, find the second column of the inverse of
$$\begin{bmatrix} 1 & 2 & 0 \\ 4 & 5 & 0 \\ 0 & 0 & 13 \end{bmatrix}.$$

18. Just write out the inverse of (no need to show any work)
$$\begin{bmatrix} 1 & 0 & 0 & 0 \\ 0 & 2 & 0 & 0 \\ 0 & 0 & 4 & 0 \\ 0 & 0 & 0 & 5 \end{bmatrix}.$$

19. Solve $[A][X]=[B]$ for $[X]$ if
$$[A]^{-1} = \begin{bmatrix} 10 & -7 & 0 \\ 2 & 2 & 5 \\ 2 & 0 & 6 \end{bmatrix},$$

and

$$[B] = \begin{bmatrix} 7 \\ 2.5 \\ 6.012 \end{bmatrix}.$$

20. Find the missing coefficients in the following matrices.
$$\begin{bmatrix} 1 & 2 & 0 \\ 4 & 5 & 0 \\ 0 & 0 & 13 \end{bmatrix} \begin{bmatrix} X & a_{12}' & X \\ X & a_{22}' & X \\ X & a_{32}' & X \end{bmatrix} = \begin{bmatrix} 1 & 0 & 0 \\ 0 & 1 & 0 \\ 0 & 0 & 1 \end{bmatrix}$$

Chapter 04.06
Gaussian Elimination

After reading this chapter, you should be able to:
1. *solve a set of simultaneous linear equations using Naïve Gauss elimination,*
2. *learn the pitfalls of the Naïve Gauss elimination method,*
3. *understand the effect of round-off error when solving a set of linear equations with the Naïve Gauss elimination method,*
4. *learn how to modify the Naïve Gauss elimination method to the Gaussian elimination with partial pivoting method to avoid pitfalls of the former method,*
5. *find the determinant of a square matrix using Gaussian elimination, and*
6. *understand the relationship between the determinant of a coefficient matrix and the solution of simultaneous linear equations.*

How is a set of equations solved numerically?

One of the most popular techniques for solving simultaneous linear equations is the Gaussian elimination method. The approach is designed to solve a general set of n equations and n unknowns

$$a_{11}x_1 + a_{12}x_2 + a_{13}x_3 + \ldots + a_{1n}x_n = b_1$$
$$a_{21}x_1 + a_{22}x_2 + a_{23}x_3 + \ldots + a_{2n}x_n = b_2$$

$\qquad \cdot \qquad \cdot$
$\qquad \cdot \qquad \cdot$
$\qquad \cdot \qquad \cdot$

$$a_{n1}x_1 + a_{n2}x_2 + a_{n3}x_3 + \ldots + a_{nn}x_n = b_n$$

Gaussian elimination consists of two steps
1. Forward Elimination of Unknowns: In this step, the unknown is eliminated in each equation starting with the first equation. This way, the equations are *reduced* to one equation and one unknown in each equation.
2. Back Substitution: In this step, starting from the last equation, each of the unknowns is found.

Forward Elimination of Unknowns:

In the first step of forward elimination, the first unknown, x_1 is eliminated from all rows below the first row. The first equation is selected as the pivot equation to eliminate x_1. So,

04.06.1

to eliminate x_1 in the second equation, one divides the first equation by a_{11} (hence called the pivot element) and then multiplies it by a_{21}. This is the same as multiplying the first equation by a_{21} / a_{11} to give

$$a_{21}x_1 + \frac{a_{21}}{a_{11}}a_{12}x_2 + \ldots + \frac{a_{21}}{a_{11}}a_{1n}x_n = \frac{a_{21}}{a_{11}}b_1$$

Now, this equation can be subtracted from the second equation to give

$$\left(a_{22} - \frac{a_{21}}{a_{11}}a_{12}\right)x_2 + \ldots + \left(a_{2n} - \frac{a_{21}}{a_{11}}a_{1n}\right)x_n = b_2 - \frac{a_{21}}{a_{11}}b_1$$

or

$$a'_{22}x_2 + \ldots + a'_{2n}x_n = b'_2$$

where

$$a'_{22} = a_{22} - \frac{a_{21}}{a_{11}}a_{12}$$

$$\vdots$$

$$a'_{2n} = a_{2n} - \frac{a_{21}}{a_{11}}a_{1n}$$

This procedure of eliminating x_1, is now repeated for the third equation to the nth equation to reduce the set of equations as

$$a_{11}x_1 + a_{12}x_2 + a_{13}x_3 + \ldots + a_{1n}x_n = b_1$$
$$a'_{22}x_2 + a'_{23}x_3 + \ldots + a'_{2n}x_n = b'_2$$
$$a'_{32}x_2 + a'_{33}x_3 + \ldots + a'_{3n}x_n = b'_3$$

$$\cdot \qquad \cdot \qquad \cdot$$
$$\cdot \qquad \cdot \qquad \cdot$$
$$\cdot \qquad \cdot \qquad \cdot$$

$$a'_{n2}x_2 + a'_{n3}x_3 + \ldots + a'_{nn}x_n = b'_n$$

This is the end of the first step of forward elimination. Now for the second step of forward elimination, we start with the second equation as the pivot equation and a'_{22} as the pivot element. So, to eliminate x_2 in the third equation, one divides the second equation by a'_{22} (the pivot element) and then multiply it by a'_{32}. This is the same as multiplying the second equation by a'_{32} / a'_{22} and subtracting it from the third equation. This makes the coefficient of x_2 zero in the third equation. The same procedure is now repeated for the fourth equation till the nth equation to give

$$a_{11}x_1 + a_{12}x_2 + a_{13}x_3 + \ldots + a_{1n}x_n = b_1$$
$$a'_{22}x_2 + a'_{23}x_3 + \ldots + a'_{2n}x_n = b'_2$$
$$a''_{33}x_3 + \ldots + a''_{3n}x_n = b''_3$$

$$\cdot \qquad \cdot$$
$$\cdot \qquad \cdot$$
$$\cdot \qquad \cdot$$

$$a''_{n3}x_3 + \ldots + a''_{nn}x_n = b''_n$$

The next steps of forward elimination are conducted by using the third equation as a pivot equation and so on. That is, there will be a total of $n-1$ steps of forward elimination. At the end of $n-1$ steps of forward elimination, we get a set of equations that look like

$$a_{11}x_1 + a_{12}x_2 + a_{13}x_3 + \ldots + a_{1n}x_n = b_1$$
$$a'_{22}x_2 + a'_{23}x_3 + \ldots + a'_{2n}x_n = b'_2$$
$$a''_{33}x_3 + \ldots + a''_{3n}x_n = b''_3$$

$$\vdots \qquad \vdots$$

$$a_{nn}^{(n-1)}x_n = b_n^{(n-1)}$$

Back Substitution:

Now the equations are solved starting from the last equation as it has only one unknown.

$$x_n = \frac{b_n^{(n-1)}}{a_{nn}^{(n-1)}}$$

Then the second last equation, that is the $(n-1)^{\text{th}}$ equation, has two unknowns: x_n and x_{n-1}, but x_n is already known. This reduces the $(n-1)^{\text{th}}$ equation also to one unknown. Back substitution hence can be represented for all equations by the formula

$$x_i = \frac{b_i^{(i-1)} - \sum\limits_{j=i+1}^{n} a_{ij}^{(i-1)}x_j}{a_{ii}^{(i-1)}} \qquad \text{for } i = n-1, n-2, \ldots, 1$$

and

$$x_n = \frac{b_n^{(n-1)}}{a_{nn}^{(n-1)}}$$

Example 1

The upward velocity of a rocket is given at three different times in Table 1.

Table 1 Velocity vs. time data.

Time, t (s)	Velocity, v (m/s)
5	106.8
8	177.2
12	279.2

The velocity data is approximated by a polynomial as

$$v(t) = a_1 t^2 + a_2 t + a_3, \qquad 5 \le t \le 12$$

The coefficients a_1, a_2, and a_3 for the above expression are given by

$$\begin{bmatrix} 25 & 5 & 1 \\ 64 & 8 & 1 \\ 144 & 12 & 1 \end{bmatrix} \begin{bmatrix} a_1 \\ a_2 \\ a_3 \end{bmatrix} = \begin{bmatrix} 106.8 \\ 177.2 \\ 279.2 \end{bmatrix}$$

Find the values of a_1, a_2, and a_3 using the Naïve Gauss elimination method. Find the velocity at $t = 6, 7.5, 9, 11$ seconds.

Solution

Forward Elimination of Unknowns

Since there are three equations, there will be two steps of forward elimination of unknowns.

First step

Divide Row 1 by 25 and then multiply it by 64, that is, multiply Row 1 by $64/25 = 2.56$.

$\begin{pmatrix}[25 & 5 & 1] & [106.8]\end{pmatrix} \times 2.56$ gives Row 1 as

$[64 \quad 12.8 \quad 2.56] \quad [273.408]$

Subtract the result from Row 2

$$\begin{array}{r} [64 \quad 8 \quad 1] \quad [177.2] \\ - [64 \quad 12.8 \quad 2.56] \quad [273.408] \\ \hline 0 \quad -4.8 \quad -1.56 \quad -96.208 \end{array}$$

to get the resulting equations as

$$\begin{bmatrix} 25 & 5 & 1 \\ 0 & -4.8 & -1.56 \\ 144 & 12 & 1 \end{bmatrix} \begin{bmatrix} a_1 \\ a_2 \\ a_3 \end{bmatrix} = \begin{bmatrix} 106.8 \\ -96.208 \\ 279.2 \end{bmatrix}$$

Divide Row 1 by 25 and then multiply it by 144, that is, multiply Row 1 by $144/25 = 5.76$.

$\begin{pmatrix}[25 & 5 & 1] & [106.8]\end{pmatrix} \times 5.76$ gives Row 1 as

$[144 \quad 28.8 \quad 5.76] \quad [615.168]$

Subtract the result from Row 3

$$\begin{array}{r} [144 \quad 12 \quad 1] \quad [279.2] \\ - [144 \quad 28.8 \quad 5.76] \quad [615.168] \\ \hline 0 \quad -16.8 \quad -4.76 \quad -335.968 \end{array}$$

to get the resulting equations as

$$\begin{bmatrix} 25 & 5 & 1 \\ 0 & -4.8 & -1.56 \\ 0 & -16.8 & -4.76 \end{bmatrix} \begin{bmatrix} a_1 \\ a_2 \\ a_3 \end{bmatrix} = \begin{bmatrix} 106.8 \\ -96.208 \\ -335.968 \end{bmatrix}$$

Second step

We now divide Row 2 by –4.8 and then multiply by –16.8, that is, multiply Row 2 by $-16.8 / -4.8 = 3.5$.

$\begin{pmatrix}[0 & -4.8 & -1.56] & [-96.208]\end{pmatrix} \times 3.5$ gives Row 2 as

$[0 \quad -16.8 \quad -5.46] \quad [-336.728]$

Subtract the result from Row 3

$$\begin{array}{cc} \begin{bmatrix} 0 & -16.8 & -4.76 \end{bmatrix} & \begin{bmatrix} -335.968 \end{bmatrix} \\ -\begin{bmatrix} 0 & -16.8 & -5.46 \end{bmatrix} & \begin{bmatrix} -336.728 \end{bmatrix} \\ \hline 0 \quad\; 0 \quad\;\; 0.7 & 0.76 \end{array}$$

to get the resulting equations as

$$\begin{bmatrix} 25 & 5 & 1 \\ 0 & -4.8 & -1.56 \\ 0 & 0 & 0.7 \end{bmatrix} \begin{bmatrix} a_1 \\ a_2 \\ a_3 \end{bmatrix} = \begin{bmatrix} 106.8 \\ -96.208 \\ 0.76 \end{bmatrix}$$

Back substitution

From the third equation

$$0.7a_3 = 0.76$$

$$a_3 = \frac{0.76}{0.7}$$

$$= 1.08571$$

Substituting the value of a_3 in the second equation,

$$-4.8a_2 - 1.56a_3 = -96.208$$

$$a_2 = \frac{-96.208 + 1.56a_3}{-4.8}$$

$$= \frac{-96.208 + 1.56 \times 1.08571}{-4.8}$$

$$= 19.6905$$

Substituting the value of a_2 and a_3 in the first equation,

$$25a_1 + 5a_2 + a_3 = 106.8$$

$$a_1 = \frac{106.8 - 5a_2 - a_3}{25}$$

$$= \frac{106.8 - 5 \times 19.6905 - 1.08571}{25}$$

$$= 0.290472$$

Hence the solution vector is

$$\begin{bmatrix} a_1 \\ a_2 \\ a_3 \end{bmatrix} = \begin{bmatrix} 0.290472 \\ 19.6905 \\ 1.08571 \end{bmatrix}$$

The polynomial that passes through the three data points is then

$$v(t) = a_1 t^2 + a_2 t + a_3$$

$$= 0.290472t^2 + 19.6905t + 1.08571, \quad 5 \le t \le 12$$

Since we want to find the velocity at $t = 6, 7.5, 9$ and 11 seconds, we could simply substitute each value of t in $v(t) = 0.290472t^2 + 19.6905t + 1.08571$ and find the corresponding velocity. For example, at $t = 6$

$$v(6) = 0.290472(6)^2 + 19.6905(6) + 1.08571$$
$$= 129.686 \text{ m/s}$$

However we could also find all the needed values of velocity at $t = 6, 7.5, 9, 11$ seconds using matrix multiplication.

$$v(t) = \begin{bmatrix} 0.290472 & 19.6905 & 1.08571 \end{bmatrix} \begin{bmatrix} t^2 \\ t \\ 1 \end{bmatrix}$$

So if we want to find $v(6), v(7.5), v(9), v(11)$, it is given by

$$\begin{bmatrix} v(6) v(7.5) & v(9) v(11) \end{bmatrix} = \begin{bmatrix} 0.290472 & 19.6905 & 1.08571 \end{bmatrix} \begin{bmatrix} 6^2 & 7.5^2 & 9^2 & 11^2 \\ 6 & 7.5 & 9 & 11 \\ 1 & 1 & 1 & 1 \end{bmatrix}$$

$$= \begin{bmatrix} 0.290472 & 19.6905 & 1.08571 \end{bmatrix} \begin{bmatrix} 36 & 56.25 & 81 & 121 \\ 6 & 7.5 & 9 & 11 \\ 1 & 1 & 1 & 1 \end{bmatrix}$$

$$= \begin{bmatrix} 129.686 & 165.104 & 201.828 & 252.828 \end{bmatrix}$$

$$v(6) = 129.686 \text{ m/s}$$
$$v(7.5) = 165.104 \text{ m/s}$$
$$v(9) = 201.828 \text{ m/s}$$
$$v(11) = 252.828 \text{ m/s}$$

Example 2

Use Naïve Gauss elimination to solve
$$20x_1 + 15x_2 + 10x_3 = 45$$
$$-3x_1 - 2.249x_2 + 7x_3 = 1.751$$
$$5x_1 + x_2 + 3x_3 = 9$$
Use six significant digits with chopping in your calculations.
Solution

Working in the matrix form
$$\begin{bmatrix} 20 & 15 & 10 \\ -3 & -2.249 & 7 \\ 5 & 1 & 3 \end{bmatrix} \begin{bmatrix} x_1 \\ x_2 \\ x_3 \end{bmatrix} = \begin{bmatrix} 45 \\ 1.751 \\ 9 \end{bmatrix}$$

Forward Elimination of Unknowns

First step
Divide Row 1 by 20 and then multiply it by –3, that is, multiply Row 1 by $-3/20 = -0.15$.
$$(\begin{bmatrix} 20 & 15 & 10 \end{bmatrix} \ \begin{bmatrix} 45 \end{bmatrix}) \times -0.15 \text{ gives Row 1 as}$$
$$\begin{bmatrix} -3 & -2.25 & -1.5 \end{bmatrix} \quad \begin{bmatrix} -6.75 \end{bmatrix}$$

Subtract the result from Row 2

$$
\begin{array}{ccc}
\begin{bmatrix} -3 & -2.249 & 7 \end{bmatrix} & \begin{bmatrix} 1.751 \end{bmatrix} \\
- \begin{bmatrix} -3 & -2.25 & -1.5 \end{bmatrix} & \begin{bmatrix} -6.75 \end{bmatrix} \\
\hline
\begin{array}{ccc} 0 & 0.001 & 8.5 \end{array} & 8.501
\end{array}
$$

to get the resulting equations as

$$
\begin{bmatrix} 20 & 15 & 10 \\ 0 & 0.001 & 8.5 \\ 5 & 1 & 3 \end{bmatrix}
\begin{bmatrix} x_1 \\ x_2 \\ x_3 \end{bmatrix}
=
\begin{bmatrix} 45 \\ 8.501 \\ 9 \end{bmatrix}
$$

Divide Row 1 by 20 and then multiply it by 5, that is, multiply Row 1 by $5/20 = 0.25$

$(\begin{bmatrix} 20 & 15 & 10 \end{bmatrix} \quad \begin{bmatrix} 45 \end{bmatrix}) \times 0.25$ gives Row 1 as

$$
\begin{bmatrix} 5 & 3.75 & 2.5 \end{bmatrix} \quad \begin{bmatrix} 11.25 \end{bmatrix}
$$

Subtract the result from Row 3

$$
\begin{array}{ccc}
\begin{bmatrix} 5 & 1 & 3 \end{bmatrix} & \begin{bmatrix} 9 \end{bmatrix} \\
- \begin{bmatrix} 5 & 3.75 & 2.5 \end{bmatrix} & \begin{bmatrix} 11.25 \end{bmatrix} \\
\hline
\begin{array}{ccc} 0 & -2.75 & 0.5 \end{array} & -2.25
\end{array}
$$

to get the resulting equations as

$$
\begin{bmatrix} 20 & 15 & 10 \\ 0 & 0.001 & 8.5 \\ 0 & -2.75 & 0.5 \end{bmatrix}
\begin{bmatrix} x_1 \\ x_2 \\ x_3 \end{bmatrix}
=
\begin{bmatrix} 45 \\ 8.501 \\ -2.25 \end{bmatrix}
$$

<u>Second step</u>

Now for the second step of forward elimination, we will use Row 2 as the pivot equation and eliminate Row 3: Column 2.

Divide Row 2 by 0.001 and then multiply it by –2.75, that is, multiply Row 2 by $-2.75/0.001 = -2750$.

$(\begin{bmatrix} 0 & 0.001 & 8.5 \end{bmatrix} \quad \begin{bmatrix} 8.501 \end{bmatrix}) \times -2750$ gives Row 2 as

$$
\begin{bmatrix} 0 & -2.75 & -23375 \end{bmatrix} \quad \begin{bmatrix} -23377.75 \end{bmatrix}
$$

Rewriting within 6 significant digits with chopping

$$
\begin{bmatrix} 0 & -2.75 & -23375 \end{bmatrix} \quad \begin{bmatrix} -23377.7 \end{bmatrix}
$$

Subtract the result from Row 3

$$
\begin{array}{ccc}
\begin{bmatrix} 0 & -2.75 & 0.5 \end{bmatrix} & \begin{bmatrix} -2.25 \end{bmatrix} \\
- \begin{bmatrix} 0 & -2.75 & -23375 \end{bmatrix} & \begin{bmatrix} -23377.7 \end{bmatrix} \\
\hline
\begin{array}{ccc} 0 & 0 & 23375.5 \end{array} & 23375.45
\end{array}
$$

Rewriting within 6 significant digits with chopping

$$
\begin{bmatrix} 0 & 0 & 23375.5 \end{bmatrix} \quad \begin{bmatrix} -23375.4 \end{bmatrix}
$$

to get the resulting equations as

$$
\begin{bmatrix} 20 & 15 & 10 \\ 0 & 0.001 & 8.5 \\ 0 & 0 & 23375.5 \end{bmatrix}
\begin{bmatrix} x_1 \\ x_2 \\ x_3 \end{bmatrix}
=
\begin{bmatrix} 45 \\ 8.501 \\ 23375.4 \end{bmatrix}
$$

This is the end of the forward elimination steps.

Back substitution

We can now solve the above equations by back substitution. From the third equation,

$$23375.5x_3 = 23375.4$$

$$x_3 = \frac{23375.4}{23375.5}$$

$$= 0.999995$$

Substituting the value of x_3 in the second equation

$$0.001x_2 + 8.5x_3 = 8.501$$

$$x_2 = \frac{8.501 - 8.5x_3}{0.001}$$

$$= \frac{8.501 - 8.5 \times 0.999995}{0.001}$$

$$= \frac{8.501 - 8.49995}{0.001}$$

$$= \frac{0.00105}{0.001}$$

$$= 1.05$$

Substituting the value of x_3 and x_2 in the first equation,

$$20x_1 + 15x_2 + 10x_3 = 45$$

$$x_1 = \frac{45 - 15x_2 - 10x_3}{20}$$

$$= \frac{45 - 15 \times 1.05 - 10 \times 0.999995}{20}$$

$$= \frac{45 - 15.75 - 9.99995}{20}$$

$$= \frac{29.25 - 9.99995}{20}$$

$$= \frac{19.2500}{20}$$

$$= 0.9625$$

Hence the solution is

$$[X] = \begin{bmatrix} x_1 \\ x_2 \\ x_3 \end{bmatrix}$$

$$= \begin{bmatrix} 0.9625 \\ 1.05 \\ 0.999995 \end{bmatrix}$$

Compare this with the exact solution of

$$[X] = \begin{bmatrix} x_1 \\ x_2 \\ x_3 \end{bmatrix}$$

$$= \begin{bmatrix} 1 \\ 1 \\ 1 \end{bmatrix}$$

Are there any pitfalls of the Naïve Gauss elimination method?

Yes, there are two pitfalls of the Naïve Gauss elimination method.
Division by zero: It is possible for division by zero to occur during the beginning of the $n-1$ steps of forward elimination.
For example

$$5x_2 + 6x_3 = 11$$
$$4x_1 + 5x_2 + 7x_3 = 16$$
$$9x_1 + 2x_2 + 3x_3 = 15$$

will result in division by zero in the first step of forward elimination as the coefficient of x_1 in the first equation is zero as is evident when we write the equations in matrix form.

$$\begin{bmatrix} 0 & 5 & 6 \\ 4 & 5 & 7 \\ 9 & 2 & 3 \end{bmatrix} \begin{bmatrix} x_1 \\ x_2 \\ x_3 \end{bmatrix} = \begin{bmatrix} 11 \\ 16 \\ 15 \end{bmatrix}$$

But what about the equations below: Is division by zero a problem?

$$5x_1 + 6x_2 + 7x_3 = 18$$
$$10x_1 + 12x_2 + 3x_3 = 25$$
$$20x_1 + 17x_2 + 19x_3 = 56$$

Written in matrix form,

$$\begin{bmatrix} 5 & 6 & 7 \\ 10 & 12 & 3 \\ 20 & 17 & 19 \end{bmatrix} \begin{bmatrix} x_1 \\ x_2 \\ x_3 \end{bmatrix} = \begin{bmatrix} 18 \\ 25 \\ 56 \end{bmatrix}$$

there is no issue of division by zero in the first step of forward elimination. The pivot element is the coefficient of x_1 in the first equation, 5, and that is a non-zero number. However, at the end of the first step of forward elimination, we get the following equations in matrix form

$$\begin{bmatrix} 5 & 6 & 7 \\ 0 & 0 & -11 \\ 0 & -7 & -9 \end{bmatrix} \begin{bmatrix} x_1 \\ x_2 \\ x_3 \end{bmatrix} = \begin{bmatrix} 18 \\ -11 \\ -16 \end{bmatrix}$$

Now at the beginning of the 2nd step of forward elimination, the coefficient of x_2 in Equation 2 would be used as the pivot element. That element is zero and hence would create the division by zero problem.

So it is important to consider that the possibility of division by zero can occur at the beginning of any step of forward elimination.

Round-off error: The Naïve Gauss elimination method is prone to round-off errors. This is true when there are large numbers of equations as errors propagate. Also, if there is subtraction of numbers from each other, it may create large errors. See the example below.

Example 3

Remember Example 2 where we used Naïve Gauss elimination to solve

$$20x_1 + 15x_2 + 10x_3 = 45$$
$$-3x_1 - 2.249x_2 + 7x_3 = 1.751$$
$$5x_1 + x_2 + 3x_3 = 9$$

using six significant digits with chopping in your calculations? Repeat the problem, but now use five significant digits with chopping in your calculations.

Solution

Writing in the matrix form

$$\begin{bmatrix} 20 & 15 & 10 \\ -3 & -2.249 & 7 \\ 5 & 1 & 3 \end{bmatrix} \begin{bmatrix} x_1 \\ x_2 \\ x_3 \end{bmatrix} = \begin{bmatrix} 45 \\ 1.751 \\ 9 \end{bmatrix}$$

Forward Elimination of Unknowns

<u>First step</u>

Divide Row 1 by 20 and then multiply it by –3, that is, multiply Row 1 by $-3/20 = -0.15$.

$([20 \quad 15 \quad 10] \quad [45]) \times -0.15$ gives Row 1 as

$[-3 \quad -2.25 \quad -1.5] \quad [-6.75]$

Subtract the result from Row 2

$$\begin{array}{cccc} [-3 & -2.249 & 7] & [1.751] \\ - [-3 & -2.25 & -1.5] & [-6.75] \\ \hline 0 & 0.001 & 8.5 & 8.501 \end{array}$$

to get the resulting equations as

$$\begin{bmatrix} 20 & 15 & 10 \\ 0 & 0.001 & 8.5 \\ 5 & 1 & 3 \end{bmatrix} \begin{bmatrix} x_1 \\ x_2 \\ x_3 \end{bmatrix} = \begin{bmatrix} 45 \\ 8.501 \\ 9 \end{bmatrix}$$

Divide Row 1 by 20 and then multiply it by 5, that is, multiply Row 1 by $5/20 = 0.25$.

$([20 \quad 15 \quad 10] \quad [45]) \times 0.25$ gives Row 1 as

$[5 \quad 3.75 \quad 2.5] \quad [11.25]$

Subtract the result from Row 3

$$\begin{array}{cccc} [5 & 1 & 3] & [9] \\ - [5 & 3.75 & 2.5] & [11.25] \\ \hline 0 & -2.75 & 0.5 & -2.25 \end{array}$$

to get the resulting equations as

$$\begin{bmatrix} 20 & 15 & 10 \\ 0 & 0.001 & 8.5 \\ 0 & -2.75 & 0.5 \end{bmatrix} \begin{bmatrix} x_1 \\ x_2 \\ x_3 \end{bmatrix} = \begin{bmatrix} 45 \\ 8.501 \\ -2.25 \end{bmatrix}$$

<u>Second step</u>

Now for the second step of forward elimination, we will use Row 2 as the pivot equation and eliminate Row 3: Column 2.

Divide Row 2 by 0.001 and then multiply it by –2.75, that is, multiply Row 2 by $-2.75/0.001 = -2750$.

$$([0 \quad 0.001 \quad 8.5] \quad [8.501]) \times -2750 \text{ gives Row 2 as}$$

$$[0 \quad -2.75 \quad -23375] \quad [-23377.75]$$

Rewriting within 5 significant digits with chopping

$$[0 \quad -2.75 \quad -23375] \quad [-23377]$$

Subtract the result from Row 3

$$\begin{array}{cccc} & [0 & -2.75 & 0.5] & [-2.25] \\ - & [0 & -2.75 & -23375] & [-23377] \\ \hline & 0 & 0 & 23375 & 23374 \end{array}$$

Rewriting within 6 significant digits with chopping

$$[0 \quad 0 \quad 23375] \quad [-23374]$$

to get the resulting equations as

$$\begin{bmatrix} 20 & 15 & 10 \\ 0 & 0.001 & 8.5 \\ 0 & 0 & 23375 \end{bmatrix} \begin{bmatrix} x_1 \\ x_2 \\ x_3 \end{bmatrix} = \begin{bmatrix} 45 \\ 8.501 \\ 23374 \end{bmatrix}$$

This is the end of the forward elimination steps.

Back substitution

We can now solve the above equations by back substitution. From the third equation,

$$23375 x_3 = 23374$$

$$x_3 = \frac{23374}{23375}$$

$$= 0.99995$$

Substituting the value of x_3 in the second equation

$$0.001 x_2 + 8.5 x_3 = 8.501$$

$$x_2 = \frac{8.501 - 8.5 x_3}{0.001}$$

$$= \frac{8.501 - 8.5 \times 0.99995}{0.001}$$

$$= \frac{8.501 - 8.499575}{0.001}$$

$$= \frac{8.501 - 8.4995}{0.001}$$

$$= \frac{0.0015}{0.001}$$

$$= 1.5$$

Substituting the value of x_3 and x_2 in the first equation,

$$20x_1 + 15x_2 + 10x_3 = 45$$

$$x_1 = \frac{45 - 15x_2 - 10x_3}{20}$$

$$= \frac{45 - 15 \times 1.5 - 10 \times 0.99995}{20}$$

$$= \frac{45 - 22.5 - 9.9995}{20}$$

$$= \frac{22.5 - 9.9995}{20}$$

$$= \frac{12.5005}{20}$$

$$= \frac{12.500}{20}$$

$$= 0.625$$

Hence the solution is

$$[X] = \begin{bmatrix} x_1 \\ x_2 \\ x_3 \end{bmatrix}$$

$$= \begin{bmatrix} 0.625 \\ 1.5 \\ 0.99995 \end{bmatrix}$$

Compare this with the exact solution of

$$[X] = \begin{bmatrix} x_1 \\ x_2 \\ x_3 \end{bmatrix} = \begin{bmatrix} 1 \\ 1 \\ 1 \end{bmatrix}$$

What are some techniques for improving the Naïve Gauss elimination method?

As seen in Example 3, round off errors were large when five significant digits were used as opposed to six significant digits. One method of decreasing the round-off error would be to use more significant digits, that is, use double or quad precision for representing the numbers. However, this would not avoid possible division by zero errors in the Naïve Gauss elimination method. To avoid division by zero as well as reduce (not eliminate) round-off error, Gaussian elimination with partial pivoting is the method of choice.

How does Gaussian elimination with partial pivoting differ from Naïve Gauss elimination?

The two methods are the same, except in the beginning of each step of forward elimination, a row switching is done based on the following criterion. If there are n equations, then there are $n-1$ forward elimination steps. At the beginning of the kth step of forward elimination, one finds the maximum of

$$\left|a_{kk}\right|, \left|a_{k+1,k}\right|, \ldots\ldots\ldots\ldots, \left|a_{nk}\right|$$

Then if the maximum of these values is $\left|a_{pk}\right|$ in the pth row, $k \le p \le n$, then switch rows p and k.

The other steps of forward elimination are the same as the Naïve Gauss elimination method. The back substitution steps stay exactly the same as the Naïve Gauss elimination method.

Example 4

In the previous two examples, we used Naïve Gauss elimination to solve

$$20x_1 + 15x_2 + 10x_3 = 45$$

$$-3x_1 - 2.249x_2 + 7x_3 = 1.751$$

$$5x_1 + x_2 + 3x_3 = 9$$

using five and six significant digits with chopping in the calculations. Using five significant digits with chopping, the solution found was

$$[X] = \begin{bmatrix} x_1 \\ x_2 \\ x_3 \end{bmatrix}$$

$$= \begin{bmatrix} 0.625 \\ 1.5 \\ 0.99995 \end{bmatrix}$$

This is different from the exact solution of

$$[X] = \begin{bmatrix} x_1 \\ x_2 \\ x_3 \end{bmatrix}$$

$$= \begin{bmatrix} 1 \\ 1 \\ 1 \end{bmatrix}$$

Find the solution using Gaussian elimination with partial pivoting using five significant digits with chopping in your calculations.

Solution

$$\begin{bmatrix} 20 & 15 & 10 \\ -3 & -2.249 & 7 \\ 5 & 1 & 3 \end{bmatrix} \begin{bmatrix} x_1 \\ x_2 \\ x_3 \end{bmatrix} = \begin{bmatrix} 45 \\ 1.751 \\ 9 \end{bmatrix}$$

Forward Elimination of Unknowns

Now for the first step of forward elimination, the absolute value of the first column elements below Row 1 is

$$|20|, |-3|, |5|$$

or

$$20, 3, 5$$

So the largest absolute value is in the Row 1. So as per Gaussian elimination with partial pivoting, the switch is between Row 1 and Row 1 to give

$$\begin{bmatrix} 20 & 15 & 10 \\ -3 & -2.249 & 7 \\ 5 & 1 & 3 \end{bmatrix} \begin{bmatrix} x_1 \\ x_2 \\ x_3 \end{bmatrix} = \begin{bmatrix} 45 \\ 1.751 \\ 9 \end{bmatrix}$$

Divide Row 1 by 20 and then multiply it by –3, that is, multiply Row 1 by $-3/20 = -0.15$.

$$(\begin{bmatrix} 20 & 15 & 10 \end{bmatrix} \begin{bmatrix} 45 \end{bmatrix}) \times -0.15 \text{ gives Row 1 as}$$

$$\begin{bmatrix} -3 & -2.25 & -1.5 \end{bmatrix} \quad \begin{bmatrix} -6.75 \end{bmatrix}$$

Subtract the result from Row 2

$$\begin{array}{ccc} \begin{bmatrix} -3 & -2.249 & 7 \end{bmatrix} & \begin{bmatrix} 1.751 \end{bmatrix} \\ - \begin{bmatrix} -3 & -2.25 & -1.5 \end{bmatrix} & \begin{bmatrix} -6.75 \end{bmatrix} \\ \hline \begin{array}{ccc} 0 & 0.001 & 8.5 \end{array} & 8.501 \end{array}$$

to get the resulting equations as

$$\begin{bmatrix} 20 & 15 & 10 \\ 0 & 0.001 & 8.5 \\ 5 & 1 & 3 \end{bmatrix} \begin{bmatrix} x_1 \\ x_2 \\ x_3 \end{bmatrix} = \begin{bmatrix} 45 \\ 8.501 \\ 9 \end{bmatrix}$$

Divide Row 1 by 20 and then multiply it by 5, that is, multiply Row 1 by $5/20 = 0.25$.

$$(\begin{bmatrix} 20 & 15 & 10 \end{bmatrix} \begin{bmatrix} 45 \end{bmatrix}) \times 0.25 \text{ gives Row 1 as}$$

$$\begin{bmatrix} 5 & 3.75 & 2.5 \end{bmatrix} \quad \begin{bmatrix} 11.25 \end{bmatrix}$$

Subtract the result from Row 3

$$\begin{array}{ccc} \begin{bmatrix} 5 & 1 & 3 \end{bmatrix} & \begin{bmatrix} 9 \end{bmatrix} \\ - \begin{bmatrix} 5 & 3.75 & 2.5 \end{bmatrix} & \begin{bmatrix} 11.25 \end{bmatrix} \\ \hline \begin{array}{ccc} 0 & -2.75 & 0.5 \end{array} & -2.25 \end{array}$$

to get the resulting equations as

$$\begin{bmatrix} 20 & 15 & 10 \\ 0 & 0.001 & 8.5 \\ 0 & -2.75 & 0.5 \end{bmatrix} \begin{bmatrix} x_1 \\ x_2 \\ x_3 \end{bmatrix} = \begin{bmatrix} 45 \\ 8.501 \\ -2.25 \end{bmatrix}$$

This is the end of the first step of forward elimination.

Now for the second step of forward elimination, the absolute value of the second column elements below Row 1 is

$$|0.001|, |-2.75|$$

or

$$0.001, 2.75$$

So the largest absolute value is in Row 3. So Row 2 is switched with Row 3 to give

$$\begin{bmatrix} 20 & 15 & 10 \\ 0 & -2.75 & 0.5 \\ 0 & 0.001 & 8.5 \end{bmatrix} \begin{bmatrix} x_1 \\ x_2 \\ x_3 \end{bmatrix} = \begin{bmatrix} 7 \\ -2.25 \\ 8.501 \end{bmatrix}$$

Divide Row 2 by -2.75 and then multiply it by 0.001, that is, multiply Row 2 by $0.001/-2.75 = -0.00036363$.

$(\begin{bmatrix} 0 & -2.75 & 0.5 \end{bmatrix} \begin{bmatrix} -2.25 \end{bmatrix}) \times -0.00036363$ gives Row 2 as

$\begin{bmatrix} 0 & 0.00099998 & -0.00018182 \end{bmatrix} \quad \begin{bmatrix} 0.00081816 \end{bmatrix}$

Subtract the result from Row 3

$$\begin{array}{r} \begin{bmatrix} 0 & 0.001 & 8.5 \end{bmatrix} \quad \begin{bmatrix} 8.501 \end{bmatrix} \\ - \begin{bmatrix} 0 & 0.00099998 & -0.00018182 \end{bmatrix} \quad \begin{bmatrix} 0.00081816 \end{bmatrix} \\ \hline \begin{matrix} 0 & 0 & 8.50018182 \end{matrix} \quad 8.50018184 \end{array}$$

Rewriting within 5 significant digits with chopping

$\begin{bmatrix} 0 & 0 & 8.5001 \end{bmatrix} \quad \begin{bmatrix} 8.5001 \end{bmatrix}$

to get the resulting equations as

$$\begin{bmatrix} 20 & 15 & 10 \\ 0 & -2.75 & 0.5 \\ 0 & 0 & 8.5001 \end{bmatrix} \begin{bmatrix} x_1 \\ x_2 \\ x_3 \end{bmatrix} = \begin{bmatrix} 45 \\ -2.25 \\ 8.5001 \end{bmatrix}$$

Back substitution

$$8.5001 x_3 = 8.5001$$

$$x_3 = \frac{8.5001}{8.5001}$$

$$= 1$$

Substituting the value of x_3 in Row 2

$$-2.75 x_2 + 0.5 x_3 = -2.25$$

$$x_2 = \frac{-2.25 - 0.5 x_2}{-2.75}$$

$$= \frac{-2.25 - 0.5 \times 1}{-2.75}$$

$$= \frac{-2.25 - 0.5}{-2.75}$$

$$= \frac{-2.75}{-2.75}$$

$$= 1$$

Substituting the value of x_3 and x_2 in Row 1

$$20 x_1 + 15 x_2 + 10 x_3 = 45$$

$$x_1 = \frac{45 - 15 x_2 - 10 x_3}{20}$$

Page 265

$$= \frac{45 - 15 \times 1 - 10 \times 1}{20}$$

$$= \frac{45 - 15 - 10}{20}$$

$$= \frac{30 - 10}{20}$$

$$= \frac{20}{20}$$

$$= 1$$

So the solution is

$$[X] = \begin{bmatrix} x_1 \\ x_2 \\ x_3 \end{bmatrix}$$

$$= \begin{bmatrix} 1 \\ 1 \\ 1 \end{bmatrix}$$

This, in fact, is the exact solution. By coincidence only, in this case, the round-off error is fully removed.

Can we use Naïve Gauss elimination methods to find the determinant of a square matrix?

One of the more efficient ways to find the determinant of a square matrix is by taking advantage of the following two theorems on a determinant of matrices coupled with Naïve Gauss elimination.

Theorem 1:

Let $[A]$ be a $n \times n$ matrix. Then, if $[B]$ is a $n \times n$ matrix that results from adding or subtracting a multiple of one row to another row, then $\det(A) = \det(B)$ (The same is true for column operations also).

Theorem 2:

Let $[A]$ be a $n \times n$ matrix that is upper triangular, lower triangular or diagonal, then

$$\det(A) = a_{11} \times a_{22} \times ... \times a_{ii} \times ... \times a_{nn}$$

$$= \prod_{i=1}^{n} a_{ii}$$

This implies that if we apply the forward elimination steps of the Naïve Gauss elimination method, the determinant of the matrix stays the same according to Theorem 1. Then since at the end of the forward elimination steps, the resulting matrix is upper triangular, the determinant will be given by Theorem 2.

Example 5

Find the determinant of

$$[A] = \begin{bmatrix} 25 & 5 & 1 \\ 64 & 8 & 1 \\ 144 & 12 & 1 \end{bmatrix}$$

Solution

Remember in Example 1, we conducted the steps of forward elimination of unknowns using the Naïve Gauss elimination method on $[A]$ to give

$$[B] = \begin{bmatrix} 25 & 5 & 1 \\ 0 & -4.8 & -1.56 \\ 0 & 0 & 0.7 \end{bmatrix}$$

According to Theorem 2

$$\begin{aligned} \det(A) &= \det(B) \\ &= 25 \times (-4.8) \times 0.7 \\ &= -84.00 \end{aligned}$$

What if I cannot find the determinant of the matrix using the Naïve Gauss elimination method, for example, if I get division by zero problems during the Naïve Gauss elimination method?

Well, you can apply Gaussian elimination with partial pivoting. However, the determinant of the resulting upper triangular matrix may differ by a sign. The following theorem applies in addition to the previous two to find the determinant of a square matrix.

Theorem 3:

Let $[A]$ be a $n \times n$ matrix. Then, if $[B]$ is a matrix that results from switching one row with another row, then $\det(B) = -\det(A)$.

Example 6

Find the determinant of

$$[A] = \begin{bmatrix} 10 & -7 & 0 \\ -3 & 2.099 & 6 \\ 5 & -1 & 5 \end{bmatrix}$$

Solution

The end of the forward elimination steps of Gaussian elimination with partial pivoting, we would obtain

$$[B] = \begin{bmatrix} 10 & -7 & 0 \\ 0 & 2.5 & 5 \\ 0 & 0 & 6.002 \end{bmatrix}$$

$$\det(B) = 10 \times 2.5 \times 6.002$$

$$= 150.05$$

Since rows were switched once during the forward elimination steps of Gaussian elimination with partial pivoting,

$$\det(A) = -\det(B)$$
$$= -150.05$$

Example 7

Prove

$$\det(A) = \frac{1}{\det\left(A^{-1}\right)}$$

Solution

$$[A][A]^{-1} = [I]$$
$$\det\left(A\,A^{-1}\right) = \det(I)$$
$$\det(A)\det\left(A^{-1}\right) = 1$$
$$\det(A) = \frac{1}{\det\left(A^{-1}\right)}$$

If $[A]$ is a $n \times n$ matrix and $\det(A) \neq 0$, what other statements are equivalent to it?

1. $[A]$ is invertible.
2. $[A]^{-1}$ exists.
3. $[A][X] = [C]$ has a unique solution.
4. $[A][X] = [0]$ solution is $[X] = [\bar{0}]$.
5. $[A][A]^{-1} = [I] = [A]^{-1}[A]$.

Key Terms:

Naïve Gauss Elimination
Partial Pivoting
Determinant

Multiple-Choice Test

Chapter 04.06
Gaussian Elimination

1. The goal of forward elimination steps in the Naïve Gauss elimination method is to reduce the coefficient matrix to a (an) _____ matrix.
    - (A) diagonal
    - (B) identity
    - (C) lower triangular
    - (D) upper triangular

2. Division by zero during forward elimination steps in Naïve Gaussian elimination of the set of equations $[A][X] = [C]$ implies the coefficient matrix $[A]$
    - (A) is invertible
    - (B) is nonsingular
    - (C) may be singular or nonsingular
    - (D) is singular

3. Using a computer with four significant digits with chopping, the Naïve Gauss elimination solution to
    $$0.0030x_1 + 55.23x_2 = 58.12$$
    $$6.239x_1 - 7.123x_2 = 47.23$$
    is
    - (A) $x_1 = 26.66;\ x_2 = 1.051$
    - (B) $x_1 = 8.769;\ x_2 = 1.051$
    - (C) $x_1 = 8.800;\ x_2 = 1.000$
    - (D) $x_1 = 8.771;\ x_2 = 1.052$

4. Using a computer with four significant digits with chopping, the Gaussian elimination with partial pivoting solution to
    $$0.0030x_1 + 55.23x_2 = 58.12$$
    $$6.239x_1 - 7.123x_2 = 47.23$$
    is
    - (A) $x_1 = 26.66;\ x_2 = 1.051$
    - (B) $x_1 = 8.769;\ x_2 = 1.051$
    - (C) $x_1 = 8.800;\ x_2 = 1.000$
    - (D) $x_1 = 8.771;\ x_2 = 1.052$

04.06.1

5.   At the end of the forward elimination steps of the Naïve Gauss elimination method on the following equations

$$\begin{bmatrix} 4.2857\times10^7 & -9.2307\times10^5 & 0 & 0 \\ 4.2857\times10^7 & -5.4619\times10^5 & -4.2857\times10^7 & 5.4619\times10^5 \\ -6.5 & -0.15384 & 6.5 & 0.15384 \\ 0 & 0 & 4.2857\times10^7 & -3.6057\times10^5 \end{bmatrix}\begin{bmatrix} c_1 \\ c_2 \\ c_3 \\ c_4 \end{bmatrix}=\begin{bmatrix} -7.887\times10^3 \\ 0 \\ 0.007 \\ 0 \end{bmatrix}$$

the resulting equations in matrix form are given by

$$\begin{bmatrix} 4.2857\times10^7 & -9.2307\times10^5 & 0 & 0 \\ 0 & 3.7688\times10^5 & -4.2857\times10^7 & 5.4619\times10^5 \\ 0 & 0 & -26.9140 & 0.579684 \\ 0 & 0 & 0 & 5.62500\times10^5 \end{bmatrix}\begin{bmatrix} c_1 \\ c_2 \\ c_3 \\ c_4 \end{bmatrix}=\begin{bmatrix} -7.887\times10^3 \\ 7.887\times10^3 \\ 1.19530\times10^{-2} \\ 1.90336\times10^4 \end{bmatrix}$$

The determinant of the original coefficient matrix is
    (A)   0.00
    (B) 4.2857×10^7
    (C) 5.486×10^{19}
    (D) -2.445×10^{20}

6.   The following data is given for the velocity of the rocket as a function of time. To find the velocity at $t=21\,\text{s}$, you are asked to use a quadratic polynomial, $v(t)=at^2+bt+c$ to approximate the velocity profile.

t	(s)	0	14	15	20	30	35
$v(t)$	(m/s)	0	227.04	362.78	517.35	602.97	901.67

The correct set of equations that will find a, b and c are

(A) $$\begin{bmatrix} 176 & 14 & 1 \\ 225 & 15 & 1 \\ 400 & 20 & 1 \end{bmatrix}\begin{bmatrix} a \\ b \\ c \end{bmatrix}=\begin{bmatrix} 227.04 \\ 362.78 \\ 517.35 \end{bmatrix}$$

(B) $$\begin{bmatrix} 225 & 15 & 1 \\ 400 & 20 & 1 \\ 900 & 30 & 1 \end{bmatrix}\begin{bmatrix} a \\ b \\ c \end{bmatrix}=\begin{bmatrix} 362.78 \\ 517.35 \\ 602.97 \end{bmatrix}$$

(C) $$\begin{bmatrix} 0 & 0 & 1 \\ 225 & 15 & 1 \\ 400 & 20 & 1 \end{bmatrix}\begin{bmatrix} a \\ b \\ c \end{bmatrix}=\begin{bmatrix} 0 \\ 362.78 \\ 517.35 \end{bmatrix}$$

(D) $$\begin{bmatrix} 400 & 20 & 1 \\ 900 & 30 & 1 \\ 1225 & 35 & 1 \end{bmatrix}\begin{bmatrix} a \\ b \\ c \end{bmatrix}=\begin{bmatrix} 517.35 \\ 602.97 \\ 901.67 \end{bmatrix}$$

Complete Solution

Problem Set

Chapter 04.06
Gauss Elimination

1. Use Naïve Gauss elimination to solve

$$4x_1 + x_2 - x_3 = -2$$
$$5x_1 + x_2 + 2x_3 = 4$$
$$6x_1 + x_2 + x_3 = 6$$

2. Assume that you are using a computer with four significant digits with chopping. Use Naïve Gauss elimination method to solve

$$4x_1 + x_2 - x_3 = -2$$
$$5x_1 + x_2 + 2x_3 = 4$$
$$6x_1 + x_2 + x_3 = 6$$

3. For

$$[A] = \begin{bmatrix} 10 & -7 & 0 \\ -3 & 2.099 & 6 \\ 5 & -1 & 5 \end{bmatrix}$$

Find the determinant of $[A]$ using forward elimination step of naïve Gauss elimination method.

4. At the end of forward elimination steps using naïve Gauss elimination method on the coefficient matrix

$$[A] = \begin{bmatrix} 25 & c & 1 \\ 64 & a & 1 \\ 144 & b & 1 \end{bmatrix}$$

$[A]$ reduces to

$$[B] = \begin{bmatrix} 25 & 5 & 1 \\ 0 & -4.8 & -1.56 \\ 0 & 0 & 0.7 \end{bmatrix}$$

What is the determinant of $[A]$?

5.   Using Gaussian elimination with partial pivoting to solve

$$4x_1 + x_2 - x_3 = -2$$
$$5x_1 + x_2 + 2x_3 = 4$$
$$6x_1 + x_2 + x_3 = 6$$

6.   Assume that you are using a computer with four significant digits with chopping, use Gaussian elimination with partial pivoting to solve

$$4x_1 + x_2 - x_3 = -2$$
$$5x_1 + x_2 + 2x_3 = 4$$
$$6x_1 + x_2 + x_3 = 6$$

Chapter 04.07
LU Decomposition

After reading this chapter, you should be able to:

1. *identify when LU decomposition is numerically more efficient than Gaussian elimination,*
2. *decompose a nonsingular matrix into LU, and*
3. *show how LU decomposition is used to find the inverse of a matrix.*

I hear about LU decomposition used as a method to solve a set of simultaneous linear equations. What is it?

We already studied two numerical methods of finding the solution to simultaneous linear equations – Naïve Gauss elimination and Gaussian elimination with partial pivoting. Then, why do we need to learn another method? To appreciate why LU decomposition could be a better choice than the Gauss elimination techniques in some cases, let us discuss first what LU decomposition is about.

For a nonsingular matrix $[A]$ on which one can successfully conduct the Naïve Gauss elimination forward elimination steps, one can always write it as

$$[A] = [L][U]$$

where

$[L]$ = Lower triangular matrix

$[U]$ = Upper triangular matrix

Then if one is solving a set of equations

$$[A][X] = [C],$$

then

$$[L][U][X] = [C] \text{ as } ([A] = [L][U])$$

Multiplying both sides by $[L]^{-1}$,

$$[L]^{-1}[L][U][X] = [L]^{-1}[C]$$

$$[I][U][X] = [L]^{-1}[C] \text{ as } \left([L]^{-1}[L] = [I]\right)$$
$$[U][X] = [L]^{-1}[C] \text{ as } \left([I][U] = [U]\right)$$

Let

$$[L]^{-1}[C] = [Z]$$

then

$$[L][Z] = [C] \tag{1}$$

and

$$[U][X] = [Z] \tag{2}$$

So we can solve Equation (1) first for $[Z]$ by using forward substitution and then use Equation (2) to calculate the solution vector $[X]$ by back substitution.

This is all exciting but LU decomposition looks more complicated than Gaussian elimination. Do we use LU decomposition because it is computationally more efficient than Gaussian elimination to solve a set of n equations given by [A][X]=[C]?

For a square matrix $[A]$ of $n \times n$ size, the computational time[1] $CT|_{DE}$ to decompose the $[A]$ matrix to $[L][U]$ form is given by

$$CT|_{DE} = T\left(\frac{8n^3}{3} + 4n^2 - \frac{20n}{3}\right),$$

where

T = clock cycle time[2].

The computational time $CT|_{FS}$ to solve by forward substitution $[L][Z] = [C]$ is given by

$$CT|_{FS} = T\left(4n^2 - 4n\right)$$

The computational time $CT|_{BS}$ to solve by back substitution $[U][X] = [Z]$ is given by

$$CT|_{BS} = T\left(4n^2 + 12n\right)$$

So, the total computational time to solve a set of equations by LU decomposition is

$$CT|_{LU} = CT|_{DE} + CT|_{FS} + CT|_{BS}$$
$$= T\left(\frac{8n^3}{3} + 4n^2 - \frac{20n}{3}\right) + T\left(4n^2 - 4n\right) + T\left(4n^2 + 12n\right)$$
$$= T\left(\frac{8n^3}{3} + 12n^2 + \frac{4n}{3}\right)$$

---

[1] The time is calculated by first separately calculating the number of additions, subtractions, multiplications, and divisions in a procedure such as back substitution, etc. We then assume 4 clock cycles each for an add, subtract, or multiply operation, and 16 clock cycles for a divide operation as is the case for a typical AMD®-K7 chip.
http://www.isi.edu/~draper/papers/mwscas07_kwon.pdf
[2] As an example, a 1.2 GHz CPU has a clock cycle of $1/(1.2 \times 10^9) = 0.833333\,\mathrm{ns}$

Now let us look at the computational time taken by Gaussian elimination. The computational time $CT|_{FE}$ for the forward elimination part,

$$CT|_{FE} = T\left(\frac{8n^3}{3} + 8n^2 - \frac{32n}{3}\right),$$

and the computational time $CT|_{BS}$ for the back substitution part is

$$CT|_{BS} = T\left(4n^2 + 12n\right)$$

So, the total computational time $CT|_{GE}$ to solve a set of equations by Gaussian Elimination is

$$CT|_{GE} = CT|_{FE} + CT|_{BS}$$

$$= T\left(\frac{8n^3}{3} + 8n^2 - \frac{32n}{3}\right) + T\left(4n^2 + 12n\right)$$

$$= T\left(\frac{8n^3}{3} + 12n^2 + \frac{4n}{3}\right)$$

The computational time for Gaussian elimination and LU decomposition is identical.

This has confused me further! Why learn LU decomposition method when it takes the same computational time as Gaussian elimination, and that too when the two methods are closely related. Please convince me that LU decomposition has its place in solving linear equations!

We have the knowledge now to convince you that LU decomposition method has its place in the solution of simultaneous linear equations. Let us look at an example where the LU decomposition method is computationally more efficient than Gaussian elimination. Remember in trying to find the inverse of the matrix $[A]$ in Chapter 04.05, the problem reduces to solving n sets of equations with the n columns of the identity matrix as the RHS vector. For calculations of each column of the inverse of the $[A]$ matrix, the coefficient matrix $[A]$ matrix in the set of equation $[A][X] = [C]$ does not change. So if we use the LU decomposition method, the $[A] = [L][U]$ decomposition needs to be done only once, the forward substitution (Equation 1) n times, and the back substitution (Equation 2) n times.

So the total computational time $CT|_{inverse\,LU}$ required to find the inverse of a matrix using LU decomposition is

$$CT|_{inverse\,LU} = 1 \times CT|_{LU} + n \times CT|_{FS} + n \times CT|_{BS}$$

$$= 1 \times T\left(\frac{8n^3}{3} + 4n^2 - \frac{20n}{3}\right) + n \times T\left(4n^2 - 4n\right) + n \times T\left(4n^2 + 12n\right)$$

$$= T\left(\frac{32n^3}{3} + 12n^2 - \frac{20n}{3}\right)$$

In comparison, if Gaussian elimination method were used to find the inverse of a matrix, the forward elimination as well as the back substitution will have to be done n times. The total computational time $CT\big|_{inverse\,GE}$ required to find the inverse of a matrix by using Gaussian elimination then is

$$CT\big|_{inverse\,GE} = n \times CT\big|_{FE} + n \times CT\big|_{BS}$$

$$= n \times T\left(\frac{8n^3}{3} + 8n^2 - \frac{32n}{3}\right) + n \times T\left(4n^2 + 12n\right)$$

$$= T\left(\frac{8n^4}{3} + 12n^3 + \frac{4n^2}{3}\right)$$

Clearly for large n, $CT\big|_{inverse\,GE} >> CT\big|_{inverse\,LU}$ as $CT\big|_{inverse\,GE}$ has the dominating terms of n^4 and $CT\big|_{inverse\,LU}$ has the dominating terms of n^3. For large values of n, Gaussian elimination method would take more computational time (approximately $n/4$ times – prove it) than the LU decomposition method. Typical values of the ratio of the computational time for different values of n are given in Table 1.

Table 1 Comparing computational times of finding inverse of a matrix using LU decomposition and Gaussian elimination.

n	10	100	1000	10000
$CT\big|_{inverse\,GE}/CT\big|_{inverse\,LU}$	3.28	25.83	250.8	2501

Are you convinced now that LU decomposition has its place in solving systems of equations? We are now ready to answer other curious questions such as
1) How do I find LU matrices for a nonsingular matrix $[A]$?
2) How do I conduct forward and back substitution steps of Equations (1) and (2), respectively?

How do I decompose a non-singular matrix $[A]$, that is, how do I find $[A]=[L][U]$?

If forward elimination steps of the Naïve Gauss elimination methods can be applied on a nonsingular matrix, then $[A]$ can be decomposed into LU as

$$[A]=\begin{bmatrix} a_{11} & a_{12} & \cdots & a_{1n} \\ a_{21} & a_{22} & \cdots & a_{2n} \\ \vdots & \vdots & \cdots & \vdots \\ a_{n1} & a_{n2} & \cdots & a_{nn} \end{bmatrix}$$

$$=\begin{bmatrix} 1 & 0 & \cdots & 0 \\ \ell_{21} & 1 & \cdots & 0 \\ \vdots & \vdots & \cdots & \vdots \\ \ell_{n1} & \ell_{n2} & \cdots & 1 \end{bmatrix}\begin{bmatrix} u_{11} & u_{12} & \cdots & u_{1n} \\ 0 & u_{22} & \cdots & u_{2n} \\ \vdots & \vdots & \cdots & \vdots \\ 0 & 0 & \cdots & u_{nn} \end{bmatrix}$$

The elements of the $[U]$ matrix are exactly the same as the coefficient matrix one obtains at the end of the forward elimination steps in Naïve Gauss elimination.

The lower triangular matrix $[L]$ has 1 in its diagonal entries. The non-zero elements on the non-diagonal elements in $[L]$ are multipliers that made the corresponding entries zero in the upper triangular matrix $[U]$ during forward elimination.

Let us look at this using the same example as used in Naïve Gaussian elimination.

Example 1

Find the LU decomposition of the matrix

$$[A] = \begin{bmatrix} 25 & 5 & 1 \\ 64 & 8 & 1 \\ 144 & 12 & 1 \end{bmatrix}$$

Solution

$$[A] = [L][U]$$

$$= \begin{bmatrix} 1 & 0 & 0 \\ \ell_{21} & 1 & 0 \\ \ell_{31} & \ell_{32} & 1 \end{bmatrix} \begin{bmatrix} u_{11} & u_{12} & u_{13} \\ 0 & u_{22} & u_{23} \\ 0 & 0 & u_{33} \end{bmatrix}$$

The $[U]$ matrix is the same as found at the end of the forward elimination of Naïve Gauss elimination method, that is

$$[U] = \begin{bmatrix} 25 & 5 & 1 \\ 0 & -4.8 & -1.56 \\ 0 & 0 & 0.7 \end{bmatrix}$$

To find ℓ_{21} and ℓ_{31}, find the multiplier that was used to make the a_{21} and a_{31} elements zero in the first step of forward elimination of the Naïve Gauss elimination method. It was

$$\ell_{21} = \frac{64}{25}$$
$$= 2.56$$
$$\ell_{31} = \frac{144}{25}$$
$$= 5.76$$

To find ℓ_{32}, what multiplier was used to make a_{32} element zero? Remember a_{32} element was made zero in the second step of forward elimination. The $[A]$ matrix at the beginning of the second step of forward elimination was

$$\begin{bmatrix} 25 & 5 & 1 \\ 0 & -4.8 & -1.56 \\ 0 & -16.8 & -4.76 \end{bmatrix}$$

So

$$\ell_{32} = \frac{-16.8}{-4.8}$$
$$= 3.5$$

Hence

$$[L] = \begin{bmatrix} 1 & 0 & 0 \\ 2.56 & 1 & 0 \\ 5.76 & 3.5 & 1 \end{bmatrix}$$

Confirm $[L][U] = [A]$.

$$[L][U] = \begin{bmatrix} 1 & 0 & 0 \\ 2.56 & 1 & 0 \\ 5.76 & 3.5 & 1 \end{bmatrix} \begin{bmatrix} 25 & 5 & 1 \\ 0 & -4.8 & -1.56 \\ 0 & 0 & 0.7 \end{bmatrix}$$

$$= \begin{bmatrix} 25 & 5 & 1 \\ 64 & 8 & 1 \\ 144 & 12 & 1 \end{bmatrix}$$

Example 2

Use the LU decomposition method to solve the following simultaneous linear equations.

$$\begin{bmatrix} 25 & 5 & 1 \\ 64 & 8 & 1 \\ 144 & 12 & 1 \end{bmatrix} \begin{bmatrix} a_1 \\ a_2 \\ a_3 \end{bmatrix} = \begin{bmatrix} 106.8 \\ 177.2 \\ 279.2 \end{bmatrix}$$

Solution

Recall that

$$[A][X] = [C]$$

and if

$$[A] = [L][U]$$

then first solving

$$[L][Z] = [C]$$

and then

$$[U][X] = [Z]$$

gives the solution vector $[X]$.

Now in the previous example, we showed

$$[A] = [L][U]$$

$$= \begin{bmatrix} 1 & 0 & 0 \\ 2.56 & 1 & 0 \\ 5.76 & 3.5 & 1 \end{bmatrix} \begin{bmatrix} 25 & 5 & 1 \\ 0 & -4.8 & -1.56 \\ 0 & 0 & 0.7 \end{bmatrix}$$

First solve

$$[L][Z] = [C]$$

$$\begin{bmatrix} 1 & 0 & 0 \\ 2.56 & 1 & 0 \\ 5.76 & 3.5 & 1 \end{bmatrix} \begin{bmatrix} z_1 \\ z_2 \\ z_3 \end{bmatrix} = \begin{bmatrix} 106.8 \\ 177.2 \\ 279.2 \end{bmatrix}$$

to give

$$z_1 = 106.8$$
$$2.56z_1 + z_2 = 177.2$$
$$5.76z_1 + 3.5z_2 + z_3 = 279.2$$

Forward substitution starting from the first equation gives

$$z_1 = 106.8$$
$$z_2 = 177.2 - 2.56z_1$$
$$= 177.2 - 2.56 \times 106.8$$
$$= -96.208$$
$$z_3 = 279.2 - 5.76z_1 - 3.5z_2$$
$$= 279.2 - 5.76 \times 106.8 - 3.5 \times (-96.208)$$
$$= 0.76$$

Hence

$$[Z] = \begin{bmatrix} z_1 \\ z_2 \\ z_3 \end{bmatrix}$$

$$= \begin{bmatrix} 106.8 \\ -96.208 \\ 0.76 \end{bmatrix}$$

This matrix is same as the right hand side obtained at the end of the forward elimination steps of Naïve Gauss elimination method. Is this a coincidence?
Now solve

$$[U][X] = [Z]$$

$$\begin{bmatrix} 25 & 5 & 1 \\ 0 & -4.8 & -1.56 \\ 0 & 0 & 0.7 \end{bmatrix} \begin{bmatrix} a_1 \\ a_2 \\ a_3 \end{bmatrix} = \begin{bmatrix} 106.8 \\ -96.208 \\ 0.76 \end{bmatrix}$$

$$25a_1 + 5a_2 + a_3 = 106.8$$
$$-4.8a_2 - 1.56a_3 = -96.208$$
$$0.7a_3 = 0.76$$

From the third equation

$$0.7a_3 = 0.76$$
$$a_3 = \frac{0.76}{0.7}$$
$$= 1.0857$$

Substituting the value of a_3 in the second equation,

$$-4.8a_2 - 1.56a_3 = -96.208$$
$$a_2 = \frac{-96.208 + 1.56a_3}{-4.8}$$
$$= \frac{-96.208 + 1.56 \times 1.0857}{-4.8}$$

$$= 19.691$$

Substituting the value of a_2 and a_3 in the first equation,

$$25a_1 + 5a_2 + a_3 = 106.8$$

$$a_1 = \frac{106.8 - 5a_2 - a_3}{25}$$

$$= \frac{106.8 - 5 \times 19.691 - 1.0857}{25}$$

$$= 0.29048$$

Hence the solution vector is

$$\begin{bmatrix} a_1 \\ a_2 \\ a_3 \end{bmatrix} = \begin{bmatrix} 0.29048 \\ 19.691 \\ 1.0857 \end{bmatrix}$$

How do I find the inverse of a square matrix using LU decomposition?

A matrix $[B]$ is the inverse of $[A]$ if

$$[A][B] = [I] = [B][A].$$

How can we use LU decomposition to find the inverse of the matrix? Assume the first column of $[B]$ (the inverse of $[A]$) is

$$[b_{11} \, b_{12} \cdots \cdots b_{n1}]^{\mathrm{T}}$$

Then from the above definition of an inverse and the definition of matrix multiplication

$$[A] \begin{bmatrix} b_{11} \\ b_{21} \\ \vdots \\ b_{n1} \end{bmatrix} = \begin{bmatrix} 1 \\ 0 \\ \vdots \\ 0 \end{bmatrix}$$

Similarly the second column of $[B]$ is given by

$$[A] \begin{bmatrix} b_{12} \\ b_{22} \\ \vdots \\ b_{n2} \end{bmatrix} = \begin{bmatrix} 0 \\ 1 \\ \vdots \\ 0 \end{bmatrix}$$

Similarly, all columns of $[B]$ can be found by solving n different sets of equations with the column of the right hand side being the n columns of the identity matrix.

Example 3

Use LU decomposition to find the inverse of

$$[A] = \begin{bmatrix} 25 & 5 & 1 \\ 64 & 8 & 1 \\ 144 & 12 & 1 \end{bmatrix}$$

Solution

Knowing that

$$[A] = [L][U]$$

$$= \begin{bmatrix} 1 & 0 & 0 \\ 2.56 & 1 & 0 \\ 5.76 & 3.5 & 1 \end{bmatrix} \begin{bmatrix} 25 & 5 & 1 \\ 0 & -4.8 & -1.56 \\ 0 & 0 & 0.7 \end{bmatrix}$$

We can solve for the first column of $[B] = [A]^{-1}$ by solving for

$$\begin{bmatrix} 25 & 5 & 1 \\ 64 & 8 & 1 \\ 144 & 12 & 1 \end{bmatrix} \begin{bmatrix} b_{11} \\ b_{21} \\ b_{31} \end{bmatrix} = \begin{bmatrix} 1 \\ 0 \\ 0 \end{bmatrix}$$

First solve

$$[L][Z] = [C],$$

that is

$$\begin{bmatrix} 1 & 0 & 0 \\ 2.56 & 1 & 0 \\ 5.76 & 3.5 & 1 \end{bmatrix} \begin{bmatrix} z_1 \\ z_2 \\ z_3 \end{bmatrix} = \begin{bmatrix} 1 \\ 0 \\ 0 \end{bmatrix}$$

to give

$$z_1 = 1$$
$$2.56 z_1 + z_2 = 0$$
$$5.76 z_1 + 3.5 z_2 + z_3 = 0$$

Forward substitution starting from the first equation gives

$$z_1 = 1$$
$$\begin{aligned} z_2 &= 0 - 2.56 z_1 \\ &= 0 - 2.56(1) \\ &= -2.56 \end{aligned}$$
$$\begin{aligned} z_3 &= 0 - 5.76 z_1 - 3.5 z_2 \\ &= 0 - 5.76(1) - 3.5(-2.56) \\ &= 3.2 \end{aligned}$$

Hence

$$[Z] = \begin{bmatrix} z_1 \\ z_2 \\ z_3 \end{bmatrix}$$

$$= \begin{bmatrix} 1 \\ -2.56 \\ 3.2 \end{bmatrix}$$

Now solve

$$[U][X] = [Z]$$

that is

$$\begin{bmatrix} 25 & 5 & 1 \\ 0 & -4.8 & -1.56 \\ 0 & 0 & 0.7 \end{bmatrix} \begin{bmatrix} b_{11} \\ b_{21} \\ b_{31} \end{bmatrix} = \begin{bmatrix} 1 \\ -2.56 \\ 3.2 \end{bmatrix}$$

$$25b_{11} + 5b_{21} + b_{31} = 1$$

$$-4.8b_{21} - 1.56b_{31} = -2.56$$

$$0.7b_{31} = 3.2$$

Backward substitution starting from the third equation gives

$$b_{31} = \frac{3.2}{0.7}$$
$$= 4.571$$
$$b_{21} = \frac{-2.56 + 1.56b_{31}}{-4.8}$$
$$= \frac{-2.56 + 1.56(4.571)}{-4.8}$$
$$= -0.9524$$
$$b_{11} = \frac{1 - 5b_{21} - b_{31}}{25}$$
$$= \frac{1 - 5(-0.9524) - 4.571}{25}$$
$$= 0.04762$$

Hence the first column of the inverse of $[A]$ is

$$\begin{bmatrix} b_{11} \\ b_{21} \\ b_{31} \end{bmatrix} = \begin{bmatrix} 0.04762 \\ -0.9524 \\ 4.571 \end{bmatrix}$$

Similarly by solving

$$\begin{bmatrix} 25 & 5 & 1 \\ 64 & 8 & 1 \\ 144 & 12 & 1 \end{bmatrix} \begin{bmatrix} b_{12} \\ b_{22} \\ b_{32} \end{bmatrix} = \begin{bmatrix} 0 \\ 1 \\ 0 \end{bmatrix} \text{ gives } \begin{bmatrix} b_{12} \\ b_{22} \\ b_{32} \end{bmatrix} = \begin{bmatrix} -0.08333 \\ 1.417 \\ -5.000 \end{bmatrix}$$

and solving

$$\begin{bmatrix} 25 & 5 & 1 \\ 64 & 8 & 1 \\ 144 & 12 & 1 \end{bmatrix} \begin{bmatrix} b_{13} \\ b_{23} \\ b_{33} \end{bmatrix} = \begin{bmatrix} 0 \\ 0 \\ 1 \end{bmatrix} \text{ gives } \begin{bmatrix} b_{13} \\ b_{23} \\ b_{33} \end{bmatrix} = \begin{bmatrix} 0.03571 \\ -0.4643 \\ 1.429 \end{bmatrix}$$

Hence

$$[A]^{-1} = \begin{bmatrix} 0.04762 & -0.08333 & 0.03571 \\ -0.9524 & 1.417 & -0.4643 \\ 4.571 & -5.000 & 1.429 \end{bmatrix}$$

Can you confirm the following for the above example?

$$[A][A]^{-1} = [I] = [A]^{-1}[A]$$

Page 284

Key Terms:

LU decomposition
Inverse

Multiple-Choice Test

Chapter 04.07
LU Decomposition Method

1. The $[L][U]$ decomposition method is computationally more efficient than Naïve Gauss elimination for solving
   - (A) a single set of simultaneous linear equations.
   - (B) multiple sets of simultaneous linear equations with different coefficient matrices and the same right hand side vectors.
   - (C) multiple sets of simultaneous linear equations with the same coefficient matrix and different right hand side vectors.
   - (D) less than ten simultaneous linear equations.

2. The lower triangular matrix $[L]$ in the $[L][U]$ decomposition of the matrix given below

$$\begin{bmatrix} 25 & 5 & 4 \\ 10 & 8 & 16 \\ 8 & 12 & 22 \end{bmatrix} = \begin{bmatrix} 1 & 0 & 0 \\ \ell_{21} & 1 & 0 \\ \ell_{31} & \ell_{32} & 1 \end{bmatrix} \begin{bmatrix} u_{11} & u_{12} & u_{13} \\ 0 & u_{22} & u_{23} \\ 0 & 0 & u_{33} \end{bmatrix}$$

   is

   (A) $\begin{bmatrix} 1 & 0 & 0 \\ 0.40000 & 1 & 0 \\ 0.32000 & 1.7333 & 1 \end{bmatrix}$

   (B) $\begin{bmatrix} 25 & 5 & 4 \\ 0 & 6 & 14.400 \\ 0 & 0 & -4.2400 \end{bmatrix}$

   (C) $\begin{bmatrix} 1 & 0 & 0 \\ 10 & 1 & 0 \\ 8 & 12 & 0 \end{bmatrix}$

   (D) $\begin{bmatrix} 1 & 0 & 0 \\ 0.40000 & 1 & 0 \\ 0.32000 & 1.5000 & 1 \end{bmatrix}$

3. The upper triangular matrix $[U]$ in the $[L][U]$ decomposition of the matrix given below

$$\begin{bmatrix} 25 & 5 & 4 \\ 0 & 8 & 16 \\ 0 & 12 & 22 \end{bmatrix} = \begin{bmatrix} 1 & 0 & 0 \\ \ell_{21} & 1 & 0 \\ \ell_{31} & \ell_{32} & 1 \end{bmatrix} \begin{bmatrix} u_{11} & u_{12} & u_{13} \\ 0 & u_{22} & u_{23} \\ 0 & 0 & u_{33} \end{bmatrix}$$

is

(A) $\begin{bmatrix} 1 & 0 & 0 \\ 0.40000 & 1 & 0 \\ 0.32000 & 1.7333 & 1 \end{bmatrix}$

(B) $\begin{bmatrix} 25 & 5 & 4 \\ 0 & 6 & 14.400 \\ 0 & 0 & -4.2400 \end{bmatrix}$

(C) $\begin{bmatrix} 25 & 5 & 4 \\ 0 & 8 & 16 \\ 0 & 0 & -2 \end{bmatrix}$

(D) $\begin{bmatrix} 1 & 0.2000 & 0.16000 \\ 0 & 1 & 2.4000 \\ 0 & 0 & -4.240 \end{bmatrix}$

4. For a given 2000×2000 matrix $[A]$, assume that it takes about 15 seconds to find the inverse of $[A]$ by the use of the $[L][U]$ decomposition method, that is, finding the $[L][U]$ once, and then doing forward substitution and back substitution 2000 times using the 2000 columns of the identity matrix as the right hand side vector. The approximate time, in seconds, that it will take to find the inverse if found by repeated use of the Naive Gauss elimination method, that is, doing forward elimination and back substitution 2000 times by using the 2000 columns of the identity matrix as the right hand side vector is most nearly
    (A) 300
    (B) 1500
    (C) 7500
    (D) 30000

5. The algorithm for solving a set of n equations $[A][X] = [C]$, where $[A] = [L][U]$ involves solving $[L][Z] = [C]$ by forward substitution. The algorithm to solve $[L][Z] = [C]$ is given by

(A) $z_1 = c_1 / l_{11}$
    for i from 2 to n do
    sum = 0
    for j from 1 to i do
    sum = sum + $l_{ij} * z_j$
    end do
    $z_i = (c_i - sum) / l_{ii}$
    end do

(B) $z_1 = c_1 / l_{11}$
    for i from 2 to n do
    sum = 0
    for j from 1 to $(i-1)$ do
    sum = sum + $l_{ij} * z_j$
    end do
    $z_i = (c_i - sum) / l_{ii}$
    end do

(C) $z_1 = c_1 / l_{11}$
    for i from 2 to n do
    for j from 1 to $(i-1)$ do
    sum = sum + $l_{ij} * z_j$
    end do
    $z_i = (c_i - sum) / l_{ii}$
    end do

(D) for i from 2 to n do
    sum = 0
    for j from 1 to $(i-1)$ do
    sum = sum + $l_{ij} * z_j$
    end do
    $z_i = (c_i - sum) / l_{ii}$
    end do

6.   To solve boundary value problems, the finite difference method is used resulting in simultaneous linear equations with tridiagonal coefficient matrices. These are solved using the specialized $[L][U]$ decomposition method. The set of equations in matrix form with a tridiagonal coefficient matrix for

$$\frac{d^2 y}{dx^2} = 6x - 0.5x^2, \ y(0) = 0, \ y(12) = 0$$

using the finite difference method with a second order accurate central divided difference   method and a step size of $h = 4$ is

(A)
$$\begin{bmatrix} 1 & 0 & 0 & 0 \\ 0.0625 & 0.125 & 0.0625 & 0 \\ 0 & 0.0625 & 0.125 & 0.0625 \\ 0 & 0 & 0 & 1 \end{bmatrix} \begin{bmatrix} y_1 \\ y_2 \\ y_3 \\ y_4 \end{bmatrix} = \begin{bmatrix} 0 \\ 16.0 \\ 16.0 \\ 0 \end{bmatrix}$$

(B)
$$\begin{bmatrix} 1 & 0 & 0 & 0 \\ 0.0625 & -0.125 & 0.0625 & 0 \\ 0 & 0.0625 & -0.125 & 0.0625 \\ 0 & 0 & 0 & 1 \end{bmatrix} \begin{bmatrix} y_1 \\ y_2 \\ y_3 \\ y_4 \end{bmatrix} = \begin{bmatrix} 0 \\ 16.0 \\ 16.0 \\ 0 \end{bmatrix}$$

(C)
$$\begin{bmatrix} 1 & 0 & 0 & 0 \\ 0 & 0 & 0 & 1 \\ 0.0625 & -0.125 & 0.0625 & 0 \\ 0 & 0.0625 & -0.125 & 0.0625 \end{bmatrix} \begin{bmatrix} y_1 \\ y_2 \\ y_3 \\ y_4 \end{bmatrix} = \begin{bmatrix} 0 \\ 0 \\ 16.0 \\ 16.0 \end{bmatrix}$$

(D)
$$\begin{bmatrix} 1 & 0 & 0 & 0 \\ 0 & 0 & 0 & 1 \\ 0.0625 & 0.125 & 0.0625 & 0 \\ 0 & 0.0625 & 0.125 & 0.0625 \end{bmatrix} \begin{bmatrix} y_1 \\ y_2 \\ y_3 \\ y_4 \end{bmatrix} = \begin{bmatrix} 0 \\ 0 \\ 16.0 \\ 16.0 \end{bmatrix}$$

Complete Solution

Problem Set

Chapter 04.07
LU Decomposition

1. Show that LU decomposition is computationally a more efficient way of finding the inverse of a square matrix than using Gaussian elimination.

2. Use LU decomposition to find [L] and [U]
$$4x_1 + x_2 - x_3 = -2$$
$$5x_1 + x_2 + 2x_3 = 4$$
$$6x_1 + x_2 + x_3 = 6$$

3. Find the inverse of
$$[A] = \begin{bmatrix} 3 & 4 & 1 \\ 2 & -7 & -1 \\ 8 & 1 & 5 \end{bmatrix}$$
using LU decomposition.

4. Fill in the blanks for the unknowns in the LU decomposition of the matrix given below
$$\begin{bmatrix} 25 & 5 & 4 \\ 75 & 7 & 16 \\ 12.5 & 12 & 22 \end{bmatrix} = \begin{bmatrix} \ell_{11} & 0 & 0 \\ \ell_{21} & \ell_{22} & 0 \\ \ell_{31} & \ell_{32} & \ell_{33} \end{bmatrix} \begin{bmatrix} 25 & 5 & 4 \\ 0 & u_{22} & u_{23} \\ 0 & 0 & u_{33} \end{bmatrix}$$

5. Show that the nonsingular matrix
$$[A] = \begin{bmatrix} 0 & 2 \\ 2 & 0 \end{bmatrix}$$
cannot be decomposed into LU form.

04.07.1

6.   The LU decomposition of

$$[A] = \begin{bmatrix} 4 & 1 & -1 \\ 5 & 1 & 2 \\ 6 & 1 & 1 \end{bmatrix}$$

is given by

$$\begin{bmatrix} 4 & 1 & -1 \\ 5 & 1 & 2 \\ 6 & 1 & 1 \end{bmatrix} = \begin{bmatrix} 1 & 0 & 0 \\ 1.25 & 1 & 0 \\ 1.5 & 2 & 1 \end{bmatrix} \begin{bmatrix} ?? & ?? & ?? \\ 0 & ?? & ?? \\ 0 & 0 & ?? \end{bmatrix}$$

Find the upper triangular matrix in the above decomposition?

Chapter 04.08
Gauss-Seidel Method

After reading this chapter, you should be able to:

1. *solve a set of equations using the Gauss-Seidel method,*
2. *recognize the advantages and pitfalls of the Gauss-Seidel method, and*
3. *determine under what conditions the Gauss-Seidel method always converges.*

Why do we need another method to solve a set of simultaneous linear equations?

In certain cases, such as when a system of equations is large, iterative methods of solving equations are more advantageous. Elimination methods, such as Gaussian elimination, are prone to large round-off errors for a large set of equations. Iterative methods, such as the Gauss-Seidel method, give the user control of the round-off error. Also, if the physics of the problem are well known, initial guesses needed in iterative methods can be made more judiciously leading to faster convergence.

What is the algorithm for the Gauss-Seidel method? Given a general set of n equations and n unknowns, we have

$$a_{11}x_1 + a_{12}x_2 + a_{13}x_3 + ... + a_{1n}x_n = c_1$$
$$a_{21}x_1 + a_{22}x_2 + a_{23}x_3 + ... + a_{2n}x_n = c_2$$
$$.\qquad\qquad .$$
$$.\qquad\qquad .$$
$$.\qquad\qquad .$$
$$a_{n1}x_1 + a_{n2}x_2 + a_{n3}x_3 + ... + a_{nn}x_n = c_n$$

If the diagonal elements are non-zero, each equation is rewritten for the corresponding unknown, that is, the first equation is rewritten with x_1 on the left hand side, the second equation is rewritten with x_2 on the left hand side and so on as follows

$$x_2 = \frac{c_2 - a_{21}x_1 - a_{23}x_3 \cdots\cdots - a_{2n}x_n}{a_{22}}$$

$$\vdots$$

$$x_{n-1} = \frac{c_{n-1} - a_{n-1,1}x_1 - a_{n-1,2}x_2 \cdots\cdots - a_{n-1,n-2}x_{n-2} - a_{n-1,n}x_n}{a_{n-1,n-1}}$$

$$x_n = \frac{c_n - a_{n1}x_1 - a_{n2}x_2 - \cdots\cdots - a_{n,n-1}x_{n-1}}{a_{nn}}$$

These equations can be rewritten in a summation form as

$$x_1 = \frac{c_1 - \displaystyle\sum_{\substack{j=1 \\ j\neq 1}}^{n} a_{1j}x_j}{a_{11}}$$

$$x_2 = \frac{c_2 - \displaystyle\sum_{\substack{j=1 \\ j\neq 2}}^{n} a_{2j}x_j}{a_{22}}$$

$$\vdots$$

$$x_{n-1} = \frac{c_{n-1} - \displaystyle\sum_{\substack{j=1 \\ j\neq n-1}}^{n} a_{n-1,j}x_j}{a_{n-1,n-1}}$$

$$x_n = \frac{c_n - \displaystyle\sum_{\substack{j=1 \\ j\neq n}}^{n} a_{nj}x_j}{a_{nn}}$$

Hence for any row i,

$$x_i = \frac{c_i - \displaystyle\sum_{\substack{j=1 \\ j\neq i}}^{n} a_{ij}x_j}{a_{ii}}, i = 1,2,\ldots,n.$$

Now to find x_i's, one assumes an initial guess for the x_i's and then uses the rewritten equations to calculate the new estimates. Remember, one always uses the most recent estimates to calculate the next estimates, x_i. At the end of each iteration, one calculates the absolute relative approximate error for each x_i as

$$|\epsilon_a|_i = \left| \frac{x_i^{new} - x_i^{old}}{x_i^{new}} \right| \times 100$$

where x_i^{new} is the recently obtained value of x_i, and x_i^{old} is the previous value of x_i.

When the absolute relative approximate error for each x_i is less than the pre-specified tolerance, the iterations are stopped.

Example 1

The upward velocity of a rocket is given at three different times in the following table

Table 1 Velocity vs. time data.

Time, t (s)	Velocity, v (m/s)
5	106.8
8	177.2
12	279.2

The velocity data is approximated by a polynomial as
$$v(t) = a_1 t^2 + a_2 t + a_3 , \qquad 5 \le t \le 12$$
Find the values of a_1, a_2, and a_3 using the Gauss-Seidel method. Assume an initial guess of the solution as
$$\begin{bmatrix} a_1 \\ a_2 \\ a_3 \end{bmatrix} = \begin{bmatrix} 1 \\ 2 \\ 5 \end{bmatrix}$$
and conduct two iterations.

Solution

The polynomial is going through three data points (t_1, v_1), (t_2, v_2), and (t_3, v_3) where from the above table
$$t_1 = 5, \quad v_1 = 106.8$$
$$t_2 = 8, \quad v_2 = 177.2$$
$$t_3 = 12, \quad v_3 = 279.2$$
Requiring that $v(t) = a_1 t^2 + a_2 t + a_3$ passes through the three data points gives
$$v(t_1) = v_1 = a_1 t_1^2 + a_2 t_1 + a_3$$
$$v(t_2) = v_2 = a_1 t_2^2 + a_2 t_2 + a_3$$
$$v(t_3) = v_3 = a_1 t_3^2 + a_2 t_3 + a_3$$
Substituting the data (t_1, v_1), (t_2, v_2), and (t_3, v_3) gives
$$a_1 (5^2) + a_2 (5) + a_3 = 106.8$$
$$a_1 (8^2) + a_2 (8) + a_3 = 177.2$$
$$a_1 (12^2) + a_2 (12) + a_3 = 279.2$$

or

$$25a_1 + 5a_2 + a_3 = 106.8$$
$$64a_1 + 8a_2 + a_3 = 177.2$$

$$144a_1 + 12a_2 + a_3 = 279.2$$

The coefficients $a_1, a_2,$ and a_3 for the above expression are given by

$$\begin{bmatrix} 25 & 5 & 1 \\ 64 & 8 & 1 \\ 144 & 12 & 1 \end{bmatrix} \begin{bmatrix} a_1 \\ a_2 \\ a_3 \end{bmatrix} = \begin{bmatrix} 106.8 \\ 177.2 \\ 279.2 \end{bmatrix}$$

Rewriting the equations gives

$$a_1 = \frac{106.8 - 5a_2 - a_3}{25}$$

$$a_2 = \frac{177.2 - 64a_1 - a_3}{8}$$

$$a_3 = \frac{279.2 - 144a_1 - 12a_2}{1}$$

Iteration #1

Given the initial guess of the solution vector as

$$\begin{bmatrix} a_1 \\ a_2 \\ a_3 \end{bmatrix} = \begin{bmatrix} 1 \\ 2 \\ 5 \end{bmatrix}$$

we get

$$a_1 = \frac{106.8 - 5(2) - (5)}{25}$$
$$= 3.6720$$

$$a_2 = \frac{177.2 - 64(3.6720) - (5)}{8}$$
$$= -7.8150$$

$$a_3 = \frac{279.2 - 144(3.6720) - 12(-7.8510)}{1}$$
$$= -155.36$$

The absolute relative approximate error for each x_i then is

$$\left| \in_a \right|_1 = \left| \frac{3.6720 - 1}{3.6720} \right| \times 100$$
$$= 72.76\%$$

$$\left| \in_a \right|_2 = \left| \frac{-7.8510 - 2}{-7.8510} \right| \times 100$$
$$= 125.47\%$$

$$\left| \in_a \right|_3 = \left| \frac{-155.36 - 5}{-155.36} \right| \times 100$$
$$= 103.22\%$$

At the end of the first iteration, the estimate of the solution vector is

$$\begin{bmatrix} a_1 \\ a_2 \\ a_3 \end{bmatrix} = \begin{bmatrix} 3.6720 \\ -7.8510 \\ -155.36 \end{bmatrix}$$

and the maximum absolute relative approximate error is 125.47%.

Iteration #2
The estimate of the solution vector at the end of Iteration #1 is

$$\begin{bmatrix} a_1 \\ a_2 \\ a_3 \end{bmatrix} = \begin{bmatrix} 3.6720 \\ -7.8510 \\ -155.36 \end{bmatrix}$$

Now we get

$$a_1 = \frac{106.8 - 5(-7.8510) - (-155.36)}{25}$$

$$= 12.056$$

$$a_2 = \frac{177.2 - 64(12.056) - (-155.36)}{8}$$

$$= -54.882$$

$$a_3 = \frac{279.2 - 144(12.056) - 12(-54.882)}{1}$$

$$= -798.34$$

The absolute relative approximate error for each x_i then is

$$\left| \epsilon_a \right|_1 = \left| \frac{12.056 - 3.6720}{12.056} \right| \times 100$$

$$= 69.543\%$$

$$\left| \epsilon_a \right|_2 = \left| \frac{-54.882 - (-7.8510)}{-54.882} \right| \times 100$$

$$= 85.695\%$$

$$\left| \epsilon_a \right|_3 = \left| \frac{-798.34 - (-155.36)}{-798.34} \right| \times 100$$

$$= 80.540\%$$

At the end of the second iteration the estimate of the solution vector is

$$\begin{bmatrix} a_1 \\ a_2 \\ a_3 \end{bmatrix} = \begin{bmatrix} 12.056 \\ -54.882 \\ -798.54 \end{bmatrix}$$

and the maximum absolute relative approximate error is 85.695%.
Conducting more iterations gives the following values for the solution vector and the corresponding absolute relative approximate errors.

Iteration	a_1	$\left|\in_a\right|_1\%$	a_2	$\left|\in_a\right|_2\%$	a_3	$\left|\in_a\right|_3\%$
1	3.6720	72.767	−7.8510	125.47	−155.36	103.22
2	12.056	69.543	−54.882	85.695	−798.34	80.540
3	47.182	74.447	−255.51	78.521	−3448.9	76.852
4	193.33	75.595	−1093.4	76.632	−14440	76.116
5	800.53	75.850	−4577.2	76.112	−60072	75.963
6	3322.6	75.906	−19049	75.972	−249580	75.931

As seen in the above table, the solution estimates are not converging to the true solution of

$a_1 = 0.29048$

$a_2 = 19.690$

$a_3 = 1.0857$

The above system of equations does not seem to converge. Why?

Well, a pitfall of most iterative methods is that they may or may not converge. However, the solution to a certain classes of systems of simultaneous equations does always converge using the Gauss-Seidel method. This class of system of equations is where the coefficient matrix $[A]$ in $[A][X] = [C]$ is diagonally dominant, that is

$$\left|a_{ii}\right| \geq \sum_{\substack{j=1 \\ j \neq i}}^{n} \left|a_{ij}\right| \text{ for all } i$$

$$\left|a_{ii}\right| > \sum_{\substack{j=1 \\ j \neq i}}^{n} \left|a_{ij}\right| \text{ for at least one } i$$

If a system of equations has a coefficient matrix that is not diagonally dominant, it may or may not converge. Fortunately, many physical systems that result in simultaneous linear equations have a diagonally dominant coefficient matrix, which then assures convergence for iterative methods such as the Gauss-Seidel method of solving simultaneous linear equations.

Example 2

Find the solution to the following system of equations using the Gauss-Seidel method.

$$12x_1 + 3x_2 - 5x_3 = 1$$
$$x_1 + 5x_2 + 3x_3 = 28$$
$$3x_1 + 7x_2 + 13x_3 = 76$$

Use

$$\begin{bmatrix} x_1 \\ x_2 \\ x_3 \end{bmatrix} = \begin{bmatrix} 1 \\ 0 \\ 1 \end{bmatrix}$$

as the initial guess and conduct two iterations.

Solution

The coefficient matrix

$$[A] = \begin{bmatrix} 12 & 3 & -5 \\ 1 & 5 & 3 \\ 3 & 7 & 13 \end{bmatrix}$$

is diagonally dominant as

$$|a_{11}| = |12| = 12 \geq |a_{12}| + |a_{13}| = |3| + |-5| = 8$$
$$|a_{22}| = |5| = 5 \geq |a_{21}| + |a_{23}| = |1| + |3| = 4$$
$$|a_{33}| = |13| = 13 \geq |a_{31}| + |a_{32}| = |3| + |7| = 10$$

and the inequality is strictly greater than for at least one row. Hence, the solution should converge using the Gauss-Seidel method.
Rewriting the equations, we get

$$x_1 = \frac{1 - 3x_2 + 5x_3}{12}$$

$$x_2 = \frac{28 - x_1 - 3x_3}{5}$$

$$x_3 = \frac{76 - 3x_1 - 7x_2}{13}$$

Assuming an initial guess of

$$\begin{bmatrix} x_1 \\ x_2 \\ x_3 \end{bmatrix} = \begin{bmatrix} 1 \\ 0 \\ 1 \end{bmatrix}$$

<u>Iteration #1</u>

$$x_1 = \frac{1 - 3(0) + 5(1)}{12}$$
$$= 0.50000$$

$$x_2 = \frac{28 - (0.50000) - 3(1)}{5}$$
$$= 4.9000$$

$$x_3 = \frac{76 - 3(0.50000) - 7(4.9000)}{13}$$
$$= 3.0923$$

The absolute relative approximate error at the end of the first iteration is

$$|\epsilon_a|_1 = \left| \frac{0.50000 - 1}{0.50000} \right| \times 100$$
$$= 100.00\%$$

$$|\epsilon_a|_2 = \left| \frac{4.9000 - 0}{4.9000} \right| \times 100$$
$$= 100.00\%$$

$$|\epsilon_a|_3 = \left| \frac{3.0923 - 1}{3.0923} \right| \times 100$$
$$= 67.662\%$$

The maximum absolute relative approximate error is 100.00%

Iteration #2

$$x_1 = \frac{1 - 3(4.9000) + 5(3.0923)}{12}$$

$$= 0.14679$$

$$x_2 = \frac{28 - (0.14679) - 3(3.0923)}{5}$$

$$= 3.7153$$

$$x_3 = \frac{76 - 3(0.14679) - 7(3.7153)}{13}$$

$$= 3.8118$$

At the end of second iteration, the absolute relative approximate error is

$$\left| \epsilon_a \right|_1 = \left| \frac{0.14679 - 0.50000}{0.14679} \right| \times 100$$

$$= 240.61\%$$

$$\left| \epsilon_a \right|_2 = \left| \frac{3.7153 - 4.9000}{3.7153} \right| \times 100$$

$$= 31.889\%$$

$$\left| \epsilon_a \right|_3 = \left| \frac{3.8118 - 3.0923}{3.8118} \right| \times 100$$

$$= 18.874\%$$

The maximum absolute relative approximate error is 240.61%. This is greater than the value of 100.00% we obtained in the first iteration. Is the solution diverging? No, as you conduct more iterations, the solution converges as follows.

Iteration	x_1	$\left|\epsilon_a\right|_1\%$	x_2	$\left|\epsilon_a\right|_2\%$	x_3	$\left|\epsilon_a\right|_3\%$
1	0.50000	100.00	4.9000	100.00	3.0923	67.662
2	0.14679	240.61	3.7153	31.889	3.8118	18.874
3	0.74275	80.236	3.1644	17.408	3.9708	4.0064
4	0.94675	21.546	3.0281	4.4996	3.9971	0.65772
5	0.99177	4.5391	3.0034	0.82499	4.0001	0.074383
6	0.99919	0.74307	3.0001	0.10856	4.0001	0.00101

This is close to the exact solution vector of

$$\begin{bmatrix} x_1 \\ x_2 \\ x_3 \end{bmatrix} = \begin{bmatrix} 1 \\ 3 \\ 4 \end{bmatrix}$$

Example 3

Given the system of equations

$$3x_1 + 7x_2 + 13x_3 = 76$$

$$x_1 + 5x_2 + 3x_3 = 28$$
$$12x_1 + 3x_2 - 5x_3 = 1$$

find the solution using the Gauss-Seidel method. Use

$$\begin{bmatrix} x_1 \\ x_2 \\ x_3 \end{bmatrix} = \begin{bmatrix} 1 \\ 0 \\ 1 \end{bmatrix}$$

as the initial guess.

Solution

Rewriting the equations, we get

$$x_1 = \frac{76 - 7x_2 - 13x_3}{3}$$

$$x_2 = \frac{28 - x_1 - 3x_3}{5}$$

$$x_3 = \frac{1 - 12x_1 - 3x_2}{-5}$$

Assuming an initial guess of

$$\begin{bmatrix} x_1 \\ x_2 \\ x_3 \end{bmatrix} = \begin{bmatrix} 1 \\ 0 \\ 1 \end{bmatrix}$$

the next six iterative values are given in the table below.

Iteration	x_1	$\left| \epsilon_a \right|_1 \%$	x_2	$\left| \epsilon_a \right|_2 \%$	x_3	$\left| \epsilon_a \right|_3 \%$
1	21.000	95.238	0.80000	100.00	50.680	98.027
2	−196.15	110.71	14.421	94.453	−462.30	110.96
3	1995.0	109.83	−116.02	112.43	4718.1	109.80
4	−20149	109.90	1204.6	109.63	−47636	109.90
5	2.0364×10^5	109.89	−12140	109.92	4.8144×10^5	109.89
6	$−2.0579 \times 10^6$	109.89	1.2272×10^5	109.89	$−4.8653 \times 10^6$	109.89

You can see that this solution is not converging and the coefficient matrix is not diagonally dominant. The coefficient matrix

$$[A] = \begin{bmatrix} 3 & 7 & 13 \\ 1 & 5 & 3 \\ 12 & 3 & -5 \end{bmatrix}$$

is not diagonally dominant as

$$\left| a_{11} \right| = \left| 3 \right| = 3 \le \left| a_{12} \right| + \left| a_{13} \right| = \left| 7 \right| + \left| 13 \right| = 20$$

Hence, the Gauss-Seidel method may or may not converge.

However, it is the same set of equations as the previous example and that converged. The only difference is that we exchanged first and the third equation with each other and that made the coefficient matrix not diagonally dominant.

Therefore, it is possible that a system of equations can be made diagonally dominant if one exchanges the equations with each other. However, it is not possible for all cases. For example, the following set of equations

$$x_1 + x_2 + x_3 = 3$$
$$2x_1 + 3x_2 + 4x_3 = 9$$
$$x_1 + 7x_2 + x_3 = 9$$

cannot be rewritten to make the coefficient matrix diagonally dominant.

Key Terms:

Gauss-Seidel method
Convergence of Gauss-Seidel method
Diagonally dominant matrix

Multiple-Choice Test

Chapter 04.08
Gauss-Seidel Method

1. A square matrix $[A]_{n \times n}$ is diagonally dominant if

    (A) $|a_{ii}| \geq \sum\limits_{\substack{j=1 \\ i \neq j}}^{n} |a_{ij}|, \ i = 1,2,...,n$

    (B) $|a_{ii}| \geq \sum\limits_{\substack{j=1 \\ i \neq j}}^{n} |a_{ij}|, \ i = 1,2,...,n$ and $|a_{ii}| > \sum\limits_{\substack{j=1 \\ i \neq j}}^{n} |a_{ij}|,$ for any $i = 1,2,...,n$

    (C) $|a_{ii}| \geq \sum\limits_{j=1}^{n} |a_{ij}|, \ i = 1,2,...,n$ and $|a_{ii}| > \sum\limits_{j=1}^{n} |a_{ij}|,$ for any $i = 1,2,...,n$

    (D) $|a_{ii}| \geq \sum\limits_{j=1}^{n} |a_{ij}|, \ i = 1,2,...,n$

2. Using $[x_1, x_2, x_3] = [1,3,5]$ as the initial guess, the values of $[x_1, x_2, x_3]$ after three iterations in the Gauss-Seidel method for

    $$\begin{bmatrix} 12 & 7 & 3 \\ 1 & 5 & 1 \\ 2 & 7 & -11 \end{bmatrix} \begin{bmatrix} x_1 \\ x_2 \\ x_3 \end{bmatrix} = \begin{bmatrix} 2 \\ -5 \\ 6 \end{bmatrix}$$

    are

    (A) [-2.8333   -1.4333   -1.9727]
    (B) [1.4959   -0.90464   -0.84914]
    (C) [0.90666 -1.0115   -1.0243]
    (D) [1.2148   -0.72060   -0.82451]

3.   To ensure that the following system of equations,

$$2x_1 + 7x_2 - 11x_3 = 6$$
$$x_1 + 2x_2 + x_3 = -5$$
$$7x_1 + 5x_2 + 2x_3 = 17$$

converges using the Gauss-Seidel method, one can rewrite the above equations as follows:

(A) $\begin{bmatrix} 2 & 7 & -11 \\ 1 & 2 & 1 \\ 7 & 5 & 2 \end{bmatrix} \begin{bmatrix} x_1 \\ x_2 \\ x_3 \end{bmatrix} = \begin{bmatrix} 6 \\ -5 \\ 17 \end{bmatrix}$

(B) $\begin{bmatrix} 7 & 5 & 2 \\ 1 & 2 & 1 \\ 2 & 7 & -11 \end{bmatrix} \begin{bmatrix} x_1 \\ x_2 \\ x_3 \end{bmatrix} = \begin{bmatrix} 17 \\ -5 \\ 6 \end{bmatrix}$

(C) $\begin{bmatrix} 7 & 5 & 2 \\ 1 & 2 & 1 \\ 2 & 7 & -11 \end{bmatrix} \begin{bmatrix} x_1 \\ x_2 \\ x_3 \end{bmatrix} = \begin{bmatrix} 6 \\ -5 \\ 17 \end{bmatrix}$

(D)   The equations cannot be rewritten in a form to ensure convergence.

4.   For $\begin{bmatrix} 12 & 7 & 3 \\ 1 & 5 & 1 \\ 2 & 7 & -11 \end{bmatrix} \begin{bmatrix} x_1 \\ x_2 \\ x_3 \end{bmatrix} = \begin{bmatrix} 22 \\ 7 \\ -2 \end{bmatrix}$ and using $\begin{bmatrix} x_1 & x_2 & x_3 \end{bmatrix} = \begin{bmatrix} 1 & 2 & 1 \end{bmatrix}$ as the initial guess,

the values of $\begin{bmatrix} x_1 & x_2 & x_3 \end{bmatrix}$ are found at the end of each iteration as

Iteration #	x_1	x_2	x_3
1	0.41667	1.1167	0.96818
2	0.93990	1.0184	1.0008
3	0.98908	1.0020	0.99931
4	0.99899	1.0003	1.0000

At what first iteration number would you trust at least 1 significant digit in your solution?
        (A) 1
        (B) 2
        (C) 3
        (D) 4

5.   The algorithm for the Gauss-Seidel method to solve $[A][X] = [C]$ is given as follows when using n max iterations. The initial value of $[X]$ is stored in $[X]$.

(A) Sub Seidel $(n, a, x, rhs, \text{nmax})$
    For $k = 1$ To nmax
    For $i = 1$ To n
    For $j = 1$ To n
    If $(i \Leftrightarrow j)$ Then
    Sum = Sum + $a(i, j) * x(j)$
    endif
    Next j
    $x(i) = (rhs(i) - Sum) / a(i,i)$
    Next i
    Next j
    End Sub

(B) Sub Seidel $(n, a, x, rhs, \text{nmax})$
    For $k = 1$ To nmax
      For $i = 1$ To n
      Sum = 0
      For $j = 1$ To n
      If $(i \Leftrightarrow j)$ Then
      Sum = Sum + $a(i, j) * x(j)$
      endif
      Next j
      $x(i) = (rhs(i) - Sum) / a(i,i)$
      Next i
      Next k
      End Sub

(C) Sub Seidel $(n, a, x, rhs, \text{nmax})$
      For $k = 1$ To nmax
      For $i = 1$ To n
      Sum = 0
      For $j = 1$ To n
      Sum = Sum + $a(i, j) * x(j)$
      Next j
      $x(i) = (rhs(i) - Sum) / a(i,i)$
      Next i
      Next k

End Sub

(D) Sub Seidel $(n, a, x, rhs, \text{nmax})$
    For $k = 1$ To nmax
    For $i = 1$ To n
    Sum = 0
    For $j = 1$ To n
    If $(i <> j)$ Then
    Sum = Sum + $a(i, j) * x(j)$
    endif
    Next j
    $x(i) = (rhs(i) - Sum)/a(i,i)$
    Next i
    Next k
    End Sub

6. Thermistors measure temperature, have a nonlinear output and are valued for a limited range. So when a thermistor is manufactured, the manufacturer supplies a resistance vs. temperature curve. An accurate representation of the curve is generally given by

$$\frac{1}{T} = a_0 + a_1 \ln(R) + a_2 \{\ln(R)\}^2 + a_3 \{\ln(R)\}^3$$

where T is temperature in Kelvin, R is resistance in ohms, and a_0, a_1, a_2, a_3 are constants of the calibration curve. Given the following for a thermistor

R	T
ohm	°C
1101.0	25.113
911.3	30.131
636.0	40.120
451.1	50.128

the value of temperature in °C for a measured resistance of 900 ohms most nearly is
    (A) 30.002
    (B) 30.473
    (C) 31.272
    (D) 31.445

Complete Solution

Problem Set

Chapter 04.08
Gauss-Seidel Method

1. Solve the following system of equations using Gauss-Seidel method.
$$12x_1 + 7x_2 + 3x_3 = 17$$
$$3x_1 + 6x_2 + 2x_3 = 9$$
$$2x_1 + 7x_2 - 11x_3 = 49$$
Conduct 3 iterations. Calculate the maximum absolute relative approximate error at the end of each iteration. Choose $\begin{bmatrix} x_1 & x_2 & x_3 \end{bmatrix} = \begin{bmatrix} 1 & 3 & 5 \end{bmatrix}$ as your initial guess.

2. Solve the following system of equations using Gauss-Seidel method.
$$3x_1 + 6x_2 + 2x_3 = 9$$
$$12x_1 + 7x_2 + 3x_3 = 17$$
$$2x_1 + 7x_2 - 11x_3 = 49$$
Conduct 3 iterations. Calculate the maximum absolute relative approximate error at the end of each iteration, and Choose $\begin{bmatrix} x_1 & x_2 & x_3 \end{bmatrix} = \begin{bmatrix} 1 & 3 & 5 \end{bmatrix}$ as your initial guess.

3. Solve the following system of equations using Gauss-Seidel method.
$$3x_1 + 6x_2 + 2x_3 = 9$$
$$12x_1 + 7x_2 + 3x_3 = 17$$
$$2x_1 + 7x_2 - 11x_3 = 49$$
Conduct 3 iterations. Calculate the maximum absolute relative approximate error at the end of each iteration, and Choose $[x_1 \quad x_2 \quad x_3] = [1.1 \quad 2.1 \quad -2.9]$ as your initial guess.

05.00A

Physical Problem of Interpolation
General Engineering

Problem

To find the altitude, velocity and acceleration profile of a rocket, a velocity probe in the rocket (Figure 1) is measuring its velocity. Below are given some typical values of a rocket velocity profile are given in Table 1.

Figure 1 A rocket launched into space[1]

[1] Source of rocket picture: NASA Langley Research Center, Office of Education, **edu.larc.nasa.gov/pstp/**

To determine the velocity at a particular time, one needs to interpolate the data. Although you may be familiar with linear interpolation, where you draw a straight line between two data points, you also want to know how accurate your estimate is. This forces you to use other interpolation functions such as quadratic and cubic polynomials.

Table 1. Velocity as a function of time

t (s)	$v(t)$ (m/s)
0	0
10	227.04
15	362.78
20	517.35
22.5	602.97
30	901.67

Can you also find the distance covered by the rocket from one point of time to the other? Can you find the acceleration of the rocket at a particular time?

INTERPOLATION	
Topic	Physical problem for interpolation
Summary	Textbook notes of a problem for interpolation using real world physics data.
Major	General Engineering
Authors	Autar Kaw
Last Revised	December 23, 2009
Web Site	http://numericalmethods.eng.usf.edu

Chapter 05.00B

Physical Problem of Interpolation
Chemical Engineering

Problem Statement

Well, I am from India and we are in the habit of drinking "afternoon tea." The other day, my wife asked me to heat up some water in our kettle. I put 4 cups (you cannot have just 1 cup) of water in the kettle and put it on over our new flat-top burner.

"You are an engineer", quipped my wife teasingly. "Can you estimate how long it would take for the water to boil and the kettle to make that whistling sound?" Yes, she clearly knows that whistling sound reminds me of all the horror movies that keep me awake at night.

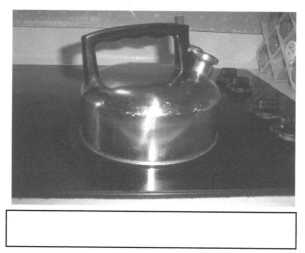

Figure 1. A kettle of water on a flat burner.

Solution

A cup of water is about 200 ml in volume. So the total volume of water is about 800 ml. The burner for our flat top is rated at 1200 W. From first law of thermodynamics [1],

$$\Delta H + \Delta E_p + \Delta E_k = Q - W_{sh}$$

where

ΔH = change in internal energy,

ΔE_p = change in potential energy,

ΔE_k = change in kinetic energy,

Q = heat added to the system,

W_{sh} = work that is called shaft work.

In this example

$\Delta E_p = 0$,

$\Delta E_k = 0$,

$W_{sh} = 0$,

giving

$\Delta H = Q$.

Assuming no heat is lost as the kettle is assumed to be thermally insulated, the amount of heat needed is

$$Q = \Delta H$$
$$= mC_p \Delta T$$

where

m = mass of water (kg),

C_p = specific heat $\left(\dfrac{J}{kg - ^\circ C} \right)$,

ΔT = change in temperature,

and the values are given as

$$m = 800ml \times \frac{1kg}{1lit}$$
$$= 0.8kg$$

$$C_p = 4814 \frac{T}{Kg - ^\circ K} \text{ from (Reference [1] - Table 8.1)}$$

$$\Delta T = 100^\circ C - 22^\circ C$$
$$= 78^0 C$$

Assuming that the room temperature is $22^0 C$ and the boiling temperature of water is $100^0 C$.

$$Q = mC_p \Delta T$$
$$= (0.8)(4814)(78)$$
$$= 300394\,J.$$

Since the wattage of the heater is 1200 W, the time it would take to boil is

$$= \frac{300394}{1200}$$
$$\cong 250\ s$$
$$\cong 4\min 10\,s$$

But, I do not see any interpolation here. One of the approximations made in the above formula is that the specific heat is constant over the temperature range of 22^0 C to 100^0 C. But it is not a constant given in the Table 1.

Table 1. Specific heat of water as a function of temperature [2].

Temperature ^{0}C	Specific heat $\dfrac{J}{kg.^\circ C}$
22	4181
42	4179
52	4186
82	4199
100	4217

One assumption one may make is to use the specific heat at the average temperature. In this case it is $\dfrac{22+100}{2}=61^0$ C .

So how do we find $C_p\left(61^\circ C\right)$? We use interpolation to do that, that is, finding the value of a discrete function at a point that is not given to us. Using $C_p\left(61^\circ C\right)$ will give us a better estimate of how much time it would take to boil the water.

References
1. Levenspiel, Octave, Understanding Engineering Thermo, Prentice Hall, New Jersey, 1996.
2. Incropera, F.P. and DeWitt, D.P., Introduction to Heat Transfer, Wiley, 4th edition, 2001.

QUESTIONS
1. Using the specific heat at the average temperature, how much is the difference in the estimated time for boiling the water.
2. Use first, second and third order polynomial interpolation to estimate $C_p\left(61^\circ C\right)$ by all the methods (except spline) you learned in class. What is the absolute relative approximate error for each order of polynomial approximation? How many significant digits are at least correct in your solution.
3. Just by looking at the data in Table 1, it may be clear that the calculated time using interpolation will not be very different from that found using the approximate specific heat. But in case of solids, it can be quite a different story. For example, to calculate heat required to raise the temperature of graphite from room temperature to 800°C for pyrolization, one needs to use proper specific heat data. Check yourself to see the difference between using specific heat at room temperature and specific heat at average temperature for the following problem. Find the heat required to raise the

temperature of 1 kg of graphite from room temperature of 22°C to 800°C, given the table of specific heat vs. temperature below.

Table 2 Specific heat of graphite as a function of temperature.

Temperature	Specific heat
^0C	$\dfrac{J}{kg.^{\circ}C}$
-73	420
127	1070
327	1370
527	1620
727	1820

INTERPOLATION	
Topic	Physical Problem
Summary	Textbook notes of a real world problem using interpolation.
Major	Chemical Engineering
Authors	Autar Kaw
Date	December 23, 2009
Web Site	http://numericalmethods.eng.usf.edu

Chapter 05.00C

Physical Problem of Interpolation
Civil Engineering

Problem Statement

This is a conversation between a former instructor (Autar) and civil engineering alumni named John Q. This is just what we heard!

Autar: "That is interesting! You are now a professional civil engineer and love to go bass fishing."

John Q: "Actually, my civil engineering education is helping me in being a good bass fisherman!"

Autar: "How is that?"

John Q: "Well, if you know where the thermocline is in the lake, you can find a lot of bass there!"

Autar: "Glad I asked? Educate me."

John Q: "Well, the water in a lake generally has three layers – epilimonon, thermocline and hypolimnion as shown in Figure 1 below. The thermocline layer is sandwiched between the epilimonon and the hypolimnion. The sun heats the water at the surface and this layer (epilimonon) of warm water floats over a layer (hypolimnion) of colder water, as the warm water is less dense then cold water. As days become hotter during the summer the layers become very distinct. Between these two layers of warm and cold water, you have a thin layer called the thermocline. Bass love the thermocline. So if you know where this thin layer of thermocline is, you can have a great catch."

Autar: "But why do bass fish like the thermocline?"

John Q: "Well, the upper layer (epilimonon) has too much light for the bass to be calm, while the lower layer (hypolimnion) has too little oxygen. The thermocline is also ideal for algae growth. So, it is the place of choice for the bass. You will be wasting your time if you fish below the thermocline."

Autar: "So how does one find where the thermocline is?"

John Q: "Well, you got electronic gadgets, such as depth finders, LCRs, and thermometers to do that. What some of these gadgets measure is the depth at which drastic change in temperature takes place? Just look at the data in Figure 2 taken in a lake in Pennsylvania. It shows the temperature data as a function of depth. You can see where it changes temperature suddenly. That is where the thermocline is.

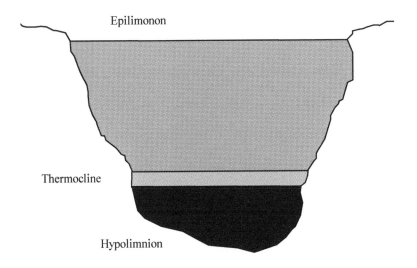

Figure 1 Three layers of lake stratification.

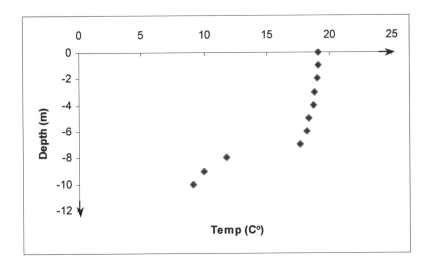

Temperature	Depth
°C	m
19.1	0
19.1	-1
19	-2
18.8	-3
18.7	-4
18.3	-5
18.2	-6
17.6	-7
11.7	-8
9.9	-9
9.1	-10

Figure 2 Temperature as a function of depth (Data courtesy of Ms. Bartlett - http://www.lehigh.edu/~infolios/becky/lakegraph.htm[1]).

Autar: "So what one can do is interpolate the temperature vs. depth data. The depth at which the thermocline occurs is the inflection point of the temperature-depth curve."

John Q: "You are still in the habit of using jargon like inflection points. I still gives me beautiful dreams of Calculus II!"

Autar: "Yes, simply said, the inflection point is where the second derivative of temperature with respect to the depth becomes zero. That is $\dfrac{d^2T}{dz^2} = 0$, where T is the temperature at depth z. I think I am going to taking this problem to the classroom to teach my students about interpolation. Thanks to you."

Topic	INTERPOLATION
Sub Topic	Physical Problem
Summary	Bass fishing never got so technical. Find how interpolation can help you to have a great catch and let you tell others a true fish story.
Authors	Autar Kaw
Last Revised	December 23, 2009
Web Site	http://numericalmethods.eng.usf.edu

---

[1] This data was gathered to teach middle school biology students about lake stratification (the three layers: epilimonon, thermocline, and hypolimnion), dissolved oxygen levels, photosynthesis, and cellular respiration."

Chapter 05.00D

Physical Problem of Interpolation
Computer Engineering

Peter: "Dr. Kaw, I am taking a course in Manufacturing. We are solving the following problem. A robot arm with a rapid laser is used to do a quick quality check, such as hole radius, on six holes on a rectangular plate 15"×10" at several points as shown in this table.

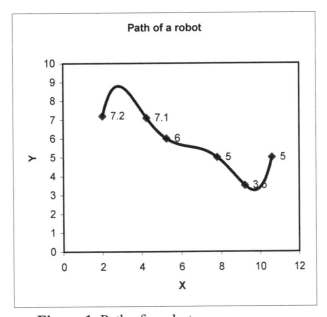

Figure 1 Path of a robot arm

Table 1   Coordinates of the points on the table

X	Y
inches	inches
2.00	7.2
4.25	7.1
5.25	6.0
7.81	5.0
9.20	3.5
10.60	5.0

I am using Excel to fit a fifth order polynomial through the 6 points. But, when I plot the polynomial, it is giving a long path!"

Kaw: "Why do you not just join the consecutive points by a straight line; just like the kids do at Pizza Hut with those 'Connect the dots' activities?"

Peter: "You are making me hungry and I wish it were that easy. The path of the robot going from one point to another needs to be smooth so as to avoid sharp jerks in the arm that can otherwise create premature wear and tear of the robot arm."

Kaw: "As I recall, you took my course in Numerical Methods. What was that – one year ago?"

Peter: "Yes, your memory is sharp but my retention from that course – can we not talk about that!"

Kaw: "Come into my office. I wrote this program using Maple as you did. See this function, $f(x) = 1/(1 + 25x^2)$. I am choosing 7 points equidistantly between –1 and 1. Now look at the sixth order interpolating polynomial and the original function (See Figure 1). See the oscillations in the interpolating polynomial. In 1901, Runge [5] used this example function to show that higher order interpolation is a bad idea. A better alternative to getting a better representation of the curve is using splines. This is the solution to your problem as well. It will give you a smooth curve with less oscillations, and a shorter path. Try it!"

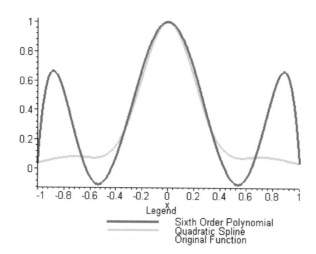

Figure 2   Runge's function interpolated

Topic	INTERPOLATION
Sub Topic	Physical Problem
Summary	A robot arm path needs to be developed over several points on a flat plate. The path needs to be smooth to avoid sudden jerky motion and at the same time needs to be short.
Authors	Autar Kaw
Last Revised	December 23, 2009
Web Site	http://numericalmethods.eng.usf.edu

Chapter 05.00E

Physical Problem of Interpolation Electrical Engineering

Thermistors are temperature-measuring devices based on the principle that the thermistor material exhibits a change in electrical resistance with a change in temperature. By measuring the resistance of the thermistor material, one can then determine the temperature. Thermistors are generally a piece of semiconductor made from metal oxides such as those of manganese, nickel, cobalt, etc. These pieces may be made into a bead, disk, wafer, etc depending on the application.

There are two types of thermistors – negative temperature coefficient (NTC) and positive temperature coefficient (PTC) thermistors. For NTCs, the resistance decreases with temperature, while for PTCs, the resistance increases with temperature. It is the NTCs that are generally used for temperature measurement.

Why would we want to use thermistors for measuring temperature as opposed to other choices such as thermocouples? It is because thermistors have high sensitivity giving more accuracy, a fast response to temperature changes for accuracy and quicker measurements, and relatively high resistance for decreasing the errors caused by the resistance of lead wires themselves.

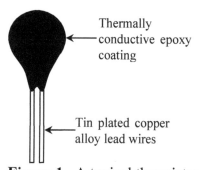

Thermally conductive epoxy coating

Tin plated copper alloy lead wires

Figure 1. A typical thermistor

But thermistors have a nonlinear output and are valued for a limited range. So, when a thermistor is manufactured, the manufacturer supplies a resistance vs. temperature curve. The curve generally used that gives an accurate representation is given by

$$\frac{1}{T} = a_0 + a_1 \ln(R) + a_2 \{\ln(R)\}^2 + a_3 \{\ln(R)\}^3 \qquad (1)$$

where

T is temperature in Kelvin, and

R is resistance in ohms.

a_0, a_1, a_2, a_3 are constants of the calibration curve.

Making change of variables

$$y = \frac{1}{T}, \text{ and}$$

$$x = \ln R,$$

we can change the calibration curve to a polynomial

$$y = a_0 + a_1 x + a_2 x^2 + a_3 x^3.$$

So if one is able to find the constants of the above formula, one can then use the calibration curve to find the temperature.

Given below is the data of resistance vs. temperature for a thermistor. Can you find the calibration curve?

Table 1 Resistance vs. temperature data for calibration of a thermistor

R	T
Ohm	°C
1101.0	25.113
911.3	30.131
636.0	40.120
451.1	50.128

References

1. Betatherm sensors, http://www.betatherm.com
2. Valvanao, J., "Measuring Temeparture Using Thermistors", Curcuit Cellar Online, August 2000, http://www.circuitcellar.com/online
3. Lavenuta, G., "Negative Temperature Coefficient Thermistors: Part 1: Characteristics, Materials, and Configurations", http://www.globalspec.com/cornerstone/ref/negtemp.html
4. Potter, D., "Measuring Temperature with Thermistors – a Tutorial", National Instruments Application Note 065, http://www.seas.upenn.edu/courses/belab/ReferenceFiles/Thermisters/an065.pdf
5. Steinhart, J.S. and Hart, S.R., 1968. "Calibration Curves for Thermistors," Deep Sea Research 15:497.
6. Sapoff, M. et al. 1982. "The Exactness of Fit of Resistance-Temperature Data of Thermistors with Third-Degree Polynomials," Temperature, Its Measurement and Control in Science and Industry, Vol. 5, James F. Schooley, ed., American Institute of Physics, New York, NY:875.

7. Siwek, W.R., et al. 1992. "A Precision Temperature Standard Based on the Exactness of Fit of Thermistor Resistance-Temperature Data Using Third Degree Polynomials," Temperature, Its Measurement and Control in Science and Industry, Vol. 6, James F. Schooley, ed., American Institute of Physics, New York, NY:491-496.

Topic	INTERPOLATION
Sub Topic	Physical Problem
Summary	Thermistors measure temperature based on the principle that resistance of thermistor material changes with temperature. Hence, a manufacturer supplies a resistance vs. temperature calibration curve. This curve is developed using interpolation.
Authors	Autar Kaw
Last Revised	December 23, 2009
Web Site	http://numericalmethods.eng.usf.edu

Chapter 05.00F

Physical Problem of Interpolation
Industrial Engineering

Problem Statement

An Industrial Engineer needs to program a Computer Numerical Control (CNC) milling machine to fabricate a cam profile that was designed by a Industrial Engineer to operate the intake valves in an internal combustion engine. The Mechanical Engineer's task was to design a disk cam (rotating counterclockwise) to move a radial roller follower (in the vertical y-direction) as shown in Figure 1 below.

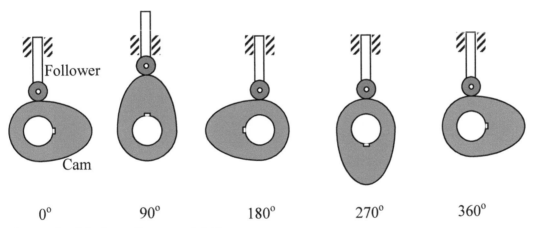

| 0° | 90° | 180° | 270° | 360° |

Figure 1 Motion of cam and follower.

Specifically, the cam is to move the follower as described in Table 1 below.

Table 1 Cam follower movement as a function of cam rotation.

Cam rotation from X-axis	Follower movement in Y-direction
0°	0.0
90°	1.0
180°	0.0
270°	0.0
360°	0.0

Solution

The Mechanical Engineer has specified seven points along the profile of the cam (see Figure below) at 30o increments as shown in Figure 2 below.

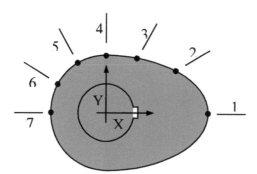

Figure 2   Schematic of cam profile

.

The geometry of the cam (i.e., coordinates of the seven points on the cam surface) are given in Table 2 below.

Table 2   Geometry of the cam.

Point	Angle from X-axis	X	Y
1	$-90°$	2.20	0.00
2	$-60°$	1.28	0.88
3	$-30°$	0.66	1.14
4	$0°$	0.00	1.20
5	$30°$	-0.60	1.04
6	$60°$	-1.04	0.60
7	$90°$	-1.20	0.00

The Industrial Engineer is responsible for fitting a *smooth* curve through the 7 points keeping in mind that the final curve must have a infinite slope at points 1 and 7, and zero slope at point 4.

Topic	INTERPOLATION
Sub Topic	Physical Problem
Summary	To program a milling machine to make a cam profile, one needs to use interpolation to develop the path of the profile.
Authors	Glen Besterfield
Last Revised	December 23, 2009
Web Site	http://numericalmethods.eng.usf.edu

Chapter 05.00G

Physical Problem of Interpolation
Mechanical Engineering

Problem Statement

To make the fulcrum (Figure 1) of a bascule bridge, a long hollow steel shaft called the trunnion is shrink fit into a steel hub.

Figure 1 Trunnion-Hub-Girder (THG) assembly.

This is done by first immersing the trunnion in a cold medium such as dry-ice/alcohol mixture. After the trunnion reaches a steady state temperature of the cold medium, the trunnion outer diameter contracts, is taken out and slid though the hole of the hub (Figure 2).

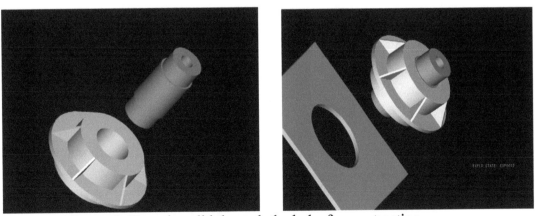

Figure 2 Trunnion slid through the hub after contracting

When the trunnion heats up, it expands and creates an interference fit with the hub. In 1995, on one of the bridges in Florida, this assembly procedure did not work as designed. Before the trunnion could be inserted fully into the hub, the trunnion got stuck. So a new trunnion and hub had to be ordered worth $50,000. Coupled with construction delays, the total loss ran into more than hundred thousand dollars.

Why did the trunnion get stuck? This was because the trunnion had not contracted enough to slide through the hole.

Now the same designer is working on making the fulcrum for another bascule bridge. Can you help him so that he does not make the same mistake?

For this new bridge, he needs to fit a hollow trunnion of outside diameter 12.363" in a hub of inner diameter 12.358". His plan is to put the trunnion in dry ice/alcohol mixture (temperature of dry ice/alcohol mixture is $-108°F$) to contract the trunnion so that it can be slid through the hole of the hub. To slide the trunnion without sticking, he has also specified a diametral clearance of at least 0.01". Assume the room temperature is $80°F$, is immersing it in dry-ice/alcohol mixture a correct decision?

Solution

Looking at the records of the designer for the previous bridge where the trunnion got stuck in the hub, it was found that he used the thermal expansion coefficient at room temperature to calculate the contraction in the trunnion diameter. In that case the reduction, ΔD in the outer diameter of the trunnion is

$$\Delta D = D\alpha\Delta T \tag{1}$$

where

D = outer diameter of the trunnion,

α = coefficient of thermal expansion coefficient at room temperature,

ΔT = change in temperature.

Given

$D = 12.363"$

$\alpha = 6.817 \times 10^{-6}\,\text{in/in/°F}$ at $80°F$

$\Delta T = T_{fluid} - T_{room}$

$\quad\quad = -108 - 80$

$\quad\quad = -188°F$

where

T_{fluid} = temperature of dry-ice/alcohol mixture

T_{room} = room temperature

the reduction in the trunnion outer diameter is given by

$$\Delta D = 12.363 \times \left(6.47 \times 10^{-6}\right)\left(-188\right)$$

$$= -0.01504"$$

So the trunnion is predicted to reduce in diameter by 0.01504". But, is this enough reduction in diameter? As per the specifications, he needs the trunnion to contract by

= trunnion outside diameter - hub inner diameter + diametric clearance

=12.363"−12.358"+0.01"

= 0.015"

So according to his calculations, it is enough to put the steel trunnion in dry-ice/alcohol mixture to get the desired contraction of 0.015" as he is predicting a contraction of 0.01504".

But as shown in the graph below, the thermal expansion coefficient of steel decreases with temperature and is not constant over the range of temperature the trunnion goes through. Hence the above formula (Equation 1) would overestimate the thermal contraction. This is the mistake he made in the calculations for the earlier bridge.

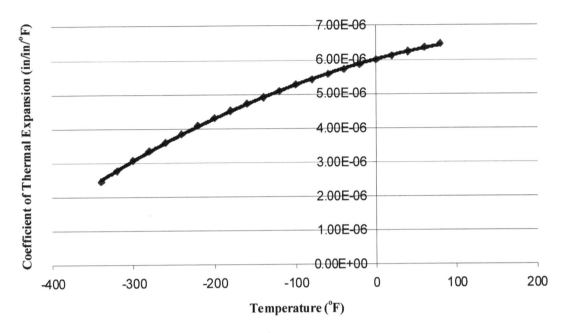

Figure 3 Varying thermal expansion coefficient as a function of temperature for cast steel.

To get a better estimate of the contraction in the diameter, we can use the thermal expansion coefficient at the average temperature. The average temperature of the steel would be

$$T_{avg} = \frac{-108 + 80}{2}$$

$$= -14^{\circ} F$$

(2)

Now given the table of thermal expansion coefficient as a function of temperature as given below, we can use polynomial interpolation to find the thermal expansion coefficient at the average temperature of $-14^{\circ} F$ and find the contraction using equation (1).

Table 1 Temperature vs thermal expansion coefficient

Temperature (^{0}F)	Thermal Expansion Coefficient ($\mu in/in/^{0}F$)
80	6.47
60	6.36
40	6.24
20	6.12
0	6.00
-20	5.86
-40	5.72
-60	5.58

-80	5.43
-100	5.28
-120	5.09
-140	4.91
-160	4.72
-180	4.52
-200	4.30
-220	4.08
-240	3.83
-260	3.58
-280	3.33
-300	3.07
-320	2.76
-340	2.45

Is cooling in dry-ice/alcohol mixture still your recommendation?

Topic	INTERPOLATION
Sub Topic	Physical Problem
Summary	Find the thermal expansion coefficient of steel at a specific temperature to find out whether a steel shaft will cool down enough to shrink fit into a hollow hub. The thermal expansion coefficient is to be found by using interpolation from a given table of thermal expansion coefficient of steel as a function of temperature.
Authors	Autar Kaw
Last Revised	December 23, 2009
Web Site	http://numericalmethods.eng.usf.edu

Multiple-Choice Test

Chapter 05.01
Background on Interpolation

1. The number of polynomials that can go through two fixed data points (x_1, y_1) and (x_2, y_2) is
   - (A) 0
   - (B) 1
   - (C) 2
   - (D) infinite

2. A unique polynomial of degree _____ passes through $n+1$ data points.
   - (A) $n+1$
   - (B) $n+1$ or less
   - (C) n
   - (D) n or less

3. The following function(s) can be used for interpolation:
   - (A) polynomial
   - (B) exponential
   - (C) trigonometric
   - (D) all of the above

4. Polynomials are the most commonly used functions for interpolation because they are easy to
   - (A) evaluate
   - (B) differentiate
   - (C) integrate
   - (D) evaluate, differentiate and integrate

5. Given $n+1$ data points $(x_0, y_0), (x_1, y_1), \dots, (x_{n-1}, y_{n-1}), (x_n, y_n)$, assume you pass a function $f(x)$ through all the data points. If now the value of the function $f(x)$ is required to be found outside the range of the given x-data, the procedure is called
   - (A) extrapolation
   - (B) interpolation
   - (C) guessing
   - (D) regression

05.01.1

6.   Given three data points $(1,6)$, $(3,28)$, and $(10, 231)$, it is found that the function $y = 2x^2 + 3x + 1$ passes through the three data points. Your estimate of y at $x = 2$ is most nearly

            (A)   6
            (B)   15
            (C)   17
            (D)   28

Complete Solution

Chapter 05.02
Direct Method of Interpolation

After reading this chapter, you should be able to:
1. *apply the direct method of interpolation,*
2. *solve problems using the direct method of interpolation, and*
3. *use the direct method interpolants to find derivatives and integrals of discrete functions.*

What is interpolation?

Many times, data is given only at discrete points such as (x_0, y_0), (x_1, y_1), ..., (x_{n-1}, y_{n-1}), (x_n, y_n). So, how then does one find the value of y at any other value of x? Well, a continuous function $f(x)$ may be used to represent the $n+1$ data values with $f(x)$ passing through the $n+1$ points (Figure 1). Then one can find the value of y at any other value of x. This is called *interpolation*.

Of course, if x falls outside the range of x for which the data is given, it is no longer interpolation but instead is called *extrapolation*.

So what kind of function $f(x)$ should one choose? A polynomial is a common choice for an interpolating function because polynomials are easy to
  (A) evaluate,
  (B) differentiate, and
  (C) integrate
relative to other choices such as a trigonometric and exponential series.

Polynomial interpolation involves finding a polynomial of order n that passes through the $n+1$ points. One of the methods of interpolation is called the direct method. Other methods include Newton's divided difference polynomial method and the Lagrangian interpolation method. We will discuss the direct method in this chapter.

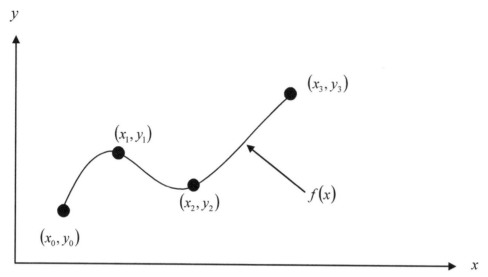

Figure 1 Interpolation of discrete data.

Direct Method

The direct method of interpolation is based on the following premise. Given $n+1$ data points, fit a polynomial of order n as given below

$$y = a_0 + a_1 x + \ldots\ldots\ldots + a_n x^n \qquad (1)$$

through the data, where $a_0, a_1, \ldots\ldots, a_n$ are $n+1$ real constants. Since $n+1$ values of y are given at $n+1$ values of x, one can write $n+1$ equations. Then the $n+1$ constants, $a_0, a_1, \ldots\ldots, a_n$ can be found by solving the $n+1$ simultaneous linear equations. To find the value of y at a given value of x, simply substitute the value of x in Equation 1.

But, it is not necessary to use all the data points. How does one then choose the order of the polynomial and what data points to use? This concept and the direct method of interpolation are best illustrated using examples.

Example 1

The upward velocity of a rocket is given as a function of time in Table 1.

Table 1 Velocity as a function of time.

t (s)	$v(t)$ (m/s)
0	0
10	227.04
15	362.78
20	517.35
22.5	602.97
30	901.67

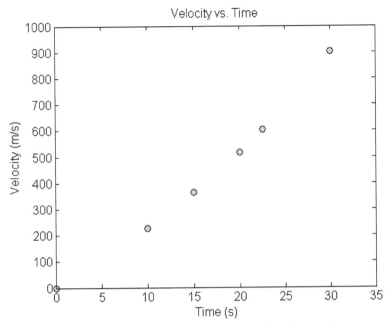

Figure 2 Graph of velocity vs. time data for the rocket example.

Determine the value of the velocity at $t = 16$ seconds using the direct method of interpolation and a first order polynomial.

Solution

For first order polynomial interpolation (also called linear interpolation), the velocity given by

$$v(t) = a_0 + a_1 t$$

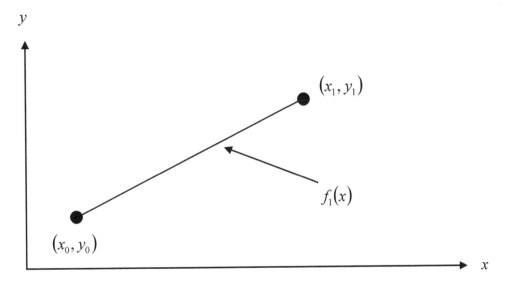

Figure 3 Linear interpolation.

Since we want to find the velocity at $t = 16$, and we are using a first order polynomial, we need to choose the two data points that are closest to $t = 16$ that also bracket $t = 16$ to evaluate it. The two points are $t_0 = 15$ and $t_1 = 20$.

Then

$$t_0 = 15, \ v(t_0) = 362.78$$
$$t_1 = 20, \ v(t_1) = 517.35$$

gives

$$v(15) = a_0 + a_1(15) = 362.78$$
$$v(20) = a_0 + a_1(20) = 517.35$$

Writing the equations in matrix form, we have

$$\begin{bmatrix} 1 & 15 \\ 1 & 20 \end{bmatrix} \begin{bmatrix} a_0 \\ a_1 \end{bmatrix} = \begin{bmatrix} 362.78 \\ 517.35 \end{bmatrix}$$

Solving the above two equations gives

$$a_0 = -100.93$$
$$a_1 = 30.914$$

Hence

$$v(t) = a_0 + a_1 t$$
$$= -100.93 + 30.914t, \ 15 \le t \le 20$$

At $t = 16$,

$$v(16) = -100.92 + 30.914 \times 16$$
$$= 393.7 \, \text{m/s}$$

Example 2

The upward velocity of a rocket is given as a function of time in Table 2.

Table 2 Velocity as a function of time.

t (s)	$v(t)$ (m/s)
0	0
10	227.04
15	362.78
20	517.35
22.5	602.97
30	901.67

Determine the value of the velocity at $t = 16$ seconds using the direct method of interpolation and a second order polynomial.

Solution

For second order polynomial interpolation (also called quadratic interpolation), the velocity is given by

$$v(t) = a_0 + a_1 t + a_2 t^2$$

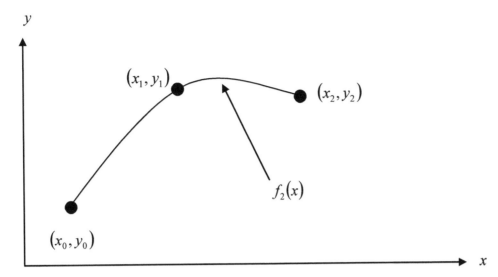

Figure 4 Quadratic interpolation.

Since we want to find the velocity at $t = 16$, and we are using a second order polynomial, we need to choose the three data points that are closest to $t = 16$ that also bracket $t = 16$ to evaluate it. The three points are $t_0 = 10$, $t_1 = 15$, and $t_2 = 20$.

Then

$$t_0 = 10, \quad v(t_0) = 227.04$$
$$t_1 = 15, \quad v(t_1) = 362.78$$
$$t_2 = 20, \quad v(t_2) = 517.35$$

gives

$$v(10) = a_0 + a_1(10) + a_2(10)^2 = 227.04$$
$$v(15) = a_0 + a_1(15) + a_2(15)^2 = 362.78$$
$$v(20) = a_0 + a_1(20) + a_2(20)^2 = 517.35$$

Writing the three equations in matrix form, we have

$$\begin{bmatrix} 1 & 10 & 100 \\ 1 & 15 & 225 \\ 1 & 20 & 400 \end{bmatrix} \begin{bmatrix} a_0 \\ a_1 \\ a_2 \end{bmatrix} = \begin{bmatrix} 227.04 \\ 362.78 \\ 517.35 \end{bmatrix}$$

Solving the above three equations gives

$$a_0 = 12.05$$
$$a_1 = 17.733$$
$$a_2 = 0.3766$$

Hence

$$v(t) = 12.05 + 17.733t + 0.3766t^2, \quad 10 \leq t \leq 20$$

At $t = 16$,

$$v(16) = 12.05 + 17.733(16) + 0.3766(16)^2$$
$$= 392.19 \text{ m/s}$$

The absolute relative approximate error $|\epsilon_a|$ obtained between the results from the first and second order polynomial is

$$|\epsilon_a| = \left| \frac{392.19 - 393.70}{392.19} \right| \times 100$$

$$= 0.38410\%$$

Example 3

The upward velocity of a rocket is given as a function of time in Table 3.

Table 3 Velocity as a function of time.

t (s)	$v(t)$ (m/s)
0	0
10	227.04
15	362.78
20	517.35
22.5	602.97
30	901.67

a) Determine the value of the velocity at $t = 16$ seconds using the direct method of interpolation and a third order polynomial.

b) Find the absolute relative approximate error for the third order polynomial approximation.

c) Using the third order polynomial interpolant for velocity from part (a), find the distance covered by the rocket from $t = 11$s to $t = 16$s.

d) Using the third order polynomial interpolant for velocity from part (a), find the acceleration of the rocket at $t = 16$s.

Solution

a) For third order polynomial interpolation (also called cubic interpolation), we choose the velocity given by

$$v(t) = a_0 + a_1 t + a_2 t^2 + a_3 t^3$$

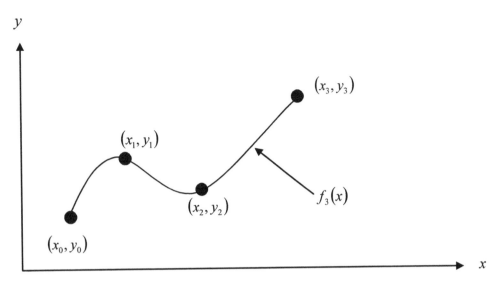

Figure 5 Cubic interpolation.

Since we want to find the velocity at $t = 16$, and we are using a third order polynomial, we need to choose the four data points closest to $t = 16$ that also bracket $t = 16$ to evaluate it. The four points are $t_0 = 10$, $t_1 = 15$, $t_2 = 20$ and $t_3 = 22.5$.

Then

$$t_0 = 10, \quad v(t_0) = 227.04$$
$$t_1 = 15, \quad v(t_1) = 362.78$$
$$t_2 = 20, \quad v(t_2) = 517.35$$
$$t_3 = 22.5, \quad v(t_3) = 602.97$$

gives

$$v(10) = a_0 + a_1(10) + a_2(10)^2 + a_3(10)^3 = 227.04$$
$$v(15) = a_0 + a_1(15) + a_2(15)^2 + a_3(15)^3 = 362.78$$
$$v(20) = a_0 + a_1(20) + a_2(20)^2 + a_3(20)^3 = 517.35$$
$$v(22.5) = a_0 + a_1(22.5) + a_2(22.5)^2 + a_3(22.5)^3 = 602.97$$

Writing the four equations in matrix form, we have

$$\begin{bmatrix} 1 & 10 & 100 & 1000 \\ 1 & 15 & 225 & 3375 \\ 1 & 20 & 400 & 8000 \\ 1 & 22.5 & 506.25 & 11391 \end{bmatrix} \begin{bmatrix} a_0 \\ a_1 \\ a_2 \\ a_3 \end{bmatrix} = \begin{bmatrix} 227.04 \\ 362.78 \\ 517.35 \\ 602.97 \end{bmatrix}$$

Solving the above four equations gives

$$a_0 = -4.2540$$
$$a_1 = 21.266$$
$$a_2 = 0.13204$$

$$a_3 = 0.0054347$$

Hence

$$v(t) = a_0 + a_1 t + a_2 t^2 + a_3 t^3$$
$$= -4.2540 + 21.266t + 0.13204t^2 + 0.0054347t^3, \quad 10 \le t \le 22.5$$
$$v(16) = -4.2540 + 21.266(16) + 0.13204(16)^2 + 0.0054347(16)^3$$
$$= 392.06 \, \text{m/s}$$

b) The absolute percentage relative approximate error $|\epsilon_a|$ for the value obtained for $v(16)$ between second and third order polynomial is

$$|\epsilon_a| = \left| \frac{392.06 - 392.19}{392.06} \right| \times 100$$
$$= 0.033269\%$$

c) The distance covered by the rocket between $t = 11\,\text{s}$ and $t = 16\,\text{s}$ can be calculated from the interpolating polynomial

$$v(t) = -4.3810 + 21.289t + 0.13064t^2 + 0.0054606t^3, \quad 10 \le t \le 22.5$$

Note that the polynomial is valid between $t = 10$ and $t = 22.5$ and hence includes the limits of integration of $t = 11$ and $t = 16$.

So

$$s(16) - s(11) = \int_{11}^{16} v(t)\,dt$$

$$= \int_{11}^{16} \left(-4.2540 + 21.266t + 0.13204t^2 + 0.0054347t^3 \right) dt$$

$$= \left[-4.2540t + 21.266\frac{t^2}{2} + 0.13204\frac{t^3}{3} + 0.0054347\frac{t^4}{4} \right]_{11}^{16}$$

$$= 1605 \, \text{m}$$

d) The acceleration at $t = 16$ is given by

$$a(16) = \frac{d}{dt} v(t) \Big|_{t=16}$$

Given that

$$v(t) = -4.2540 + 21.266t + 0.13204t^2 + 0.0054347t^3, \quad 10 \le t \le 22.5$$
$$a(t) = \frac{d}{dt} v(t)$$
$$= \frac{d}{dt} \left(-4.2540 + 21.266t + 0.13204t^2 + 0.0054347t^3 \right)$$
$$= 21.289 + 0.26130t + 0.016382t^2, \quad 10 \le t \le 22.5$$
$$a(16) = 21.266 + 0.26408(16) + 0.016304(16)^2$$
$$= 29.665 \, \text{m/s}^2$$

INTERPOLATION	
Topic	Direct Method of Interpolation
Summary	Textbook notes on the direct method of interpolation.
Major	General Engineering
Authors	Autar Kaw, Peter Warr, Michael Keteltas
Date	August 11, 2010
Web Site	http://numericalmethods.eng.usf.edu

Multiple-Choice Test

Chapter 05.02
Direct Method of Interpolation

1. A unique polynomial of degree _____ passes through $n+1$ data points.
    (A) $n+1$
    (B) $n+1$ or less
    (C) n
    (D) n or less

2. The following data of the velocity of a body is given as a function of time.

Time (s)	0	15	18	22	24
Velocity (m/s)	22	24	37	25	123

    The velocity in m/s at 16 s using linear polynomial interpolation is most nearly
    (A) 27.867
    (B) 28.333
    (C) 30.429
    (D) 43.000

3. The following data of the velocity of a body is given as a function of time.

Time (s)	0	15	18	22	24
Velocity (m/s)	22	24	37	25	123

    The velocity in m/s at 16 s using quadratic polynomial interpolation is most nearly
    (A) 27.867
    (B) 28.333
    (C) 30.429
    (D) 43.000

4. The following data of the velocity of a body is given as a function of time.

Time (s)	0	15	18	22	24
Velocity (m/s)	22	24	37	25	123

    Using quadratic interpolation, the interpolant
    $$v(t) = 8.667t^2 - 349.67t + 3523, \quad 18 \le t \le 24$$
    approximates the velocity of the body. From this information, the time in seconds at which the velocity of the body is 35 m/s during the above time interval of $t = 18$ s to $t = 24$ s is
    (A) 18.667
    (B) 20.850
    (C) 22.200
    (D) 22.294

5.   The following data of the velocity of a body is given as a function of time.

Time (s)	0	15	18	22	24
Velocity (m/s)	22	24	37	25	123

One of the interpolant approximations for the velocity from the above data is given as

$$v(t) = 8.6667t^2 - 349.67t + 3523, \quad 18 \le t \le 24$$

Using the above interpolant, the distance in meters covered by the body between $t = 19$ s and $t = 22$ s is most nearly

(A) 10.337
(B) 88.500
(C) 93.000
(D) 168.00

6.   The following data of the velocity of a body is given as a function of time.

Time (s)	0	15	18	22	24
Velocity (m/s)	22	24	37	25	123

If you were going to use quadratic interpolation to find the value of the velocity at $t = 14.9$ seconds, what three data points of time would you choose for interpolation?

(A) 0, 15, 18
(B) 15, 18, 22
(C) 0, 15, 22
(D) 0, 18, 24

Complete Solution

Problem Set

Chapter 05.02
Direct Method of Interpolation

1. The following data of the velocity of a body as a function of time is given

Time (s)	0	15	18	22	24
Velocity (m/s)	22	24	37	25	123

   What is the velocity at $t = 14$ seconds using linear polynomial interpolation?

2. The following data of the velocity of a body as a function of time is given

Time (s)	0	15	18	22	24
Velocity (m/s)	22	24	37	25	123

   What is the velocity at $t = 14$ seconds using quadratic polynomial interpolation?

3. The following data of the velocity of a body as a function of time is given

Time (s)	0	15	18	22	24
Velocity (m/s)	22	24	37	25	123

   What is the velocity at $t = 14$ seconds using cubic polynomial interpolation?

4. The following data of the velocity of a body as a function of time is given as follows.

Time (s)	0	15	18	22	24
Velocity (m/s)	22	24	37	25	123

   Using quadratic interpolation, the interpolant
   $$v(t) = 9.500t^2 - 383.0t + 3853$$

   approximates the velocity of the body between 18 and 24 seconds. From this information, can you find out when the velocity of the body is 26 m/s during the above time interval?

5. The following data of the velocity of a body as a function of time is given as follows.

Time (s)	0	15	18	22	24
Velocity (m/s)	22	24	37	25	123

   Find the value of velocity at $t = 16$ seconds using the following interpolation function for the velocity of the body
   $$v(t) = a_0 + a_1 \sin(t) + a_2 \sin(2t)$$

   where a_0, a_1, and a_2 are the unknown constants.

6.   You are given data for the upward velocity of a rocket as a function of time in the table below.

t, s	0	10	15	20	22.5	30
$v(t)$, m/s	0	227.04	362.78	517.35	602.97	901.67

   a) Determine the value of the velocity at $t = 16$ seconds using first order polynomial direct method.
   b) Determine the value of the velocity at $t = 16$ seconds using second order polynomial direct method. Find the absolute relative approximate error for approximation from the second order polynomial. How many significant digits would you at least trust in the solution?
   c) Determine the value of the velocity at $t = 16$ seconds using third order polynomial direct method. Find the absolute relative approximate error for approximation from the third order polynomial. How many significant digits would you at least trust in the solution?
   d) What is the true error for part (a), (b) and (c), if I told you that the data given in the table above was derived from the formula

$$v(t) = 2000 \ln \left[\frac{14 \times 10^4}{14 \times 10^4 - 2100t} \right] - 9.8t, \quad 0 \le t \le 30$$

7.   You are given data for the upward velocity of a rocket as a function of time in the table below.

t, s	0	10	15	20	22.5	30
$v(t)$, m/s	0	227.04	362.78	517.35	602.97	901.67

   a) Use linear interpolant approximation of velocity to find the acceleration at $t = 16$s.
   b) Use quadratic interpolant approximation of velocity to find the acceleration at $t = 16$s.
   c) Find the distance covered by the rocket from $t = 5$s to 16s? Use any method.

Chapter 05.03
Newton's Divided Difference Interpolation

After reading this chapter, you should be able to:
  1. *derive Newton's divided difference method of interpolation,*
  2. *apply Newton's divided difference method of interpolation, and*
  3. *apply Newton's divided difference method interpolants to find derivatives and integrals.*

What is interpolation?

Many times, data is given only at discrete points such as (x_0, y_0), (x_1, y_1), ..., (x_{n-1}, y_{n-1}), (x_n, y_n). So, how then does one find the value of y at any other value of x? Well, a continuous function $f(x)$ may be used to represent the $n+1$ data values with $f(x)$ passing through the $n+1$ points (Figure 1). Then one can find the value of y at any other value of x. This is called *interpolation*.

Of course, if x falls outside the range of x for which the data is given, it is no longer interpolation but instead is called *extrapolation*.

So what kind of function $f(x)$ should one choose? A polynomial is a common choice for an interpolating function because polynomials are easy to
  (A) evaluate,
  (B) differentiate, and
  (C) integrate,
relative to other choices such as a trigonometric and exponential series.

Polynomial interpolation involves finding a polynomial of order n that passes through the $n+1$ points. One of the methods of interpolation is called Newton's divided difference polynomial method. Other methods include the direct method and the Lagrangian interpolation method. We will discuss Newton's divided difference polynomial method in this chapter.

Newton's Divided Difference Polynomial Method

To illustrate this method, linear and quadratic interpolation is presented first. Then, the general form of Newton's divided difference polynomial method is presented. To illustrate the general form, cubic interpolation is shown in Figure 1.

05.02.1

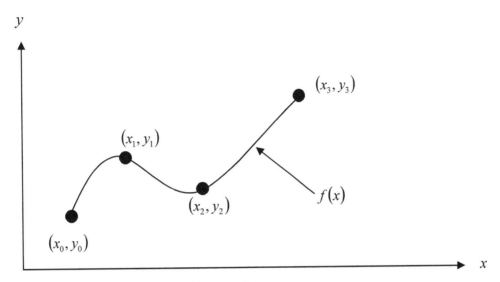

Figure 1 Interpolation of discrete data.

<u>Linear Interpolation</u>
Given (x_0, y_0) and (x_1, y_1), fit a linear interpolant through the data. Noting $y = f(x)$ and $y_1 = f(x_1)$, assume the linear interpolant $f_1(x)$ is given by (Figure 2)

$$f_1(x) = b_0 + b_1(x - x_0)$$

Since at $x = x_0$,

$$f_1(x_0) = f(x_0) = b_0 + b_1(x_0 - x_0) = b_0$$

and at $x = x_1$,

$$f_1(x_1) = f(x_1) = b_0 + b_1(x_1 - x_0)$$
$$= f(x_0) + b_1(x_1 - x_0)$$

giving

$$b_1 = \frac{f(x_1) - f(x_0)}{x_1 - x_0}$$

So

$$b_0 = f(x_0)$$
$$b_1 = \frac{f(x_1) - f(x_0)}{x_1 - x_0}$$

giving the linear interpolant as

$$f_1(x) = b_0 + b_1(x - x_0)$$
$$f_1(x) = f(x_0) + \frac{f(x_1) - f(x_0)}{x_1 - x_0}(x - x_0)$$

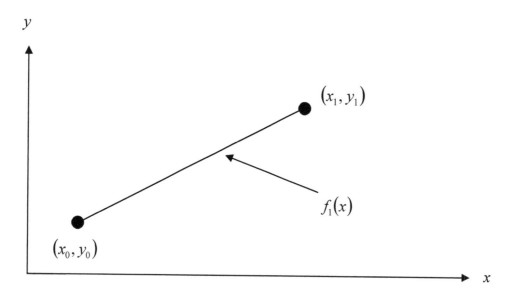

Figure 2 Linear interpolation.

Example 1

The upward velocity of a rocket is given as a function of time in Table 1 (Figure 3).

Table 1 Velocity as a function of time.

t (s)	$v(t)$ (m/s)
0	0
10	227.04
15	362.78
20	517.35
22.5	602.97
30	901.67

Determine the value of the velocity at $t = 16$ seconds using first order polynomial interpolation by Newton's divided difference polynomial method.

Solution

For linear interpolation, the velocity is given by

$$v(t) = b_0 + b_1(t - t_0)$$

Since we want to find the velocity at $t = 16$, and we are using a first order polynomial, we need to choose the two data points that are closest to $t = 16$ that also bracket $t = 16$ to evaluate it. The two points are $t = 15$ and $t = 20$.

Then

$$t_0 = 15, \ v(t_0) = 362.78$$
$$t_1 = 20, \ v(t_1) = 517.35$$

gives

$$b_0 = v(t_0)$$

$$= 362.78$$

$$b_1 = \frac{v(t_1) - v(t_0)}{t_1 - t_0}$$

$$= \frac{517.35 - 362.78}{20 - 15}$$

$$= 30.914$$

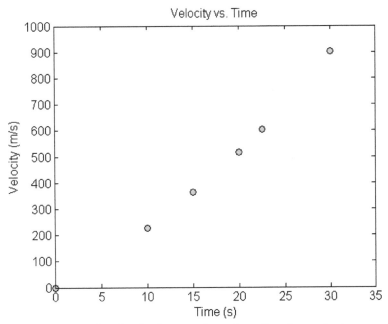

Figure 3 Graph of velocity vs. time data for the rocket example.

Hence

$$v(t) = b_0 + b_1(t - t_0)$$
$$= 362.78 + 30.914(t - 15), \qquad 15 \le t \le 20$$

At $t = 16$,

$$v(16) = 362.78 + 30.914(16 - 15)$$
$$= 393.69 \text{ m/s}$$

If we expand

$$v(t) = 362.78 + 30.914(t - 15), \qquad 15 \le t \le 20$$

we get

$$v(t) = -100.93 + 30.914t, \qquad 15 \le t \le 20$$

and this is the same expression as obtained in the direct method.

Quadratic Interpolation

Given (x_0, y_0), (x_1, y_1), and (x_2, y_2), fit a quadratic interpolant through the data. Noting $y = f(x)$, $y_0 = f(x_0)$, $y_1 = f(x_1)$, and $y_2 = f(x_2)$, assume the quadratic interpolant $f_2(x)$ is given by

$$f_2(x) = b_0 + b_1(x - x_0) + b_2(x - x_0)(x - x_1)$$

At $x = x_0$,

$$f_2(x_0) = f(x_0) = b_0 + b_1(x_0 - x_0) + b_2(x_0 - x_0)(x_0 - x_1)$$
$$= b_0$$
$$b_0 = f(x_0)$$

At $x = x_1$

$$f_2(x_1) = f(x_1) = b_0 + b_1(x_1 - x_0) + b_2(x_1 - x_0)(x_1 - x_1)$$
$$f(x_1) = f(x_0) + b_1(x_1 - x_0)$$

giving

$$b_1 = \frac{f(x_1) - f(x_0)}{x_1 - x_0}$$

At $x = x_2$

$$f_2(x_2) = f(x_2) = b_0 + b_1(x_2 - x_0) + b_2(x_2 - x_0)(x_2 - x_1)$$
$$f(x_2) = f(x_0) + \frac{f(x_1) - f(x_0)}{x_1 - x_0}(x_2 - x_0) + b_2(x_2 - x_0)(x_2 - x_1)$$

Giving

$$b_2 = \frac{\dfrac{f(x_2) - f(x_1)}{x_2 - x_1} - \dfrac{f(x_1) - f(x_0)}{x_1 - x_0}}{x_2 - x_0}$$

Hence the quadratic interpolant is given by

$$f_2(x) = b_0 + b_1(x - x_0) + b_2(x - x_0)(x - x_1)$$

$$= f(x_0) + \frac{f(x_1) - f(x_0)}{x_1 - x_0}(x - x_0) + \frac{\dfrac{f(x_2) - f(x_1)}{x_2 - x_1} - \dfrac{f(x_1) - f(x_0)}{x_1 - x_0}}{x_2 - x_0}(x - x_0)(x - x_1)$$

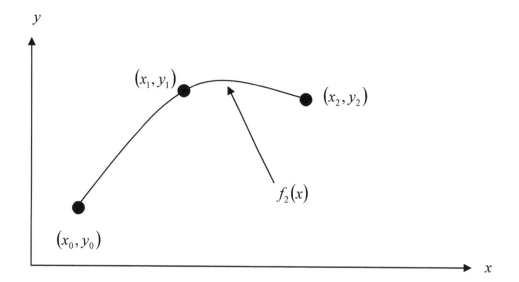

Figure 4   Quadratic interpolation.

Example 2

The upward velocity of a rocket is given as a function of time in Table 2.

Table 2 Velocity as a function of time.

t (s)	$v(t)$ (m/s)
0	0
10	227.04
15	362.78
20	517.35
22.5	602.97
30	901.67

Determine the value of the velocity at $t = 16$ seconds using second order polynomial interpolation using Newton's divided difference polynomial method.

Solution

For quadratic interpolation, the velocity is given by

$$v(t) = b_0 + b_1(t - t_0) + b_2(t - t_0)(t - t_1)$$

Since we want to find the velocity at $t = 16$, and we are using a second order polynomial, we need to choose the three data points that are closest to $t = 16$ that also bracket $t = 16$ to evaluate it. The three points are $t_0 = 10$, $t_1 = 15$, and $t_2 = 20$.

Then

$$t_0 = 10, \ v(t_0) = 227.04$$
$$t_1 = 15, \ v(t_1) = 362.78$$
$$t_2 = 20, \ v(t_2) = 517.35$$

gives

$$b_0 = v(t_0)$$
$$\quad = 227.04$$

$$b_1 = \frac{v(t_1) - v(t_0)}{t_1 - t_0}$$

$$\quad = \frac{362.78 - 227.04}{15 - 10}$$

$$\quad = 27.148$$

$$b_2 = \frac{\dfrac{v(t_2) - v(t_1)}{t_2 - t_1} - \dfrac{v(t_1) - v(t_0)}{t_1 - t_0}}{t_2 - t_0}$$

$$\quad = \frac{\dfrac{517.35 - 362.78}{20 - 15} - \dfrac{362.78 - 227.04}{15 - 10}}{20 - 10}$$

$$\quad = \frac{30.914 - 27.148}{10}$$

$$= 0.37660$$

Hence

$$v(t) = b_0 + b_1(t - t_0) + b_2(t - t_0)(t - t_1)$$
$$= 227.04 + 27.148(t - 10) + 0.37660(t - 10)(t - 15), \qquad 10 \le t \le 20$$

At $t = 16$,

$$v(16) = 227.04 + 27.148(16 - 10) + 0.37660(16 - 10)(16 - 15)$$
$$= 392.19 \text{ m/s}$$

If we expand

$$v(t) = 227.04 + 27.148(t - 10) + 0.37660(t - 10)(t - 15), \ 10 \le t \le 20$$

we get

$$v(t) = 12.05 + 17.733t + 0.37660t^2, \quad 10 \le t \le 20$$

This is the same expression obtained by the direct method.

General Form of Newton's Divided Difference Polynomial

In the two previous cases, we found linear and quadratic interpolants for Newton's divided difference method. Let us revisit the quadratic polynomial interpolant formula

$$f_2(x) = b_0 + b_1(x - x_0) + b_2(x - x_0)(x - x_1)$$

where

$$b_0 = f(x_0)$$

$$b_1 = \frac{f(x_1) - f(x_0)}{x_1 - x_0}$$

$$b_2 = \frac{\dfrac{f(x_2) - f(x_1)}{x_2 - x_1} - \dfrac{f(x_1) - f(x_0)}{x_1 - x_0}}{x_2 - x_0}$$

Note that b_0, b_1, and b_2 are finite divided differences. b_0, b_1, and b_2 are the first, second, and third finite divided differences, respectively. We denote the first divided difference by

$$f[x_0] = f(x_0)$$

the second divided difference by

$$f[x_1, x_0] = \frac{f(x_1) - f(x_0)}{x_1 - x_0}$$

and the third divided difference by

$$f[x_2, x_1, x_0] = \frac{f[x_2, x_1] - f[x_1, x_0]}{x_2 - x_0}$$

$$= \frac{\dfrac{f(x_2) - f(x_1)}{x_2 - x_1} - \dfrac{f(x_1) - f(x_0)}{x_1 - x_0}}{x_2 - x_0}$$

where $f[x_0]$, $f[x_1, x_0]$, and $f[x_2, x_1, x_0]$ are called bracketed functions of their variables enclosed in square brackets.

Rewriting,

$$f_2(x) = f[x_0] + f[x_1, x_0](x - x_0) + f[x_2, x_1, x_0](x - x_0)(x - x_1)$$

This leads us to writing the general form of the Newton's divided difference polynomial for $n+1$ data points, $(x_0, y_0), (x_1, y_1), \ldots, (x_{n-1}, y_{n-1}), (x_n, y_n)$, as

$$f_n(x) = b_0 + b_1(x - x_0) + \ldots + b_n(x - x_0)(x - x_1)\ldots(x - x_{n-1})$$

where

$$b_0 = f[x_0]$$
$$b_1 = f[x_1, x_0]$$
$$b_2 = f[x_2, x_1, x_0]$$
$$\vdots$$
$$b_{n-1} = f[x_{n-1}, x_{n-2}, \ldots, x_0]$$
$$b_n = f[x_n, x_{n-1}, \ldots, x_0]$$

where the definition of the mth divided difference is

$$b_m = f[x_m, \ldots, x_0]$$
$$= \frac{f[x_m, \ldots, x_1] - f[x_{m-1}, \ldots, x_0]}{x_m - x_0}$$

From the above definition, it can be seen that the divided differences are calculated recursively.

For an example of a third order polynomial, given (x_0, y_0), (x_1, y_1), (x_2, y_2), and (x_3, y_3),

$$f_3(x) = f[x_0] + f[x_1, x_0](x - x_0) + f[x_2, x_1, x_0](x - x_0)(x - x_1)$$
$$+ f[x_3, x_2, x_1, x_0](x - x_0)(x - x_1)(x - x_2)$$

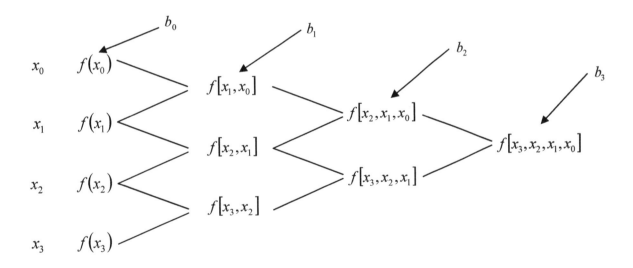

Figure 5   Table of divided differences for a cubic polynomial.

Example 3

The upward velocity of a rocket is given as a function of time in Table 3.

Table 3 Velocity as a function of time.

t (s)	$v(t)$ (m/s)
0	0
10	227.04
15	362.78
20	517.35
22.5	602.97
30	901.67

a) Determine the value of the velocity at $t = 16$ seconds with third order polynomial interpolation using Newton's divided difference polynomial method.
b) Using the third order polynomial interpolant for velocity, find the distance covered by the rocket from $t = 11\,\text{s}$ to $t = 16\,\text{s}$.
c) Using the third order polynomial interpolant for velocity, find the acceleration of the rocket at $t = 16\,\text{s}$.

Solution

a) For a third order polynomial, the velocity is given by
$$v(t) = b_0 + b_1(t - t_0) + b_2(t - t_0)(t - t_1) + b_3(t - t_0)(t - t_1)(t - t_2)$$
Since we want to find the velocity at $t = 16$, and we are using a third order polynomial, we need to choose the four data points that are closest to $t = 16$ that also bracket $t = 16$ to evaluate it. The four data points are $t_0 = 10$, $t_1 = 15$, $t_2 = 20$, and $t_3 = 22.5$.
Then
$$t_0 = 10, \quad v(t_0) = 227.04$$
$$t_1 = 15, \quad v(t_1) = 362.78$$
$$t_2 = 20, \quad v(t_2) = 517.35$$
$$t_3 = 22.5, \quad v(t_3) = 602.97$$
gives
$$b_0 = v[t_0]$$
$$\quad = v(t_0)$$
$$\quad = 227.04$$
$$b_1 = v[t_1, t_0]$$
$$\quad = \frac{v(t_1) - v(t_0)}{t_1 - t_0}$$
$$\quad = \frac{362.78 - 227.04}{15 - 10}$$
$$\quad = 27.148$$
$$b_2 = v[t_2, t_1, t_0]$$
$$\quad = \frac{v[t_2, t_1] - v[t_1, t_0]}{t_2 - t_0}$$

$$v[t_2, t_1] = \frac{v(t_2) - v(t_1)}{t_2 - t_1}$$

$$= \frac{517.35 - 362.78}{20 - 15}$$

$$= 30.914$$

$$v[t_1, t_0] = 27.148$$

$$b_2 = \frac{v[t_2, t_1] - v[t_1, t_0]}{t_2 - t_0}$$

$$= \frac{30.914 - 27.148}{20 - 10}$$

$$= 0.37660$$

$$b_3 = v[t_3, t_2, t_1, t_0]$$

$$= \frac{v[t_3, t_2, t_1] - v[t_2, t_1, t_0]}{t_3 - t_0}$$

$$v[t_3, t_2, t_1] = \frac{v[t_3, t_2] - v[t_2, t_1]}{t_3 - t_1}$$

$$v[t_3, t_2] = \frac{v(t_3) - v(t_2)}{t_3 - t_2}$$

$$= \frac{602.97 - 517.35}{22.5 - 20}$$

$$= 34.248$$

$$v[t_2, t_1] = \frac{v(t_2) - v(t_1)}{t_2 - t_1}$$

$$= \frac{517.35 - 362.78}{20 - 15}$$

$$= 30.914$$

$$v[t_3, t_2, t_1] = \frac{v[t_3, t_2] - v[t_2, t_1]}{t_3 - t_1}$$

$$= \frac{34.248 - 30.914}{22.5 - 15}$$

$$= 0.44453$$

$$v[t_2, t_1, t_0] = 0.37660$$

$$b_3 = \frac{v[t_3, t_2, t_1] - v[t_2, t_1, t_0]}{t_3 - t_0}$$

$$= \frac{0.44453 - 0.37660}{22.5 - 10}$$

$$= 5.4347 \times 10^{-3}$$

Hence

$$v(t) = b_0 + b_1(t - t_0) + b_2(t - t_0)(t - t_1) + b_3(t - t_0)(t - t_1)(t - t_2)$$

$$= 227.04 + 27.148(t-10) + 0.37660(t-10)(t-15)$$
$$+ 5.5347 \times 10^{-3}(t-10)(t-15)(t-20)$$

At $t = 16$,

$$v(16) = 227.04 + 27.148(16-10) + 0.37660(16-10)(16-15)$$
$$+ 5.5347 \times 10^{-3}(16-10)(16-15)(16-20)$$
$$= 392.06 \text{ m/s}$$

b) The distance covered by the rocket between $t = 11\text{ s}$ and $t = 16\text{ s}$ can be calculated from the interpolating polynomial

$$v(t) = 227.04 + 27.148(t-10) + 0.37660(t-10)(t-15)$$
$$+ 5.5347 \times 10^{-3}(t-10)(t-15)(t-20)$$
$$= -4.2541 + 21.265t + 0.13204t^2 + 0.0054347t^3, \quad 10 \le t \le 22.5$$

Note that the polynomial is valid between $t = 10$ and $t = 22.5$ and hence includes the limits of $t = 11$ and $t = 16$.
So

$$s(16) - s(11) = \int_{11}^{16} v(t)dt$$

$$= \int_{11}^{16} (-4.2541 + 21.265t + 0.13204t^2 + 0.0054347t^3)dt$$

$$= \left[-4.2541t + 21.265\frac{t^2}{2} + 0.13204\frac{t^3}{3} + 0.0054347\frac{t^4}{4} \right]_{11}^{16}$$

$$= 1605 \text{ m}$$

c) The acceleration at $t = 16$ is given by

$$a(16) = \frac{d}{dt}v(t)\Big|_{t=16}$$

$$a(t) = \frac{d}{dt}v(t)$$

$$= \frac{d}{dt}\left(-4.2541 + 21.265t + 0.13204t^2 + 0.0054347t^3\right)$$

$$= 21.265 + 0.26408t + 0.016304t^2$$

$$a(16) = 21.265 + 0.26408(16) + 0.016304(16)^2$$

$$= 29.664 \text{ m/s}^2$$

INTERPOLATION	
Topic	Newton's Divided Difference Interpolation
Summary	Textbook notes on Newton's divided difference interpolation.
Major	General Engineering
Authors	Autar Kaw, Michael Keteltas
Last Revised	December 23, 2009
Web Site	http://numericalmethods.eng.usf.edu

Multiple-Choice Test

Chapter 05.03
Newton's Divided Difference Polynomial Method

1. If a polynomial of degree n has $n+1$ zeros, then the polynomial is
   (A) oscillatory
   (B) zero everywhere
   (C) quadratic
   (D) not defined

2. The following x, y data is given.

x	15	18	22
y	24	37	25

   The Newton's divided difference second order polynomial for the above data is given by
   $$f_2(x) = b_0 + b_1(x-15) + b_2(x-15)(x-18)$$
   The value of b_1 is most nearly
   (A) -1.0480
   (B) 0.14333
   (C) 4.3333
   (D) 24.000

3. The polynomial that passes through the following x, y data

x	18	22	24
y	?	25	123

   is given by
   $$8.125x^2 - 324.75x + 3237, \quad 18 \le x \le 24$$
   The corresponding polynomial using Newton's divided difference polynomial is given by
   $$f_2(x) = b_0 + b_1(x-18) + b_2(x-18)(x-22)$$
   The value of b_2 is most nearly
   (A) 0.25000
   (B) 8.1250
   (C) 24.000
   (D) not obtainable with the information given

05.04.1

4. Velocity vs. time data for a body is approximated by a second order Newton's divided difference polynomial as

$$v(t) = b_0 + 39.622(t - 20) + 0.5540(t - 20)(t - 15), \quad 10 \leq t \leq 20$$

The acceleration in m/s^2 at $t = 15$ is
    (A) 0.5540
    (B) 39.622
    (C) 36.852
    (D) not obtainable with the given information

5. The path that a robot is following on a $x - y$ plane is found by interpolating the following four data points as

x	2	4.5	5.5	7
y	7.5	7.5	6	5

$$y(x) = 0.1524x^3 - 2.257x^2 + 9.605x - 3.900$$

The length of the path from $x = 2$ to $x = 7$ is

   (A) $\sqrt{(7.5 - 7.5)^2 + (4.5 - 2)^2} + \sqrt{(6 - 7.5)^2 + (5.5 - 4.5)^2} + \sqrt{(5 - 6)^2 + (7 - 5.5)^2}$

   (B) $\int_2^7 \sqrt{1 + (0.1524x^3 - 2.257x^2 + 9.605x - 3.900)^2}\, dx$

   (C) $\int_2^7 \sqrt{1 + (0.4572x^2 - 4.514x + 9.605)^2}\, dx$

   (D) $\int_2^7 (0.1524x^3 - 2.257x^2 + 9.605x - 3.900)\, dx$

6. The following data of the velocity of a body is given as a function of time.

Time (s)	0	15	18	22	24
Velocity (m/s)	22	24	37	25	123

If you were going to use quadratic interpolation to find the value of the velocity at $t = 14.9$ seconds, the three data points of time you would choose for interpolation are
    (A) 0, 15, 18
    (B) 15, 18, 22
    (C) 0, 15, 22
    (D) 0, 18, 24

Complete Solution

Problem Set

Chapter 05.03
Newton's Divided Difference Polynomial

1. The following data of the velocity of a body as a function of time is given

Time (s)	0	15	18	22	24
Velocity (m/s)	22	24	37	25	123

Find the coefficients of the Newton's divided difference interpolating first order polynomial to find the velocity at $t = 14s$.

2. The following data of the velocity of a body as a function of time is given

Time (s)	0	15	18	22	24
Velocity (m/s)	22	24	37	25	123

Find the coefficients of the Newton's divided difference interpolating second order polynomial to find the velocity at $t = 14s$.

3. The following data of the velocity of a body as a function of time is given

Time (s)	0	15	18	22	24
Velocity (m/s)	22	24	37	25	123

Find the coefficients of the Newton's divided difference interpolating third order polynomial to find the velocity at $t = 14s$.

4. You are given data for the upward velocity of a rocket as a function of time in the table below.

t, s	0	10	15	20	22.5	30
$v(t)$, m/s	0	227.04	362.78	517.35	602.97	901.67

   a) Use Newton's divided difference linear interpolant approximation of velocity to find the acceleration at $t = 16$ s.
   b) Use Newton's divided difference quadratic interpolant approximation of velocity to find the acceleration at $t = 16$ s.
   c) Find the distance covered by the rocket from $t = 5$ s to 16 s? Use any method.

5. The acceleration-time data for a small rocket is given in tabular form below.

Time (s)	10	12	14	16	18	20	22	24
Acceleration (m/s^2)	106.6	94.1	80.9	68.0	56.2	45.8	37.1	30.1

a) Use Newton's divided difference quadratic polynomial interpolation to find the acceleration at $t = 15.5$ seconds. Be sure to choose your base points for good accuracy.

b) Use the quadratic interpolant of part (a) to find the change in the velocity of the rocket between $t = 14.1$ and $t = 15.8$ seconds.

6. A robot follows a path generated by a quadratic interpolant from $x = 2$ to $x = 4$. The interpolant passes through three consecutive data points (2,4), (3,9) and (4,16) and is given by $y = x^2$. Find the length of the interpolant path from $x = 2$ to $x = 4$. You can approximate a general integral by

$$\int_a^b f(x)dx \approx \frac{(b-a)}{6}\left[f(a) + 4f\left(\frac{a+b}{2}\right) + f(b) \right]$$

Chapter 05.05
Spline Method of Interpolation

After reading this chapter, you should be able to:
1. *interpolate data using spline interpolation, and*
2. *understand why spline interpolation is important.*

What is interpolation?

Many times, data is given only at discrete points such as (x_0, y_0), (x_1, y_1), ..., (x_{n-1}, y_{n-1}), (x_n, y_n). So, how then does one find the value of y at any other value of x? Well, a continuous function $f(x)$ may be used to represent the $n+1$ data values with $f(x)$ passing through the $n+1$ points (Figure 1). Then one can find the value of y at any other value of x. This is called *interpolation*.

Of course, if x falls outside the range of x for which the data is given, it is no longer interpolation but instead is called *extrapolation*.

So what kind of function $f(x)$ should one choose? A polynomial is a common choice for an interpolating function because polynomials are easy to
(A) evaluate,
(B) differentiate, and
(C) integrate
relative to other choices such as a trigonometric and exponential series.

Polynomial interpolation involves finding a polynomial of order n that passes through the $n+1$ points. Several methods to obtain such a polynomial include the direct method, Newton's divided difference polynomial method and the Lagrangian interpolation method.

So is the spline method yet another method of obtaining this n^{th} order polynomial. ...... NO! Actually, when n becomes large, in many cases, one may get oscillatory behavior in the resulting polynomial. This was shown by Runge when he interpolated data based on a simple function of

$$y = \frac{1}{1 + 25x^2}$$

on an interval of [–1, 1]. For example, take six equidistantly spaced points in [–1, 1] and find y at these points as given in Table 1.

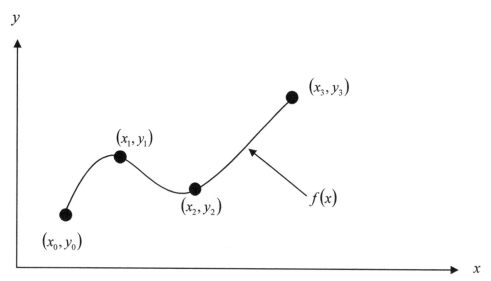

Figure 1 Interpolation of discrete data.

Table 1 Six equidistantly spaced points in [–1, 1].

x	$y = \dfrac{1}{1+25x^2}$
–1.0	0.038461
–0.6	0.1
–0.2	0.5
0.2	0.5
0.6	0.1
1.0	0.038461

Now through these six points, one can pass a fifth order polynomial

$$f_5(x) = 3.1378 \times 10^{-11} x^5 + 1.2019x^4 - 3.3651 \times 10^{-11} x^3 - 1.7308x^2 + 1.0004 \times 10^{-11} x + 5.6731 \times 10^{-1},$$
$$-1 \le x \le 1$$

through the six data points. On plotting the fifth order polynomial (Figure 2) and the original function, one can see that the two do not match well. One may consider choosing more points in the interval [–1, 1] to get a better match, but it diverges even more (see Figure 3), where 20 equidistant points were chosen in the interval [–1, 1] to draw a 19th order polynomial. In fact, Runge found that as the order of the polynomial becomes infinite, the polynomial diverges in the interval of $-1 < x < -0.726$ and $0.726 < x < 1$.

So what is the answer to using information from more data points, but at the same time keeping the function true to the data behavior? The answer is in spline interpolation. The most common spline interpolations used are linear, quadratic, and cubic splines.

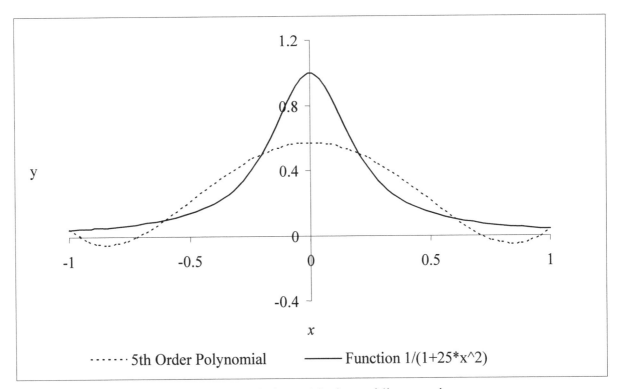

Figure 2   5th order polynomial interpolation with six equidistant points.

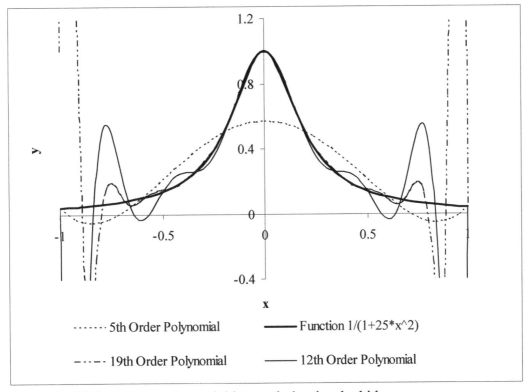

Figure 3   Higher order polynomial interpolation is a bad idea.

Linear Spline Interpolation

Given $(x_0, y_0), (x_1, y_1), \ldots\ldots, (x_{n-1}, y_{n-1})(x_n, y_n)$, fit linear splines (Figure 4) to the data. This simply involves forming the consecutive data through straight lines. So if the above data is given in an ascending order, the linear splines are given by $y_i = f(x_i)$.

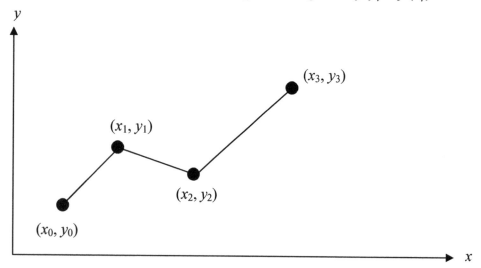

Figure 4   Linear splines.

$$f(x) = f(x_0) + \frac{f(x_1) - f(x_0)}{x_1 - x_0}(x - x_0), \qquad x_0 \le x \le x_1$$

$$= f(x_1) + \frac{f(x_2) - f(x_1)}{x_2 - x_1}(x - x_1), \qquad x_1 \le x \le x_2$$

$$\vdots$$

$$= f(x_{n-1}) + \frac{f(x_n) - f(x_{n-1})}{x_n - x_{n-1}}(x - x_{n-1}), \quad x_{n-1} \le x \le x_n$$

Note the terms of

$$\frac{f(x_i) - f(x_{i-1})}{x_i - x_{i-1}}$$

in the above function are simply slopes between x_{i-1} and x_i.

Example 1

The upward velocity of a rocket is given as a function of time in Table 2 (Figure 5).

Table 2 Velocity as a function of time.

t (s)	$v(t)$ (m/s)
0	0
10	227.04
15	362.78
20	517.35
22.5	602.97
30	901.67

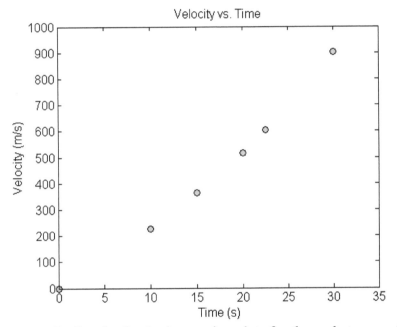

Figure 5 Graph of velocity vs. time data for the rocket example.

Determine the value of the velocity at $t = 16$ seconds using linear splines.

Solution

Since we want to evaluate the velocity at $t = 16$, and we are using linear splines, we need to choose the two data points closest to $t = 16$ that also bracket $t = 16$ to evaluate it. The two points are $t_0 = 15$ and $t_1 = 20$.

Then

$$t_0 = 15, \quad v(t_0) = 362.78$$
$$t_1 = 20, \quad v(t_1) = 517.35$$

gives

$$v(t) = v(t_0) + \frac{v(t_1) - v(t_0)}{t_1 - t_0}(t - t_0)$$

$$= 362.78 + \frac{517.35 - 362.78}{20 - 15}(t - 15)$$

$$= 362.78 + 30.913(t - 15), \ 15 \le t \le 20$$

At $t = 16$,

$$v(16) = 362.78 + 30.913(16 - 15)$$

$$= 393.7 \, \text{m/s}$$

Linear spline interpolation is no different from linear polynomial interpolation. Linear splines still use data only from the two consecutive data points. Also at the interior points of the data, the slope changes abruptly. This means that the first derivative is not continuous at these points. So how do we improve on this? We can do so by using quadratic splines.

Quadratic Splines

In these splines, a quadratic polynomial approximates the data between two consecutive data points. Given $(x_0, y_0), (x_1, y_1), \ldots, (x_{n-1}, y_{n-1}), (x_n, y_n)$, fit quadratic splines through the data. The splines are given by

$$f(x) = a_1 x^2 + b_1 x + c_1, \qquad x_0 \le x \le x_1$$

$$= a_2 x^2 + b_2 x + c_2, \qquad x_1 \le x \le x_2$$

$$\vdots$$

$$= a_n x^2 + b_n x + c_n, \qquad x_{n-1} \le x \le x_n$$

So how does one find the coefficients of these quadratic splines? There are $3n$ such coefficients

$$a_i, \ i = 1, 2, \ldots, n$$

$$b_i, \ i = 1, 2, \ldots, n$$

$$c_i, \ i = 1, 2, \ldots, n$$

To find $3n$ unknowns, one needs to set up $3n$ equations and then simultaneously solve them. These $3n$ equations are found as follows.

1. Each quadratic spline goes through two consecutive data points

$$a_1 x_0^2 + b_1 x_0 + c_1 = f(x_0)$$

$$a_1 x_1^2 + b_1 x_1 + c_1 = f(x_1)$$

$$\vdots$$

$$a_i x_{i-1}^2 + b_i x_{i-1} + c_i = f(x_{i-1})$$

$$a_i x_i^2 + b_i x_i + c_i = f(x_i)$$

$$\vdots$$

$$a_n x_{n-1}{}^2 + b_n x_{n-1} + c_n = f(x_{n-1})$$
$$a_n x_n{}^2 + b_n x_n + c_n = f(x_n)$$

This condition gives $2n$ equations as there are n quadratic splines going through two consecutive data points.

2. The first derivatives of two quadratic splines are continuous at the interior points. For example, the derivative of the first spline

$$a_1 x^2 + b_1 x + c_1$$

is

$$2a_1 x + b_1$$

The derivative of the second spline

$$a_2 x^2 + b_2 x + c_2$$

is

$$2a_2 x + b_2$$

and the two are equal at $x = x_1$ giving

$$2a_1 x_1 + b_1 = 2a_2 x_1 + b_2$$
$$2a_1 x_1 + b_1 - 2a_2 x_1 - b_2 = 0$$

Similarly at the other interior points,

$$2a_2 x_2 + b_2 - 2a_3 x_2 - b_3 = 0$$

$$\cdot$$
$$\cdot$$
$$\cdot$$

$$2a_i x_i + b_i - 2a_{i+1} x_i - b_{i+1} = 0$$

$$\cdot$$
$$\cdot$$
$$\cdot$$

$$2a_{n-1} x_{n-1} + b_{n-1} - 2a_n x_{n-1} - b_n = 0$$

Since there are $(n-1)$ interior points, we have $(n-1)$ such equations. So far, the total number of equations is $(2n) + (n-1) = (3n-1)$ equations. We still then need one more equation.

We can assume that the first spline is linear, that is

$$a_1 = 0$$

This gives us $3n$ equations and $3n$ unknowns. These can be solved by a number of techniques used to solve simultaneous linear equations.

Example 2

The upward velocity of a rocket is given as a function of time as

Table 3 Velocity as a function of time.

t (s)	$v(t)$ (m/s)
0	0
10	227.04
15	362.78
20	517.35
22.5	602.97
30	901.67

a) Determine the value of the velocity at $t = 16$ seconds using quadratic splines.
b) Using the quadratic splines as velocity functions, find the distance covered by the rocket from $t = 11\text{s}$ to $t = 16\text{s}$.
c) Using the quadratic splines as velocity functions, find the acceleration of the rocket at $t = 16\text{s}$.

Solution

a) Since there are six data points, five quadratic splines pass through them.

$$
\begin{aligned}
v(t) &= a_1 t^2 + b_1 t + c_1, \quad 0 \le t \le 10 \\
     &= a_2 t^2 + b_2 t + c_2, \quad 10 \le t \le 15 \\
     &= a_3 t^2 + b_3 t + c_3, \quad 15 \le t \le 20 \\
     &= a_4 t^2 + b_4 t + c_4, \quad 20 \le t \le 22.5 \\
     &= a_5 t^2 + b_5 t + c_5, \quad 22.5 \le t \le 30
\end{aligned}
$$

The equations are found as follows.
1. Each quadratic spline passes through two consecutive data points.
$a_1 t^2 + b_1 t + c_1$ passes through $t = 0$ and $t = 10$.

$$a_1 (0)^2 + b_1 (0) + c_1 = 0 \tag{1}$$

$$a_1 (10)^2 + b_1 (10) + c_1 = 227.04 \tag{2}$$

$a_2 t^2 + b_2 t + c_2$ passes through $t = 10$ and $t = 15$.

$$a_2 (10)^2 + b_2 (10) + c_2 = 227.04 \tag{3}$$

$$a_2 (15)^2 + b_2 (15) + c_2 = 362.78 \tag{4}$$

$a_3 t^2 + b_3 t + c_3$ passes through $t = 15$ and $t = 20$.

$$a_3 (15)^2 + b_3 (15) + c_3 = 362.78 \tag{5}$$

$$a_3 (20)^2 + b_3 (20) + c_3 = 517.35 \tag{6}$$

$a_4 t^2 + b_4 t + c_4$ passes through $t = 20$ and $t = 22.5$.

$$a_4 (20)^2 + b_4 (20) + c_4 = 517.35 \tag{7}$$

$$a_4 (22.5)^2 + b_4 (22.5) + c_4 = 602.97 \tag{8}$$

$a_5 t^2 + b_5 t + c_5$ passes through $t = 22.5$ and $t = 30$.

$$a_5 (22.5)^2 + b_5 (22.5) + c_5 = 602.97 \tag{9}$$

$$a_5 (30)^2 + b_5 (30) + c_5 = 901.67 \tag{10}$$

2. Quadratic splines have continuous derivatives at the interior data points.

At $t = 10$

$$2a_1 (10) + b_1 - 2a_2 (10) - b_2 = 0 \tag{11}$$

At $t = 15$

$$2a_2 (15) + b_2 - 2a_3 (15) - b_3 = 0 \tag{12}$$

At $t = 20$

$$2a_3 (20) + b_3 - 2a_4 (20) - b_4 = 0 \tag{13}$$

At $t = 22.5$

$$2a_4 (22.5) + b_4 - 2a_5 (22.5) - b_5 = 0 \tag{14}$$

3. Assuming the first spline $a_1 t^2 + b_1 t + c_1$ is linear,

$$a_1 = 0 \tag{15}$$

Combining Equation (1) –(15) in matrix form gives

$$
\begin{bmatrix}
0 & 0 & 1 & 0 & 0 & 0 & 0 & 0 & 0 & 0 & 0 & 0 & 0 & 0 & 0 \\
100 & 10 & 1 & 0 & 0 & 0 & 0 & 0 & 0 & 0 & 0 & 0 & 0 & 0 & 0 \\
0 & 0 & 0 & 100 & 10 & 1 & 0 & 0 & 0 & 0 & 0 & 0 & 0 & 0 & 0 \\
0 & 0 & 0 & 225 & 15 & 1 & 0 & 0 & 0 & 0 & 0 & 0 & 0 & 0 & 0 \\
0 & 0 & 0 & 0 & 0 & 0 & 225 & 15 & 1 & 0 & 0 & 0 & 0 & 0 & 0 \\
0 & 0 & 0 & 0 & 0 & 0 & 400 & 20 & 1 & 0 & 0 & 0 & 0 & 0 & 0 \\
0 & 0 & 0 & 0 & 0 & 0 & 0 & 0 & 0 & 400 & 20 & 1 & 0 & 0 & 0 \\
0 & 0 & 0 & 0 & 0 & 0 & 0 & 0 & 0 & 506.25 & 22.5 & 1 & 0 & 0 & 0 \\
0 & 0 & 0 & 0 & 0 & 0 & 0 & 0 & 0 & 0 & 0 & 0 & 506.25 & 22.5 & 1 \\
0 & 0 & 0 & 0 & 0 & 0 & 0 & 0 & 0 & 0 & 0 & 0 & 900 & 30 & 1 \\
20 & 1 & 0 & -20 & -1 & 0 & 0 & 0 & 0 & 0 & 0 & 0 & 0 & 0 & 0 \\
0 & 0 & 0 & 30 & 1 & 0 & -30 & -1 & 0 & 0 & 0 & 0 & 0 & 0 & 0 \\
0 & 0 & 0 & 0 & 0 & 0 & 40 & 1 & 0 & -40 & -1 & 0 & 0 & 0 & 0 \\
0 & 0 & 0 & 0 & 0 & 0 & 0 & 0 & 0 & 45 & 1 & 0 & -45 & -1 & 0 \\
1 & 0 & 0 & 0 & 0 & 0 & 0 & 0 & 0 & 0 & 0 & 0 & 0 & 0 & 0
\end{bmatrix}
\begin{bmatrix}
a_1 \\ b_1 \\ c_1 \\ a_2 \\ b_2 \\ c_2 \\ a_3 \\ b_3 \\ c_3 \\ a_4 \\ b_4 \\ c_4 \\ a_5 \\ b_5 \\ c_5
\end{bmatrix}
=
\begin{bmatrix}
0 \\ 227.04 \\ 227.04 \\ 362.78 \\ 362.78 \\ 517.35 \\ 517.35 \\ 602.97 \\ 602.97 \\ 901.67 \\ 0 \\ 0 \\ 0 \\ 0 \\ 0
\end{bmatrix}
$$

Solving the above 15 equations give the 15 unknowns as

i	a_i	b_i	c_i
1	0	22.704	0
2	0.8888	4.928	88.88
3	−0.1356	35.66	−141.61
4	1.6048	−33.956	554.55
5	0.20889	28.86	−152.13

Therefore, the splines are given by

$$v(t) = 22.704t, \qquad\qquad\qquad 0 \leq t \leq 10$$
$$= 0.8888t^2 + 4.928t + 88.88, \qquad 10 \leq t \leq 15$$
$$= -0.1356t^2 + 35.66t - 141.61, \qquad 15 \leq t \leq 20$$
$$= 1.6048t^2 - 33.956t + 554.55, \qquad 20 \leq t \leq 22.5$$
$$= 0.20889t^2 + 28.86t - 152.13, \qquad 22.5 \leq t \leq 30$$

At $t = 16\,\text{s}$

$$v(16) = -0.1356(16)^2 + 35.66(16) - 141.61$$
$$= 394.24\,\text{m/s}$$

b) The distance covered by the rocket between 11 and 16 seconds can be calculated as

$$s(16) - s(11) = \int_{11}^{16} v(t)\,dt$$

But since the splines are valid over different ranges, we need to break the integral accordingly as

$$v(t) = 0.8888t^2 + 4.928t + 88.88, \quad 10 \leq t \leq 15$$
$$= -0.1356t^2 + 35.66t - 141.61, \quad 15 \leq t \leq 20$$

$$\int_{11}^{16} v(t)\,dt = \int_{11}^{15} v(t)\,dt + \int_{15}^{16} v(t)\,dt$$

$$s(16) - s(11) = \int_{11}^{15}(0.8888t^2 + 4.928t + 88.88)\,dt + \int_{15}^{16}(-0.1356t^2 + 35.66t - 141.61)\,dt$$

$$= \left[0.8888\frac{t^3}{3} + 4.928\frac{t^2}{2} + 88.88t \right]_{11}^{15}$$

$$+ \left[-0.1356\frac{t^3}{3} + 35.66\frac{t^2}{2} - 141.61t \right]_{15}^{16}$$

$$= 1217.35 + 378.53$$
$$= 1595.9 \text{ m}$$

c) What is the acceleration at $t = 16$?

$$a(16) = \frac{d}{dt}v(t)\Big|_{t=16}$$

$$a(t) = \frac{d}{dt}v(t) = \frac{d}{dt}(-0.1356t^2 + 35.66t - 141.61)$$
$$= -0.2712t + 35.66, \qquad 15 \leq t \leq 20$$
$$a(16) = -0.2712(16) + 35.66$$
$$= 31.321\,\text{m/s}^2$$

INTERPOLATION	
Topic	Spline Method of Interpolation
Summary	Textbook notes on the spline method of interpolation
Major	General Engineering
Authors	Autar Kaw, Michael Keteltas
Date	December 23, 2009
Web Site	http://numericalmethods.eng.usf.edu

Multiple-Choice Test

Chapter 05.05
Spline Method of Interpolation

1.   The following n data points, (x_1, y_1), (x_2, y_2), ... (x_n, y_n), are given. For conducting quadratic spline interpolation the x-data needs to be
     (A) equally spaced
     (B) placed in ascending or descending order of x-values
     (C) integers
     (D) positive

2.   In cubic spline interpolation,
     (A) the first derivatives of the splines are continuous at the interior data points
     (B) the second derivatives of the splines are continuous at the interior data points
     (C) the first and the second derivatives of the splines are continuous at the interior data points
     (D) the third derivatives of the splines are continuous at the interior data points

3.   The following incomplete y vs. x data is given.

x	1	2	4	6	7
y	5	11	????	????	32

The data is fit by quadratic spline interpolants given by
$$f(x) = ax - 1, \ 1 \le x \le 2$$
$$f(x) = -2x^2 + 14x - 9, \ 2 \le x \le 4$$
$$f(x) = bx^2 + cx + d, \ 4 \le x \le 6$$
$$f(x) = 25x^2 - 303x + 928, \ 6 \le x \le 7$$
where a, b, c, and d are constants. The value of c is most nearly
     (A) -303.00
     (B) -144.50
     (C) 0.0000
     (D) 14.000

4. The following incomplete y vs. x data is given.

x	1	2	4	6	7
y	5	11	????	????	32

The data is fit by quadratic spline interpolants given by

$$f(x) = ax - 1, \ 1 \le x \le 2,$$
$$f(x) = -2x^2 + 14x - 9, \ 2 \le x \le 4$$
$$f(x) = bx^2 + cx + d, \ 4 \le x \le 6$$
$$f(x) = ex^2 + fx + g, \ 6 \le x \le 7$$

where $a, b, c, d, e, f,$ and g are constants. The value of $\dfrac{df}{dx}$ at $x = 2.6$ most nearly is

(A) -144.50
(B) -4.0000
(C) 3.6000
(D) 12.200

5. The following incomplete y vs. x data is given.

x	1	2	4	6	7
y	5	11	????	????	32

The data is fit by quadratic spline interpolants given by

$$f(x) = ax - 1, \ 1 \le x \le 2,$$
$$f(x) = -2x^2 + 14x - 9, \ 2 \le x \le 4$$
$$f(x) = bx^2 + cx + d, \ 4 \le x \le 6$$
$$f(x) = 25x^2 - 303x + 928, \ 6 \le x \le 7$$

where $a, b, c,$ and d are constants. What is the value of $\displaystyle\int_{1.5}^{3.5} f(x)dx$?

(A) 23.500
(B) 25.667
(C) 25.750
(D) 28.000

6.   A robot needs to follow a path that passes consecutively through six points as shown in the figure. To find the shortest path that is also smooth you would recommend which of the following?

(A)   Pass a fifth order polynomial through the data
(B)   Pass linear splines through the data
(C)   Pass quadratic splines through the data
(D)   Regress the data to a second order polynomial

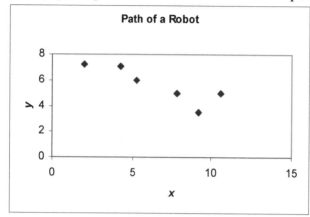

Complete Solution

Problem Set

Chapter 05.05
Spline Method of Interpolation

1. The following y vs. x data is given.

x	2	3	6
y	4.75	5.25	45

    a) Set up the equations to solve for the quadratic spline interpolants that go through the data.
    b) Use a program such as MATLAB to solve the equations and then write down the spline interpolants.
    c) Estimate the value of $y(3.6)$.

2. The following y vs. x data is given.

x	1	2	3	5	6
y	4.75	4	5.25	15	45

    The data is fit by quadratic spline interpolants given by
    $$f(x) = -0.75x + 5.5, \ 1 \le x \le 2,$$
    $$= 2x^2 - 8.75x + 13.5, \ 2 \le x \le 3,$$
    $$= cx^2 + gx + h, \ 3 \le x \le 5,$$
    $$= jx^2 + kx + l, \ 5 \le x \le 6.$$

    where $c, g, h, j, k,$ and l are constants.

    a) Find the value of $c, g, h, j, k,$ and l.
    b) Compare the value of the function at $x = 2.3$ using linear spline interpolation and quadratic spline interpolation.

3. The following incomplete y vs. x data is given.

x	1	2.2	3.7	5.1	6
y	4.25	6	5.25	15.1	?????

    The data is fit by quadratic spline interpolants given by
    $$f(x) = 1.4583x + 2.7917, \ 1 \le x \le 2.2$$
    $$= -1.3056x^2 + 7.2028x - 3.5278, \ 2.2 \le x \le 3.7$$
    $$= cx^2 + gx + h, \ 3.7 \le x \le 5.1$$
    $$= jx^2 + kx + 1, \ 5.1 \le x \le 6$$

    where $c, g, h, j, k,$ and l are constants. What is the value of g? Show all your steps clearly.

4.   The following incomplete y vs. x data is given.

x	1	2.2	3.7	5.1	6
y	4.25	6	5.25	????	?????

The data is fit by quadratic spline interpolants given by
$$f(x) = 1.4583x + 2.7917, \quad 1 \le x \le 2.2$$
$$= -1.3056x^2 + 7.2028x - 3.5272, \quad 2.2 \le x \le 3.7$$
$$= cx^2 + gx + h, \quad 3.7 \le x \le 5.1$$
$$= jx^2 + kx + l, \quad 5.1 \le x \le 6$$

where $c, g, h, j, k,$ and l are constants. What is the value of $\dfrac{df}{dx}$ at $x = 2.67$?

5.   The following incomplete y vs. x data is given.

x	1	2.2	3.7	5.1	6
y	4.25	6	5.25	????	?????

The data is fit by quadratic spline interpolants given by
$$f(x) = 1.4583x + 2.7917, \quad 1 \le x \le 2.2$$
$$= -1.3056x^2 + 7.2028x - 3.5272, \quad 2.2 \le x \le 3.7$$
$$= cx^2 + gx + h, \quad 3.7 \le x \le 5.1$$
$$= jx^2 + kx + l, \quad 5.1 \le x \le 6$$

where $c, g, h, j, k,$ and l are constants. What is the value of $\int_{1.5}^{2.5} f(x)dx$?

6.   Given three data points (1,6), (3,28), and (10, 231), it is found that the function $y = 2x^2 + 3x + 1$ passes through the three data points. To find the length of the polynomial curve from $x = 5$ to $x = 8$, a student uses the formula, $S = \int_a^b \sqrt{1 + (dy/dx)^2}\,dx$. However, this formula gives the student an integral that cannot be solved exactly. Instead, the student approximates the polynomial curve by drawing linear splines from $x = 5$ to $x = 6$, from $x = 6$ to $x = 7$ and from $x = 7$ to $x = 8$. The student then finds the lengths of these three linear splines. What is the student's estimate of the length of the polynomial curve from $x = 5$ to $x = 8$?

Chapter 05.06
Extrapolation is a Bad Idea

After reading this chapter, you should be able to:

1. *understand why using extrapolation can be a bad idea.*

Example
(Due to certain reasons, this student wishes to remain anonymous.)
This takes place in Summer Session B – July 2001

Student: "Hey, Dr. Kaw! Look at this cool new cell phone I just got!"
Kaw: "That's nice. It better not ring in my class or it's mine."
Student: "What would you think about getting stock in this company?"
Kaw: "What company is that?"
Student: "WorldCom! They're the world's leading global data and internet company."
Kaw: "So?"
Student: "They've just closed the deal today to merge with Intermedia Communications, based right here in Tampa!"
Kaw: "Yeah, and ...?"
Student: "The stock's booming! It's at $14.11 per share and promised to go only one way—up! We'll be millionaires if we invest now!"
Kaw: "You might not want to assume their stock will keep rising ... besides, I'm skeptical of their success. I don't want you putting yourself in financial 'jeopardy!' over some silly extrapolation. Take a look at these NASDAQ composite numbers (Table 1)"
Student: "That's only up to two years ago ..."
Kaw: "That's right. Looking at this data, don't you think you should've invested back then?"
Student: "Well, didn't the composite drop after that?"
Kaw: "Right again, but look what you would've hoped for if you had depended on that trend continuing (Figure 1)."
Student: "So you're saying that ...?"
Kaw: "You should seldom depend on extrapolation as a source of approximation! Just take a look at how wrong you would have been (Table 2)."

Table 1. End of year NASDAQ composite data

End of year[1]	NASDAQ
1	751.96
2	1052.13
3	1291.03
4	1570.35
5	2192.69
6	4069.31

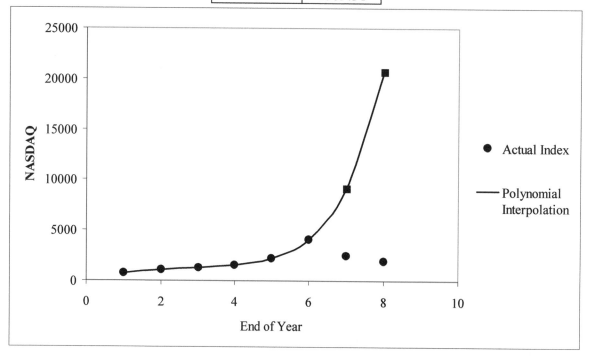

Figure 1 Data from 1994 to 1999 extrapolated to yield results for 2000 and 2001 using polynomial extrapolation.

---

[1] Range of years actually between 1994 (Year 1) and 1999 (Year 9). Numbers start from 1 to avoid round-off errors and near singularity in matrix calculations.

Table 2 Absolute relative true error of polynomial interpolation.

End of Year	Actual	Fifth order polynomial interpolation	Absolute relative true error
2000	2471	9128	269.47 %
2001	1950	20720	962.36 %

Student: "Now wait a sec! I wouldn't have been quite that wrong. What if I had used cubic splines instead of a fifth order interpolant?"
Kaw: "Let's find out."

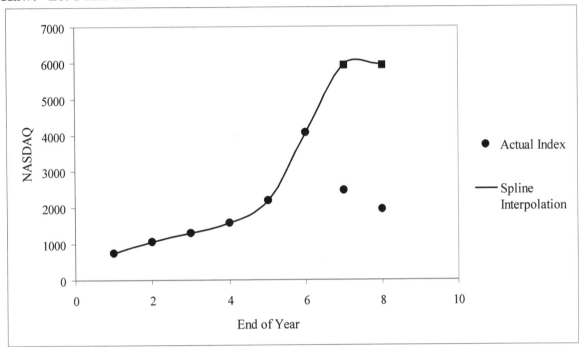

Figure 2 Data from 1994 to 1999 extrapolated to yield results for 2000 and 2001 using cubic spline interpolation.

Table 3 Absolute relative true error of cubic spline interpolation

End of Year	Actual	Cubic spline interpolation	Absolute relative true error
2000	2471	5945.9	140.63 %
2001	1950	5947.4	204.99 %

Student: "There you go. That didn't take so long (Figure 2 and Table 3)."
Kaw: "Well, let's think about what this data means. If you had gone ahead and invested, thinking your projected yield would follow the spline, you would have only been 205% (Table 3) wrong, as opposed to being 962% (Table 2) wrong by following the polynomial. That's not so bad, is it?"
Student: "Okay, you've got a point. Maybe I'll hold off on being an investor and just use the cell phone."

Kaw: "You've got a point, too—you're brighter than you look … that is if you turn off the phone before coming to class."

*   *   *   *   *

<One year later … July 2002>
Student: "Hey, Dr. Kaw! Whatcha got for me today?"
Kaw: "The Computational Methods students just took their interpolation test today, so here you go. <hands stack of tests to student> Time to grade them!"
Student: <Grunt!> "That's a lot of paper! Boy, interpolation … learned that a while ago."
Kaw: "You haven't forgotten my lesson to you about not extrapolating, have you?"
Student: "Of course not! Haven't you seen the news? WorldCom just closed down 93% from 83¢ on June 25 to 6¢ per share! They've had to recalculate their earnings, so your skepticism really must've spread. Did you have an "in" on what was going on?"
Kaw: "Oh, of course not. I'm just an ignorant numerical methods professor."

INTERPOLATION	
Topic	Extrapolation is a bad idea
Summary	Textbook notes on errors that can occur when extrapolating data
Major	All majors of engineering
Authors	Autar Kaw
Last Revised	December 23, 2009
Web Site	http://numericalmethods.eng.usf.edu

Chapter 05.07
Higher Order Interpolation is a Bad Idea

After reading this chapter, you should be able to:

1. *Understand why higher order interpolation is a bad idea*

Example

Peter: "Dr. Kaw, what is this you were talking about in class that higher order interpolation is a bad idea? More points, more accuracy; isn't that the way it works?"

Kaw: "Come on in. In 1901, Runge wanted to show that higher order interpolation is a bad idea. He took this function, $f(x) = 1/(1 + 25x^2)$ in the domain [-1,1]."

Table 1. Six equidistant points of $f(x) = 1/(1 + 25x^2)$

x	y
-1	0.038462
-0.6	0.1
-0.2	0.5
0.2	0.5
0.6	0.1
1	0.038462

Let us choose 6 points equidistantly between –1 and 1 as given in Table 1. You can interpolate these 6 data points by a 5th order polynomial. In Figure 1, I am then plotting the fifth order polynomial and the original function. See the oscillations in the interpolating polynomial. The polynomial does go through the six points, but at many other points it does not even come close to the original function. Just look at $x = 0.85$, the value of the function is 0.052459, but the fifth order polynomial gives you a value of –0.055762. That is a whopping 206.30 % relative error and also note the opposite sign.

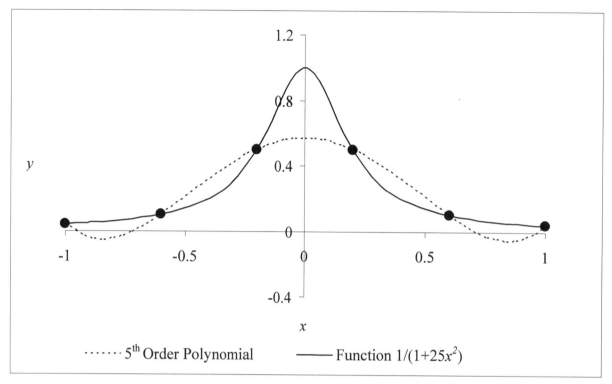

Figure 1 5th order polynomial interpolation with six equidistant points.

Peter: "Maybe you are not taking enough points. Six points may be too small a number to approximate the function."

Kaw: "How many points do you want to choose?"

Peter: "Ok! Let's get crazy. How about 20? That will give us a 19th order polynomial"

Kaw: "I chose 20 points equidistantly in [-1,1]. It is not any better; the oscillations continue and get worse near the end points (Figure 2)."

Peter: "Yes, it is wild. It, however, did do a better job of approximating the data except near the ends, but at the ends it is worse than before. At our chosen point, $x = 0.85$, the value of the function is 0.052459, while we get –0.62944 from the 19th order polynomial, and that is a big whopper error of 1299.9 %. Higher order interpolation is a bad idea. What is the solution to the problem then? What if we choose more points close to the end points?"

Kaw: "You are on to something. But, I need to go to teach my other class. You can get your question answered by seeing other anecdotes on the numerical methods web site. Just choose any interpolation module. You will get the answers to the questions you just asked."

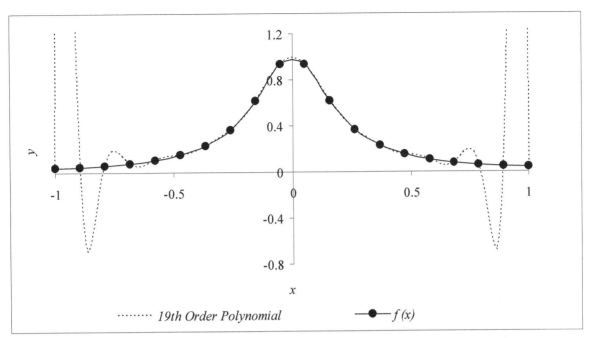

Figure 2 19th order polynomial interpolation with twenty equidistant points

INTERPOLATION	
Topic	Higher order interpolation is a bad idea
Summary	Textbook notes on errors which occur when using higher order interpolation.
Major	All majors of engineering
Authors	Autar Kaw
Last Revised	December 23, 2009
Web Site	http://numericalmethods.eng.usf.edu

Chapter 05.08
Why Do we Need Splines?

After reading this chapter, you should be able to:

1. *understand why we use splines for interpolation.*

Example

Peter: "Dr. Kaw, in class, you were talking about higher order interpolation being a bad idea and then telling us that taking more points is not going to get you a better approximation."

Kaw: "Yes, we were talking in class about the classic example taken by Runge. He took $f(x) = 1/(1 + 25x^2)$ in the domain [-1,1]. Choosing 20 equidistant points (Figure 1) on [-1,1] to approximate the function by a 19th order polynomial gave worse results than when we chose 6 equidistant points to approximate the function by a 5th order polynomial."

Peter: "Yes, it was wild. So what do we do? Accept this fact and roll over?"

Kaw: "Now, we do not have to do that. We can use interpolation such as cubic splines. Cubic splines approximate data between consecutive data points by cubic polynomials but at the same time use all the data to approximate the function. You can see from Figure 2 how cubic splines do a better job of approximating the data. The thin dash line is a 19th order polynomial approximation of the function by choosing 20 equidistant data points in [-1, 1], while the thick dash line is the cubic spline approximation of the data. See how close the cubic splines are to the original function (continuous line)."

05.08.1

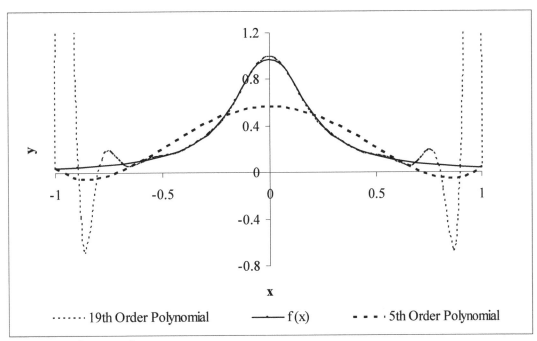

Figure 1 5th and 19th order polynomial approximations of Runge's function.

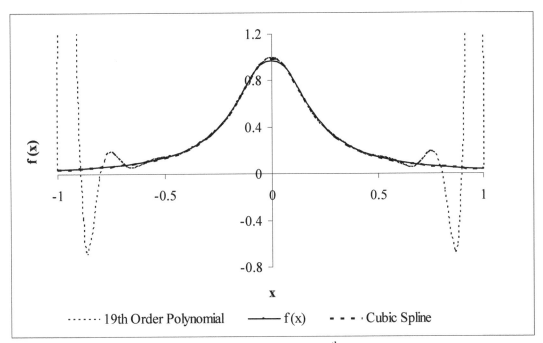

Figure 2 Approximating Runge's function by a 19th order polynomial and a cubic spline.

INTERPOLATION	
Topic	Why do we need splines?
Summary	Textbook notes on understanding why we use splines for interpolation.

Major	All majors of engineering
Authors	Autar Kaw
Last Revised	December 23, 2009
Web Site	http://numericalmethods.eng.usf.edu

Chapter 05.10
Shortest Path of a Robot

After reading this chapter, you should be able to:

1. *find the shortest smooth path through consecutive points, and*
2. *compare the lengths of different paths.*

Example

Peter: "Dr. Kaw, I am taking a course in manufacturing. We are solving the following problem. A robot arm with a rapid laser is used to do a quick quality check, such as the radius of hole, on six holes on a rectangular plate 15"×10" at several points as shown in Table 1 and Figure 1.

Table 1 The coordinate values of six holes on a rectangle plate.

x	y
2.00	7.2
4.5	7.1
5.25	6.0
7.81	5.0
9.20	3.5
10.60	5.0

I am using Excel to fit a fifth order polynomial through the 6 points. But, when I plot the polynomial, it is taking a long path! (Figure 2)"

Kaw: "Why do you not just join the consecutive points by a straight line; just like the kids do at Pizza Hut™ with those 'Connect the dots' activities?"

Peter: "You are making me hungry and I wish it were that easy. The path of the robot going from one point to another point needs to be smooth so as to avoid sharp jerks in the arm that can otherwise create premature wear and tear of the robot arm."

Kaw: "As I recall, you took my course in Numerical Methods. What was that ...... one year ago?"

Peter: "Yes, your memory is sharp, but my retention from that course – can we not talk about that?!?"

05.11.1

Kaw: "Come into my office. I wrote this program using Maple. See this function, $f(x) = 1/(1 + 25x^2)$. I am choosing 7 points equidistantly (Table 2) between −1 and 1.

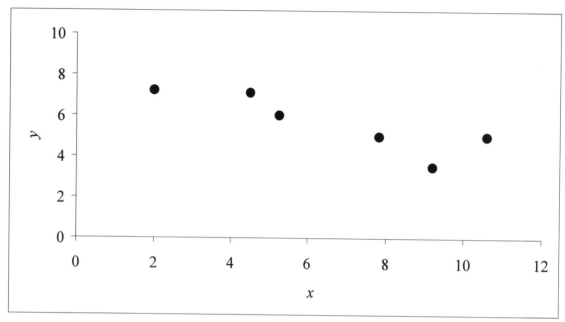

Figure 1 Locations of holes on the rectangular plate.

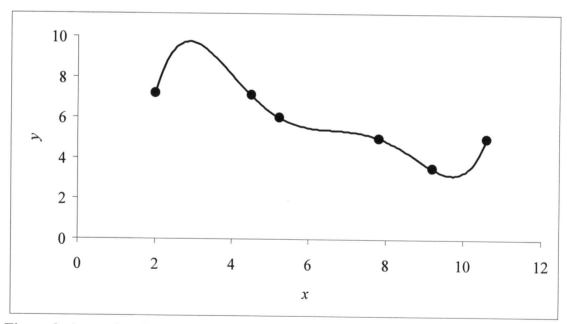

Figure 2 Approximating the path of the robot using 5th order polynomial.

Now look at the sixth order interpolating polynomial and the original function (Figure 3). See the oscillations in the interpolating polynomial. In 1901, Runge used this example function to show that higher order interpolation is a bad idea. One of the solutions to your robot path problem is to use quadratic or cubic spline interpolation. That will give you a smooth curve with fewer oscillations, and a smoother and shorter path."

Table 2 The coordinate values of 7 equidistantly spaced points.

x	$y = \dfrac{1}{1+25x^2}$
-1	0.038462
-0.66667	0.0826
-0.33333	0.264706
0	1
0.333333	0.264706
0.666667	0.082569
1	0.0385

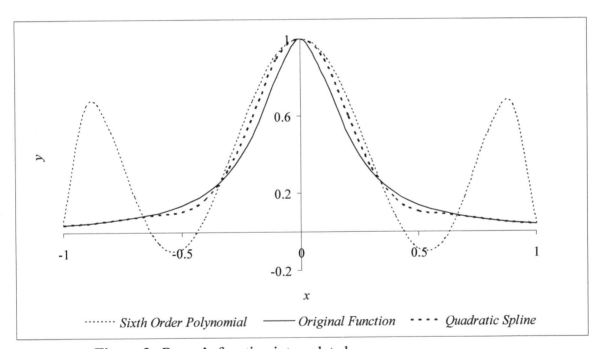

Figure 3 Runge's function interpolated.

Peter: "Okay. Let's give that a try."
Kaw: "Now, let's try generating a set of cubic splines to go through the data:"

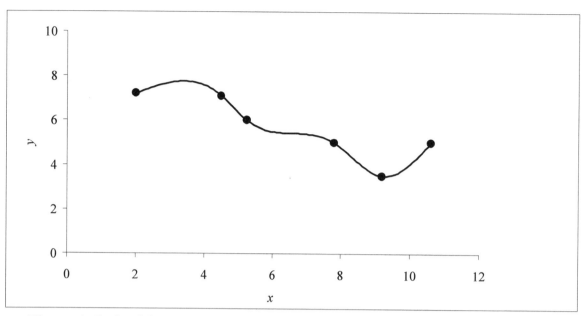

Figure 4 Path of the robot arm using cubic spline interpolation.

Peter: "Wow! That (Figure 4) looks much better!"
Kaw: "It may look better, but let's find out for sure. See if you can combine the two plots (Figure 5) and compare the lengths of each path."
Peter: "The length of a path S if $y = f(x)$ from a to b is given by

$$S = \int_a^b \sqrt{1 + \left(\frac{df}{dx}\right)^2}\, dx$$

Right?"

Table 3 Comparison of the length of curves.

Type of interpolation	5th order polynomial	Cubic Spline
Length of Curve	14.919"	11.248"

Kaw: "Yes! You solved the problem. See Table 3 for answers."
Peter: "I guess your class was good for something after all, Dr. Kaw."
Kaw: "Are you sure? You could have always fallen back on the connecting-the-dots method. Besides, you don't want to grow up … you're a Pizza Hut™ kid, right?"
Peter: "That's a Toys Я' Us™ kid. You'll do anything to be reminded of songs, won't you?"

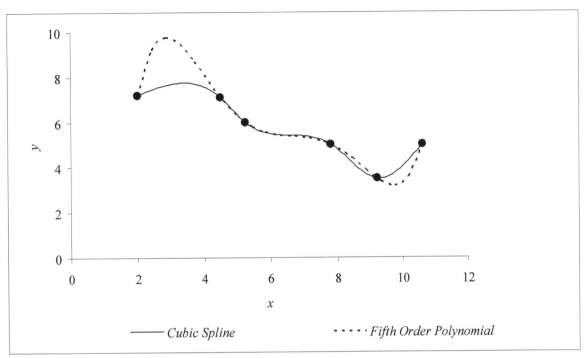

Figure 5 Path of robot arm compared using polynomial interpolation and cubic spline interpolation.

INTERPOLATION	
Topic	Shortest path of a robot
Summary	An example of interpolation: A robot arm path needs to be developed over several points on a flat plate. The path needs to be smooth to avoid sudden jerky motion and at the same time needs to be short.
Major	General Engineering
Authors	Autar Kaw, Michael Keteltas
Date	December 23, 2009
Web Site	http://numericalmethods.eng.usf.edu

Chapter 6.00A

Physical Problem for Regression
General Engineering

Problem Statement

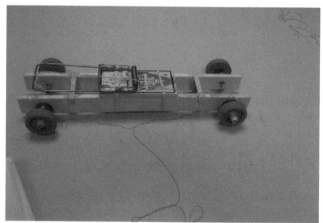

Figure 1 Mousetrap car.

In Summer of 2003, a high school student worked with me to study the physics of a mousetrap car so that he can build the car that would go the fastest and/or the farthest.

So what is a mousetrap car?

A mousetrap car (Figure 1) is a vehicle that is powered by the energy stored in the spring of a mousetrap. One of the basic ways in which most mousetrap vehicles are set into motion is by connecting the lever of the mousetrap bar through a string to the axle of the car. As the mousetrap lever is released, the tension that was built up in the spring is released, and the car sets into motion.

So to get the car to go the farthest and fastest, we need to store as much potential energy in the mousetrap spring. Since there is no specification on the mousetrap other than using a certain brand, we could use a mousetrap that had the largest spring constant as that would translate to the largest potential energy stored.

Therefore, we bought several mousetrap springs and conducted a simple experiment to determine the spring constant of the mousetrap spring. This would then allow us to find the potential energy stored in the mousetrap.

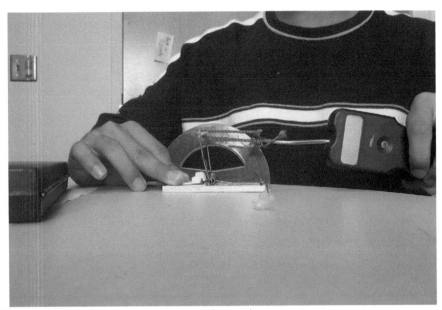

Figure 2 Experimental setup to measure the spring constant.

To find the spring constant of the mousetrap spring, we conducted the following experiment. We pulled the end of the mousetrap lever by a force probe (a fish hook) and measured the angle through which it is pulled by a protractor (Figure 2). We pulled on the end of the spring via a string so that the force on the lever is applied at right angle to the lever. This way the torque applied is simply the product of the force, as measured by the fishhook (Figure 3), and the length of the lever arm.

Figure 3 Force probe designed to measure the amount of force an object contains.

We measured the force needed to pull the lever for several different angles. The data for one of the mousetraps is given in Table 1.

The relationship between the torque applied and the angle of the rotation of the spring rotation is assumed to be a straight line

$$T = k_0 + k_1 \theta$$

where

T = Torque (N-m)

θ = Angle through which the spring is rotated

Table 1 Force vs. angle of lever rotation (Mousetrap#1).

Angle (degrees)	Force (lbs)
40	0.9
55	1.0
65	1.1
90	1.2
110	1.5

The data in Table 1 is converted to SI system of units, and the torque is calculated using the measured lever moment arm of 47 mm, that is

$T = FL$

where,

T = Torque (N-m)

F = Force applied (N)

L = Moment arm (m)

Angle Radians	Torque N-m
0.698132	0.188224
0.959931	0.209138
1.134464	0.230052
1.570796	0.250965
1.919862	0.313707

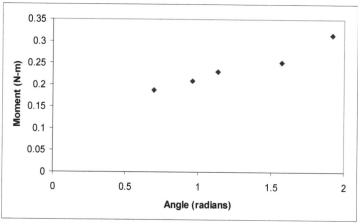

Figure 4 Data and plot of torque vs angle of rotation.

Other mousetrap springs were tested accordingly and the data is given in Tables 2 and 3.

From these tables, we can find the $T = k_0 + k_1 \theta$ relationship for each of three mousetraps. The potential energy, U stored in the spring would be given by

$$U = \int_{\theta_{low}}^{\theta_{high}} T d\theta$$

$$= \int_{\theta_{low}}^{\theta_{high}} (k_0 + k_1 \theta) d\theta$$

Knowing that in our case, $\theta_{low} = 0$ and $\theta_{high} = \pi$, the maximum potential energy stored

$$U_{max} = \int_0^\pi (k_0 + k_1 \theta) d\theta$$

$$= k_0 \pi + k_1 \frac{\pi^2}{2}$$

Table 2 Force vs. angle of lever rotation (Mousetrap#2).

Angle (degrees)	Force (lbs)
38	0.9
58	1.0
65	1.1
90	1.2
120	1.6

Table 3 Force vs. angle of lever rotation (Mousetrap#3).

Angle (degrees)	Force (lbs)
40	0.9
57	1.0
65	1.1
90	1.2
135	1.7

Questions

1. Find the constants of the regression model for the spring for the three cases (Tables 1, 2 and 3).
2. Which of the three springs would you chose based on maximum potential energy stored?

REGRESSION	
Topic	Physical problem for regression
Summary	Conducting regression for the mousetrap spring to find the best mousetrap for use in a mousetrap-car.
Major	General Engineering
Authors	Autar Kaw
Date	December 23, 2009
Web Site	http://numericalmethods.eng.usf.edu

Chapter 06.00B

Physical Problem for Regression
Chemical Engineering

Problem Statement

Chemical bonds have specific frequencies at which they will vibrate. These frequencies depend on the length of the bonds and the mass of the atoms at either end of bonds. Hence, vibrations of a molecule can be studied by shining infrared light onto the surface of the molecule. If one end of the molecular bond has a different charge from the other end (dipole moment), then the molecule can absorb infrared spectrum. However, this absorption occurs only at a certain fixed frequencies characteristic of the molecule and its component parts. Thus, an infrared light reflected from the surface of the bond will show absorption peaks characteristic of the molecule. This forms the basis of Infrared Spectroscopy (IRS).

To measure a sample, infrared light at a specific frequency is beamed onto the sample and the amount of energy absorbed is recorded. A chart is built up when this is repeated for several other frequencies. By examining the chart, one experienced in the art can identify the substance.

Fourier Transform Infrared Spectroscopy is a measurement technique for collecting infrared spectra and analyzing it. The wavenumber is the inverse of frequency while absorbance is proportional to the energy of the infrared light absorbed.

Table 1gives the FT-IR (Fourier Transform Infra Red) data of a 1:1 (by weight) mixture of ethylene carbonate (EC) and dimethyl carbonate (DMC). One would like to develop an equation which relates the absorbance as a function of wave number.

06.00B.1

Table 1 Absorbance as a function of wavenumber

Wavenumber	Absorbance
(cm^{-1})	(arbitrary unit)
804.184	0.1591
808.041	0.1447
815.755	0.1045
821.540	0.0731
827.326	0.0439
829.254	0.0357
831.183	0.0285
833.111	0.0226
835.040	0.0178
836.968	0.0140
838.897	0.0109
840.825	0.0087
846.611	0.0050
852.396	0.0039
860.110	0.0045
869.753	0.0073
877.467	0.0142
881.324	0.0206
883.252	0.0250
885.181	0.0304
889.038	0.0448
892.895	0.0649
896.752	0.0910
900.609	0.1204

QUESTIONS

1. Find a best-fit equation (polynomial) to the data trend.
2. A student had used only the first 8 data points in his best-fit equation in (a), What conclusion would he/she reach about the data? Would the conclusion reached from the use of the first 8 data points be valid for the whole data set?

REGRESSION	
Topic	Regression
Summary	Infrared Spectroscopy
Major	Chemical Engineering
Authors	Egwu Eric Kalu
Date	December 23, 2009
Web Site	http://numericalmethods.eng.usf.edu

Chapter 06.00C

Physical Problem for Regression
Civil Engineering

Problem Statement

A composite is a structural material that consists of combining two or more constituents. The constituents are combined at a macroscopic level and are not soluble in each other. One constituent is called the *reinforcing phase* and the one in which it is embedded is called the *matrix*. The reinforcing phase material may be in the form of fibers, particles, or flakes. The matrix phase materials are generally continuous. Examples of composite systems include concrete reinforced with steel and epoxy reinforced with graphite fibers, etc.

A special case of composite materials are advanced composites, and are defined as composite materials which are traditionally used in the aerospace industries. These composites have high performance reinforcements of a thin diameter in a matrix material such as epoxy and aluminum. Examples are Graphite/Epoxy, Kevlar[1]/Epoxy, and Boron/Aluminum composites. These materials have now found applications in commercial industries as well.

Monolithic metals and their alloys cannot always meet the demands of today's advanced technologies. Only by combining several materials can one meet the performance requirements. For example, trusses and benches used in satellites need to be dimensionally stable in space during temperature changes between $-256°F$ $(-160°C)$ and $200°F$ $(93.3°C)$. Limitations on coefficient of thermal expansion[2] hence are low and may be of the order of 1×10^{-7} in/in/°F $(1.8 \times 10^{-7}$ m/m/°C$)$. Monolithic materials cannot meet these requirements, which leave composites, such as Graphite/Epoxy, as the only materials to satisfy this requirement.

In many cases, using composites is more efficient. For example, in the highly competitive

---

[1] Kevlar is a registered trademark of E.I. duPont deNemours and Company, Inc., Wilmington, Delaware.

[2] Coefficient of thermal expansion is the change in length per unit length of a material when heated through a unit temperature. The units are in/in/°F and m/m/°C. A typical value for steel is 6.5×10^{-6} in/in/°F $(11.7 \times 10^{-6}$ m/m/°C$)$.

airline market, one is continuously looking for ways to lower the overall mass of the aircraft without decreasing the stiffness and strength of its components. This is possible by replacing conventional metal alloys with composite materials. Even if the composite material costs may be higher, the reduction in the number of parts in an assembly and the savings in fuel costs make them more profitable. Reducing one pound (0.453 kg) of mass in a commercial aircraft can save up to 360 gallons (1360 liters) of fuel per year; and fuel expenses are 25% of the total operating costs of a commercial airline.

The general test method to find the Young's modulus of a composite material is the ASTM Test Method for Tensile Properties of Fiber-Resin Composites (D3039).

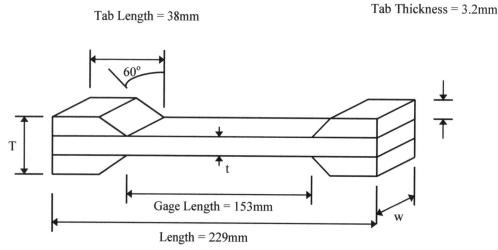

Figure 1 Schematic of Test Specimen used to find the Young's modulus of a composite.

A tensile test geometry (Figure 1) to find the longitudinal tensile strength consists of 6-8 plies of 0^0 plies which are 12.5 mm (2 inches) wide and 229 mm (10 inches) long. The specimen is mounted with strain gages in the longitudinal and transverse direction. Tensile stresses are applied on the specimen at a rate of about 0.5 - 1 mm/min (0.02 to 0.04 in/min). A total of 40-50 data points for stress and strain are taken until a specimen fails. The stress in the longitudinal direction is plotted as a function of longitudinal strain as shown in Figure 2. The data is reduced using linear regression. The longitudinal Young's modulus is the initial slope of the longitudinal stress, σ_1 vs strain, longitudinal strain, ε_1 curve.

Strain	Stress
(%)	(MPa)
0	0
0.183	306
0.36	612
0.5324	917
0.702	1223
0.867	1529
1.0244	1835
1.1774	2140
1.329	2446
1.479	2752
1.5	2767
1.56	2896

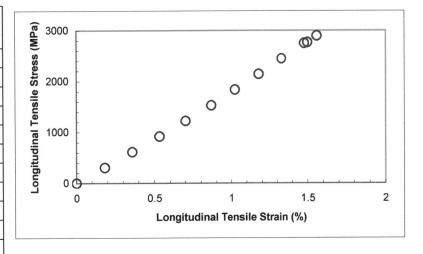

Figure 2 Longitudinal stress as a function of longitudinal strain for a graphite/epoxy composite.

The first order polynomial that one may fit to the data is

$$\sigma = E_1 \varepsilon \tag{1}$$

Questions

1. Find the Young's modulus, E_1?
2. What is the longitudinal ultimate tensile strength?
3. What is the longitudinal ultimate strain?
4. What value of E_1 do you get if you use the general linear regression model?

REGRESSION	
Topic	Physical problem for regression
Summary	Find the Young's modulus of a unidirectional graphite/epoxy composite material.
Major	Civil Engineering
Authors	Autar Kaw
Date	December 23, 2009
Web Site	http://numericalmethods.eng.usf.edu

Chapter 06.00D

Physical Problem for Regression
Computer Engineering

Problem Statement

Automated cartography deals with building or updating maps automatically from aerial or satellite images. Gone are the days when map updating was a laborious process that took a long period to accomplish. There are now many computer vision methods that one can employ to assist and ease the job of the cartographer. For instance, consider the aerial image shown, which is of a park with a lake. One of the tasks is to extract the road network that is visible. The road network appears as bright linear strips. On the right of that figure is shown the road network

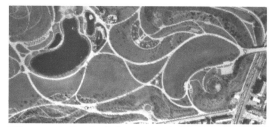

Figure 1 On left is an aerial image of park in Munich, Germany. We see the roads and a lake. On the right is the road network extracted from the image.

that is automatically extracted from the image. In this module, we will see how to achieve this by fitting models to the local intensities in the image.

Image is a collection of gray level values at set of predetermined sites known as pixels, arranged in an array. These gray level values are also known as image intensities. In the above figure we see the profile of the intensity value along a line (shown in red) cutting a road in an image. We represent small values to represent dark points in the image and large values to detect bright regions in the image. The value increases and then decreases. This intensity profile can be modeled as an inverted parabola. The road can be detected by identifying pixels in the image that exhibit this intensity profile around it. To detect all the road pixels, we would have to repeat this process for intensity profile along the vertical as well along the horizontal directions at each pixel.

Let the intensities profile at a pixel be denoted by the values: $y_{-K}, \ldots, y_0, \ldots, y_K$, the index 0 is used to denote the pixel location under consideration and we look at K pixels on either sides of it. We will use $x = -K, \ldots, 0, \ldots K$ to denote these pixel locations that are the independent variables.

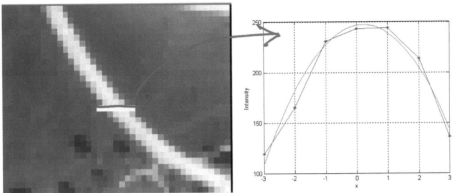

Figure 2 On left is a magnified portion of an image with a piece of the road. Note we can observe the individual pixels. On the right, we plot the intensities of the pixels marked by a red line. The raw intensities are plotted in blue, with fitted function in red.

Consider a polynomial model of the intensities.

$$y(x) = ax^2 + bx + c$$

We fit this second order polynomial model to the observed intensities to minimize the fit error denoted by

$$e = \sum_{k=-K}^{k=K} (y_k - y(k))^2 = \sum_{k=-K}^{k=K} (y_k - ak^2 - bk - c)^2$$

The unknown parameters, a, b, and c can be estimated to be the values that minimize the above error. The necessary condition is that the derivative of the error with respect to these parameters be zero.

$$\frac{\partial e}{\partial a} = -\sum 2k^2 (y_k - ak^2 - bk - c) = 0$$

$$\frac{\partial e}{\partial b} = -\sum 2k (y_k - ak^2 - bk - c) = 0$$

$$\frac{\partial e}{\partial c} = -\sum 2(y_k - ak^2 - bk - c) = 0$$

The three equations can be expressed in matrix form as

$$\begin{bmatrix} \sum_k k^4 & \sum_k k^3 & \sum_k k^2 \\ \sum_k k^3 & \sum_k k^2 & \sum_k k^1 \\ \sum_k k^2 & \sum_k k^1 & \sum_k 1 \end{bmatrix} \begin{bmatrix} a \\ b \\ c \end{bmatrix} = \begin{bmatrix} \sum_k k^2 y_k \\ \sum_k k\, y_k \\ \sum_k y_k \end{bmatrix}$$

We thus have three linear equations with three unknown, which can be solved using a variety of methods. The conditions corresponding to the road intensity profile, which is an inverted parabola, can be found by using the observation that the maximum of the fitted polynomial should happen at or near $k = 0$. The condition for a maximum value is given by $a < 0$ and the location of the maximum is given by $-b/2a$, which should be between -0.5 and 0.5 pixels. Note that 0.5 denotes the halfway location between the pixel at location 0 and the next pixel, which is at 1. The value of the maximum is given by c, which should be high because we are looking of bright road edges.

Worked Out Example

Consider the following intensity profile: $\{y_k\} = 119, 165, 231, 243, 244, 214, 136,$ corresponding to $k = -3, -2, -1, 0, 1, 2, 3$. This intensity profile corresponds to the one shown in Figure 2. The corresponding simultaneous equation for best least square fit is given by

$$\begin{bmatrix} 196 & 0 & 28 \\ 0 & 28 & 0 \\ 28 & 0 & 0 \end{bmatrix} \begin{bmatrix} a \\ b \\ c \end{bmatrix} = \begin{bmatrix} 4286 \\ 162 \\ 1352 \end{bmatrix}$$

The solution is given by $a = -13.3571$, $b = 5.7857$, and $c = 246.5714$. Since a is negative, we have a maximum value, which is located at $-b/2a = -0.2166$. This location is near 0 and the value at zero is 246.57, which denotes a bright value. All of these quantities suggest that we have a road at the pixel we are considering.

QUESTIONS

Instead of processing the an image, which is laid out in a 2D plane, along just the horizontal and vertical directions, it is more natural to consider fitting a 2D surface model, whose general form is given by

$$y(x, y) = ax^2 + by^2 + cxy + dx + ey + f$$

1. Work out the regression equation for fitting this surface model to intensities in a K by K neighborhood around a pixel.
2. How would you determine, based on the values of the estimated parameters, whether the pixel is on a road edge or not, that is, the fitted surface has a *roof-like* shape?

REGRESSION	
Topic	Physical problem for regression
Summary	Extraction of road networks in images by function fitting
Major	Computer Science
Authors	Sudeep Sarkar
Date	December 23, 2009
Web Site	http://numericalmethods.eng.usf.edu

Chapter 06.00E

Physical Problem for Regression
Electrical Engineering

Problem Statement

All electrical devices exhibit non-linear behavior to some extent. This is caused by many factors including material and thermal properties. For most of the basic components, a simple linear model is used that is sufficient for most operating conditions. This is the case for resistors, capacitors, and inductors. Semiconductor devices, however, are specifically chosen for their non-linear behaviors. This allows them to perform gating, switching, and amplifying operations. Consider the case of a simple diode, like the 1N4001, whose forward-bias VI-characteristic is shown in Figure 1.

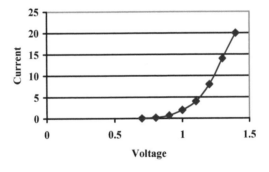

Figure 1 VI Forward-Bias Characteristic of a 1N4001 Diode [1]

In many applications it is suitable to model the forward-bias behavior of the diode as a simple voltage drop of about 0.7 V [2, pp. 70,1]. Other types of diodes, such as LEDs, have voltage drops on the order of 2.0 to 2.5 V. This modeling is not very realistic because it fails to account for the increasing voltage drop as current flow through the diode increases as is shown in Figure 1. If our analysis requires us to know how much current a diode can supply, then the ideal model is clearly inadequate.

It would be, of course, possible to model the diode using some form of interpolated curve, but that would almost certainly force any kind of analysis to be able to only use numerical tools. A much better solution would be to develop a model using simpler linear components that could be used in place of the diode. This is typically done using a DC supply and a series resistor as shown in Figure 2 [2, pp. 72-5].

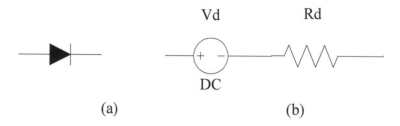

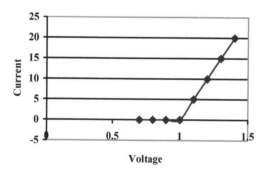

Figure 2. (a) Ideal Diode and (b) Forward Bias Model

The question then becomes, what are the appropriate values for V_d and R_d? The answer will vary from diode to diode, but good values can be determined using the numerical method of linear regression. The model of Figure 2b in effect replaces the characteristic of Figure 1 with that of Figure 3. Remember that for this to work we are still assuming the diode is sufficiently forward-biased to turn it on which means that the voltage across the diode must exceed V_d.

Figure 3. VI Characteristic of Forward Bias Model

Choosing suitable values for V_d and R_d will depend on the potential use for the diode. In a small signal application (low current) it would be more appropriate to choose current values from the original characteristic curve that are well-below 5 A. and for large-signal applications it would be a better fit to use current values of 5 A and above. To study this problem, let us take a closer look at the actual data used to generate the characteristic in Figure 1. This is shown in Table 1.

The simplest way to determine the V_d and R_d from the selected data is to generate a trend line for the region in question. This can be done using linear regression since a linear regression trend line has the effect of minimizing the mean-square error between the modeled line and the actual data. Using the standard linear regression model using β_0 and β_1 parameters yields the following equation for the trend line.

$$I \cong \beta_1 V + \beta_0$$

Once β_0 and β_1 are known V_d and R_d can be computed as follows:

$$V_d = -\frac{\beta_0}{\beta_1}$$

$$R_d = \frac{1}{\beta_1}$$

Voltage, V	Current, A	Small Signal	Large Signal
0.0	0.00	N	N
0.6	0.01	Y	N
0.7	0.05	Y	N
0.8	0.20	Y	N
0.9	0.70	Y	Y
1.0	2.00	Y	Y
1.1	4.00	Y	Y
1.2	8.00	N	Y
1.3	14.00	N	Y
1.4	20.00	N	Y

Table 1. VI Characteristic of a Forward-Biased Diode

The effects of this choice are shown in Figure 4. When the data from the small-signal column of Table 1 is used to generate the regression line, it results in the model of Figure 4a and when the data from the large-signal column of Table 2 is used, the result is the model of Figure 4b.

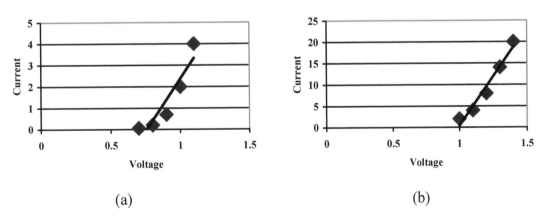

(a)   (b)

Figure 4 (a) Small-Signal Model and (b) Large-Signal Model for a Diode

The small-signal model agrees with the typical diode modeling where V_d is approximately 0.7V and will model the diode fairly well for currents below about 4 A. For a higher-current circuit the large-signal model with V_d approximately 1 V is a better choice, but will not model the data as well when the current is 2 A or below.

Complete the analysis by determining more exact values for V_d and R_d for both of these models. Use the small signal and large signal columns of Table 1 to select the data to use in your analysis.

QUESTIONS

1. This analysis can be extended to handle other diodes. Find the data sheet for a 1N4150 or an LED, which shows the VI-Characteristic and derive suitable small- and large-signal forward-bias models.
2. A similar analysis can be used to model the reverse-bias behavior of a diode. Use the datasheet from (1) to develop an appropriate model.
3. Model the reverse-bias characteristics for a zener diode (e.g. the 1N4678 to 1N4717 family).
4. The use of linear regression only reduces the modeling/approximating error for the sample data points provided. In this problem, we actually have a two-piece linear model (the flat portion up to V_d when the diode turns on and the forward-bias model involving R_d after the diode is on). This may not adequately model the entire forward-bias characteristic. Using your model values for V_d and R_d as a start, examine the overall characteristic and pick values for V_d and R_d that minimize the mean-square error over the entire forward bias region. This will have to be a combination of the error caused by having V_d to the right of the actual turn-on point as well as the error in the turned-on region. How close is this model to our simpler approach that modeled each piece separately?

References

[1]   1N4001 Data Sheet, Fairchild Semiconductor, http://www.fairchildsemi.com/ds/1N/1N4007.pdf, accessed May 12, 2005.
[2]   Malvino, A., Electronic Principles, Sixth Edition, Glencoe McGraw-Hill, 1999.

REGRESSION	
Topic	Physical Problem for Regression
Summary	Many electrical devices have non-linear behavior. It is often advantageous to substitute a model for the device using simpler linear components. In the case of a diode, this is often done with a DC supply and a series resistor. To determine an appropriate value for the resistor, regression is used.
Major	Electrical Engineering
Authors	Henry Welch
Date	December 23, 2009
Web Site	http://numericalmethods.eng.usf.edu

Chapter 06.00F

Physical Problem for Regression
Industrial Engineering

Problem Statement

An industrial engineer working for a manufacturing company has noticed a deviation in the accuracy of a machine after it runs for long periods without a cool down cycle. This is especially concerning because the company wants to increase production (longer machine operating times without a cool down) because of a large contract the company will start in 3-4 months. The industrial engineer decides to monitor the machining process to determine the point (hours of operation) when the machine is producing parts that could be out of tolerance. Over the course of several months, the industrial engineer monitored the machining process to determine a relationship between hours of machine use and millimeters off target the machine was. The data collected is shown in tabular form (Table 1) and scatter plot (Figure 1).

Table 1. Off target measured as a fubtion of machine use.

Hours of machine use	30	31	32	33	34	35	36	37	38	39	40	41	42	43	44	45
Millimeters off target	1.10	1.21	1.00	1.21	1.25	1.23	1.24	1.28	1.30	1.30	1.38	1.35	1.38	1.38	1.40	1.42

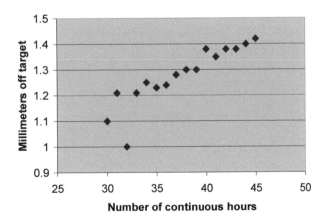

Figure 1. Off target measurement as a function of machine use.

Based on the above data, the industrial engineer would like to determine the number of hours of machine use that would produce a 2 millimeters off target because many parts would fail quality check at that point. Determine the number of hours of operation that produces 2 millimeter off target based on a least squares fit for the data.

Background

In order to determine a relationship between millimeters off target and hours of machine use, a curve (for example, a linear polynomial) needs to be fit to the data. This is done by regression where we best fit a curve through the data given in the previous table. In this case, we may best fit the data to a first order polynomial, that is

$$h = a_0 + a_1 t$$

Where h is the hours of machine use and t is the millimeters off target. The values of the coefficients in the above equations will be found by linear regression. Knowing the values of a_0 and a_1, we can determine the millimeters off target as a function of hours of machine use. For example, if we want to find the time when the machine will be 2 mm off target, then

$$2 = a_0 + a_1 t$$

giving

$$t = \frac{2 - a_0}{a_1}$$

Questions

1. Fit the data in the previous table using a linear regression, and determine the hours of machine use that will make the machine 2 mm off target.
2. Fit the data in the previous table using a second order polynomial regression, and determine the hours of machine use that will make the machine 2 millimeters off target.
3. Find whether a linear or second order polynomial regression is a better fit to the data.

REGRESSION	
Topic	A physical problem for regression.
Summary	Find the number of toys a company should manufacture per day to maximize their injection molding and assembly line.
Major	Industrial Engineering
Authors	Glen Besterfield
Date	December 23, 2009
Web Site	http://numericalmethods.eng.usf.edu

Chapter 06.00G

Physical Problem for Regression Mechanical Engineering

Problem Statement

To make the fulcrum (Figure 1) of a bascule bridge, a long hollow steel shaft called the trunnion is shrink fit into a steel hub. The resulting steel trunnion-hub assembly is then shrink fit into the girder of the bridge.

Figure 1 Trunnion-Hub-Girder (THG) assembly.

This is done by first immersing the trunnion in a cold medium such as dry-ice/alcohol mixture. After the trunnion reaches the steady state temperature of the cold medium, the trunnion outer diameter contracts. The trunnion is taken out of the medium and slid though the hole of the hub (Figure 2).

When the trunnion heats up, it expands and creates an interference fit with the hub. In 1995, on one of the bridges in Florida, this assembly procedure did not work as designed. Before the trunnion could be inserted fully into the hub, the trunnion got stuck. Luckily, the trunnion was taken out before it got stuck permanently. Otherwise, a new trunnion and hub would needed to be ordered at a cost of $50,000. Coupled with construction delays, the total loss could have been more than hundred thousand dollars.

Why did the trunnion get stuck? This was because the trunnion had not contracted enough to slide through the hole. Can you find out why?

A hollow trunnion of outside diameter 12.363″ is to be fitted in a hub of inner diameter 12.358″. The trunnion was put in dry ice/alcohol mixture (temperature of the fluid - dry ice/alcohol mixture is $-108°F$) to contract the trunnion so that it can be slid through the hole of the hub. To slide the trunnion without sticking, a diametrical clearance of at least $0.01''$ is required between the trunnion and the hub. Assuming the room temperature is $80°F$, is immersing it in dry-ice/alcohol mixture a correct decision?

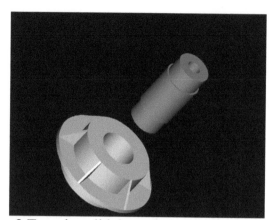

Figure 2 Trunnion slid through the hub after contracting.

Solution

To calculate the contraction in the diameter of the trunnion, thermal expansion coefficient at room temperature is used. In that case the reduction, ΔD in the outer diameter of the trunnion is

$$\Delta D = D\alpha\Delta T \tag{1}$$

where

   $D =$ outer diameter of the trunnion,
   $\alpha =$ coefficient of thermal expansion coefficient at room temperature, and
   $\Delta T =$ change in temperature.

Given

   $D = 12.363''$
   $\alpha = 6.817 \times 10^{-6}$ in/in/°F at 80°F
   $\Delta T = T_{fluid} - T_{room}$
   $\qquad = -108 - 80$
   $\qquad = -188°F$

where

   $T_{fluid} =$ temperature of dry-ice/alcohol mixture,

   $T_{room} =$ room temperature,

the reduction in the trunnion outer diameter is given by

   $\Delta D = (12.363)\left(6.47 \times 10^{-6}\right)\left(-188\right)$
   $\qquad = -0.01504''$

So the trunnion is predicted to reduce in diameter by $0.01504''$. But, is this enough reduction in diameter? As per specifications, he needs the trunnion to contract by

   $=$ trunnion outside diameter - hub inner diameter + diametric clearance
   $= 12.363'' - 12.358'' + 0.01''$
   $= 0.015''$

So according to his calculations, immersing the steel trunnion in dry-ice/alcohol mixture gives the desired contraction of $0.015''$ as we predict a contraction of $0.01504''$.

But as shown in Figure 3 and Table 1, the thermal expansion coefficient of steel decreases with temperature and is not constant over the range of temperature the trunnion goes through. Hence, the above formula (Equation 1) would overestimate the thermal contraction.

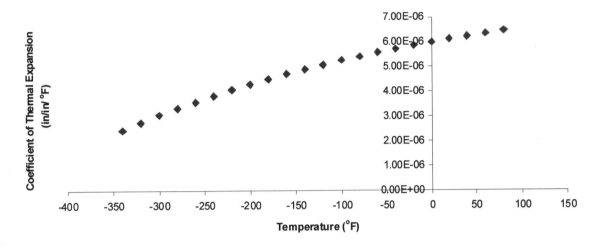

Figure 3 Varying thermal expansion coefficient as a function of temperature for cast steel.

The contraction in the diameter for the trunnion for which the thermal expansion coefficient varies as a function of temperature is given by

$$\Delta D = D \int_{T_{room}}^{T_{fluid}} \alpha \, dT \qquad (2)$$

So one needs to find the curve to find the coefficient of thermal expansion as a function of temperature. This is done by regression where we best fit a curve through the data given in Table 1. In this case, we may fit a second order polynomial

$$\alpha = a_0 + a_1 \times T + a_2 \times T^2. \qquad (3)$$

The values of the coefficients in the above equations will be found by polynomial regression. Knowing the values of a_0, a_1, and a_2, we can then find the contraction in the trunnion diameter as

$$\Delta D = D \int_{T_{room}}^{T_{fluid}} (a_0 + a_1 \times T + a_2 \times T^2) dT$$

$$= D[a_0 \times (T_{fluid} - T_{room}) + a_1 \times \frac{(T_{fluid}^2 - T_{room}^2)}{2} + a_2 \times \frac{(T_{fluid}^3 - T_{room}^3)}{3}]$$

Questions

1. Find the contraction in the outer diameter of the trunnion.
2. As required, is the magnitude of contraction more than $0.015''$?

3. If the magnitude of contraction is less than 0.015″, what if the trunnion were immersed in liquid nitrogen (boiling temperature = −321°F) ? Will that give enough contraction in the trunnion?
4. Rather than regressing the data to a second order polynomial so that one can find the contraction in the outer diameter of the trunnion, how would you use Trapezoidal rule of integration for unequal segments to find the contraction? What is the relative difference between the two results? The data for the thermal expansion coefficient as function of temperature is given in Table 1.
5. We chose a second order polynomial for regression. What would make a different order polynomial a better choice for regression? Is there an optimum order of polynomial you can find?

Table 1 Instantaneous thermal expansion coefficient as a function of temperature.

Temperature	Instantaneous Thermal Expansion
°F	μ in / in/°F
80	6.47
60	6.36
40	6.24
20	6.12
0	6.00
-20	5.86
-40	5.72
-60	5.58
-80	5.43
-100	5.28
-120	5.09
-140	4.91
-160	4.72
-180	4.52
-200	4.30
-220	4.08
-240	3.83
-260	3.58
-280	3.33
-300	3.07
-320	2.76
-340	2.45

REGRESSION	
Topic	A physical problem for regression.
Summary	Finding the regression model for thermal expansion coefficient as a function of temperature to calculate the contraction in the diameter of a trunnion for purposes of shrink fitting.
Major	Mechanical Engineering
Authors	Autar Kaw
Date	December 23, 2009
Web Site	http://numericalmethods.eng.usf.edu

Chapter 06.01
Statistics Background of Regression Analysis

After reading this chapter, you should be able to:

1. *review the statistics background needed for learning regression, and*
2. *know a brief history of regression.*

Review of Statistical Terminologies

Although the language of statistics may be used at an elementary and descriptive level in this chapter, it makes an integral part of our every day discussions. When two friends talk about the weather (whether it will rain or not - probability), or the time it takes to drive from point A to point B (speed - mean or average), or baseball facts (all time career RBI or home runs of a sportsman -sorting, range), or about class grades (lowest and highest score - range and sorting), they are invariably using statistical tools. From the foregoing, it is imperative then that we review some of the statistical terminologies that we may encounter in studying the topic of regression. Some key terms we need to review are sample, arithmetic mean (average), error or deviation, standard deviation, variance, coefficient of variation, probability, Gaussian or normal distribution, degrees of freedom, and hypothesis.

Elementary Statistics

A statistical sample is a fraction or a portion of the whole (population) that is studied. This is a concept that may be confusing to many and is best illustrated with examples. Consider that a chemical engineer is interested in understanding the relationship between the rate of a reaction and temperature. It is impractical for the engineer to test all possible and measurable temperatures. Apart from the fact that the instrument for temperature measurement have limited temperature ranges for which they can function, the sheer number of hours required to measure every possible temperature makes it impractical. What the engineer does is choose a temperature range (based on his/her knowledge of the chemistry of the system) in which to study. Within the chosen temperature range, the engineer further chooses specific temperatures that span the range within which to conduct the experiments. These chosen temperatures for study constitute the sample while all possible temperatures are the population. In statistics, the sample is the fraction of the population chosen for study.

The location of the center of a distribution - the mean or average - is an item of interest in our every day lives. We use the concept when we talk about the average income, the class average for a test, the average height of some persons or about one being overweight (based on the average weight expected of an individual with similar

06.01.1

characteristics) or not. The arithmetic mean of a sample is a measure of its central tendency and is evaluated by dividing the sum of individual data points by the number of points.

Consider Table 1 which 14 measurements of the concentration of sodium chlorate produced in a chemical reactor operated at a pH of 7.0.

Table 1 Chlorate ion concentration in mmol/cm^3

12.0	15.0	14.1	15.9	11.5	14.8	11.2	13.7	15.9	12.6	14.3	12.6	12.1	14.8

The arithmetic mean $\bar{y}$ is mathematically defined as

$$\bar{y} = \frac{\sum\limits_{i=1}^{n} y_i}{n} \tag{1}$$

which is the sum of the individual data points y_i divided by the number of data points n.

One of the measures of the spread of the data is the range of the data. The range R is defined as the difference between the maximum and minimum value of the data as

$$R = y_{max} - y_{min} \tag{2}$$

where

y_{max} is the maximum of the values of y_i, $i = 1, 2, ..., n,$

y_{min} is the minimum of the values of y_i, $i = 1, 2, ..., n.$.

However, range may not give a good idea of the spread of the data as some data points may be far away from most other data points (such data points are called outliers). That is why the deviation from the average or arithmetic mean is looked as a better way to measure the spread. The residual between the data point and the mean is defined as

$$e_i = y_i - \bar{y} \tag{3}$$

The difference of each data point from the mean can be negative or positive depending on which side of the mean the data point lies (recall the mean is centrally located) and hence if one calculates the sum of such differences to find the overall spread, the differences may simply cancel each other. That is why the sum of the square of the differences is considered a better measure. The sum of the squares of the differences, also called summed squared error (SSE), S_t, is given by

$$S_t = \sum_{i=1}^{n} (y_i - \bar{y})^2 \tag{4}$$

Since the magnitude of the summed squared error is dependent on the number of data points, an average value of the summed squared error is defined as the variance, σ^2

$$\sigma^2 = \frac{S_t}{n-1} = \frac{\sum\limits_{i=1}^{n} (y_i - \bar{y})^2}{n-1} \tag{5}$$

The variance, σ^2 is sometimes written in two different convenient formulas as

$$\sigma^2 = \frac{\sum_{i=1}^{n} y_i^2 - \dfrac{\left(\sum_{i=1}^{n} y_i\right)^2}{n}}{n-1} \tag{6}$$

or

$$\sigma^2 = \frac{\sum_{i=1}^{n} y_i^2 - n\bar{y}^2}{n-1} \tag{7}$$

However, why is the variance divided by $(n-1)$ and not n as we have n data points? This is because with the use of the mean in calculating the variance, we lose the independence of one of the data points. That is, if you know the mean of n data points, then the value of one of the n data points can be calculated by knowing the other $(n-1)$ data points.

To bring the variation back to the same level of units as the original data, a new term called standard deviation, σ, is defined as

$$\sigma = \sqrt{\frac{S_t}{n-1}} = \sqrt{\frac{\sum_{i=1}^{n} (y_i - \bar{y})^2}{n-1}} \tag{8}$$

Furthermore, the ratio of the standard deviation to the mean, known as the coefficient variation $c.v$ is also used to normalize the spread of a sample.

$$c.v = \frac{\sigma}{\bar{y}} \times 100 \tag{9}$$

Example 1

Use the data in Table 1 to calculate the
   a) mean chlorate concentration,
   b) range of data,
   c) residual of each data point,
   d) sum of the square of the residuals.
   e) sample standard deviation,
   f) variance, and
   g) coefficient of variation.

Solution

Set up a table (see Table 2) containing the data, the residual for each data point and the square of the residuals.

Table 2 Data and data summations for statistical calculations.

i	y_i	y_i^2	$y_i - \bar{y}$	$(y_i - \bar{y})^2$
1	12	144	-1.6071	2.5829
2	15	225	1.3929	1.9401
3	14.1	198.81	0.4929	0.24291

4	15.9	252.81	2.2929	5.2572
5	11.5	132.25	-2.1071	4.4401
6	14.8	219.04	1.1929	1.4229
7	11.2	125.44	-2.4071	5.7943
8	13.7	187.69	0.0929	0.0086224
9	15.9	252.81	2.2929	5.2572
10	12.6	158.76	-1.0071	1.0143
11	14.3	204.49	0.6929	0.48005
12	12.6	158.76	-1.0071	1.0143
13	12.1	146.41	-1.5071	2.2715
14	14.8	219.04	1.1929	1.4229
$\sum_{i=1}^{14}$	190.50	2625.3	0.0000	33.149

a) Mean chlorate concentration as from Equation (1)

$$\bar{y} = \frac{\sum_{i=1}^{n} y_i}{n} = \frac{190.5}{14} = 13.607$$

b) The range of data as per Equation (2) is

$$R = y_{max} - y_{min}$$
$$= 15.9 - 11.2$$
$$= 4.7$$

c) Residual at each point is shown in Table 2. For example, at the first data point as per Equation (3)

$$e_1 = y_1 - \bar{y}$$
$$= 12.0 - 13.607$$
$$= -1.6071$$

d) The sum of the square of the residuals as from Equation (4) is

$$S_t = \sum_{i=1}^{n} (y_i - \bar{y})^2$$
$$= 33.149 \text{ (See Table 2)}$$

e) The standard deviation as per Equation (8) is

$$\sigma = \sqrt{\frac{\sum_{i=1}^{n} (y_i - \bar{y})^2}{n-1}}$$
$$= \sqrt{\frac{33.149}{14-1}}$$
$$= 1.5969$$

f) The variance is calculated as from Equation (5)

$$\sigma^2 = (1.597)^2$$
$$= 2.5499$$

The variance can be calculated using Equation (6)

$$\sigma^2 = \frac{\sum\limits_{i=1}^{n} y_i^2 - \dfrac{\left(\sum\limits_{i=1}^{n} y_i\right)^2}{n}}{n-1}$$

$$= \frac{2625.31 - \dfrac{(190.5)^2}{14}}{14-1}$$

$$= 2.5499$$

or by using Equation (7)

$$\sigma^2 = \frac{\sum\limits_{i=1}^{n} y_i^2 - n\bar{y}^2}{n-1}$$

$$= \frac{2625.3 - 14 \times 13.607^2}{14-1}$$

$$= 2.5499$$

g) The coefficient of variation, $c.v$ as from Equation (9) is

$$c.v = \frac{\sigma}{\bar{y}} \times 100$$

$$= \frac{1.5969}{13.607} \times 100$$

$$= 11.735\%$$

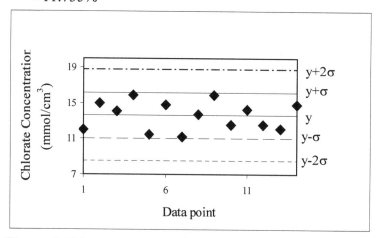

Figure 1 Chlorate concentration data points.

A Brief History of Regression

Anyone who is familiar with the Pearson Product Moment Correlation (PPMC) will no doubt associate regression principles with the name of Pearson. Although this association may be right, the concept of linear regression was largely due to the work of Galton, a cousin of Charles Darwin of the evolution theory fame. Sir Galton's work on inherited characteristics of sweet peas led to the initial conception of linear regression. His treatment of regression was not mathematically rigorous. The mathematical rigor and subsequent development of multiple regression were due largely to the contributions of his assistant and co-worker - Karl Pearson.

It is however instructive to note for historical accuracy that the development of regression could be attributed to the attempt at answering the question of hereditary - how and what characteristics offspring acquire from their progenitor. Sweet peas were used by Galton in his observations of characteristics of next generations of a given species. Despite his poor choice of descriptive statistics and limited mathematical rigor, Galton was able to generalize his work over a variety of hereditary problems. He further arrived at the idea that the differences in regression slopes were due to differences in variability between different sets of measurements. In today's appreciation of this, one can say that Galton recognized the ratio of variability of two measures was a key factor in determining the slope of the regression line.

The first rigorous treatment of correlation and regression was the work of Pearson in 1896. In the paper in the Philosophical Transactions of the Royal Society of London, Pearson showed that the optimum values of both the regression slope and the correlation coefficient for a straight line could be evaluated from the product-moment,

$$\sum_{i=1}^{n} \frac{(x_i - \bar{x})(y_i - \bar{y})}{n},$$

where $\bar{x}$ and $\bar{y}$ are the means of observed x and y values, respectively. In the 1896 paper, Pearson had attributed the initial mathematical formula for correlation to Auguste Bravais' work fifty years earlier. Pearson stated that although Bravais did demonstrate the use of product-moment for calculating the correlation coefficient, he did not show that it provided the best fit for the data.

REGRESSION	
Topic	Statistics Background for Regression
Summary	Textbook notes for the background of regression
Major	All engineering majors
Authors	Egwu Kalu, Autar Kaw
Date	October 11, 2008
Web Site	http://numericalmethods.eng.usf.edu

Chapter 06.02
Introduction of Regression Analysis

After reading this chapter, you should be able to:

1. *know what regression analysis is,*
2. *know the effective use of regression, and*
3. *enumerate uses and abuses of regression.*

What is regression analysis?

Regression analysis gives information on the relationship between a response (dependent) variable and one or more (predictor) independent variables to the extent that information is contained in the data. The goal of regression analysis is to express the response variable as a function of the predictor variables. The duality of fit and the accuracy of conclusion depend on the data used. Hence non-representative or improperly compiled data result in poor fits and conclusions. Thus, for effective use of regression analysis one must

1. investigate the data collection process,
2. discover any limitations in data collected, and
3. restrict conclusions accordingly.

Once a regression analysis relationship is obtained, it can be used to predict values of the response variable, identify variables that most affect the response, or verify hypothesized causal models of the response. The value of each predictor variable can be assessed through statistical tests on the estimated coefficients (multipliers) of the predictor variables.

An example of a regression model is the linear regression model which is a linear relationship between response variable, y and the predictor variable, $x_i, i = 1,2...,n$ of the form

$$y = \beta_0 + \beta_1 x_1 + \beta_2 x_2 + ... + \beta_n x_n + \varepsilon \tag{1}$$

where

$\beta_0, \beta_1 ....\beta_n$ are regression coefficients (unknown model parameters), and

ε is the error due to variability in the observed responses.

Example 1

In the transformation of raw or uncooked potato to cooked potato, heat is applied for some specific tune. One might postulate that the amount of untransformed portion of the starch (y) inside the potato is a linear function of time (t) and temperature (θ) of cooking. This is represented as

$$y = \beta_0 + \beta_1 t + \beta_2 \theta + \varepsilon \tag{2}$$

Linear as used in linear regression refers to the form of occurrence of the unknown parameters, β_1 and β_2 as ,simple linear multipliers of the predictor variable. Thus, the two equations below are also both linear.

$$y = \beta_0 + \beta_1 t + \beta_2 t\theta + \beta_3 \theta + \varepsilon \tag{3}$$

$$y = \beta_0 + \beta_1 t\theta + \beta_2 \theta + \varepsilon \tag{4}$$

Comparison of Regression and Correlation

Unlike regression, correlation analysis assesses the simultaneous variability of a collection of variables. The relationship is not directional and interest is not on how some variables respond to others but on how they are mutually associated. Thus, simultaneous variability of a collection of variables is referred to as correlation analysis.

Uses of Regression Analysis

Three uses for regression analysis are for
1. prediction
2. model specification and
3. parameter estimation.

Regression analysis equations are designed only to make predictions. Good predictions will not be possible if the model is not correctly specified and accuracy of the parameter not ensured. However, accurate prediction and model specification require that all relevant variables be accounted for in the data and the prediction equation be defined in the correct functional form for all predictor variables.

Parameter estimation is the most difficult to perform because not only is the model required to be correctly specified, the prediction must also be accurate and the data should allow for good estimation. For example, multicolinearity creates a problem and requires that some estimators may not be used. Thus, limitations of data and inability to measure all predictor variables relevant in a study restrict the use of prediction equations.

Abuses of Regression Analysis

Let us examine three common abuses of regression analysis.
1. Extrapolation
2. Generalization
3. Causation

Extrapolation

If you were dealing in the stock market or even interested in it, then you might remember the stock market crash of March 2000. During 1997-1999, investors thought they would double their money every year. They started buying fancy cars and houses on credit, and living the high life. Little did they know that the whole market was hyped on speculation and little economic sense. The Enron and MCI financial fiascos soon followed.

Let us look if we could have safely extrapolated the NASDAQ index[1] from past years. Below is the table of NASDAQ index, S, as a function of end of year number, t (Year 1 is the end of year 1994, and Year 6 is the end of year 1999).

Table 1 NASDAQ index as a function of year number.

Year Number (t)	NASDAQ Index (S)
1 (1994)	752
2 (1995)	1052
3 (1996)	1291
4 (1997)	1570
5 (1998)	2193
6 (1999)	4069

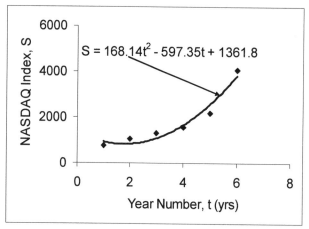

Figure 1 The regression line of NASDAQ Index as a function of year number.

---

[1] NASDAQ (National Association of Securities Dealers Automated Quotations) index is a composite index based on the stock market value of 3,000 companies. The NASDAQ index began on February 5, 1971 with a base value of 100. Twenty years later in 1995, NASDAQ index crossed the 1000 mark. It rose as high as 5132 on March 10, 2000 and currently is at a value of 2282 (February 19, 2006).

A relationship $S = a_0 + a_1 t + a_2 t^2$ between the NASDAQ index, S, and the year number, t, is developed using least square regression and is found to be $S = 168.14t^2 - 597.37t + 1361.8$. The data and the regression line are shown in Figure 1. The data is given only for Years 1 through 6 and it is desired to calculate the value for $t > 6$. This is extrapolation outside the model data. The error inherent in this model is shown in Table 2 and Figure 2. Look at the Year 7 and 8 that was not included in the data – the error between the predicted and actual values is 119% and 277%, respectively.

Table 2 NASDAQ index as a function of year number.

Year Number (t)	NASDAQ Index (S)	Predicted Index	Absolute Relative True Error (%)
1 (1994)	752	933	24
2 (1995)	1052	840	20
3 (1996)	1291	1083	16
4 (1997)	1570	1663	6
5 (1998)	2193	2579	18
6 (1999)	4069	3831	6
7 (2000)	2471	5419	119
8 (2001)	1951	7344	276

This illustration is not exaggerated and it is important that a careful use of any given model equations is always employed. At all times, it is imperative to infer the domain of independent variables for which a given equation is valid.

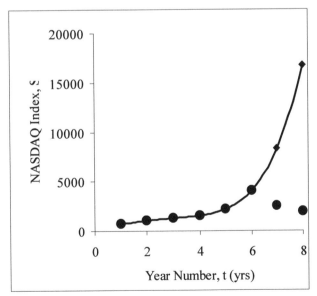

Figure 2 Extrapolated curve and actual data for Years 7 and 8.

Generalization

Generalization could arise when unsupported or over exaggerated claims are made. It is not often possible to measure all predictor variables relevant in a study. For example, a study carried out about the behavior of men might have inadvertently restricted the survey to Caucasian men only. Shall we then generalize the result as the attributes of all men irrespective of race? Such use of regression equation is an abuse since the limitations imposed by the data restrict the use of the prediction equations to Caucasian men.

Misidentification

Finally, misidentification of causation is a classic abuse of regression analysis equations. Regression analysis can only aid in the confirmation or refutation of a causal model - the model must however have a theoretical basis. In a chemical reacting system in which two species react to form a product, the amount of product formed or amount of reacting species vary with time. Although a regression equation of species concentration and time can be obtained, one cannot attribute time as the causal agent for the varying species concentration. Regression analysis cannot prove causality, rather it can only substantiate or contradict causal assumptions. Anything outside this is an abuse of regression analysis method.

Least Squares Methods

This is the most popular method of parameter estimation for coefficients of regression models. It has well known probability distributions and gives unbiased estimators of regression parameters with the smallest variance.

We wish to predict the response to n data points $(x_1, y_1), (x_2, y_2), \ldots, (x_n, y_n)$ by a regression model given by

$$y = f(x) \tag{6}$$

where, the function $f(x)$ has regression constants that need to be estimated.

For example

$f(x) = a_0 + a_1 x$ is a straight-line regression model with constants a_0 and a_1

$f(x) = a_0 e^{a_1 x}$ is an exponential model with constants a_0 and a_1

$f(x) = a_0 + a_1 x + a_2 x^2$ is a quadratic model with constants a_0, a_1 and a_2

A measure of goodness of fit, that is how the regression model $f(x)$ predicts the response variable y is the magnitude of the residual, E_i at each of the n data points.

$$E_i = y_i - f(x_i), \ i = 1, 2, \ldots n \tag{7}$$

Ideally, if all the residuals E_i are zero, one may have found an equation in which

all the points lie on a model. Thus, minimization of the residual is an objective of obtaining regression coefficients. In the least squares method, estimates of the constants of the models are chosen such that minimization of the sum of the squared residuals is achieved, that is

minimize $\sum\limits_{i=1}^{n} E_i^2$.

Why minimize the sum of the square of the residuals?

Why not for instance minimize the sum of the residual errors, $\sum_{i=1}^{n} E_i$, or the sum of the absolute values of the residuals, $\sum_{i=1}^{n} |E_i|$? Alternatively, constants of the model can be chosen such that the average residual is zero without making individual residuals small. Will any of these criteria yield unbiased parameters with the smallest variance? All of these questions will be answered when we discuss linear regression in the next chapter (Chapter 06.03).

Regression	
Topic	Introduction to Regression
Summary	Textbook notes for the introduction to regression
Major	All engineering majors
Authors	Egwu Kalu, Autar Kaw
Date	October 11, 2008
Web Site	http://numericalmethods.eng.usf.edu

Multiple-Choice Test

Chapter 06.01
Background

1. The average and standard deviation of the following numbers

2	4	10	12	1.6	6.4

   are
   - (A) 6.0, 4.0857
   - (B) 6.0, 4.2783
   - (C) 7.2, 4.0857
   - (D) 7.2, 4.4757

2. The average of 7 numbers is given as 12.6. If 6 of the numbers are 5, 7, 9, 12, 17 and 10, the remaining number is
   - (A) -47.9
   - (B) -47.4
   - (C) 15.6
   - (D) 28.2

3. The average and standard deviation of 7 numbers is given as 8.142 and 5.005, respectively. If 5 numbers are 5, 7, 9, 12 and 17, the other two numbers are
   - (A) -0.1738, 7.175
   - (B) 3.396, 12.890
   - (C) 3.500, 3.500
   - (D) 4.488, 2.512

4. The sum of the square of the difference between data point and its average for the data

2	5	10	12	2.5	6.7

   is
   - (A) 4.023
   - (B) 13.49
   - (C) 16.19
   - (D) 80.93

5.   Two medications are tried to heal esophageal ulcers in patients. The time to heal is reported as the time the patient reports 1 or less heartburn episode per week.

Pacalo	Reggon
26	25
23	31
21	32
25	23
32	19
37	26

The medication with less recovery time with standard deviation and mean is

(A) Pacalo, $\bar{x} = 27.33, \sigma = 6.022$

(B) Reggon, $\bar{x} = 26.00, \sigma = 4.900$

(C) Pacalo, $\bar{x} = 27.33, \sigma = 5.497$

(D) Pacalo, $\bar{x} = 27.33, \sigma = 6.022$

6.   A very large number of data points are chosen on a function $y = 3e^{2x}$ from $x = 0.2$ to 2.1. The average value of these data points most nearly is

(A) 51.5
(B) 78.2
(C) 97.8
(D) 102

Complete Solution

Problem Set

Chapter 06.02
Introduction of Regression Analysis

1. Enumerate three items that a scientist should do for effective use of regression analysis.

2. Enumerate three uses of regression analysis.

3. Enumerate three common abuses of regression analysis.

4. Does regression analysis prove causality? If not, what does it do.

5. Give an example of each of abuses of regression – extrapolation, generalization, and misidentification.

6. What are the differences between regression and interpolation?

06.02.1

Chapter 06.03
Linear Regression

After reading this chapter, you should be able to
1. *define regression,*
2. *use several minimizing of residual criteria to choose the right criterion,*
3. *derive the constants of a linear regression model based on least squares method criterion,*
4. *use in examples, the derived formulas for the constants of a linear regression model, and*
5. *prove that the constants of the linear regression model are unique and correspond to a minimum.*

Linear regression is the most popular regression model. In this model, we wish to predict response to n data points $(x_1, y_1), (x_2, y_2),......,(x_n, y_n)$ by a regression model given by

$$y = a_0 + a_1 x \tag{1}$$

where a_0 and a_1 are the constants of the regression model.

A measure of goodness of fit, that is, how well $a_0 + a_1 x$ predicts the response variable y is the magnitude of the residual ε_i at each of the n data points.

$$E_i = y_i - (a_0 + a_1 x_i) \tag{2}$$

Ideally, if all the residuals ε_i are zero, one may have found an equation in which all the points lie on the model. Thus, minimization of the residual is an objective of obtaining regression coefficients.

The most popular method to minimize the residual is the least squares methods, where the estimates of the constants of the models are chosen such that the sum of the squared residuals is minimized, that is minimize $\sum_{i=1}^{n} E_i^{2}$.

Why minimize the sum of the square of the residuals? Why not, for instance, minimize the sum of the residual errors or the sum of the absolute values of the residuals? Alternatively, constants of the model can be chosen such that the average residual is zero without making individual residuals small. Will any of these criteria yield unbiased

06.03.1

parameters with the smallest variance? All of these questions will be answered below. Look at the data in Table 1.

Table 1 Data points.

x	y
2.0	4.0
3.0	6.0
2.0	6.0
3.0	8.0

To explain this data by a straight line regression model,

$$y = a_0 + a_1 x \tag{3}$$

and using minimizing $\sum_{i=1}^{n} E_i$ as a criteria to find a_0 and a_1, we find that for (Figure 1)

$$y = 4x - 4 \tag{4}$$

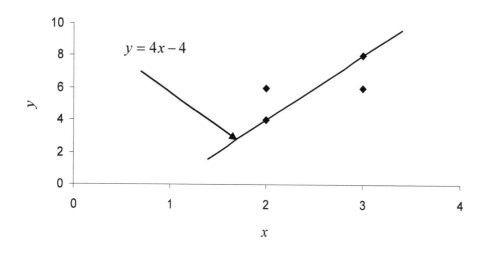

Figure 1 Regression curve $y = 4x - 4$ for y vs. x data.

the sum of the residuals, $\sum_{i=1}^{4} E_i = 0$ as shown in the Table 2.

Table 2 The residuals at each data point for regression model $y = 4x - 4$.

x	y	$y_{predicted}$	$\varepsilon = y - y_{predicted}$
2.0	4.0	4.0	0.0
3.0	6.0	8.0	-2.0
2.0	6.0	4.0	2.0
3.0	8.0	8.0	0.0
			$\sum_{i=1}^{4} \varepsilon_i = 0$

So does this give us the smallest error? It does as $\sum_{i=1}^{4} E_i = 0$. But it does not give unique values for the parameters of the model. A straight-line of the model

$$y = 6 \tag{5}$$

also makes $\sum_{i=1}^{4} E_i = 0$ as shown in the Table 3.

Table 3 The residuals at each data point for regression model $y = 6$

x	y	$y_{predicted}$	$\varepsilon = y - y_{predicted}$
2.0	4.0	6.0	-2.0
3.0	6.0	6.0	0.0
2.0	6.0	6.0	0.0
3.0	8.0	6.0	2.0
			$\sum_{i=1}^{4} E_i = 0$

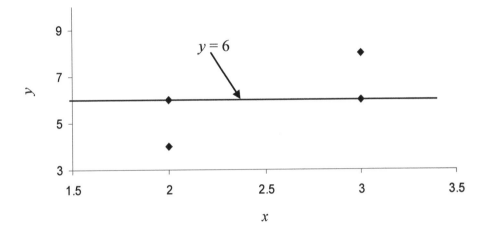

Figure 2 Regression curve $y = 6$ for y vs. x data.

Since this criterion does not give a unique regression model, it cannot be used for finding the regression coefficients. Let us see why we cannot use this criterion for any general data. We want to minimize

$$\sum_{i=1}^{n} E_i = \sum_{i=1}^{n} (y_i - a_0 - a_1 x_i) \tag{6}$$

Differentiating Equation (6) with respect to a_0 and a_1, we get

$$\frac{\partial \sum_{i=1}^{n} E_i}{\partial a_0} = -\sum_{i=1}^{n} 1 = -n \tag{7}$$

$$\frac{\partial \sum\limits_{i=1}^{n} E_i}{\partial a_1} = -\sum\limits_{i=1}^{n} x_i = -n\bar{x} \tag{8}$$

Putting these equations to zero, give $n = 0$ but that is not possible. Therefore, unique values of a_0 and a_1 do not exist.

You may think that the reason the minimization criterion $\sum\limits_{i=1}^{n} E_i$ does not work is that negative residuals cancel with positive residuals. So is minimizing $\sum\limits_{i=1}^{n} |E_i|$ better? Let us look at the data given in the Table 2 for equation $y = 4x - 4$. It makes $\sum\limits_{i=1}^{4} |E_i| = 4$ as shown in the following table.

Table 4 The absolute residuals at each data point when employing $y = 4x - 4$.

x	y	$y_{predicted}$	$\varepsilon = y - y_{predicted}$
2.0	4.0	4.0	0.0
3.0	6.0	8.0	2.0
2.0	6.0	4.0	2.0
3.0	8.0	8.0	0.0
			$\sum\limits_{i=1}^{4} |\varepsilon_i| = 4$

The value of $\sum\limits_{i=1}^{4} |E_i| = 4$ also exists for the straight line model $y = 6$. No other straight line model for this data has $\sum\limits_{i=1}^{4} |E_i| < 4$. Again, we find the regression coefficients are not unique, and hence this criterion also cannot be used for finding the regression model.

Let us use the least squares criterion where we minimize

$$S_r = \sum\limits_{i=1}^{n} E_i^2 = \sum\limits_{i=1}^{n} \left(y_i - a_0 - a_1 x_i\right)^2 \tag{9}$$

S_r is called the sum of the square of the residuals.

To find a_0 and a_1, we minimize S_r with respect to a_0 and a_1.

$$\frac{\partial S_r}{\partial a_0} = 2\sum\limits_{i=1}^{n} \left(y_i - a_0 - a_1 x_i\right)(-1) = 0 \tag{10}$$

$$\frac{\partial S_r}{\partial a_1} = 2\sum\limits_{i=1}^{n} \left(y_i - a_0 - a_1 x_i\right)(-x_i) = 0 \tag{11}$$

giving

$$-\sum\limits_{i=1}^{n} y_i + \sum\limits_{i=1}^{n} a_0 + \sum\limits_{i=1}^{n} a_1 x_i = 0 \tag{12}$$

$$-\sum_{i=1}^{n} y_i x_i + \sum_{i=1}^{n} a_0 x_i + \sum_{i=1}^{n} a_1 x_i^2 = 0 \tag{13}$$

Noting that $\displaystyle\sum_{i=1}^{n} a_0 = a_0 + a_0 + \ldots + a_0 = na_0$

$$na_0 + a_1 \sum_{i=1}^{n} x_i = \sum_{i=1}^{n} y_i \tag{14}$$

$$a_0 \sum_{i=1}^{n} x_i + a_1 \sum_{i=1}^{n} x_i^2 = \sum_{i=1}^{n} x_i y_i \tag{15}$$

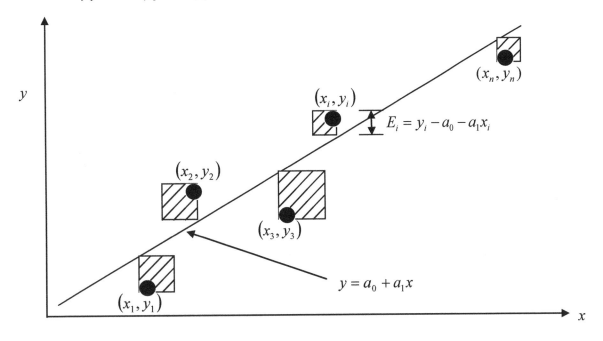

Figure 3 Linear regression of y vs. x data showing residuals and square of residual at a typical point, x_i.

Solving the above Equations (14) and (15) gives

$$a_1 = \frac{n\displaystyle\sum_{i=1}^{n} x_i y_i - \sum_{i=1}^{n} x_i \sum_{i=1}^{n} y_i}{n\displaystyle\sum_{i=1}^{n} x_i^2 - \left(\sum_{i=1}^{n} x_i\right)^2} \tag{16}$$

$$a_0 = \frac{\displaystyle\sum_{i=1}^{n} x_i^2 \sum_{i=1}^{n} y_i - \sum_{i=1}^{n} x_i \sum_{i=1}^{n} x_i y_i}{n\displaystyle\sum_{i=1}^{n} x_i^2 - \left(\sum_{i=1}^{n} x_i\right)^2} \tag{17}$$

Redefining

$$S_{xy} = \sum_{i=1}^{n} x_i y_i - n \bar{x} \bar{y} \tag{18}$$

$$S_{xx} = \sum_{i=1}^{n} x_i^2 - n \bar{x}^2 \tag{19}$$

$$\bar{x} = \frac{\sum_{i=1}^{n} x_i}{n} \tag{20}$$

$$\bar{y} = \frac{\sum_{i=1}^{n} y_i}{n} \tag{21}$$

we can rewrite

$$a_1 = \frac{S_{xy}}{S_{xx}} \tag{22}$$

$$a_0 = \bar{y} - a_1 \bar{x} \tag{23}$$

Example 1

The torque T needed to turn the torsional spring of a mousetrap through an angle, θ is given below

Table 5 Torque versus angle for a torsion spring.

Angle, θ Radians	Torque, T N·m
0.698132	0.188224
0.959931	0.209138
1.134464	0.230052
1.570796	0.250965
1.919862	0.313707

Find the constants k_1 and k_2 of the regression model
$$T = k_1 + k_2 \theta$$

Solution

Table 6 shows the summations needed for the calculation of the constants of the regression model.

Table 6 Tabulation of data for calculation of needed summations.

i	θ	T	θ^2	$T\theta$
1	radians	N·m	radians^2	N·m
2	0.698132	0.188224	4.87388×10^{-1}	1.31405×10^{-1}
3	0.959931	0.209138	9.21468×10^{-1}	2.00758×10^{-1}
4	1.134464	0.230052	1.2870	2.60986×10^{-1}

5	1.570796	0.250965	2.4674	3.94215×10^{-1}
6	1.919862	0.313707	3.6859	6.02274×10^{-1}
$\displaystyle\sum_{i=1}^{5}$	**6.2831**	**1.1921**	**8.8491**	**1.5896**

$n = 5$

$$k_2 = \frac{n \displaystyle\sum_{i=1}^{5} \theta_i T_i - \sum_{i=1}^{5} \theta_i \sum_{i=1}^{5} T_i}{n \displaystyle\sum_{i=1}^{5} \theta_i^2 - \left(\sum_{i=1}^{5} \theta_i\right)^2}$$

$$= \frac{5(1.5896) - (6.2831)(1.1921)}{5(8.8491) - (6.2831)^2}$$

$$= 9.6091 \times 10^{-2} \text{ N - m/rad}$$

$$\bar{T} = \frac{\displaystyle\sum_{i=1}^{5} T_i}{n}$$

$$= \frac{1.1921}{5}$$

$$= 2.3842 \times 10^{-1} \text{N-m}$$

$$\bar{\theta} = \frac{\displaystyle\sum_{i=1}^{5} \theta_i}{n}$$

$$= \frac{6.2831}{5}$$

$$= 1.2566 \text{ radians}$$

$$k_1 = \bar{T} - k_2 \bar{\theta}$$

$$= 2.3842 \times 10^{-1} - (9.6091 \times 10^{-2})(1.2566)$$

$$= 1.1767 \times 10^{-1} \text{ N - m}$$

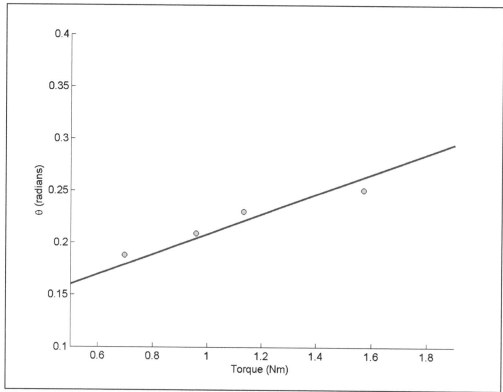

Figure 4 Linear regression of torque vs. angle data

Example 2

To find the longitudinal modulus of a composite material, the following data, as given in Table 7, is collected.

Table 7 Stress vs. strain data for a composite material.

Strain (%)	Stress (MPa)
0	0
0.183	306
0.36	612
0.5324	917
0.702	1223
0.867	1529
1.0244	1835
1.1774	2140
1.329	2446
1.479	2752
1.5	2767
1.56	2896

Find the longitudinal modulus E using the regression model.

$$\sigma = E\varepsilon \tag{24}$$

Solution

Rewriting data from Table 7, stresses versus strain data in Table 8

Table 8 Stress vs strain data for a composite in SI system of units

Strain (m/m)	Stress (Pa)
0.0000	0.0000
1.8300×10^{-3}	3.0600×10^{8}
3.6000×10^{-3}	6.1200×10^{8}
5.3240×10^{-3}	9.1700×10^{8}
7.0200×10^{-3}	1.2230×10^{9}
8.6700×10^{-3}	1.5290×10^{9}
1.0244×10^{-2}	1.8350×10^{9}
1.1774×10^{-2}	2.1400×10^{9}
1.3290×10^{-2}	2.4460×10^{9}
1.4790×10^{-2}	2.7520×10^{9}
1.5000×10^{-2}	2.7670×10^{9}
1.5600×10^{-2}	2.8960×10^{9}

Applying the least square method, the residuals γ_i at each data point is

$$\gamma_i = \sigma_i - E\varepsilon_i$$

The sum of square of the residuals is

$$S_r = \sum_{i=1}^{n} \gamma_i^2$$

$$= \sum_{i=1}^{n} (\sigma_i - E\varepsilon_i)^2$$

Again, to find the constant E, we need to minimize S_r by differentiating with respect to E and then equating to zero

$$\frac{dS_r}{dE} = \sum_{i=1}^{n} 2(\sigma_i - E\varepsilon_i)(-\varepsilon_i) = 0$$

From there, we obtain

$$E = \frac{\sum_{i=1}^{n} \sigma_i \varepsilon_i}{\sum_{i=1}^{n} \varepsilon_i^2} \tag{25}$$

Note, Equation (25) only so far has shown that it corresponds to a local minimum or maximum. Can you show that it corresponds to an absolute minimum.
The summations used in Equation (25) are given in the Table 9.

Table 9 Tabulation for Example 2 for needed summations

i	ε	σ	ε^2	$\varepsilon\sigma$
1	0.0000	0.0000	0.0000	0.0000
2	1.8300×10^{-3}	3.0600×10^{8}	3.3489×10^{-6}	5.5998×10^{5}
3	3.6000×10^{-3}	6.1200×10^{8}	1.2960×10^{-5}	2.2032×10^{6}
4	5.3240×10^{-3}	9.1700×10^{8}	2.8345×10^{-5}	4.8821×10^{6}
5	7.0200×10^{-3}	1.2230×10^{9}	4.9280×10^{-5}	8.5855×10^{6}
6	8.6700×10^{-3}	1.5290×10^{9}	7.5169×10^{-5}	1.3256×10^{7}
7	1.0244×10^{-2}	1.8350×10^{9}	1.0494×10^{-4}	1.8798×10^{7}
8	1.1774×10^{-2}	2.1400×10^{9}	1.3863×10^{-4}	2.5196×10^{7}
9	1.3290×10^{-2}	2.4460×10^{9}	1.7662×10^{-4}	3.2507×10^{7}
10	1.4790×10^{-2}	2.7520×10^{9}	2.1874×10^{-4}	4.0702×10^{7}
11	1.5000×10^{-2}	2.7670×10^{9}	2.2500×10^{-4}	4.1505×10^{7}
12	1.5600×10^{-2}	2.8960×10^{9}	2.4336×10^{-4}	4.5178×10^{7}
$\sum\limits_{i=1}^{12}$			1.2764×10^{-3}	2.3337×10^{8}

$$n = 12$$

$$\sum_{i=1}^{12}\varepsilon_i^2 = 1.2764\times10^{-3}$$

$$\sum_{i=1}^{12}\sigma_i\varepsilon_i = 2.3337\times10^{8}$$

$$E = \frac{\sum\limits_{i=1}^{12}\sigma_i\varepsilon_i}{\sum\limits_{i=1}^{12}\varepsilon_i^2}$$

$$= \frac{2.3337\times10^{8}}{1.2764\times10^{-3}}$$

$$= 182.84 \text{ GPa}$$

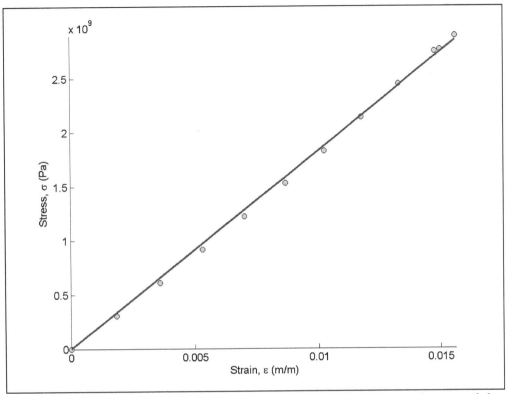

Figure 5 Linear regression model of stress vs. strain for a composite material.

Appendix

Do the values of the constants of the least squares straight-line regression model correspond to a minimum? Is the straight line unique?

ANSWER:

Given n data pairs, $(x_1, y_1), \ldots, (x_n, y_n)$, the best fit for the straight line regression model

$$y = a_0 + a_1 x \tag{A.1}$$

is found by the method of least squares.

Starting with the sum of the square of the residuals S_r, we get

$$S_r = \sum_{i=1}^{n} \left(y_i - a_0 - a_1 x_i \right)^2 \tag{A.2}$$

and using

$$\frac{\partial S_r}{\partial a_0} = 0 \tag{A.3}$$

$$\frac{\partial S_r}{\partial a_1} = 0 \tag{A.4}$$

gives two simultaneous linear equations whose solution is

$$a_1 = \frac{n\sum_{i=1}^{n} x_i y_i - \sum_{i=1}^{n} x_i \sum_{i=1}^{n} y_i}{n\sum_{i=1}^{n} x_i^2 - \left(\sum_{i=1}^{n} x_i\right)^2} \tag{A.5a}$$

$$a_0 = \frac{\sum_{i=1}^{n} x_i^2 \sum_{i=1}^{n} y_i - \sum_{i=1}^{n} x_i \sum_{i=1}^{n} x_i y_i}{n\sum_{i=1}^{n} x_i^2 - \left(\sum_{i=1}^{n} x_i\right)^2} \tag{A.5b}$$

But does this give the minimum of value of S_r? The first derivative only tells us about a local minima or maxima, and not whether it is an absolute minimum or a maximum.

We need to conduct a second derivative test to find out whether the point (a_0, a_1) from Equation (A.5) gives the minimum or maximum of S_r.

What is the second derivative test for a minimum if we have a function of two variables?

If you have a function $f(x, y)$ and we found a critical point (a, b) from the first derivative test, then (a, b) is a minimum point if

$$\frac{\partial^2 f}{\partial x^2} \frac{\partial^2 f}{\partial y^2} - \left(\frac{\partial^2 f}{\partial x \partial y}\right)^2 > 0 \text{, and} \tag{A.6}$$

$$\frac{\partial^2 f}{\partial x^2} > 0 \text{ OR } \frac{\partial^2 f}{\partial y^2} > 0 \tag{A.7}$$

From Equation (2)

$$\frac{\partial S_r}{\partial a_0} = \sum_{i=1}^{n} 2(y_i - a_0 - a_1 x_i)(-1)$$

$$= -2\sum_{i=1}^{n} (y_i - a_0 - a_1 x_i) \tag{A.8}$$

$$\frac{\partial S_r}{\partial a_1} = \sum_{i=1}^{n} 2(y_i - a_0 - a_1 x_i)(-x_i)$$

$$= -2\sum_{i=1}^{n} (x_i y_i - a_0 x_i - a_1 x_i^2) \tag{A.9}$$

then

$$\frac{\partial^2 S_r}{\partial a_0^2} = -2\sum_{i=1}^{n} -1$$

$$= 2n \tag{A.10}$$

$$\frac{\partial^2 S_r}{\partial a_1^2} = 2\sum_{i=1}^{n} x_i^2 \tag{A.11}$$

$$\frac{\partial^2 S_r}{\partial a_0 \partial a_1} = 2\sum_{i=1}^{n} x_i \qquad\qquad\qquad\qquad\qquad\qquad (A.12)$$

So we satisfy condition (A.7) as from Equation (A.10), $2n$ is a positive number and from Equation (A.11) $2\sum_{i=1}^{n} x_i^2$ is a positive number as assuming that all data points are NOT zero is reasonable.

Is the other condition for being a minimum as given by Equation (A.6) met? Yes, we can show (*the proof is not given*)

$$\frac{\partial^2 S_r}{\partial a_0^2}\frac{\partial^2 S_r}{\partial a_1^2} - \left(\frac{\partial^2 S_r}{\partial a_0 \partial a_1}\right)^2 = (2n)\left(2\sum_{i=1}^{n} x_i^2\right) - \left(2\sum_{i=1}^{n} x_i\right)^2$$

$$= 4\left[n\sum_{i=1}^{n} x_i^2 - \left(\sum_{i=1}^{n} x_i\right)^2\right] > 0 \qquad\qquad (A.13)$$

So the values of a_0 and a_1 that we have in Equations (A.5a) and (A.5b), are in fact corresponding to a local minimum of S_r. But this local minimum is an absolute minimum because the first derivative is zero for only one point as given by Equations (A.5a) and (A.5b). The solution given by Equations (A.5a) and (A.5b) can be shown to be unique because the denominator of the solution is nonzero as shown by Equation (A.13). Hence, this also makes the straight-line regression model unique.

LINEAR REGRESSION	
Topic	Linear Regression
Summary	Textbook notes of Linear Regression
Major	General Engineering
Authors	Egwu Kalu, Autar Kaw, Cuong Nguyen
Date	April 9, 2010
Web Site	http://numericalmethods.eng.usf.edu

Multiple-Choice Test

Chapter 06.03
Linear Regression

1. Given $(x_1, y_1), (x_2, y_2), \ldots\ldots\ldots, (x_n, y_n)$, best fitting data to $y = f(x)$ by least squares requires minimization of

   (A) $\displaystyle\sum_{i=1}^{n} [y_i - f(x_i)]$

   (B) $\displaystyle\sum_{i=1}^{n} |y_i - f(x_i)|$

   (C) $\displaystyle\sum_{i=1}^{n} (y_i - f(x_i))^2$

   (D) $\displaystyle\sum_{i=1}^{n} [y_i - \bar{y}]^2$, $\bar{y} = \dfrac{\displaystyle\sum_{i=1}^{n} y_i}{n}$

2. The following data

x	1	20	30	40
y	1	400	800	1300

   is regressed with least squares regression to $y = a_0 + a_1 x$. The value of a_1 most nearly is
   - (A) 27.480
   - (B) 28.956
   - (C) 32.625
   - (D) 40.000

3. The following data is regressed with least squares regression to $y = a_1 x$. The value of a_1 most nearly is

x	1	20	30	40
y	1	400	800	1300

   - (A) 27.480
   - (B) 28.956
   - (C) 32.625
   - (D) 40.000

06.03.1

4. An instructor gives the same y vs. x data as given below to four students and asks them to regress the data with least squares regression to $y = a_0 + a_1 x$.

x	1	10	20	30	40
y	1	100	400	600	1200

They each come up with four different answers for the straight-line regression model. Only one is correct. The correct model is

(A) $y = 60x - 1200$

(B) $y = 30x - 200$

(C) $y = -139.43 + 29.684x$

(D) $y = 1 + 22.782x$

5. A torsion spring of a mousetrap is twisted through an angle of $180°$. The torque vs. angle data is given below.

Torsion, T (N-m)	0.110	0.189	0.230	0.250
Angle, θ (rad)	0.10	0.50	1.1	1.5

The relationship between the torque and the angle is $T = a_0 + a_1\theta$.

The amount of strain energy stored in the mousetrap spring in Joules is

(A) 0.29872

(B) 0.41740

(C) 0.84208

(D) 1561.8

6. A scientist finds that regressing the y vs. x data given below to $y = a_o + a_1 x$ results in the coefficient of determination for the straight-line model, r^2 being zero.

x	1	3	11	17
y	2	6	22	?

The missing value for y at $x = 17$ most nearly is

(A) -2.4444

(B) 2.000

(C) 6.889

(D) 34.00

Complete Solution

Problem Set

Chapter 06.03
Linear Regression

1. Given the following data of y vs x

x	1	2	3	4	5
y	1	4	9	16	25

   The data is regressed to a straight line $y = -7 + 6x$. What is the residual at $x = 4$?

2. The force vs. displacement data for a linear spring is given below. F is the force in Newtons and x is the displacement in meters. Assume displacement data is known more accurately.

Displacement, x (m)	10	15	20
Force, F (N)	100	200	400

   If the F vs x data is regressed to $F = a + kx$, what is the value of k by minimizing the sum of the square of the residuals?

3. A torsion spring of a mousetrap is twisted through an angle of 180^0. The torque vs angle data is given below.

θ (rad)	0.12	0.50	1.1
T (Nm)	0.25	1.00	2.0

   Assuming that the torque and the angle are related via a general straight line as $T = k_0 + k_1 \theta$, regress the above data to the straight-line model.

4. The force vs. displacement data for a linear spring is given below. F is the force in Newtons and x is the displacement in meters. Assume displacement data is known more accurately.

Displacement, x (m)	10	15	20
Force, F (N)	100	200	400

   If the F vs x data is regressed to $F = kx$, what is the value of k by minimizing the sum of the square of the residuals.

5. Given the following data of y vs x

x	1	2	3	4	5
y	1	1.1	0.9	0.96	1.01

   If the y vs x data is regressed to a constant line given by $y = a$, where a is a constant, what is the value of a by minimizing the sum of the square of the residuals.

6.   To find the longitudinal modulus of composite, the following data as given in Table 1.

Strain (%)	Stress (MPa)
0	0
0.183	306
0.36	612
0.5324	917
0.702	1223
0.867	1529
1.0244	1835
1.1774	2140
1.329	2446
1.479	2752
1.5	2767
1.56	2896

Table 1 Stress versus strain data for a composite material.

Find the longitudinal modulus, E using the regression model. (Hint: $\sigma = E\varepsilon$)

Chapter 06.04
Nonlinear Models for Regression

After reading this chapter, you should be able to
1. *derive constants of nonlinear regression models,*
2. *use in examples, the derived formula for the constants of the nonlinear regression model, and*
3. *linearize (transform) data to find constants of some nonlinear regression models.*

From fundamental theories, we may know the relationship between two variables. An example in chemical engineering is the Clausius-Clapeyron equation that relates vapor pressure P of a vapor to its absolute temperature, T.

$$\log(P) = A + \frac{B}{T} \tag{1}$$

where A and B are the unknown parameters to be determined. The above equation is not linear in the unknown parameters. Any model that is not linear in the unknown parameters is described as a nonlinear regression model.

Nonlinear models using least squares

The development of the least squares estimation for nonlinear models does not generally yield equations that are linear and hence easy to solve. An example of a nonlinear regression model is the exponential model.

<u>Exponential model</u>

Given $(x_1, y_1), (x_2, y_2), \ldots (x_n, y_n)$, best fit $y = ae^{bx}$ to the data. The variables a and b are the constants of the exponential model. The residual at each data point x_i is

$$E_i = y_i - ae^{bx_i} \tag{2}$$

The sum of the square of the residuals is

$$S_r = \sum_{i=1}^{n} E_i^2$$

$$= \sum_{i=1}^{n} \left(y_i - ae^{bx_i} \right)^2 \tag{3}$$

06.04.1

To find the constants a and b of the exponential model, we minimize S_r by differentiating with respect to a and b and equating the resulting equations to zero.

$$\frac{\partial S_r}{\partial a} = \sum_{i=1}^{n} 2\left(y_i - ae^{bx_i}\right)\left(-e^{bx_i}\right) = 0$$

$$\frac{\partial S_r}{\partial b} = \sum_{i=1}^{n} 2\left(y_i - ae^{bx_i}\right)\left(-ax_i e^{bx_i}\right) = 0 \tag{4a,b}$$

or

$$-\sum_{i=1}^{n} y_i e^{bx_i} + a\sum_{i=1}^{n} e^{2bx_i} = 0$$

$$\sum_{i=1}^{n} y_i x_i e^{bx_i} - a\sum_{i=1}^{n} x_i e^{2bx_i} = 0 \tag{5a,b}$$

Equations (5a) and (5b) are nonlinear in a and b and thus not in a closed form to be solved as was the case for linear regression. In general, iterative methods (such as Gauss-Newton iteration method, method of steepest descent, Marquardt's method, direct search, etc) must be used to find values of a and b.

However, in this case, from Equation (5a), a can be written explicitly in terms of b as

$$a = \frac{\sum_{i=1}^{n} y_i e^{bx_i}}{\sum_{i=1}^{n} e^{2bx_i}} \tag{6}$$

Substituting Equation (6) in (5b) gives

$$\sum_{i=1}^{n} y_i x_i e^{bx_i} - \frac{\sum_{i=1}^{n} y_i e^{bx_i}}{\sum_{i=1}^{n} e^{2bx_i}} \sum_{i=1}^{n} x_i e^{2bx_i} = 0 \tag{7}$$

This equation is still a nonlinear equation in b and can be solved best by numerical methods such as the bisection method or the secant method.

Example 1

Many patients get concerned when a test involves injection of a radioactive material. For example for scanning a gallbladder, a few drops of Technetium-99m isotope is used. Half of the technetium-99m would be gone in about 6 hours. It, however, takes about 24 hours for the radiation levels to reach what we are exposed to in day-to-day activities. Below is given the relative intensity of radiation as a function of time.

Table 1 Relative intensity of radiation as a function of time

t (hrs)	0	1	3	5	7	9
γ	1.000	0.891	0.708	0.562	0.447	0.355

If the level of the relative intensity of radiation is related to time via an exponential formula $\gamma = Ae^{\lambda t}$, find

    a) the value of the regression constants A and λ,

    b) the half-life of Technium-99m, and

    c) the radiation intensity after 24 hours.

Solution

a) The value of λ is given by solving the nonlinear Equation (7),

$$f(\lambda) = \sum_{i=1}^{n} \gamma_i t_i e^{\lambda t_i} - \frac{\sum_{i=1}^{n} \gamma_i e^{\lambda t_i}}{\sum_{i=1}^{n} e^{2\lambda t_i}} \sum_{i=1}^{n} t_i e^{2\lambda t_i} = 0 \tag{8}$$

and then the value of A from Equation (6),

$$A = \frac{\sum_{i=1}^{n} \gamma_i e^{\lambda t_i}}{\sum_{i=1}^{n} e^{2\lambda t_i}} \tag{9}$$

    Equation (8) can be solved for λ using bisection method. To estimate the initial guesses, we assume $\lambda = -0.120$ and $\lambda = -0.110$. We need to check whether these values first bracket the root of $f(\lambda) = 0$. At $\lambda = -0.120$, the table below shows the evaluation of $f(-0.120)$.

Table 2 Summation value for calculation of constants of model

i	t_i	γ_i	$\gamma_i t_i e^{\lambda t_i}$	$\gamma_i e^{\lambda t_i}$	$e^{2\lambda t_i}$	$t_i e^{2\lambda t_i}$
1	0	1	0.00000	1.00000	1.00000	0.00000
2	1	0.891	0.79205	0.79205	0.78663	0.78663
3	3	0.708	1.4819	0.49395	0.48675	1.4603
4	5	0.562	1.5422	0.30843	0.30119	1.5060
5	7	0.447	1.3508	0.19297	0.18637	1.3046
6	9	0.355	1.0850	0.12056	0.11533	1.0379
$\sum_{i=1}^{6}$			6.2501	2.9062	2.8763	6.0954

From Table 2

$$n = 6$$

$$\sum_{i=1}^{6} \gamma_i t_i e^{-0.120 t_i} = 6.2501$$

$$\sum_{i=1}^{6} \gamma_i e^{-0.120 t_i} = 2.9062$$

$$\sum_{i=1}^{6} e^{2(-0.120) t_i} = 2.8763$$

$$\sum_{i=1}^{6} t_i e^{2(-0.120)t_i} = 6.0954$$

$$f(-0.120) = (6.2501) - \frac{2.9062}{2.8763}(6.0954)$$

$$= 0.091357$$

Similarly

$$f(-0.110) = -0.10099$$

Since

$$f(-0.120) \times f(-0.110) < 0,$$

the value of λ falls in the bracket of $[-0.120, -0.110]$. The next guess of the root then is

$$\lambda = \frac{-0.120 + (-0.110)}{2}$$

$$= -0.115$$

Continuing with the bisection method, the root of $f(\lambda) = 0$ is found as $\lambda = -0.11508$. This value of the root was obtained after 20 iterations with an absolute relative approximate error of less than 0.000008%.

From Equation (9), A can be calculated as

$$A = \frac{\displaystyle\sum_{i=1}^{6} \gamma_i e^{\lambda t_i}}{\displaystyle\sum_{i=1}^{6} e^{2\lambda t_i}}$$

$$= \frac{\begin{array}{l} 1 \times e^{-0.11508(0)} + 0.891 \times e^{-0.11508(1)} + 0.708 \times e^{-0.11508(3)} + \\ 0.562 \times e^{-0.11508(5)} + 0.447 \times e^{-0.11508(7)} + 0.355 \times e^{-0.11508(9)} \end{array}}{\begin{array}{l} e^{2(-0.11508)(0)} + e^{2(-0.11508)(1)} + e^{2(-0.11508)(3)} + \\ e^{2(-0.11508)(5)} + e^{2(-0.11508)(7)} + e^{2(-0.11508)(9)} \end{array}}$$

$$= \frac{2.9373}{2.9378}$$

$$= 0.99983$$

The regression formula is hence given by

$$\gamma = 0.99983 \, e^{-0.11508t}$$

b) Half life of Technetium-99m is when $\gamma = \left.\frac{1}{2}\gamma\right|_{t=0}$

$$0.99983 \times e^{-0.11508t} = \frac{1}{2}(0.99983)e^{-0.11508(0)}$$

$$e^{-0.11508t} = 0.5$$

$$-0.11508t = \ln(0.5)$$

$$t = 6.0232 \text{ hours}$$

c) The relative intensity of the radiation after 24 hrs is

$$\gamma = 0.99983 \times e^{-0.11508(24)}$$

$$= 6.3160 \times 10^{-2}$$

This implies that only $\dfrac{6.3160 \times 10^{-2}}{0.99983} \times 100 = 6.3171\%$ of the initial radioactive intensity is left after 24 hrs.

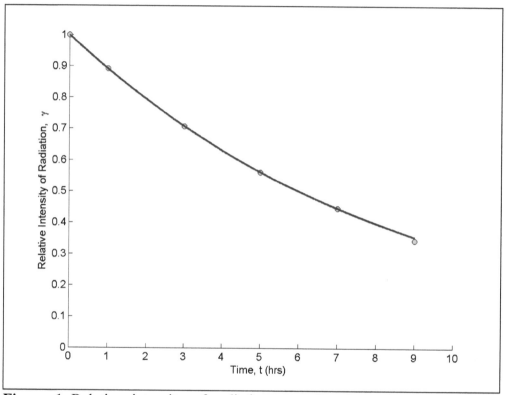

Figure 1 Relative intensity of radiation as a function of temperature using an exponential regression model.

Growth model

      Growth models common in scientific fields have been developed and used successfully for specific situations. The growth models are used to describe how something grows with changes in the regressor variable (often the time). Examples in this category include growth of thin films or population with time. Growth models include

$$y = \frac{a}{1 + be^{-cx}} \tag{10}$$

where a, b and c are the constants of the model. At $x = 0$, $y = \dfrac{a}{1+b}$ and as $x \to \infty$,

$y \to a$.

The residuals at each data point x_i, are

$$E_i = y_i - \frac{a}{1 + be^{-cx_i}} \tag{11}$$

The sum of the square of the residuals is

$$S_r = \sum_{i=1}^{n} E_i^2$$

$$= \sum_{i=1}^{n} \left(y_i - \frac{a}{1 + be^{-cx_i}} \right)^2 \tag{12}$$

To find the constants a, b and c we minimize S_r by differentiating with respect to a, b and c, and equating the resulting equations to zero.

$$\frac{\partial S_r}{\partial a} = \sum_{i=1}^{n} \left(\frac{2e^{cx_i}\left[ae^{c \times x_i} - y_i\left(e^{cx_i} + b\right)\right]}{\left(e^{cx_i} + b\right)^2} \right) = 0,$$

$$\frac{\partial S_r}{\partial b} = \sum_{i=1}^{n} \left(\frac{2ae^{cx_i}\left[by_i + e^{cx_i}\left(y_i - a\right)\right]}{\left(e^{cx_i} + b\right)^3} \right) = 0,$$

$$\frac{\partial S_r}{\partial c} = \sum_{i=1}^{n} \left(\frac{-2abx_i e^{cx_i}\left[by_i + e^{cx_i}\left(y_i - a\right)\right]}{\left(e^{cx_i} + b\right)^3} \right) = 0. \tag{13a,b,c}$$

One can use the Newton-Raphson method to solve the above set of simultaneous nonlinear equations for a, b and c.

Example 2

The height of a child is measured at different ages as follows.

Table 3 Height of the child at different ages.

t (yrs)	0	5.0	8	12	16	18
H(in)	20	36.2	52	60	69.2	70

Estimate the height of the child as an adult of 30 years of age using the growth model,

$$H = \frac{a}{1 + be^{-ct}}$$

Solution

The saturation growth model of height, H vs. age, t is given as

$$H = \frac{a}{1 + be^{-ct}}$$

where the constants a, b and c are the roots of the simultaneous nonlinear equation system

$$\sum_{i=1}^{6} \left(\frac{2e^{ct_i} \left[ae^{ct_i} - H_i \left(e^{ct_i} + b \right) \right]}{\left(e^{ct_i} + b \right)^2} \right) = 0$$

$$\sum_{i=1}^{6} \left(\frac{2ae^{ct_i} \left[bH_i + e^{ct_i} \left(H_i - a \right) \right]}{\left(e^{ct_i} + b \right)^3} \right) = 0$$

$$\sum_{i=1}^{6} \left(\frac{-2abt_i e^{ct_i} \left[bH_i + e^{ct_i} \left(H_i - a \right) \right]}{\left(e^{ct_i} + b \right)^3} \right) = 0 \qquad \text{(14a,b,c)}$$

We need initial guesses of the roots to get the iterative process started to find the root of those equations. Suppose we use three of the given data points such as $(0, 20)$, $(12, 60)$ and $(18, 70)$ to find the initial guesses of roots; we have

$$20 = \frac{a}{1 + be^{-c(0)}}$$

$$60 = \frac{a}{1 + be^{-c(12)}}$$

$$70 = \frac{a}{1 + be^{-c(18)}}$$

One can solve three unknowns a, b and c from the three equations as

$$a = 7.5534 \times 10^1$$
$$b = 2.7767$$
$$c = 1.9772 \times 10^{-1}$$

Applying the Newton-Raphson method for simultaneous nonlinear equations, one can get the roots

$$a = 7.4321 \times 10^1$$
$$b = 2.8233$$
$$c = 2.1715 \times 10^{-1}$$

The saturation growth model of the height of the child then is

$$H = \frac{7.4321 \times 10^1}{1 + 2.8233e^{-2.1715 \times 10^{-1} t}}$$

The height of the child as an adult of 30 years of age is

$$H = \frac{7.4321 \times 10^1}{1 + 2.8233e^{-2.1715 \times 10^{-1} \times (30)}}$$
$$= 74"$$

Polynomial Models

Given n data points $(x_1, y_1), (x_2, y_2), \ldots, (x_n, y_n)$ use least squares method to regress the data to an mth order polynomial.

$$y = a_0 + a_1 x + a_2 x^2 + \cdots + a_m x^m, m < n \qquad (15)$$

The residual at each data point is given by

$$E_i = y_i - a_0 - a_1 x_i - \ldots - a_m x_i^m \qquad (16)$$

The sum of the square of the residuals is given by

$$S_r = \sum_{i=1}^{n} E_i^2$$

$$= \sum_{i=1}^{n} \left(y_i - a_0 - a_1 x_i - \ldots - a_m x_i^m \right)^2$$

(17)

To find the constants of the polynomial regression model, we put the derivatives with respect to a_i to zero, that is,

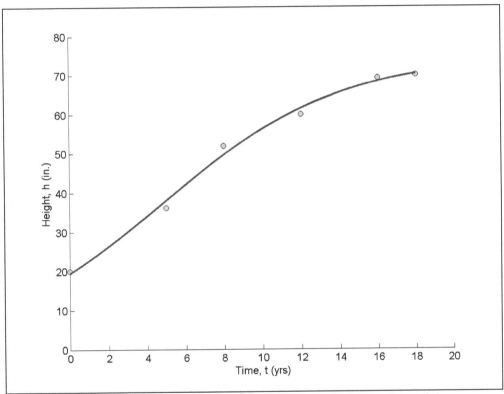

Figure 2 Height of child as a function of age saturation growth model.

$$\frac{\partial S_r}{\partial a_0} = \sum_{i=1}^{n} 2 \left(y_i - a_0 - a_1 x_i - \ldots - a_m x_i^m \right)(-1) = 0$$

$$\frac{\partial S_r}{\partial a_1} = \sum_{i=1}^{n} 2 \left(y_i - a_0 - a_1 x_i - \ldots - a_m x_i^m \right)(-x_i) = 0$$

.   . . .

.   . . .

(18)

$$\frac{\partial S_r}{\partial a_m} = \sum_{i=1}^{n} 2 \left(y_i - a_0 - a_1 x_i - \ldots - a_m x_i^m \right)(-x_i^m) = 0$$

Setting those equations in matrix form gives

$$
\begin{bmatrix}
n & \left(\displaystyle\sum_{i=1}^{n} x_i\right) & \cdots & \left(\displaystyle\sum_{i=1}^{n} x_i^{m}\right) \\
\left(\displaystyle\sum_{i=1}^{n} x_i\right) & \left(\displaystyle\sum_{i=1}^{n} x_i^{2}\right) & \cdots & \left(\displaystyle\sum_{i=1}^{n} x_i^{m+1}\right) \\
\cdots & \cdots & \cdots & \cdots \\
\left(\displaystyle\sum_{i=1}^{n} x_i^{m}\right) & \left(\displaystyle\sum_{i=1}^{n} x_i^{m+1}\right) & \cdots & \left(\displaystyle\sum_{i=1}^{n} x_i^{2m}\right)
\end{bmatrix}
\begin{bmatrix} a_0 \\ a_1 \\ \cdots \\ a_m \end{bmatrix}
=
\begin{bmatrix}
\displaystyle\sum_{i=1}^{n} y_i \\
\displaystyle\sum_{i=1}^{n} x_i y_i \\
\cdots \\
\displaystyle\sum_{i=1}^{n} x_i^{m} y_i
\end{bmatrix}
\qquad (19)
$$

The above are solved for $a_0, a_1, ..., a_m$

Example 3

To find contraction of a steel cylinder, one needs to regress the thermal expansion coefficient data to temperature

Table 4 The thermal expansion coefficient at given different temperatures

Temperature, T ($^\circ$F)	Coefficient of thermal expansion, α (in/in/$^\circ$F)
80	6.47×10^{-6}
40	6.24×10^{-6}
-40	5.72×10^{-6}
-120	5.09×10^{-6}
-200	4.30×10^{-6}
-280	3.33×10^{-6}
-340	2.45×10^{-6}

Fit the above data to $\alpha = a_0 + a_1 T + a_2 T^2$

Solution

Since $\alpha = a_0 + a_1 T + a_2 T^2$ is the quadratic relationship between the thermal expansion coefficient and the temperature, the coefficients a_0, a_1, a_2 are found as follows

$$
\begin{bmatrix}
n & \left(\displaystyle\sum_{i=1}^{n} T_i\right) & \left(\displaystyle\sum_{i=1}^{n} T_i^{2}\right) \\
\left(\displaystyle\sum_{i=1}^{n} T_i\right) & \left(\displaystyle\sum_{i=1}^{n} T_i^{2}\right) & \left(\displaystyle\sum_{i=1}^{n} T_i^{3}\right) \\
\left(\displaystyle\sum_{i=1}^{n} T_i^{2}\right) & \left(\displaystyle\sum_{i=1}^{n} T_i^{3}\right) & \left(\displaystyle\sum_{i=1}^{n} T_i^{4}\right)
\end{bmatrix}
\begin{bmatrix} a_0 \\ a_1 \\ a_2 \end{bmatrix}
=
\begin{bmatrix}
\displaystyle\sum_{i=1}^{n} \alpha_i \\
\displaystyle\sum_{i=1}^{n} T_i \alpha_i \\
\displaystyle\sum_{i=1}^{n} T_i^{2} \alpha_i
\end{bmatrix}
$$

Table 5 Summations for calculating constants of model

i	$T(^\circ F)$	α (in/in/$^\circ$F)	T^2	T^3
1	80	6.4700×10^{-6}	6.4000×10^3	5.1200×10^5
2	40	6.2400×10^{-6}	1.6000×10^3	6.4000×10^4
3	-40	5.7200×10^{-6}	1.6000×10^3	-6.4000×10^4
4	-120	5.0900×10^{-6}	1.4400×10^4	-1.7280×10^6
5	-200	4.3000×10^{-6}	4.0000×10^4	-8.0000×10^6
6	-280	3.3300×10^{-6}	7.8400×10^4	-2.1952×10^7
7	-340	2.4500×10^{-6}	1.1560×10^5	-3.9304×10^7
$\sum_{i=1}^{7}$	-8.6000×10^2	3.3600×10^{-5}	2.5800×10^5	-7.0472×10^7

Table 5 (cont)

i	T^4	$T\times\alpha$	$T^2\times\alpha$
1	4.0960×10^7	5.1760×10^{-4}	4.1408×10^{-2}
2	2.5600×10^6	2.4960×10^{-4}	9.9840×10^{-3}
3	2.5600×10^6	-2.2880×10^{-4}	9.1520×10^{-3}
4	2.0736×10^8	-6.1080×10^{-4}	7.3296×10^{-2}
5	1.6000×10^9	-8.6000×10^{-4}	1.7200×10^{-1}
6	6.1466×10^9	-9.3240×10^{-4}	2.6107×10^{-1}
7	1.3363×10^{10}	-8.3300×10^{-4}	2.8322×10^{-1}
$\sum_{i=1}^{7}$	2.1363×10^{10}	-2.6978×10^{-3}	8.5013×10^{-1}

$n = 7$

$$\sum_{i=1}^{7} T_i = -8.6000\times10^{-2}$$

$$\sum_{i=1}^{7} T_i^2 = 2.5580 \times 10^5$$

$$\sum_{i=1}^{7} T_i^3 = -7.0472 \times 10^7$$

$$\sum_{i=1}^{7} T_i^4 = 2.1363 \times 10^{10}$$

$$\sum_{i=1}^{7} \alpha_i = 3.3600 \times 10^{-5}$$

$$\sum_{i=1}^{7} T_i \alpha_i = -2.6978 \times 10^{-3}$$

$$\sum_{i=1}^{7} T_i^2 \alpha_i = 8.5013 \times 10^{-1}$$

We have

$$\begin{bmatrix} 7.0000 & -8.6000 \times 10^2 & 2.5800 \times 10^5 \\ -8.600 \times 10^2 & 2.5800 \times 10^5 & -7.0472 \times 10^7 \\ 2.5800 \times 10^5 & -7.0472 \times 10^7 & 2.1363 \times 10^{10} \end{bmatrix} \begin{bmatrix} a_0 \\ a_1 \\ a_2 \end{bmatrix} = \begin{bmatrix} 3.3600 \times 10^{-5} \\ -2.6978 \times 10^{-3} \\ 8.5013 \times 10^{-1} \end{bmatrix}$$

Solving the above system of simultaneous linear equations, we get

$$\begin{bmatrix} a_0 \\ a_1 \\ a_2 \end{bmatrix} = \begin{bmatrix} 6.0217 \times 10^{-6} \\ 6.2782 \times 10^{-9} \\ -1.2218 \times 10^{-11} \end{bmatrix}$$

The polynomial regression model is

$$\alpha = a_0 + a_1 T + a_2 T^2$$
$$= 6.0217 \times 10^{-6} + 6.2782 \times 10^{-9} T - 1.2218 \times 10^{-11} T^2$$

Transforming the data to use linear regression formulas

Examination of the nonlinear models above shows that in general iterative methods are required to estimate the values of the model parameters. It is sometimes useful to use simple linear regression formulas to estimate the parameters of a nonlinear model. This involves first transforming the given data such as to regress it to a linear model. Following the transformation of the data, the evaluation of model parameters lends itself to a direct solution approach using the least squares method. Data for nonlinear models such as exponential, power, and growth can be transformed.

<u>Exponential Model</u>

As given in Example 1, many physical and chemical processes are governed by the exponential function.

$$\gamma = ae^{bx} \tag{20}$$

Taking natural log of both sides of Equation (20) gives

$$\ln \gamma = \ln a + bx \tag{21}$$

Let

$$z = \ln \gamma$$

$$a_0 = \ln a \quad \text{implying} \quad a = e^{a_o}$$

$$a_1 = b$$

then

$$z = a_0 + a_1 x \tag{22}$$

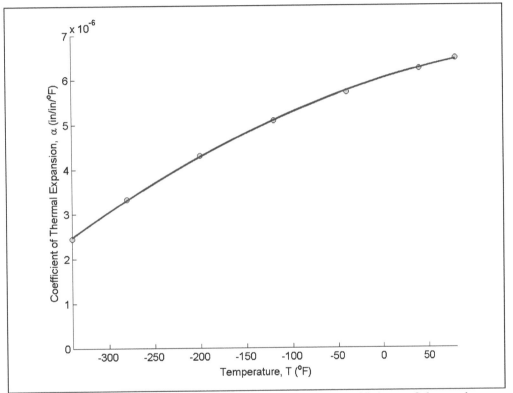

Figure 3 Second-order polynomial regression model for coefficient of thermal expansion as a function of temperature.

The data z versus x is now a linear model. The constants a_0 and a_1 can be found using the equation for the linear model as

$$a_1 = \frac{n \sum_{i=1}^{n} x_i z_i - \sum_{i=1}^{n} x_i \sum_{i=1}^{n} z_i}{n \sum_{i=1}^{n} x_i^2 - \left(\sum_{i=1}^{n} x_i\right)^2} \tag{23a,b}$$

$$a_0 = \bar{z} - a_1 \bar{x}$$

Now since a_0 and a_1 are found, the original constants with the model are found as

$$b = a_1$$
$$a = e^{a_0}$$

(24a,b)

Example 4

Repeat Example 1 using linearization of data.

Solution

$$\gamma = A e^{\lambda t}$$
$$\ln(\gamma) = \ln(A) + \lambda t$$

Assuming

$$y = \ln \gamma$$
$$a_0 = \ln(A)$$
$$a_1 = \lambda$$

We get

$$y = a_0 + a_1 t$$

This is a linear relationship between y and t.

$$a_1 = \frac{n \sum\limits_{i=1}^{n} t_i y_i - \sum\limits_{i=1}^{n} t_i \sum\limits_{i=1}^{n} y_i}{n \sum\limits_{i=1}^{n} t_i^2 - \left(\sum\limits_{i=1}^{n} t_i\right)^2}$$

$$a_0 = \bar{y} - a_1 \bar{t}$$

(25a,b)

Table 6 Summations of data to calculate constants of model.

i	t_i	γ_i	$y_i = \ln \gamma_i$	$t_i y_i$	t_i^2
1	0	1	0.00000	0.0000	0.0000
2	1	0.891	-0.11541	-0.11541	1.0000
3	3	0.708	-0.34531	-1.0359	9.0000
4	5	0.562	-0.57625	-2.8813	25.000
5	7	0.447	-0.80520	-5.6364	49.000
6	9	0.355	-1.0356	-9.3207	81.000
$\sum\limits_{i=1}^{6}$	25.000		-2.8778	-18.990	165.00

$$n = 6$$

$$\sum\limits_{i=1}^{6} t_i = 25.000$$

$$\sum\limits_{i=1}^{6} y_i = -2.8778$$

$$\sum_{i=1}^{6} t_i y_i = -18.990$$

$$\sum_{i=1}^{6} t_i^2 = 165.00$$

From Equation (25a,b) we have

$$a_1 = \frac{6(-18.990) - (25)(-2.8778)}{6(165.00) - (25)^2}$$

$$= -0.11505$$

$$a_0 = \frac{-2.8778}{6} - (-0.11505)\frac{25}{6}$$

$$= -2.6150 \times 10^{-4}$$

Since

$$a_0 = \ln(A)$$

$$A = e^{a_0}$$

$$= e^{-2.6150 \times 10^{-4}}$$

$$= 0.99974$$

$$\lambda = a_1 = -0.11505$$

The regression formula then is

$$\gamma = 0.99974 \times e^{-0.11505t}$$

Compare the formula to the one obtained without data linearization,

$$\gamma = 0.99983 \times e^{-0.11508t}$$

b) Half-life is when

$$\gamma = \frac{1}{2}\gamma\Big|_{t=0}$$

$$0.99974 \times e^{-0.11505t} = \frac{1}{2}(0.99974)e^{-0.11505(0)}$$

$$e^{-0.11508t} = 0.5$$

$$-0.11505t = \ln(0.5)$$

$$t = 6.0248 \text{ hours}$$

c) The relative intensity of radiation, after 24 hours is

$$\gamma = 0.99974e^{-0.11505(24)}$$

$$= 0.063200$$

This implies that only $\dfrac{6.3200 \times 10^{-2}}{0.99974} \times 100 = 6.3216\%$ of the initial radioactivity is left after 24 hours.

Logarithmic Functions

The form for the log regression models is

$$y = \beta_0 + \beta_1 \ln(x) \tag{26}$$

This is a linear function between y and $\ln(x)$ and the usual least squares method applies in which y is the response variable and $\ln(x)$ is the regressor.

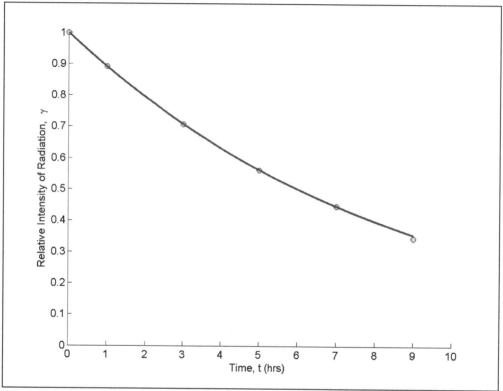

Figure 4 Exponential regression model with transformed data for relative intensity of radiation as a function of temperature.

Example 5

Sodium borohydride is a potential fuel for fuel cell. The following overpotential (η) vs. current (i) data was obtained in a study conducted to evaluate its electrochemical kinetics.

Table 7 Electrochemical Kinetics of borohydride data.

$\eta\,(V)$	-0.29563	-0.24346	-0.19012	-0.18772	-0.13407	-0.0861
$i\,(A)$	0.00226	0.00212	0.00206	0.00202	0.00199	0.00195

At the conditions of the study, it is known that the relationship that exists between the overpotential (η) and current (i) can be expressed as

$$\eta = a + b\ln i \tag{27}$$

where a is an electrochemical kinetics parameter of borohydride on the electrode. Use the data in Table 7 to evaluate the values of a and b.

Solution

Following the least squares method, Table 8 is tabulated where

$$x = \ln i$$
$$y = \eta$$

We obtain

$$y = a + bx \tag{28}$$

This is a linear relationship between y and x, and the coefficients b and a are found as follow

$$b = \frac{n\sum_{i=1}^{n} x_i y_i - \sum_{i=1}^{n} x_i \sum_{i=1}^{n} y_i}{n\sum_{i=1}^{n} x_i^2 - \left(\sum_{i=1}^{n} x_i\right)^2}$$

$$a = \bar{y} - b\bar{x} \tag{29a,b}$$

Table 8 Summation values for calculating constants of model

#	i	$y = \eta$	$x = \ln(i)$	x^2	$x \times y$
1	0.00226	-0.29563	-6.0924	37.117	1.8011
2	0.00212	-0.24346	-6.1563	37.901	1.4988
3	0.00206	-0.19012	-6.1850	38.255	1.1759
4	0.00202	-0.18772	-6.2047	38.498	1.1647
5	0.00199	-0.13407	-6.2196	38.684	0.83386
6	0.00195	-0.08610	-6.2399	38.937	0.53726
$\sum_{i=1}^{6}$	0.012400	-1.1371	-37.098	229.39	7.0117

$$n = 6$$

$$\sum_{i=1}^{6} x_i = -37.098$$

$$\sum_{i=1}^{6} y_i = -1.1371$$

$$\sum_{i=1}^{6} x_i y_i = 7.0117$$

$$\sum_{i=1}^{6} x_i^2 = 229.39$$

$$b = \frac{6(7.0117) - (-37.098)(-1.1371)}{6(229.39) - (-37.098)^2}$$

$$= -1.3601$$

$$a = \frac{-1.1371}{6} - (-1.3601)\frac{-37.098}{6}$$
$$= -8.5990$$

Hence

$$\eta = -8.5990 - 1.3601 \times \ln i$$

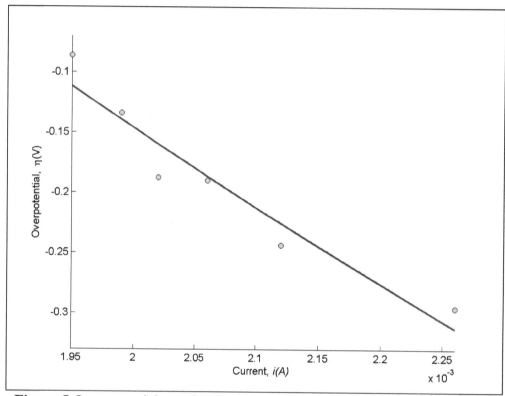

Figure 5 Overpotential as a function of current. $\eta(V)$

Power Functions

The power function equation describes many scientific and engineering phenomena. In chemical engineering, the rate of chemical reaction is often written in power function form as

$$y = ax^b \tag{30}$$

The method of least squares is applied to the power function by first linearizing the data (the assumption is that b is not known). If the only unknown is a, then a linear relation exists between x^b and y. The linearization of the data is as follows.

$$\ln(y) = \ln(a) + b\ln(x) \tag{31}$$

The resulting equation shows a linear relation between $\ln(y)$ and $\ln(x)$.

Let

$$z = \ln y$$

$$w = \ln(x)$$

$$a_0 = \ln a \quad \text{implying} \quad a = e^{a_0}$$

$$a_1 = b$$

we get

$$z = a_0 + a_1 w \tag{32}$$

$$a_1 = \frac{n\sum_{i=1}^{n} w_i z_i - \sum_{i=1}^{n} w_i \sum_{i=1}^{n} z_i}{n\sum_{i=1}^{n} w_i^2 - \left(\sum_{i=1}^{n} w_i\right)^2} \tag{33a,b}$$

$$a_0 = \frac{\sum_{i=1}^{n} z_i}{n} - a_1 \frac{\sum_{i=1}^{n} w_i}{n}$$

Since a_0 and a_1 can be found, the original constants of the model are

$$b = a_1 \tag{34a,b}$$

$$a = e^{a_0}$$

Example 6

The progress of a homogeneous chemical reaction is followed and it is desired to evaluate the rate constant and the order of the reaction. The rate law expression for the reaction is known to follow the power function form

$$-r = kC^n \tag{35}$$

Use the data provided in the table to obtain n and k.

Table 9 Chemical kinetics.

C_A(gmol/l)	4	2.25	1.45	1.0	0.65	0.25	0.006
$-r_A$(gmol/l·s)	0.398	0.298	0.238	0.198	0.158	0.098	0.048

Solution

Taking the natural log of both sides of Equation (35), we obtain

$$\ln(-r) = \ln(k) + n\ln(C)$$

Let

$$z = \ln(-r)$$

$$w = \ln(C)$$

$$a_0 = \ln(k) \quad \text{implying that} \quad k = e^{a_0} \tag{36}$$

$$a_1 = n \tag{37}$$

We get

$$z = a_0 + a_1 w$$

This is a linear relation between z and w, where

$$a_1 = \frac{n \sum_{i=1}^{n} w_i z_i - \sum_{i=1}^{n} w_i \sum_{i=1}^{n} z_i}{n \sum_{i=1}^{n} w_i^2 - \left(\sum_{i=1}^{n} w_i \right)^2}$$

$$a_0 = \left(\frac{\sum_{i=1}^{n} z_i}{n} \right) - a_1 \left(\frac{\sum_{i=1}^{n} w_i}{n} \right) \qquad (38a,b)$$

Table 10 Kinetics rate law using power function

i	C	$-r$	w	z	$w \times z$	w^2
1	4	0.398	1.3863	-0.92130	-1.2772	1.9218
2	2.25	0.298	0.8109	-1.2107	-0.9818	0.65761
3	1.45	0.238	0.3716	-1.4355	-0.5334	0.13806
4	1	0.198	0.0000	-1.6195	0.0000	0.00000
5	0.65	0.158	-0.4308	-1.8452	0.7949	0.18557
6	0.25	0.098	-1.3863	-2.3228	3.2201	1.9218
7	0.006	0.048	-5.1160	-3.0366	15.535	26.173
$\sum_{i=1}^{7}$			-4.3643	-12.391	16.758	30.998

$n = 7$

$$\sum_{i=1}^{7} w_i = -4.3643$$

$$\sum_{i=1}^{7} z_i = -12.391$$

$$\sum_{i=1}^{7} w_i z_i = 16.758$$

$$\sum_{i=1}^{7} w_i^2 = 30.998$$

From Equation (38a,b)

$$a_1 = \frac{7 \times (16.758) - (-4.3643) \times (-12.391)}{7 \times (30.998) - (-4.3643)^2}$$

$$= 0.31943$$

$$a_0 = \frac{-12.391}{7} - (.31943)\frac{-4.3643}{7}$$

$$= -1.5711$$

From Equation (36) and (37), we obtain

$$k = e^{-1.5711}$$

$$= 0.20782$$

$$n = a_1$$

$$= 0.31941$$

Finally, the model of progress of that chemical reaction is

$$-r = 0.20782 \times C^{0.31941}$$

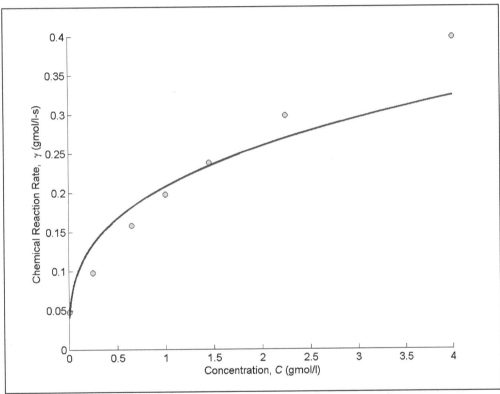

Figure 6 Kinetic chemical reaction rate as a function of concentration.

Growth Model
Growth models common in scientific fields have been developed and used successfully for specific situations. The growth models are used to describe how something grows with changes in a regressor variable (often the time). Examples in this category include growth of thin films or population with time. In the logistic growth model, an example of a growth model in which a measurable quantity y varies with some quantity x is

$$y = \frac{ax}{b+x} \tag{39}$$

For $x = 0$, $y = 0$ while as $x \to \infty$, $y \to a$. To linearize the data for this method,

$$\frac{1}{y} = \frac{b+x}{ax}$$

$$= \frac{b}{a}\frac{1}{x} + \frac{1}{a} \qquad (40)$$

Let

$$z = \frac{1}{y}$$

$$w = \frac{1}{x},$$

$$a_0 = \frac{1}{a} \text{ implying that } a = \frac{1}{a_0}$$

$$a_1 = \frac{b}{a} \text{ implying } b = a_1 \times a = \frac{a_1}{a_0}$$

Then

$$z = a_0 + a_1 w \qquad (41)$$

The relationship between z and w is linear with the coefficients a_0 and found as follows.

$$a_1 = \frac{n\displaystyle\sum_{i=1}^{n} w_i z_i - \sum_{i=1}^{n} w_i \sum_{i=1}^{n} z_i}{n\displaystyle\sum_{i=1}^{n} w_i^2 - \left(\sum_{i=1}^{n} w_i\right)^2}$$

$$a_0 = \left(\frac{\displaystyle\sum_{i=1}^{n} z_i}{n}\right) - a_1 \left(\frac{\displaystyle\sum_{i=1}^{n} w_i}{n}\right) \qquad (42a,b)$$

Finding a_0 and a_1, then gives the constants of the original growth model as

$$a = \frac{1}{a_0}$$

$$b = \frac{a_1}{a_0} \qquad (43a,b)$$

NONLINEAR REGRESSION	
Topic	Nonlinear Regression
Summary	Textbook notes of Nonlinear Regression
Major	General Engineering
Authors	Egwu Kalu, Autar Kaw, Cuong Nguyen
Date	April 1, 2010
Web Site	http://numericalmethods.eng.usf.edu

Multiple-Choice Test

Chapter 06.04
Non-Linear Regression

1. When using the linearized data model to find the constants of the regression model $y = ae^{bx}$ to best fit $(x_1, y_1), (x_2, y_2), \ldots, (x_n, y_n)$, the sum of the square of the residuals that is minimized is

   (A) $\displaystyle\sum_{i=1}^{n} \left(y_i - ae^{bx_i}\right)^2$

   (B) $\displaystyle\sum_{i=1}^{n} \left(\ln(y_i) - \ln(a) - bx_i\right)^2$

   (C) $\displaystyle\sum_{i=1}^{n} \left(y_i - \ln(a) - bx_i\right)^2$

   (D) $\displaystyle\sum_{i=1}^{n} \left(\ln(y_i) - \ln(a) - b\ln(x_i)\right)^2$

2. It is suspected from theoretical considerations that the rate of water flow from a firehouse is proportional to some power of the nozzle pressure. Assume pressure data is more accurate. You are transforming the data.

Flow rate, F (gallons/min)	96	129	135	145	168	235
Pressure, p (psi)	11	17	20	25	40	55

   The exponent of the nozzle pressure in the regression model $F = ap^b$ most nearly is
   (A) 0.49721
   (B) 0.55625
   (C) 0.57821
   (D) 0.67876

3. The linearized data model for the stress-strain curve $\sigma = k_1 \varepsilon e^{-k_2 \varepsilon}$ for concrete in compression, where σ is the stress and ε is the strain, is

   (A) $\ln(\sigma) = \ln(k_1) + \ln(\varepsilon) - k_2 \varepsilon$

   (B) $\ln\left(\dfrac{\sigma}{\varepsilon}\right) = \ln(k_1) - k_2 \varepsilon$

   (C) $\ln\left(\dfrac{\sigma}{\varepsilon}\right) = \ln(k_1) + k_2 \varepsilon$

   (D) $\ln(\sigma) = \ln(k_1 \varepsilon) - k_2 \varepsilon$

06.04.1

4. In nonlinear regression, finding the constants of the model requires solving simultaneous nonlinear equations. However in the exponential model $y = ae^{bx}$ that is best fit to $(x_1, y_1), (x_2, y_2), \ldots, (x_n, y_n)$, the value of b can be found as a solution of a nonlinear equation. That equation is given by

(A) $\displaystyle\sum_{i=1}^{n} y_i x_i e^{bx_i} - \sum_{i=1}^{n} y_i e^{bx_i} \sum_{i=1}^{n} x_i = 0$

(B) $\displaystyle\sum_{i=1}^{n} y_i x_i e^{bx_i} - \frac{\displaystyle\sum_{i=1}^{n} y_i e^{bx_i}}{\displaystyle\sum_{i=1}^{n} e^{2bx_i}} \sum_{i=1}^{n} x_i e^{2bx_i} = 0$

(C) $\displaystyle\sum_{i=1}^{n} y_i x_i e^{bx_i} - \frac{\displaystyle\sum_{i=1}^{n} y_i e^{bx_i}}{\displaystyle\sum_{i=1}^{n} e^{2bx_i}} \sum_{i=1}^{n} e^{bx_i} = 0$

(D) $\displaystyle\sum_{i=1}^{n} y_i e^{bx_i} - \frac{\displaystyle\sum_{i=1}^{n} y_i e^{bx_i}}{\displaystyle\sum_{i=1}^{n} e^{2bx_i}} \sum_{i=1}^{n} x_i e^{2bx_i} = 0$

5. There is a functional relationship between the mass density p of air and the altitude h above the sea level.

Altitude above sea level, h (km)	0.32	0.64	1.28	1.60
Mass Density, ρ (kg/m^3)	1.15	1.10	1.05	0.95

In the regression model $\rho = k_1 e^{-k_2 h}$, the constant k_2 is found as $k_2 = 0.1315$. Assuming the mass density of air at the top of the atmosphere is $1/1000^{th}$ of the mass density of air at sea level. The altitude in kilometers of the top of the atmosphere most nearly is
(A) 46.2
(B) 46.6
(C) 49.7
(D) 52.5

6. A steel cylinder at $80°$ F of length 12" is placed in a commercially available liquid nitrogen bath $(-315°$ F$)$. If the thermal expansion coefficient of steel behaves as a second order polynomial that is a function of temperature and the polynomial is found by regressing the data below,

Temperature, T (°F)	Thermal expansion Coefficient, α (μ in/in/°F)
-320	2.76
-240	3.83
-160	4.72
-80	5.43
0	6.00
80	6.47

the reduction in the length of the cylinder in inches most nearly is

(A)   0.0219
(B)   0.0231
(C)   0.0235
(D)   0.0307

Complete Solution

Problem Set

Chapter 06.04
Nonlinear Regression

1. It is suspected from theoretical considerations that the rate of flow from a fire hose is proportional to some power of the nozzle pressure. Determine whether the speculation is true. What is the exponent of the data? Assume pressure data is more accurate. You are allowed to linearize the data.

Flow rate (gallons/min), F	94	118	147	180	230
Pressure (psi), p	10	16	25	40	60

2. The following force vs. displacement data is given for a nonlinear spring.

Displacement, x (m)	10	15	20
Force, F (N)	100	200	400

    By minimizing the sum of the square of the residuals and without data linearization, the above F vs x data is regressed to $F = kx^2$. Find the value of k.

3. Data points $(x_1, y_1), (x_2, y_2), \ldots, (x_n, y_n)$ is regressed to $y = \dfrac{1}{(ax+b)^2}$. The constants of the model a and b are solved by data linearization. Find the formulas for calculating a and b?
    Hint: Take the inverse and square-root of both sides.

4. Fit $\sigma = K_1 \varepsilon e^{-K_2 \varepsilon}$ to the following stress-strain curve data of concrete. You are allowed to linearize the data. Units of stress, σ are psi and units of strain, ε are $\mu\,\text{in/in}$.

σ	2250	3575	4250	4400	4200
ε	500	1000	1500	2000	2375

5. It is desired to obtain a functional relationship between the mass density ρ of air and the altitude h above the sea level for the dynamic analysis of bodies moving within earth's atmosphere. Use the approximation $\rho = k_1 e^{-k_2 h}$ to fit the data given below by regression analysis. Find the constants k_1 and k_2. You are allowed to linearize the data.

Altitude (kilometers)	Mass density (kg/m^3)
0.32	1.15
0.64	1.10
1.28	1.05
1.60	0.95

06.04.1

6.   You are working for Valdez SpillProof Oil Company as a petroleum engineer. Your boss is asking you to estimate the life of an oil well. The analysis used in the industry is called the *decline curve analysis* where the barrels of oil produced per unit time are plotted against time, and the curve is extrapolated. One of the standard curves used is the harmonic decline model, that is

$$q = \frac{b}{1+at}$$

where q is the rate of production and t is the time, b and a are the constants of the regression model.

Time (t), month	2	6	10	14	18
Rate of production (q), barrels per day	260	189	120	87	75

a) Find the constants of the regression model. Hint: You are allowed to linearize the data if possible.
b) Find the total life of an oil field if 5 barrels per day is considered the production at which the field needs to be abandoned for further production.
c) What does b stand for physically?

7.   From the physical understanding of a phenomenon, the velocity of a body is suspected to follow the relationship $v = at^2$, where v is the velocity and t is the time. Given n data points $(t_1, v_1), (t_2, v_2), \ldots, (t_n, v_n)$, start from the fundamentals of minimizing the sum of the squares of the residuals to derive a single equation in terms of the time and velocity data to find the value of a. Simplify the equation. You are not allowed to linearize the data.

8.   The population for a small community is given as a function of time.

t (years)	0	5	10
Population, p	100	165	314

By minimizing the sum of the square of the residuals and without data linearization, the model is regressed to $p = ae^{bt}$, where a and b are constants of the model. The value of b was found to be 0.1199. Find the value of a?

9.   Fit $W = at^2 + bt + c$ to the following data to find $W(360)$

t	0	2	4	6	18
W	7.5	11.25	14.30	16.00	26.00

The data given above is actually the weight (lbs) of a baby as a function of the age (months) of the baby. We expect that the weight of the baby to saturate as the baby reaches adulthood. Suggest a different model and estimate $W(360)$.

10. The temperature of a copper sphere cooling in air is measured as a function of time to yield the following data.

Time, t (s)	0.2	0.6	1.0	2.0
Temperature, T (°C)	146.0	129.5	114.8	85.1

From theoretical considerations, an exponential decrease of temperature is expected as a function of time. One can assume a regression model given by $T = Ae^{-0.3t}$. Starting from minimizing the sum of the residuals, find the constant of the model, A .

11. There is a functional relationship between the mass density ρ of air and altitude h above the sea level, and is found from the data below.

Altitude above sea level, h (km)	0.32	0.64	1.28	1.60
Mass Density, ρ (kg/m^3)	1.15	1.10	1.05	0.95

This functional relationship is found by regression using the model $\rho = k_1 e^{-k_2 h}$. The constant k_2 is found as $k_2 = 0.1315$. Assuming the mass density of air at the top of the atmosphere is $1/1000^{th}$ of the mass density of air at sea level, find the altitude above the sea level in km of the top of the atmosphere.

Chapter 06.05
Adequacy of Models for Regression

Quality of Fitted Model

In the application of regression models, one objective is to obtain an equation $y = f(x)$ that best describes the n response data points $(x_1, y_1), (x_2, y_2), \ldots, (x_n, y_n)$. Consequently, we are faced with answering two basic questions.

1. Does the model $y = f(x)$ describe the data adequately, that is, is there an adequate fit?
2. How well does the model predict the response variable (predictability)?

To answer these questions, let us limit our discussion to straight line models as nonlinear models require a different approach. Some authors [1] claim that nonlinear model parameters are not unbiased.

To exemplify our discussion, we will take example data to go through the process of model evaluation. Given below is the data for the coefficient of thermal expansion vs. temperature for steel. We assume a linear relationship between the data as
$$\alpha(T) = a_0 + a_1 T$$

Table 1 Values of coefficient of thermal expansion vs. temperature.

$T(^\circ\mathrm{F})$	α (μin/in/$^\circ$F)
-340	2.45
-260	3.58
-180	4.52
-100	5.28
-20	5.86
60	6.36

Following the procedure for conducting linear regression as given in Chapter 06.03, we get
$$\alpha(T) = 6.0325 + 0.0096964 T$$
Let us now look at how we can evaluate the adequacy of a linear regression model.

1. Plot the data and the regression model.
Figure 1 shows the data and the regression model. From a visual check, it looks like the model explains the data adequately.

06.05.1

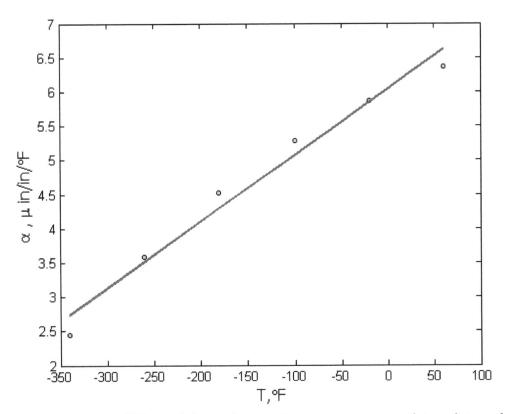

Figure 1 Plot of coefficient of thermal expansion vs. temperature data points and regression line.

2. **Calculate the standard error of estimate**.
The standard error of estimate is defined as

$$s_{\alpha/T} = \sqrt{\frac{S_r}{n-2}}$$

where

$$S_r = \sum_{i=1}^{n} (\alpha_i - a_0 - a_1 T_i)^2$$

Table 2 Residuals for data.

T_i	α_i	$a_0 + a_1 T_i$	$\alpha_i - a_0 - a_1 T_i$
-340	2.45	2.7357	-0.28571
-260	3.58	3.5114	0.068571
-180	4.52	4.2871	0.23286
-100	5.28	5.0629	0.21714
-20	5.86	5.8386	0.021429
60	6.36	6.6143	-0.25429

Table 2 shows the residuals of the data to calculate the sum of the square of residuals as

$$S_r = (-0.28571)^2 + (0.068571)^2 + (0.23286)^2 + (0.21714)^2$$
$$+ (0.021429)^2 + (-0.25429)^2$$
$$= 0.25283$$

The standard error of estimate

$$s_{\alpha/T} = \sqrt{\frac{S_r}{n-2}}$$
$$= \sqrt{\frac{0.25283}{6-2}}$$
$$= 0.25141$$

The units of $s_{\alpha/T}$ are same as the units of α. How is the value of the standard error of estimate interpreted? We may say that on average the difference between the observed and predicted values is $0.25141\,\mu in/in/^\circ F$. Also, we can look at the value as follows. About 95% of the observed α values are between $\pm 2s_{\alpha/T}$ of the predicted value (see Figure 2). This would lead us to believe that the value of α in the example is expected to be accurate within $\pm 2s_{\alpha/T} = \pm 2 \times 0.25141 = \pm 0.50282\,\mu in/in/^\circ F$.

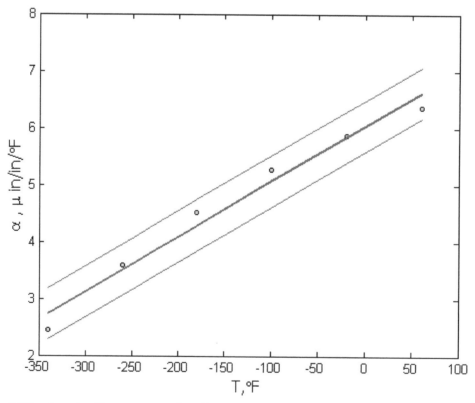

Figure 2 Plotting the linear regression line and showing the regression standard error.

One can also look at this criterion as finding if 95% of the scaled residuals for the model are in the domain [-2,2], that is

$$\text{Scaled residual} = \frac{\alpha_i - a_0 - a_1 T_i}{s_{\alpha/T}}$$

For the example,

$$s_{\alpha/T} = 0.25141$$

Table 4 Residuals and scaled residuals for data.

T_i	α_i	$\alpha_i - a_0 - a_1 T_i$	Scaled Residuals
-340	2.45	-0.28571	-1.1364
-260	3.58	0.068571	0.27275
-180	4.52	0.23286	0.92622
-100	5.28	0.21714	0.86369
-20	5.86	0.021429	0.085235
60	6.36	-0.25429	-1.0115

and the scaled residuals are calculated in Table 4. All the scaled residuals are in the [-2,2] domain.

3. **Calculate the coefficient of determination.**

Denoted by r^2, the coefficient of determination is another criterion to use for checking the adequacy of the model.

To answer the above questions, let us start from the examination of some measures of discrepancies between the whole data and some key central tendency. Look at the two equations given below.

$$S_r = \sum_{i=1}^{n} (\alpha_i - \hat{\alpha}_i)^2 \tag{1}$$

$$= \sum_{i=1}^{n} (\alpha_i - a_0 - a_1 T_i)^2$$

$$S_t = \sum_{i=1}^{n} (\alpha_i - \overline{\alpha})^2 \tag{2}$$

where

$$\overline{\alpha} = \frac{\sum_{i=1}^{n} \alpha_i}{n}$$

For the example data

$$\overline{\alpha} = \frac{\sum_{i=1}^{6} \alpha_i}{6}$$

$$= \frac{2.45 + 3.58 + 4.52 + 5.28 + 5.86 + 6.36}{6}$$

$$= 4.6750 \, \mu\text{in/in/}^\circ\text{F}$$

$$S_t = \sum_{i=1}^{n} (\alpha_i - \overline{\alpha})^2$$

$$= (-2.2250)^2 + (-1.0950)^2 + (-0.15500)^2 + (0.60500)^2 + (1.1850)^2 + (1.6850)^2$$
$$= 10.783$$

Table 5 Difference between observed and average value.

T_i	α_i	$\alpha_i - \overline{\alpha}$
-340	2.45	-2.2250
-260	3.58	-1.0950
-180	4.52	-0.15500
-100	5.28	0.60500
-20	5.86	1.1850
60	6.36	1.6850

where S_r is the sum of the square of the residuals (residual is the difference between the observed value and the predicted value), and S_t is the sum of the square of the difference between the observed value and the average value.

What inferences can we make about the two equations? Equation (2) measures the discrepancy between the data and the mean. Recall that the mean of the data is a measure of a single point that measures the central tendency of the whole data. Equation (2) contrasts with Equation (1) as Equation (1) measures the discrepancy between the vertical distance of the point from the regression line (another measure of central tendency). This line obtained by the least squares method gives the best estimate of a line with least sum of deviation. S_r as calculated quantifies the spread around the regression line.

The objective of least squares method is to obtain a compact equation that best describes all the data points. The mean can also be used to describe all the data points. The magnitude of the sum of squares of deviation from the mean or from the least squares line **is therefore a good indicator of how well the mean or least squares characterizes the whole data.** We can liken the sum of squares deviation around the mean, S_t as the error or variability in y without considering the regression variable x, while S_r, the sum of squares deviation around the least square regression line is error or variability in y remaining after the dependent variable x has been considered.

The difference between these two parameters measures the error due to describing or characterizing the data in one form instead of the other. A relative comparison of this difference $(S_t - S_r)$, with the sum of squares deviation associated with the mean S_t describes a quantity called **coefficient of determination**, r^2

$$r^2 = \frac{S_t - S_r}{S_t} \tag{5}$$
$$= \frac{10.783 - 0.25283}{10.783}$$
$$= 0.97655$$

Based on the value obtained above, we can claim that 97.7% of the original uncertainty in the value of α can be explained by the straight-line regression model of $\alpha(T) = 6.0325 + 0.0096964T$.

Going back to the definition of the coefficient of determination, one can see that S_t is the variation without any relationship of y vs. x, while S_r is the variation with the straight-line relationship.

The limits of the values of r^2 are between 0 and 1. What do these limiting values of r^2 mean? If $r^2 = 0$, then $S_t = S_r$, which means that regressing the data to a straight line does nothing to explain the data any further. If $r^2 = 1$, then $S_r = 0$, which means that the straight line is passing through all the data points and is a perfect fit.

Caution in the use of r^2

a) The coefficient of determination, r^2 can be made larger (assumes no collinear points) by adding more terms to the model. For instance, $n-1$ terms in a regression equation for which n data points are used will give an r^2 value of 1 if there are no collinear points.

b) The magnitude of r^2 also depends on the range of variability of the regressor (x) variable. Increase in the spread of x increases r^2 while a decrease in the spread of x decreases r^2.

c) Large regression slope will also yield artificially high r^2.

d) The coefficient of determination, r^2 does not measure the appropriateness of the linear model. r^2 may be large for nonlinearly related x and y values.

e) Large coefficient of determination r^2 value does not necessarily imply the regression will predict accurately.

f) The coefficient of determination , r^2 does not measure the magnitude of the regression slope.

g) These statements above imply that one should not choose a regression model solely based on consideration of r^2.

4. Find if the model meets the assumptions of random errors.

These assumptions include that the residuals are negative as well as positive to give a mean of zero, the variation of the residuals as a function of the independent variable is random, the residuals follow a normal distribution, and that there is no auto correlation between the data points.

To illustrate this better, we have an extended data set for the example that we took. Instead of 6 data points, this set has 22 data points (Table 6). Drawing conclusions from small or large data sets for checking assumption of random error is not recommended.

Table 6 Instantaneous thermal expansion coefficient as a function of temperature.

Temperature	Instantaneous Thermal Expansion
°F	μin/in/°F
80	6.47

60	6.36
40	6.24
20	6.12
0	6.00
-20	5.86
-40	5.72
-60	5.58
-80	5.43
-100	5.28
-120	5.09
-140	4.91
-160	4.72
-180	4.52
-200	4.30
-220	4.08
-240	3.83
-260	3.58
-280	3.33
-300	3.07
-320	2.76
-340	2.45

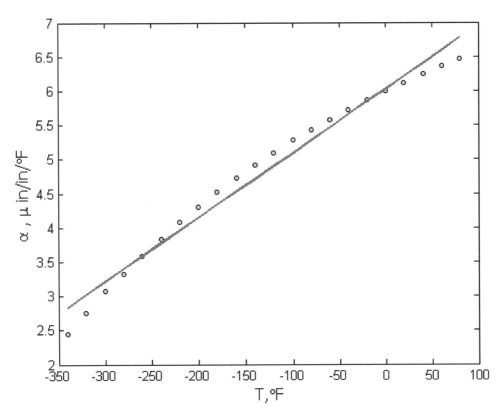

Figure 3 Plot of thermal expansion coefficient vs. temperature data points and regression line for more data points.

Regressing the data from Table 2 to the straight line regression line

$$\alpha(T) = a_0 + a_1 T$$

and following the procedure for conducting linear regression as given in Chapter 06.03, we get (Figure 3)

$$\alpha = 6.0248 + 0.0093868T$$

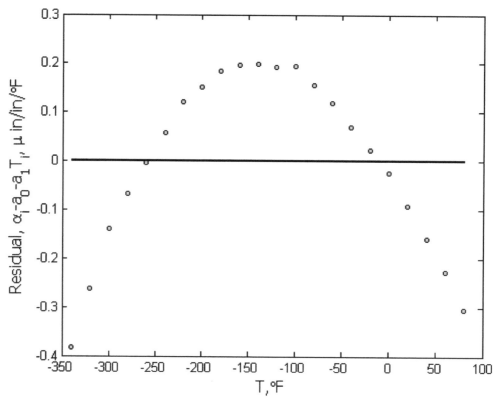

Figure 4 Plot of residuals.

Figure 4 shows the residuals for the example as a function of temperature. Although the residuals seem to average to zero, but within a range, they do not exhibit this zero mean. For an initial value of T, the averages are below zero. For the middle values of T, the averages are below zero, and again for the final values of T, the averages are below zero. This may be considered a violation of the model assumption.

Figure 4 also shows the residuals for the example are following a nonlinear variance. This is a clear violation of the model assumption of constant variance.

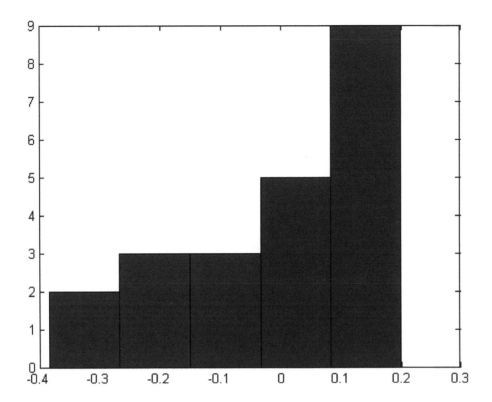

Figure 5 Histogram of residuals.

Figure 5 shows the histogram of the residuals. Clearly, the histogram is not showing a normal distribution, and hence violates the model assumption of normality.

To check that there is no autocorrelation between observed values, the following rule of thumb can be used. If n is the number of data points, and q is the number of times the sign of the residual changes, then if

$$\frac{(n-1)}{2} - \sqrt{n-1} \le q \le \frac{n-1}{2} + \sqrt{n-1},$$

you most likely do not have an autocorrelation. For the example, $n = 22$, then

$$\frac{(22-1)}{2} - \sqrt{22-1} \le q \le \frac{22-1}{2} + \sqrt{22-1}$$

$$5.9174 \le q \le 15.083$$

is not satisfied as $q = 2$. So this model assumption is violated.

References

ADEQUACY OF REGRESSION MODELS	
Topic	Adequacy of Regression Models
Summary	Textbook notes of Adequacy of Regression Models
Major	General Engineering
Authors	Autar Kaw, Egwu Kalu

Date	April 1, 2010
Web Site	http://numericalmethods.eng.usf.edu

Problem Set

Chapter 06.05
Adequacy of Regression Models

1. Water is flowing through a circular pipe of 0.5 ft radius and flow velocity (ft/s) measurements are made from the center to the wall of the pipe as follows.

Radial location, r (ft)	0	0.083	0.17	0.25	0.33	0.42	0.50
Velocity, v (ft/s)		10	9.72	8.88	7.5	5.6	3.1	0

A scientist regresses the data to a straight line and is given by $v(r) = -19.92r + 11.39$.

   a) How much is the absolute relative true error in the flow rate using the above velocity expression if the actual flow rate is $3.9 \text{ ft}^3/\text{s}$?

   b) Regress the data to a second order polynomial of r. What is the absolute relative true error for this case?

   c) Regress the data to a specified second order polynomial, $v = a_0(1 - 4r^2)$. Find the value of a_0. What is the absolute relative true error in this case.

2. The following y vs. x data is regressed to a straight line and is given by $y = -1.398 + 0.3x$.

x	5	6	7	8	9
y	0.3	0.4	0.51	0.6	1.7

Find the coefficient of determination.

3. Many times, you may not know what regression model to use for the given data. In such cases, a suggestion maybe to use a polynomial. But the question remains, what order of polynomial to use? For example, if you are given 10 data points, you can regress the data to a polynomial of order 1, 2, 3, 4, 5, 6, 7, 8 or 9. What order of polynomial would you use? An instructor suggests four different criteria. Only one is correct. Which one would you choose?

   (A) Find the sum of the square of residuals, S_r for all possible polynomials and choose the order for which S_r is minimum.

   (B) Find $\dfrac{\text{sum of the square of residuals}}{(\text{number of data points - order of polynomial})}$ for all possible polynomials and choose the order for which it is minimum.

   (C) Find $\dfrac{\text{sum of the square of residuals}}{(\text{number of data points - order of polynomial - 1})}$ for all possible polynomials and choose the order for which it is minimum.

(D) Find $\dfrac{\text{sum of the square of residuals}}{\text{(number of data points - order of polynomial} + 1)}$ for all possible polynomials and choose the order for which it is minimum.

4. The following y vs. x data is regressed to a straight line and is given by $y = -1.398 + 0.3x$.

x	5	6	7	8	9
y	0.3	0.4	0.51	0.6	1.7

Find the scaled residuals and check how many of them are between in the range $[-2,2]$.

5. Water is flowing through a circular pipe of 0.5 ft radius and flow velocity (ft/s) measurements are made from the center to the wall of the pipe as follows

Radial Location, r (ft)	0	0.083	0.17	0.25	0.33	0.42	0.50
Velocity, v (ft/s)	10	9.72	8.88	7.5	5.6	3.1	0

A scientist regresses the data to a straight line and is given by $v(r) = -19.92r + 11.39$. Verify if the model is adequate based on what you learned in class.

6. Water is flowing through a circular pipe of 0.5ft radius and flow velocity (ft/s) measurements are made from the center to the wall of the pipe as follows

Radial Location, r (ft)	0	0.083	0.17	0.25	0.33	0.42	0.50
Velocity, v (ft/s)	10	9.72	8.88	7.5	5.6	3.1	0

Use an appropriate regression model to find the following.

a) Velocity at $r = 0.3\,\text{ft}$.
b) Rate of change of velocity with respect to radial location at $r = 0.3\,\text{ft}$.
c) An engineer, who thinks he knows everything, calculates the flow rate out of the pipe by averaging the given velocities and multiplying it by the cross-sectional area of the pipe. How will you convince him/her that he/she needs to use a different (better) approach. Hint: The flow rate Q out of the pipe is given by the formula $Q = \displaystyle\int_0^{0.5} v\,dA = \int_0^{0.5} 2\pi r v\,dr$.

7. For the purpose of shrinking a trunnion into a hub, the reduction of diameter, ΔD of a trunnion shaft by cooling it through a temperature change of ΔT, is given by

$$\Delta D = D \int_{T_{room}}^{T_{fluid}} \alpha\,dT$$

where

$D =$ original diameter (in)
$\alpha =$ coefficient of thermal expansion (in/in/$^\circ$F)
$T_{fluid} =$ temperature of dry-ice/alcohol mixture, ($^\circ$F)

T_{room} = room temperature, ($^\circ$ F)

Given below is the table of the coefficient of thermal expansion vs. temperature

Temperature (°F)	Thermal expansion coefficient (μ in/in/°F)
80	6.47
0	6.00
−60	5.58
−160	4.72
−260	3.58
−340	2.45

A diametric contraction of 0.015″ is needed in the trunnion.

Nominal outer diameter of the trunnion =12.363″.

Temperature of dry-ice/alcohol mixture $=-108^\circ$ F

Temperature of liquid nitrogen $=-321^\circ$ F

Room temperature $=80^\circ$ F

    a) Find the regression curve (straight line is not acceptable) for the coefficient of thermal expansion as a function of temperature.

    b) Find the diametric contraction of the trunnion if it is cooled in dry-ice/alcohol mixture? Can this cooling method be recommended to get the needed contraction?

    c) If the answer to part (b) is no, would you recommend cooling it in liquid nitrogen? Why?

Chapter 07.00A

Physical Problem for Integration
General Engineering

Problem

A rocket is going vertically up and expels fuel at a velocity $2000\,\text{m/s}$ at a consumption rate of $2100\,\text{kg/s}$. The initial mass of the rocket is $140{,}000\,\text{kg}$. If the rocket starts from rest at $t = 0$ seconds, how can I calculate the vertical distance covered by the rocket from $t = 8$ to $t = 30$ seconds?

Figure 1 A rocket launched into space

Solution

If

m_0 = initial mass of rocket at $t = 0$ (kg)

q = rate at which fuel is expelled (kg/sec)

u = velocity at which the fuel is being expelled (m/s)

Then since fuel is expelled from the rocket, the mass of the rocket keeps decreasing with time. The mass of rocket, m at any time t

$$m = m_0 - qt$$

The forces on the rocket at any time are found by applying Newton's second law of motion. Then

$$\sum F = ma$$

07.00A.1

$$uq - mg = ma$$

$$uq - (m_0 - qt)g = (m_0 - qt)a$$

where

g = acceleration due to gravity (m/s^2)

$$a = \frac{uq}{m_0 - qt} - g$$

$$\frac{d^2x}{dt^2} = \frac{uq}{m_0 - qt} - g$$

$$\frac{dx}{dt} = -u\log_e(m_0 - qt) - gt + C$$

Since the rocket starts from rest

$$\frac{dx}{dt} = 0 \text{ at } t = 0$$

$$0 = u\log_e(m_0) + C$$

$$C = u\log_e(m_0)$$

Hence

$$\frac{dx}{dt} = -u\log_e(m_0 - qt) - gt + u\log_e(m_0)$$

$$\frac{dx}{dt} = u\log_e\left(\frac{m_0}{m_0 - qt}\right) - gt$$

Then the distance covered by the rocket from $t = t_0$ to $t = t_1$ is,

$$x = \int_{t_0}^{t_1}\left[u\log_e\left(\frac{m_0}{m_0 - qt}\right) - gt\right]dt$$

Let us substitute the values into the above equation. A rocket is going vertically up and expels fuel at a velocity 2000 m/s at a consumption rate of 2100 kg/s. The initial mass of the rocket is 140,000 kg. If the rocket starts from rest at $t = 0$ seconds, how can I calculate the vertical distance covered by the rocket from $t = 8$ to $t = 30$ seconds?

Substituting

$u = 2000 \text{ m/s}$

$m_0 = 140000 \text{ kg}$

$q = 2100 \text{ kg/s}$

$g = 9.8 \text{ m/s}^2$

$t_0 = 8 \text{ s}$

$t_1 = 30 \text{ s}$

$$x = \int_{8}^{30}\left(2000\ln\left[\frac{140000}{140000 - 2100t}\right] - 9.8t\right)dt$$

INTEGRATION	
Topic	Integration
Summary	These are textbook notes of a physical problem for integration
Major	General Engineering
Authors	Autar Kaw, Michael Keteltas
Date	December 23, 2009
Web Site	http://numericalmethods.eng.usf.edu

Chapter 07.00B

Physical Problem for Integration
Chemical Engineering

Although a fuel cell provides DC electricity like an ordinary battery, it differs from an ordinary battery from the fact that its fuel source is externally supplied and as long as the fuel is being supplied, the fuel cell can in theory run continuously without needing a recharge. The two electrochemical reactions in a fuel cell occur at the electrodes (or poles) to which reactants are continuously fed. The reaction at the negative electrode (anode) is maintained by supplying a fuel such as hydrogen or methanol, whereas the positive electrode (cathode) reaction is maintained by the supply of oxygen or air. The two electrodes (anode and cathode) are separated by a proton conducting membrane – polymer electrolyte membrane (PEM).

A schematic diagram showing the operating principles of fuel cell that utilizes methanol as fuel, i.e., a Direct Methanol Fuel Cell (DMFC) is shown below.

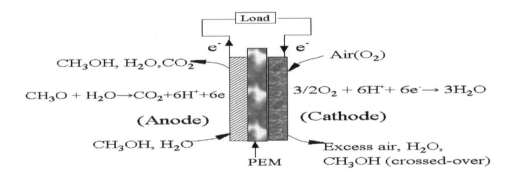

Figure 1. Direct methanol fuel cell

DC current is produced in the DMFC when methanol is electrochemically oxidized at the anode electrocatalyst. The electrons produced from the oxidation reaction leave the anode and travel through the external circuit to the cathode electrocatalyst where they are consumed together with oxygen in a reduction reaction. The circuit is maintained within the cell by the conduction of protons in the electrolyte (PEM).

07.00B.1

Because of ease of design and its ability to withstand high temperature and pressure operation, most fuel cells today use PEM such as Nafion™.

The overall reaction occurring in the DMFC is equivalent to the direct combustion of methanol:

$$2CH_3OH + 3O_2 \rightarrow 4H_2O + 2CO_2$$

One of the problems affecting the performance and hence commercialization of the direct methanol fuel cell (DMFC) is the depolarization of the oxygen reduction electrode caused by methanol cross-over. Depolarization as used here means that the presence of methanol limits the oxygen reduction and hence the amount of electricity produced. The exact role of methanol in limiting oxygen reduction can be inferred by understanding the physics and chemistry of the reaction. In an attempt to understand the mechanism of the depolarization process, an electro-kinetic model for mixed oxygen-methanol current on platinum was developed in our laboratory. A very simplified model [1] of the reaction developed suggests a functional relation of the form

$$T = -\int_{x_1}^{x_2} \left(\frac{6.73x + 6.725 \times 10^{-8} + 7.26 \times 10^{-4} C_{me}}{3.62 \times 10^{-12} x + 3.908 \times 10^{-8} x C_{me}} \right) dx$$

where

T = time in s

x = Concentration of oxygen, moles/cm^3,

C_{me} = Concentration of methanol, moles/cm^3,

The parameters [1] in the above equation are

$C_{me} = 5 \times 10^{-4}$ moles/cm^3

The initial concentration is

$x(t = 0) = 1.22 \times 10^{-6}$ moles/cm^3

QUESTIONS

1. Evaluate the time required for 50% of the initial oxygen concentration to be consumed in the fuel cell in the presence of methanol.
2. Repeat (a) in the absence of methanol (that is, $C_{me} = 0$). What can you infer from the result in (a) and (b)?
3. Plot time vs. oxygen concentration for the following concentrations of oxygen - $x = [1.22, 1.20, 1.0, 0.8, 0.6, 0.4, 0.2] \times 10^{-6}$ moles/cm^3 both in the presence and absence of methanol.

References

1. Itoe, R.N., Analysis of simultaneous oxygen reduction and methanol oxidation process in a direct methanol fuel cell, MS Thesis, Department of Chemical and Biomedical Engineering, Florida A&M University (1999).

INTEGRATION	
Topic	Integration
Summary	These are textbook notes of a physical problem for integration
Major	Chemical Engineering
Authors	Egwu Kalu
Date	December 23, 2009
Web Site	http://numericalmethods.eng.usf.edu

Chapter 07.00C

Physical Problem for Integration
Civil Engineering

Problem Statement

In a class X528 well in New York State, you are asked to find if the concentration of benzene is below the toxicity level of $0.5\,\text{mg/l}$ at a distance of $36\,\text{m}$ from the point of contamination. The contamination at the source is constant at $3.5\,\text{mg/l}$ for a whole year.

Solution

The equations governing transport of groundwater contaminant are quite complex. They depend on several parameters such as "the molecular diffusion of the contaminant, physical and chemical isotropy of the medium, and actual direction of the groundwater flow" [1].

Here we consider that the groundwater is flowing in one-direction, x and the aquifer has isotropic and homogeneous physical and chemical characteristics. In that case, the governing equation [2] for the concentration $c(x,t)$ of the contaminant is given by

$$\frac{\partial c}{\partial t} + u\frac{\partial c}{\partial x} = D\frac{\partial^2 c}{\partial x^2}. \tag{1}$$

where

$u =$ velocity of ground water flow in the x-direction (m/s)

$t =$ time (s)

$x =$ distance from source (m)

$D =$ dispersion coefficient (m^2).

To solve this partial differential equation (1) [3], we use Laplace transforms. Applying Laplace transform to both sides on the variable t,

$$L\left(\frac{\partial c}{\partial t} + u\frac{\partial c}{\partial x}\right) = L\left(D\frac{\partial^2 c}{\partial x^2}\right)$$

$$sC - c(x,0) + u\frac{dC}{dx} = D\frac{d^2C}{dx^2}. \tag{2}$$

where

$$L[c(x,t)] = C(x,s)$$

Since the initial concentration is zero,

$$c(x,0) = 0,$$

Equation (2) becomes

$$sC + u\frac{dc}{dx} = D\frac{d^2C}{dx^2}$$

$$D\frac{d^2C}{dx^2} - u\frac{dC}{dx} - sC = 0 \tag{3}$$

This is a homogenous ordinary differential equation. It is linear with fixed coefficients. The characteristics equation of the above ordinary differential equation (3) is

$$Dm^2 - um - s = 0$$

$$m = \frac{u \pm \sqrt{u^2 + 4Ds}}{2D} \tag{4}$$

The homogeneous as well as the complete solution of Equation (3) is

$$C(x,s) = A(s)e^{\frac{u+\sqrt{u^2+4Ds}}{2D}x} + B(s)e^{\frac{u-\sqrt{u^2+4Ds}}{2D}x} \tag{5}$$

At $x = \infty$, that is far away from the source, the concentration of the pollutant is zero, that is $c(\infty, s) = 0$, that is, $C(\infty, s) = 0$. This forces $A(s) = 0$ as the exponent of the exponential term is always positive as $u, D, s > 0$. The exponent of the exponential term on the second term will be negative as $\sqrt{u^2 + uDs} > u$ for all values of u, D, s as $u, D, s > 0$. Equation (5) hence reduces to

$$C(x,s) = B(s)e^{\frac{u-\sqrt{u^2+4Ds}}{2D}x} \tag{6}$$

At $x = 0$, $c = c_0$ (initial concentration, c_0), then $C(0,s) = \frac{c_0}{s}$. Substituting this in equation (6) gives

$$\frac{c_o}{s} = B(s)$$

then equation (6) is

$$C(x,s) = \frac{c_0}{s}e^{\frac{u-\sqrt{u^2+4Ds}}{2D}x}$$

$$= \left(c_0e^{\frac{ux}{2D}}\right)\left(\frac{e^{-\frac{\sqrt{u^2+4Ds}}{2D}x}}{s}\right)$$

$$L^{-1}[C(x,s)] = L^{-1}\left[\left(c_0e^{\frac{ux}{2D}}\right)\left(\frac{e^{-\frac{\sqrt{u^2+4Ds}}{2D}x}}{s}\right)\right]$$

$$c(x,t) = c_0e^{\frac{ux}{2D}}L^{-1}\left(\frac{e^{-\frac{\sqrt{u^2+4Ds}}{2D}x}}{s}\right)$$

$$= C_0 e^{\frac{ux}{2D}} L^{-1} \left[\frac{e^{-\frac{x}{\sqrt{D}}\sqrt{\frac{u^2}{4D}+s}}}{S} \right] \tag{7}$$

Let

$$a = \frac{x}{\sqrt{D}}$$

$$b = \frac{u}{2\sqrt{D}}$$

Then Equation (7) becomes

$$c(x,t) = c_0 e^{ab} L^{-1} \left(\frac{e^{-a\sqrt{b^2+s}}}{s} \right) \tag{8}$$

Using the formulas

$$L^{-1}(e^{-a\sqrt{s}}) = \left(\frac{a}{2\sqrt{\pi t^3}} e^{-\frac{a^2}{4t}} \right), a > 0, \text{ and}$$

$$L^{-1}(F(s+a)) = e^{-at} f(t)$$

then

$$L^{-1}\left(e^{-a\sqrt{b^2+s}}\right) = \frac{a}{2\sqrt{\pi t^3}} e^{-\frac{a^2}{4t}-b^2 t} \tag{9}$$

Then from

$$\int_0^t f(\tau) d\tau = \frac{F(s)}{s}$$

we get

$$L^{-1}\left(\frac{e^{-a\sqrt{b^2+s}}}{s} \right) = \int_0^t \frac{a}{2\sqrt{\pi \tau^3}} e^{-\frac{a^2}{4\tau}} e^{-b^2 \tau} d\tau$$

$$= e^{-ab} \int_0^t \frac{a}{2\sqrt{\pi \tau^3}} e^{-\frac{(a-2b\tau)^2}{4\tau}} d\tau$$

$$= e^{-ab} \int_0^t \left(\frac{a+2b\tau}{4\sqrt{\pi \tau^3}} + \frac{a-2b\tau}{4\sqrt{\pi \tau^3}} \right) e^{-\frac{(a-2b\tau)^2}{4\tau}} d\tau$$

$$= e^{-ab} \int_0^t \frac{a+2b\tau}{4\sqrt{\pi \tau^3}} e^{-\frac{(a-2b\tau)^2}{4\tau}} d\tau + e^{-ab} \int_0^t \frac{a-2b\tau}{4\sqrt{\pi \tau^3}} e^{-\frac{(a-2b\tau)^2}{4\tau}} d\tau$$

$$= e^{-ab} \int_0^t \frac{a+2b\tau}{4\sqrt{\pi \tau^3}} e^{-\frac{(a-2b\tau)^2}{4\tau}} d\tau + e^{-ab} \int_0^t \frac{a-2b\tau}{4\sqrt{\pi \tau^3}} e^{-\frac{(a-2b\tau)^2}{4\tau} - \frac{8ab\tau}{4\tau} + \frac{8ab\tau}{4\tau}} d\tau$$

$$= e^{-ab} \int_0^t \frac{a+2b\tau}{4\sqrt{\pi \tau^3}} e^{-\frac{(a-2b\tau)^2}{4\tau}} d\tau + e^{ab} \int_0^t \frac{a-2b\tau}{4\sqrt{\pi \tau^3}} e^{-\frac{(a+2b\tau)^2}{4\tau}} d\tau$$

Let

$$p = \frac{a - 2b\tau}{\sqrt{4\tau}},$$

$$q = \frac{a + 2b\tau}{\sqrt{4\tau}}$$

then

$$L^{-1}\left(\frac{e^{-a\sqrt{b^2+s}}}{s}\right) = \frac{e^{-ab}}{\sqrt{\pi}} \int_{\infty}^{\frac{a-2bt}{\sqrt{4t}}} e^{-p^2} dp - \frac{e^{ab}}{\sqrt{\pi}} \int_{\infty}^{\frac{a+2bt}{\sqrt{4t}}} e^{-q^2} dq$$

$$= \frac{e^{-ab}}{2} erfc\left(\frac{a - 2bt}{2\sqrt{t}}\right) + \frac{e^{ab}}{2} erfc\left(\frac{a + 2bt}{2\sqrt{t}}\right) \qquad (10)$$

Using Equation (10), Equation (8) becomes

$$c(x,t) = c_0 e^{ab}\left[\frac{e^{-ab}}{2} erfc\left(\frac{a - 2bt}{2\sqrt{t}}\right) + \frac{e^{ab}}{2} erfc\left(\frac{a + 2bt}{2\sqrt{t}}\right)\right]$$

$$= \frac{c_0}{2}\left[erfc\left(\frac{a - 2bt}{2\sqrt{t}}\right) + \frac{e^{2ab}}{2} erfc\left(\frac{a + 2bt}{2\sqrt{t}}\right)\right] \qquad (11)$$

Substituting back

$$a = -\frac{x}{\sqrt{D}},$$

$$b = \frac{u}{2\sqrt{D}}$$

$$c(x,t) = \frac{c_0}{2}\left[erfc\left(\frac{x - ut}{2\sqrt{Dt}}\right) + e^{\frac{ux}{D}} erfc\left(\frac{x + ut}{2\sqrt{Dt}}\right)\right] \qquad (12)$$

The velocity of the ground flow, u is given by

$$u = \frac{k}{n_{ed}} \frac{dh}{d\ell} \qquad (13)$$

where

n_{ed} = effective Darcian porosity,

K = permeability,

$\frac{dh}{dl}$ = ground water gradient.

Assuming

$n_{ed} = 22\% = 0.22$

$K = 0.002 \dfrac{cm}{s}$

$\dfrac{dh}{dl} = 0.01 \dfrac{cm}{cm}$.

Then from Equation (13),

$$u = \frac{0.002}{0.22}(0.01)$$

$$= 9.091 \times 10^{-5}\,\frac{\text{cm}}{\text{s}}.$$

So in the formula for concentration given by Equation (12), substituting

$$D = 0.01\frac{\text{cm}^2}{\text{s}}$$

$$c_0 = 3.5\frac{\text{mg}}{\text{L}}$$

$$x = 36\,\text{m}$$

$$t = 1\,\text{year} = 3.15 \times 10^7\,\text{s}$$

the concentration of benzene after 1 year at a distance of $36\,\text{m}$ is

$$c = \frac{3.5}{2}\left[erfc\left(\frac{3.6 - \left(9.091 \times 10^{-5}\right)\left(3.15 \times 10^7\right)}{2\sqrt{(0.01)\left(3.15 \times 10^7\right)}} \right) + e^{\frac{\left(9.091 \times 10^{-5}\right)(36)}{0.01}}\, erfc\left(\frac{36 + \left(9.091 \times 10^{-5}\right)\left(3.15 \times 10^7\right)}{2\sqrt{(0.01)\left(3.15 \times 10^7\right)}} \right) \right]$$

$$= 1.75[erfc(0.6560) + e^{32.73}\,erfc(5.758)] \qquad (14)$$

As you can see to calculate the concentration of benzene at $x = 36\,\text{m}$, we need to calculate $erfc(0.6560)$ and $erfc(5.758)$. How is $erfc(x)$ defined?

$$erfc(x) = \int_{\infty}^{x} e^{-z^2}\,dz$$

So

$$erfc(0.6560) = \int_{\infty}^{0.6560} e^{-z^2}\,dz$$

Since e^{-z^2} decays rapidly as $z \to \infty$, we will approximate

$$erfc(0.6560) = \int_{5}^{0.6560} e^{-z^2}\,dz$$

So to find whether the concentration of benzene is below toxicity level, we need to find the integral numerically.

QUESTIONS

1. What is the concentration of benzene after 2 years?
2. After 1 year, at what distance does the concentration go below the toxicity level of 0.5 mg/L?

REFERENCES

1. EPA Region 5 Water Draft UIC Class IV and V Site Assessment Guidelines, http://www.epa.gov/R5water/uic/r5guid/siteasst.htm, last accessed July 2004.
2. Fetter, C.W., Jr., Applied Hydrology, Merill Publishing Co, Columbus, 1980.

3. Li, W., Differential Equations of Hydraulic Transients, Dispersion, and Groundwater
    Flow, Prentice Hall, Englewood Cliffs, NJ, 1972

Topic	INTEGRATION
Sub Topic	Physical problem
Summary	Find if the concentration of benzene is above or below the toxicity limit at a critical distance from its source.
Authors	Autar Kaw
Last Revised	December 23, 2009
Web Site	http://numericalmethods.eng.usf.edu

Chapter 07.00D

Physical Problem for Integration
Computer Engineering

Problem

Human vision has the remarkable ability to infer 3D shapes from 2D images. When we look at 2D photographs or TV we do not see them as 2D shapes, rather as 3D entities with surfaces and volumes. Perception research has unraveled many of the cues that are used by us. The intriguing question is: can we replicate some of these abilities on a computer? To this end, in this assignment we are going to look at one way to engineer a solution to the 3D shape from 2D images problem. Apart from the pure fun of solving a new problem, there are many practical applications of this technology such as in automated inspection of machine parts, inference of obstructing surfaces for robot navigation, and even in robot-assisted surgery.

Image is a collection of gray level values at a set of predetermined sites known as pixels, arranged in an array. These gray level values are also known as image intensities. The registered intensity at an image pixel is dependent on a number of factors such as the lighting conditions, surface orientation, and surface material properties. The nature of lighting and its placement can drastically affect the appearance of a scene. In another module on simultaneous linear equations, we saw how to infer the surface normal vectors for each point in the scene, given three images of the scene taken with three different light sources. In Figure 1 we see vector field that we have inferred form the three images. In this module, we will see how we can *integrate this vector field to arrive at a surface.*

Physics of the Problem

To be able to reconstruct the shape of the underlying surface, we have to first understand the how the surface normal is related to the underlying surface. Figure 2 shows the schematic of the camera centered coordinate axis that we can use to formulate the problem. The z-direction is away from the camera towards the scene. Let the scene surface be parameterized by the function.

$$z = g(x, y)$$

The equation of the local surface normal can be related to this function as follows. If we find two tangents on the surface then the cross product of these tangents will give us the surface normal. Two tangents along the x and y-directions can easily be specified in terms of the derivatives along these directions. Figure 2 shows the underlying geometry that can be used to arrive at these equations.

Figure 1 The first three images are of a sphere taken with three different light source positions. The right image is a vector field representation of the surface normal vectors estimated from these three images. Can you compute the underlying surface representation from this vector field?

$$\vec{t}_x = \begin{bmatrix} 1 \\ 0 \\ \dfrac{\partial g(x,y)}{\partial x} \end{bmatrix} \quad \text{and} \quad \vec{t}_y = \begin{bmatrix} 0 \\ 1 \\ \dfrac{\partial g(x,y)}{\partial y} \end{bmatrix}$$

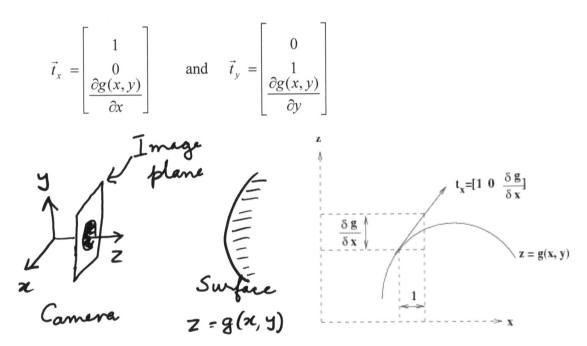

Figure 2   Relationship between surface tangent at a point to underlying surface equation. On the left is a simplified representation of the imaging geometry. The surface is assumed to be far away from the camera. On the right is a schematic of the local geometry on the scene surface.

The local surface normal, n, will be along the direction of the cross product of t_x and t_y.

$$c\vec{n} = -\vec{t}_x \times \vec{t}_y = \begin{bmatrix} \dfrac{\partial g(x,y)}{\partial x} \\ \dfrac{\partial g(x,y)}{\partial x} \\ -1 \end{bmatrix}$$

Note that there is 1800 ambiguity in the specification of the surface normal. We need the negative sign because we want the surface normal to be oriented towards the camera and the z-axis is pointed away from the camera. Also, note that the cross product gives as a vector along the surface normal. We have to normalize the vector to arrive at the surface normal. For notational ease let

$$p = \frac{\partial g(x,y)}{\partial x} \text{ and } q = \frac{\partial g(x,y)}{\partial y}$$

Then,

$$\vec{n} = \begin{bmatrix} n_x \\ n_y \\ n_z \end{bmatrix} = \frac{1}{\sqrt{p^2 + q^2 + 1}} \begin{bmatrix} p \\ q \\ -1 \end{bmatrix}$$

We see that the surface normal can be expressed in terms of the derivatives of the underlying surface. From this equation, we can express the local surface derivatives in terms of ratios of the surface normal components.

$$\frac{\partial g(x,y)}{\partial x} = \frac{n_x}{n_y} \qquad \text{and} \qquad \frac{\partial g(x,y)}{\partial y} = \frac{n_y}{n_z}$$

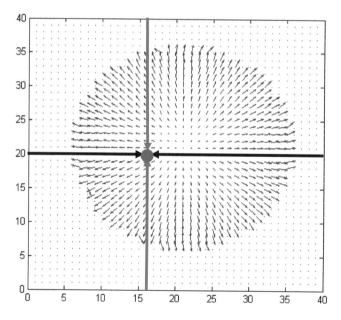

Figure 3 Integration paths to arrive at the depth surface value for the point marked by the red dot.

The black lines denote possible paths over which the x-partial derivative can be integrated. And, the purple lines denote possible paths to integrate the y-partial derivative. The paths are shown overlaid on the input vector field representing the partial derivatives of the surface along x and y directions.

Solution

We arrive at the final surface equation by integration these partial derivatives. Since we have a 2D field, we can perform the integration along many paths. The simplest paths are along the x (or y) axis.

$$g(u,v) = \int_o^u \frac{\partial g(x,v)}{\partial x}\, dx \qquad \text{or} \qquad g(u,v) = \int_o^v \frac{\partial g(u,y)}{\partial y}\, dy$$

One could also start from the right edge of the image and integrate the partial derivative with respect to x towards the left edge, or start from the bottom of the image and integrate the y-partial derivative towards the top. These directions are depicted in

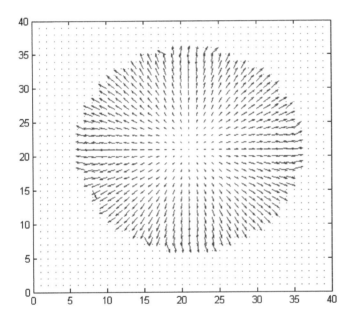

Figure 3 Integration paths to arrive at the depth surface value for the point marked by the red dot.

. The equivalent integrals are as follows. The image is assumed to N pixels by M pixels in size and the negative sign arises because of the direction of the integration.

$$g(u,v) = -\int_N^u \frac{\partial g(x,v)}{\partial x}\, dx \qquad \text{or} \qquad g(u,v) = -\int_M^v \frac{\partial g(u,y)}{\partial y}\, dy$$

Ideally, all the four integrals should result in the same value, however, for noisy, real world data they will never be the same. One solution is to take the average of these four integrals as the final value. Note that these integrals have to be evaluated for each location (u,v) in the image to arrive at the full surface.

Worked Out Example

Consider the problem of estimating the surface height along the line passing through the center of the sphere in Figure 1. Figure 4 (a) shows the input estimates for the partial derivatives along the x direction, $p = \dfrac{\partial g(x,y)}{\partial x}$ for the sphere along this line. The raw data for this plot is given below.

x	g
1.00000	0.00000
2.00000	0.00000
3.00000	0.00000
4.00000	0.00000
5.00000	0.00000
6.00000	0.00000
7.00000	0.00000
8.00000	0.00000
9.00000	0.00000
10.00000	0.00000
11.00000	0.00000
12.00000	0.00000
13.00000	0.00000
14.00000	0.00000
15.00000	0.00000
16.00000	0.00000
17.00000	0.00000
18.00000	0.00000
19.00000	0.00000
20.00000	0.00000
21.00000	0.00000
22.00000	0.00000
23.00000	0.00000
24.00000	0.00000
25.00000	0.00000
26.00000	0.00000
27.00000	0.00000
28.00000	0.00000
29.00000	0.00000
30.00000	5.42857
31.00000	4.40000
32.00000	3.82362
33.00000	3.23097
34.00000	2.74844
35.00000	2.43579
36.00000	2.19293
37.00000	2.04677

38.00000	1.91851
39.00000	1.88649
40.00000	1.62019
41.00000	1.55007
42.00000	1.47428
43.00000	1.44755
44.00000	1.36134
45.00000	1.28187
46.00000	1.14868
47.00000	1.15089
48.00000	1.14027
49.00000	1.05379
50.00000	0.98459
51.00000	1.00329
52.00000	0.96249
53.00000	0.90161
54.00000	0.88597
55.00000	0.83243
56.00000	0.78901
57.00000	0.80149
58.00000	0.74730
59.00000	0.73934
60.00000	0.70364
61.00000	0.67288
62.00000	0.66161
63.00000	0.62773
64.00000	0.61402
65.00000	0.60783
66.00000	0.58271
67.00000	0.55106
68.00000	0.52999
69.00000	0.50641
70.00000	0.50146
71.00000	0.46053
72.00000	0.45829
73.00000	0.43148
74.00000	0.41627
75.00000	0.39025
76.00000	0.38186
77.00000	0.35635
78.00000	0.34187
79.00000	0.32304
80.00000	0.31064
81.00000	0.27967
82.00000	0.27367

83.00000	0.26137
84.00000	0.24340
85.00000	0.23128
86.00000	0.20758
87.00000	0.19566
88.00000	0.19566
89.00000	0.17807
90.00000	0.16632
91.00000	0.14409
92.00000	0.12686
93.00000	0.11039
94.00000	0.10481
95.00000	0.08266
96.00000	0.06623
97.00000	0.04945
98.00000	0.04383
99.00000	0.03309
100.00000	0.00038
101.00000	-0.00516
102.00000	-0.02149
103.00000	-0.03232
104.00000	-0.04317
105.00000	-0.05421
106.00000	-0.06513
107.00000	-0.09250
108.00000	-0.09820
109.00000	-0.11468
110.00000	-0.12011
111.00000	-0.13697
112.00000	-0.14808
113.00000	-0.18176
114.00000	-0.18776
115.00000	-0.19904
116.00000	-0.20511
117.00000	-0.22784
118.00000	-0.25084
119.00000	-0.26862
120.00000	-0.26960
121.00000	-0.30463
122.00000	-0.30577
123.00000	-0.33591
124.00000	-0.33720
125.00000	-0.35061
126.00000	-0.37626
127.00000	-0.38823

128.00000	-0.40213
129.00000	-0.42330
130.00000	-0.44994
131.00000	-0.47173
132.00000	-0.47897
133.00000	-0.50129
134.00000	-0.54231
135.00000	-0.54480
136.00000	-0.57621
137.00000	-0.56790
138.00000	-0.61925
139.00000	-0.63884
140.00000	-0.65569
141.00000	-0.68145
142.00000	-0.73088
143.00000	-0.75263
144.00000	-0.76928
145.00000	-0.79030
146.00000	-0.80970
147.00000	-0.81065
148.00000	-0.88367
149.00000	-0.89782
150.00000	-0.92400
151.00000	-1.00067
152.00000	-1.03536
153.00000	-1.08947
154.00000	-1.09584
155.00000	-1.20465
156.00000	-1.22123
157.00000	-1.26090
158.00000	-1.30056
159.00000	-1.33557
160.00000	-1.49718
161.00000	-1.53483
162.00000	-1.70123
163.00000	-1.69167
164.00000	-1.89507
165.00000	-2.06525
166.00000	-2.24788
167.00000	-2.45874
168.00000	-2.80478
169.00000	-3.22446
170.00000	-3.86839
171.00000	-4.00000
172.00000	-4.00000

173.00000	0.00000
174.00000	0.00000
175.00000	0.00000
176.00000	0.00000
177.00000	0.00000
178.00000	0.00000
179.00000	0.00000
180.00000	0.00000
181.00000	0.00000
182.00000	0.00000
183.00000	0.00000
184.00000	0.00000
185.00000	0.00000
186.00000	0.00000
187.00000	0.00000
188.00000	0.00000
189.00000	0.00000
190.00000	0.00000
191.00000	0.00000
192.00000	0.00000
193.00000	0.00000
194.00000	0.00000
195.00000	0.00000
196.00000	0.00000
197.00000	0.00000
198.00000	0.00000
199.00000	0.00000
200.00000	0.00000

This data needs to be numerically integrated to arrive at height values.

Figure 4 (b) shows the plot of the surface height, as computed by integrating starting from left and from right. We used the trapezoidal integration method. Notice the small discrepancy, which is due to real world data noise. The overall shape does look circular, which should serve as a sanity check on the calculations.

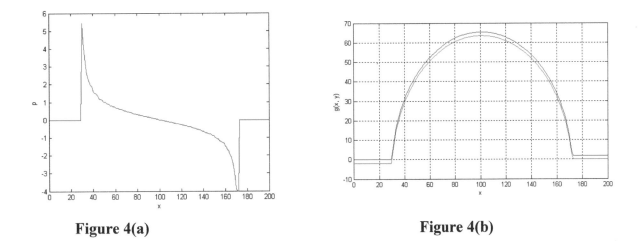

Figure 4(a)   **Figure 4(b)**

Figure 4(a) The plot of the estimates for the partial derivatives along the x direction, $p = \dfrac{\partial g(x,y)}{\partial x}$ for the sphere along a horizontal line passing through the middle of the sphere.

Figure 4(b) Plot of the integrated value at each point along the horizontal. The blue plot corresponds to integrating from left to right and the red plot corresponds to integrating from right to left.

If we repeat the above process along the vertical direction (along image columns), then we will arrive at two more estimates for the middle point of the sphere, which can be averaged to arrive at one estimate. If we repeat this for each point on the sphere, not just the middle, then we will arrive at the surface representation for the full sphere. Figure 5 shows the averaged estimate of the sphere as estimated from the input vector field. Note the spherical nature of the final estimate.

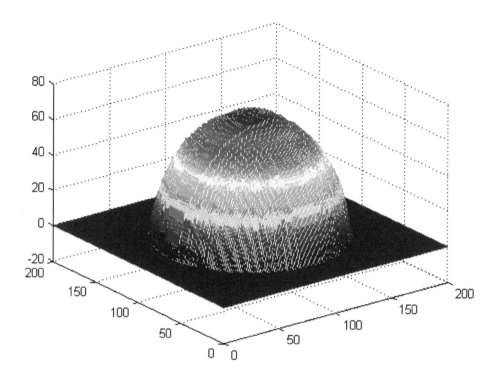

Figure 5 Estimated surface height for the vector field in Figure 1(c) as computed by averaging the estimates of the integrals along four directions, for each point.

QUESTIONS

1. Write code to recover the surface height at each point in the image given the vector field.
2. For any point on the sphere, specify 25 different paths along which you can integrate.
3. Study how the roughness of the estimated surface changes with number of path integrals that are averaged.

INTEGRATION	
Topic	Integration
Summary	To infer the surfaces from vector fields
Major	General Engineering
Authors	Sudeep Sarkar
Date	September 10, 2005
Web Site	http://numericalmethods.eng.usf.edu

Chapter 07.00E

Physical Problem for Integration
Electrical Engineering

Today's consumer products rely heavily on small electronic circuits to provide much of their functionality. Each of these circuits is built around electrical components that, like all devices, vary in value due to variations in materials, manufacturing, and operating conditions. For example, capacitors are notoriously variable often operating as much as $+/-20\%$ from their nominal value. Clearly, a variation in capacitor value can have an affect on the operation of an electronic circuit. If the statistical properties of the capacitor and resistor value distributions are known, stochastic methods can be used to compute this effect. Unfortunately, this is often not the case and we are frequently left to use empirical methods to determine this effect. A common technique is to use a Monte Carlo method where a circuit will be built (or simulated) many times with different components from a lot and the resulting behavior analyzed. The goal will be to determine a confidence value that a randomly selected circuit built with these components will behave within a certain interval.

Consider the case of an op-amp based square wave generator as shown in Figure 1. Its operative behavior in terms of period is described by the equation (1, pp. 625-627]

$$T = 2RC \ln\left(1 + 2\frac{R_2}{R_1}\right)$$

Clearly, the period/frequency of this circuit is quite susceptible to variations in all the components[1] except the op-amp, resistor, R_3 and the zener diodes. How then can the likely behavior to all the possible combination of variations in the components R, C, R_1 and R_2 be determined? The answer is to apply a Monte Carlo method and some basic statistics.
If we assume that the statistical distribution of the circuit behavior is normal1 then a two-tailed confidence interval test can be used to determine the likelihood that the circuit will

---

[1] This assumption should be tested, but that is beyond the scope of this example. See question 5 for more information.

behave acceptably [2, pp. 113-27]. An examination of the literature will show that a confidence interval can be established through the use of the z-test. For a sample of size n with known standard deviation σ it can be determined with confidence $(1-\alpha)$ that the measured value will stay in the following range

$$\bar{x} - z(\alpha/2)\sigma < value < \bar{x} + z(\alpha/2)\sigma,$$

where

$\bar{x}$ is the sample mean of the measured value.

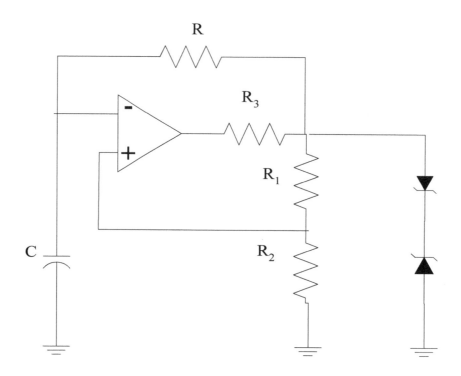

Figure 1 Square-Wave Oscillator

If α is 0.05 then there is 90% confidence that the value of all possible circuits will be within the indicated range about the sample mean. When the sample size n is smaller than 30 or the population standard deviation, σ is not known the sample standard deviation, s can be substituted and the normal distribution must be replaced with the Student-T distribution [2, pp. 174-7].

Interpretation of the term $z(\alpha/2)$ and $t(\alpha/2, n-2)$ often leads to a lot of confusion. It is the $z-$ or $t-$score value that is necessary so that $(1-\alpha)$ of the area under the probability distribution is inside the desired range. This is often referred to, in part, as a two-tailed test. Figure 2 shows this graphically.

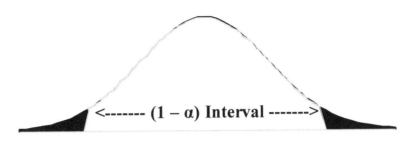

Figure 2 $(1-\alpha)$ Confidence Interval

$z(\alpha/2)$ is the value so that when the normal distribution is integrated from $-z(\alpha/2)$ to $+z(\alpha/2)$ that the resulting area is $(1-\alpha)$. This integration is summarized by the following equation.

$$(1-\alpha)=\int_{-z(\alpha/2)}^{z(\alpha/2)}\frac{1}{\sqrt{2\pi}}e^{-\frac{x^2}{2}}dx$$

The analysis is similar for the Student-T distribution and $t(\alpha/2,n-2)$.

The problem is that there is no closed-form solution to the integration of either the normal distribution or the Student-T distribution. These are typically handled via look-up tables of the cumulative distributions from $-\infty$ to z [2, pp. 513-14].

In the case of a confidence interval computation generally everything is known except for $z(\alpha/2)$. However, in the case of a circuit, that analysis can be reversed to determine with what confidence the average circuit behavior will be in a given interval. In other words, suppose that the goal is to determine how likely it is that the square-wave generator for Figure 1 will behave with a frequency of 11 kHz. For example, suppose that suitable components have been chosen for R, C, R_1 and R_2 for a lot and that 25 circuits were built with the following results being measured:

　　　Number of Samples: $n=25$

　　　Average Period: $\bar{x}=0.995$ ms

　　　Standard Deviation: $\sigma=0.02$ ms

What is the likelihood, with this batch of components, that any given oscillator will have its frequency within 5% of the target of 1 kHz? Rearranging the confidence interval formula and solving for $z(\alpha/2)$ yields the following two equations. One for the upper end for $\mu<1.053$ ms and the other for the upper end for $\mu>0.952$ ms^3.

$$z(\alpha_1/2)=\frac{(\mu_1-\bar{x})}{\sigma}=\frac{(1.053m-0.995m)}{0.02m}=2.9$$

$$z(\alpha_2/2)=\frac{(\mu_2-\bar{x})}{\sigma}=\frac{(0.952m-0.995m)}{0.02m}=-2.15$$

The likelihood of this happening can then be determined by finding the total area under the normal distribution for the range in question

$$(1-\alpha) = \int_{-2.15}^{2.9} \frac{1}{\sqrt{2\pi}} e^{-\frac{x^2}{2}} dx$$

QUESTIONS

1. There is no real way to know the population standard deviation, σ, so the more complex formula using the sample standard deviation, s, and the Student-T distribution would have to be used, especially when n is less than 30   30 [2, pp. 174-19]. The entire analysis is the same except the integral is now the more complicated.

$$(1-\alpha) = \int_{-t(\alpha/2,m)}^{t(\alpha/2,m)} \left\{ \frac{\Gamma\left(\frac{m+1}{2}\right)}{\sqrt{m\pi}\,\Gamma\left(\frac{m}{2}\right)} \left(1+\frac{x^2}{m}\right)^{-\left(\frac{m+1}{2}\right)} \right\} dx$$

where

$$\Gamma(1) = 1$$
$$\Gamma(1/2) = \sqrt{\pi}$$
$$\Gamma(m) = (m-1)\Gamma(m-1)$$

Perform the computations using the Student-T distribution.

2. The more common way of using these statistics is to compute the actual confidence interval centered about the sample data. This means that α is known and $z(\alpha/2)$ or $t(\alpha/2, n-2)$ have to be computed. This can be done by repeatedly trying possible values for z or t and evaluating the integral. This is an excellent application for a root-finding algorithm. If an algorithm like bisection method of solving nonlinear equations were used, how would you pick the initial bounds for the x or t value?

3. Because there are actual formulas for the functional inside the integral and not just sampled points on the curve in question, it is possible to apply an interval halving approach and a Romberg extrapolation to solve these integrals. Set up the algorithm for doing this.

4. Normal and Student-T distribution tables like those in [2, pp. 513-4] are limited in their choices. Integrating these distributions from $-\infty$ can be used to generate a more complete table. To do this an algorithm must take advantage of the symmetry in the distributions since it is not possible to integrate numerically with an infinite bound. When the z or t value is less than zero simply report 0.5 minus the integral from 0 to z or t, and when the z or t value is greater than zero simply report 0.5 plus the integral from 0 to z or t. Set-up the algorithm for doing this.

5. In the analysis above it was assumed that the population of circuits was roughly normal, this should generally be tested before applying the assumption. There exist goodness-of-fit tests to see if the population is sufficiently normal. For more information, see [2, pp. 265-8].

References

[1] Millman, J., Micro-Electronics: Digital and Analog Circuits and Systems, McGraw Hill, 1979.

[2] Walpole, R. and Myers, R., Probability and Statistics for Engineers and Scientists, 2nd Ed., MacMillan, 1978.

Topic	INTEGRATION
Sub Topic	Physical Problem
Summary	Not all electrical components, especially off-the-shelf components match their nominal value. Variations in materials and manufacturing as well as operating conditions can affect their value. Suppose a circuit is designed such that it requires a specific component value, how confident can we be that the variation in the component value will result in acceptable circuit behavior? To solve this problem a probability density function will need to be integrated to determine the confidence interval.
Authors	Henry Welch
Last Revised	May 24, 2005
Web Site	http://numericalmethods.eng.usf.edu

Chapter 07.00F

Physical Problem for Integration
Industrial Engineering

Problem Statement

An industrial engineer works as a quality control engineer for a company making toilet paper. The company advertises that every roll of toilet paper has at least 250 sheets. It is the industrial (quality) engineer's responsibility to validate this claim by sampling rolls off of the assembly line and determining the probability (that is, confidence) that the company can make the claim. Note that validating the claim is important to avoid frivolous lawsuits associated with false advertising.

Background: Let us assume that the number of sheets in a roll of toilet paper, y, is governed by the normal probability distribution (see figure on next page), that is,

$$y \sim N(\mu, \sigma^2)$$

where N is a normal random variable described by it's mean, μ, and standard deviation, σ. The probability distribution function of the normal random variable y is

$$f(y) = \frac{1}{\sigma\sqrt{2\pi}} e^{-(1/2)[(y-\mu)/\sigma]^2}$$

and is shown in the Figure 1.

Note that the previously described normal probability density function was first derived by Abraham de Moivre in 1733 in his book called *The Doctrine of Chance*. Initially, the discovery went unnoticed until it was re-derived by Laplace and Gauss about 50 years. Hence, it is often called the Gaussian distribution. The normal probability distribution, which is a continuous distribution, is derived from the binomial probability distribution, which is a discrete distribution. The discrete binomial distribution is given below

$$f(y) = \frac{n!}{k!(n-k)!} p^k (1-p)^{n-k}$$

where n is the number of samples and k is the number of successes with a probability of p. When n is large the binomial distribution approaches the normal distribution. In fact, when n is greater than or equal to 6, the normal distribution is an excellent approximation to the binomial distribution (Figure 2).

07.00F.1

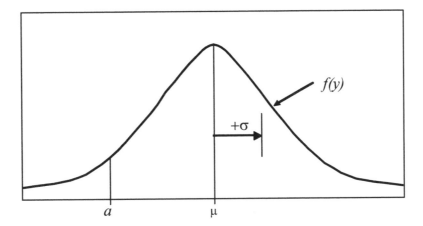

Figure 1 Probability distribution function, $f(y) = \dfrac{1}{\sigma\sqrt{2\pi}}e^{-(1/2)[(y-\mu)/\sigma]^2}$

The actual proof that the binomial distribution approaches the normal distribution involves a special case of the central limit theorem and is beyond the scope of this problem. Furthermore, the derivation also involves the inclusion of a continuity correction factor.

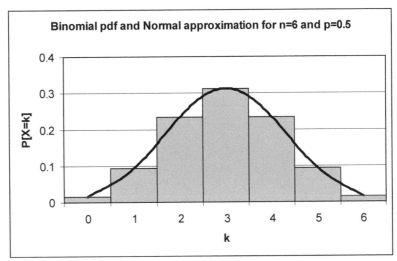

Figure 2 Binomial pdf and normal approximation for $n = 6$ and $p = 0.5$

Since the quality engineer cannot sample every roll of toilet paper and count the number of sheets, the mean and standard deviation are estimated based on a sample size of n rolls of toilet paper. The mean, $\bar{y}$, and standard deviation, s, of the sample (that is, sample mean and sample standard deviation) are estimates of the actual mean, μ, and standard deviation, σ, and are given by

$$\bar{y} = \frac{\displaystyle\sum_{i=1}^{n} y_i}{n} \approx \mu$$

$$s = \sqrt{\frac{\sum\limits_{i=1}^{n}(y_i - \bar{y})^2}{n-1}} \approx \sigma$$

where n is the number of samples (that is, rolls of toilet paper). The probability that the number of sheets in a roll is greater than or equal to some specified number, a, is the area under the probability density function (that is, integral) from a to ∞, and is given by

$$P(y \ge a) = \int_a^\infty f(y)dy = \int_a^\infty \frac{1}{\sigma\sqrt{2\pi}} e^{-(1/2)[(y-\mu)/\sigma]^2} dy$$

Note that the result of the previous equation is a number from 0 to 1 that correlates to a 0% to 100% probability, respectively.

Solution

A co-operative education student working for the industrial (quality) engineer samples 10 rolls of toilet paper on a monthly basis and determines that the number of sheets in each roll is

Roll	Number of sheets
1	253
2	250
3	251
4	252
5	253
6	253
7	252
8	254
9	252
10	252

The industrial (quality) engineer calculates the following mean and standard deviation of the sample of 10 rolls of toilet paper.

$$\bar{y} = \frac{253 + 250 + 251 + 252 + 253 + 253 + 252 + 254 + 252 + 252}{10} = 252.2 \approx \mu$$

$$s = \sqrt{\frac{\begin{array}{l}(253-252.2)^2 + (250-252.2)^2 + (251-252.2)^2 + \\ (252-252.2)^2 + (253-252.2)^2 + (253-252.2)^2 + \\ (252-252.2)^2 + (254-252.2)^2 + (252-252.2)^2 + (252-252.2)^2\end{array}}{10-1}} = 1.135 \approx \sigma$$

Finally, the probability that the number of sheets in a roll is greater $a = 250$ sheets is

$$P(y \ge 250) = \int_{250}^\infty \frac{1}{1.135\sqrt{2\pi}} e^{-(1/2)[(y-252.2)/1.135]^2} dy$$

$$P(y \ge 250) = \int_{250}^\infty 0.3515 \; e^{-0.3881(y-252.2)^2} dy$$

$$P(y \ge 250) = ??$$

Solution to the previous equation yields the probability that the number of sheets in a roll is greater than or equal to 250.

QUESTIONS

1. Although all the samples have more than 250 sheets, why do we not get 100% probability that all the rolls will have more than 250 sheets.
2. Change one of the data points to 248 sheets and rework the problem.
3. To find the integral numerically, one may substitute infinity by 5. How will you justify this substitution quantitatively.

Topic	INTEGRATION
Sub Topic	Physical Problem
Summary	Find the probability, based on a sampling of the assembly line that the number of sheets in a roll of toilet paper is greater than a specified number.
Authors	Glen Besterfield
Last Revised	December 23, 2009
Web Site	http://numericalmethods.eng.usf.edu

Chapter 07.00G

Physical Problem for Integration
Mechanical Engineering

Problem Statement

To make the fulcrum (Figure 1) of a bascule bridge, a long hollow steel shaft called the trunnion is shrink fit into a steel hub. The resulting steel trunnion-hub assembly is then shrink fit into the girder of the bridge.

Figure 1 Trunnion-Hub-Girder (THG) assembly.

This is done by first immersing the trunnion in a cold medium such as dry-ice/alcohol mixture. After the trunnion reaches the steady state temperature of the cold medium, the trunnion outer diameter contracts. The trunnion is taken out of the medium and slid though the hole of the hub (Figure 2).

When the trunnion heats up, it expands and creates an interference fit with the hub. In 1995, on one of the bridges in Florida, this assembly procedure did not work as designed. Before the trunnion could be inserted fully into the hub, the trunnion got stuck. Luckily the trunnion was taken out before it got stuck permanently. Otherwise, a new trunnion and hub would needed to be ordered at a cost of $50,000. Coupled with construction delays, the total loss could have been more than hundred thousand dollars.

Why did the trunnion get stuck? This was because the trunnion had not contracted enough to slide through the hole. Can you find out why?

A hollow trunnion of outside diameter 12.363″ is to be fitted in a hub of inner diameter 12.358″. The trunnion was put in dry ice/alcohol mixture (temperature of the fluid

- dry ice/alcohol mixture is $-108°F$) to contract the trunnion so that it can be slid through the hole of the hub. To slide the trunnion without sticking, a diametrical clearance of at least $0.01''$ is required between the trunnion and the hub. Assuming the room temperature is $80°F$, is immersing it in dry-ice/alcohol mixture a correct decision?

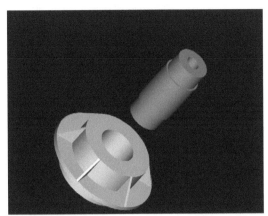

Figure 2 Trunnion slided through the hub after contracting

Solution

To calculate the contraction in the diameter of the trunnion, thermal expansion coefficient at room temperature is used. In that case the reduction, ΔD in the outer diameter of the trunnion is

$$\Delta D = D\alpha\Delta T \qquad (1)$$

where

D = outer diameter of the trunnion,

α = coefficient of thermal expansion coefficient at room temperature, and

ΔT = change in temperature,

Given

$D = 12.363''$

$\alpha = 6.817 \times 10^{-6}$ in/in/°F at 80°F

$\Delta T = T_{fluid} - T_{room}$

$\quad = -108 - 80$

$\quad = -188°F$

where

T_{fluid} = temperature of dry-ice/alcohol mixture,

T_{room} = room temperature,

the reduction in the trunnion outer diameter is given by

$$\Delta D = (12.363)(6.47 \times 10^{-6})(-188)$$

$$= -0.01504''$$

So the trunnion is predicted to reduce in diameter by 0.01504". But, is this enough reduction in diameter? As per specifications, he needs the trunnion to contract by

= trunnion outside diameter - hub inner diameter + diametral clearance

= 12.363"−12.358"+0.01"

= 0.015"

So according to his calculations, immersing the steel trunnion in dry-ice/alcohol mixture gives the desired contraction of 0.015" as we predict a contraction of 0.01504".

But as shown in Figure 3, the thermal expansion coefficient of steel decreases with temperature and is not constant over the range of temperature the trunnion goes through. Hence the above formula (Equation 1) would overestimate the thermal contraction.

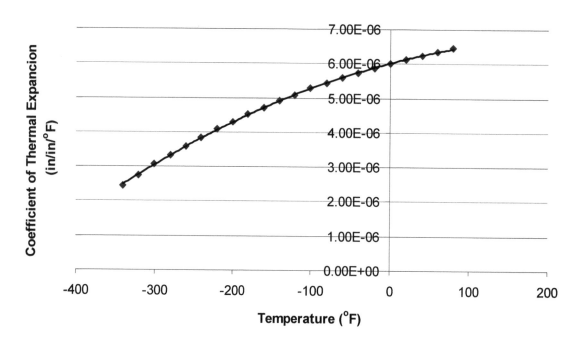

Figure 3 Varying thermal expansion coefficient as a function of temperature for cast steel.

The contraction in the diameter for the trunnion for which the thermal expansion coefficient varies as a function of temperature is given by

$$\Delta D = D \int_{T_{room}}^{T_{fluid}} \alpha \, dT \tag{2}$$

Note that Equation (2) reduces to Equation (1) if the coefficient of thermal expansion is assumed to be constant. In Figure 3, the thermal expansion coefficient of a typical cast steel is approximated by a second order polynomial[1] as

$$\alpha = -1.2278 \times 10^{-11} T^2 + 6.1946 \times 10^{-9} T + 6.0150 \times 10^{-6}$$

$$\Delta D = 12.363 \int_{80}^{-108} \left(-1.2278 \times 10^{-11} T^2 + 6.1946 \times 10^{-9} T + 6.015 \times 10^{-6} \right) dT$$

QUESTIONS

1. Can you now find the contraction in the trunnion OD?
2. Is the magnitude of contraction more than 0.015" as required?
3. If that is not the case, what if the trunnion were immersed in liquid nitrogen (boiling temperature= $-321° F$)? Will that give enough contraction in the trunnion?

4. Rather than regressing the data to a second order polynomial so that one can find the contraction in the trunnion outer diameter, how would you use trapezoidal rule of integration for unequal segments? What is the relative difference between the two results? The data for the thermal expansion coefficients as function of temperature is given below.

Table 1 Instantaneous thermal expansion coefficient as a function of temperature.

Temperature	Instantaneous Thermal Expansion
°F	μ in / in/°F
80	6.47
60	6.36
40	6.24
20	6.12
0	6.00
-20	5.86
-40	5.72
-60	5.58
-80	5.43
-100	5.28
-120	5.09
-140	4.91
-160	4.72
-180	4.52
-200	4.30
-220	4.08
-240	3.83
-260	3.58
-280	3.33
-300	3.07
-320	2.76
-340	2.45

[1] The second order polynomial is derived using regression analysis which is another mathematical procedure where numerical methods are employed. Regression analysis approximates discrete data such as the thermal expansion coefficient vs. temperature data as a continuous function. This is an excellent example of where one has to use numerical methods of more than one procedure to solve a real life problem.

Topic	INTEGRATION
Sub Topic	Physical Problem
Summary	A physical problem of finding if the shaft has contracted enough to be shrink fit into a hollow hub.
Authors	Autar Kaw
Date	December 7, 2008
Web Site	http://numericalmethods.eng.usf.edu

Multiple-Choice Test

Chapter 07.01
Background

1. Physically, integrating $\int_a^b f(x)dx$ means finding the

   (A) area under the curve from a to b
   (B) area to the left of point a
   (C) area to the right of point b
   (D) area above the curve from a to b

2. The mean value of a function $f(x)$ from a to b is given by

   (A) $\dfrac{f(a)+f(b)}{2}$

   (B) $\dfrac{f(a)+2f\left(\dfrac{a+b}{2}\right)+f(b)}{4}$

   (C) $\int_a^b f(x)dx$

   (D) $\dfrac{\int_a^b f(x)dx}{b-a}$

3. The exact value of $\int_{0.2}^{2.2} xe^x dx$ is most nearly

   (A) 7.8036
   (B) 11.807
   (C) 14.034
   (D) 19.611

4. $\int_{0.2}^{2} f(x)dx$ for

   $$f(x) = x, \qquad 0 \le x \le 1.2$$
   $$= x^2, \quad 1.2 < x \le 2.4$$

   is most nearly
   (A) 1.9800
   (B) 2.6640
   (C) 2.7907
   (D) 4.7520

5.   The area of a circle of radius a can be found by the following integral

(A) $\int\limits_{0}^{a}\left(a^2 - x^2\right)dx$

(B) $\int\limits_{0}^{2\pi}\sqrt{a^2 - x^2}\,dx$

(C) $4\int\limits_{0}^{a}\sqrt{a^2 - x^2}\,dx$

(D) $\int\limits_{0}^{a}\sqrt{a^2 - x^2}\,dx$

6.   Velocity distribution of a fluid flow through a pipe varies along the radius and is given by $v(r)$. The flow rate through the pipe of radius a is given by

(A) $\pi v(a)a^2$

(B) $\pi\dfrac{v(0) + v(a)}{2}a^2$

(C) $\int\limits_{0}^{a}v(r)dr$

(D) $2\pi\int\limits_{0}^{a}v(r)r\,dr$

Complete Solution

Problem Set

Chapter 07.01
Background of Integration

1. Integrate exactly $\displaystyle\int_0^{\pi} 3\sin 2x\, dx$

2. Integrate exactly $\displaystyle\int_0^3 xe^{2x}\, dx$

3. Integrate exactly $\displaystyle\int_1^5 4e^{-2t}\, dt$

4. The rod fixed at left end as shown in the Figure 1 is being heated from room temperature. Find the change in length of the rod if heated from room temperature to $120°\,\mathrm{F}$. Given

$$\Delta L = L \int_{T_{room}}^{T_{final}} \alpha\, dT$$

where

$\Delta L = $ change in length due to temperature change (in),

$L = $ length of rod at room temperature (in),

$\alpha = $ temperature dependent coefficient of thermal expansion (in/in/$°\,$F),

$T_{final} = $ Final temperature to which the rod is heated ($°\,$F),

$T_{room} = $ room temperature ($°\,$F).

Given

$L = 9\,\mathrm{in}$,

$T_{room} = 70°\,\mathrm{F}$,

$\alpha = 9.4\times 10^{-9}T + 6\times 10^{-6}$ (in/in/$°\,$F),

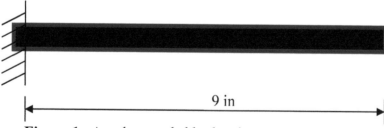

9 in

Figure 1 A rod expanded by heating.

07.01.1

5.   The rod fixed at left end as shown in the Figure 2 is being heated from room temperature. At what temperature would the rod touch the wall on the right side? Given that

$$\Delta L = L \int_{T_{room}}^{T_{final}} \alpha \, dT$$

where

ΔL = change in length due to temperature change (in),

L = length of rod at room temperature (in),

α = temperature dependent coefficient of thermal expansion (in/in/$^\circ$F),

T_{final} = Final temperature to which the rod is heated ($^\circ$F),

T_{room} = room temperature ($^\circ$F),

Given

$L = 9$ in,

$T_{room} = 70^\circ$F,

$\alpha = 9.4 \times 10^{-9}\, T + 6 \times 10^{-6}$ in/in/$^\circ$F,

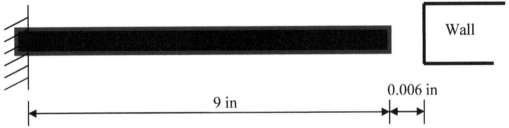

Figure 2 A rod expanding to touch the wall.

6.   The integral $\int_{3}^{9} x^2 dx$ can be calculated approximately by finding the area of the four rectangles as shown in the Figure 3.   What is the truncation error due to this approximation?

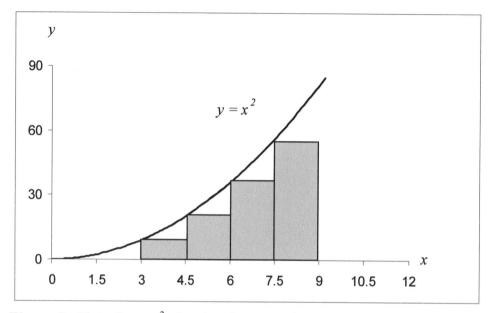

Figure 3   Plot of $y = x^2$ showing the approximate area under the curve from $x = 3$ to $x = 9$ using four rectangles.

Chapter 07.02
Trapezoidal Rule of Integration

After reading this chapter, you should be able to:

1. *derive the trapezoidal rule of integration,*
2. *use the trapezoidal rule of integration to solve problems,*
3. *derive the multiple-segment trapezoidal rule of integration,*
4. *use the multiple-segment trapezoidal rule of integration to solve problems, and*
5. *derive the formula for the true error in the multiple-segment trapezoidal rule of integration.*

What is integration?

Integration is the process of measuring the area under a function plotted on a graph. Why would we want to integrate a function? Among the most common examples are finding the velocity of a body from an acceleration function, and displacement of a body from a velocity function. Throughout many engineering fields, there are (what sometimes seems like) countless applications for integral calculus. You can read about some of these applications in Chapters 07.00A-07.00G.

Sometimes, the evaluation of expressions involving these integrals can become daunting, if not indeterminate. For this reason, a wide variety of numerical methods has been developed to simplify the integral.

Here, we will discuss the trapezoidal rule of approximating integrals of the form

$$I = \int_{a}^{b} f(x)dx$$

where

$f(x)$ is called the integrand,
$a =$ lower limit of integration
$b =$ upper limit of integration

What is the trapezoidal rule?

The trapezoidal rule is based on the Newton-Cotes formula that if one approximates the integrand by an nth order polynomial, then the integral of the function is approximated by the integral of that n^{th} order polynomial. Integrating polynomials is simple and is based on the calculus formula.

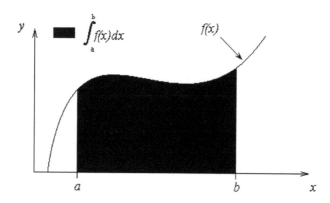

Figure 1 Integration of a function

$$\int_a^b x^n dx = \left(\frac{b^{n+1} - a^{n+1}}{n+1} \right), \quad n \neq -1 \tag{1}$$

So if we want to approximate the integral

$$I = \int_a^b f(x)dx \tag{2}$$

to find the value of the above integral, one assumes

$$f(x) \approx f_n(x) \tag{3}$$

where

$$f_n(x) = a_0 + a_1 x + \ldots + a_{n-1}x^{n-1} + a_n x^n. \tag{4}$$

where $f_n(x)$ is a nth order polynomial. The trapezoidal rule assumes $n = 1$, that is, approximating the integral by a linear polynomial (straight line),

$$\int_a^b f(x)dx \approx \int_a^b f_1(x)dx$$

Derivation of the Trapezoidal Rule

Method 1: Derived from Calculus

$$\int_a^b f(x)dx \approx \int_a^b f_1(x)dx$$

$$= \int_a^b (a_0 + a_1 x)dx$$

$$= a_0(b-a) + a_1 \left(\frac{b^2 - a^2}{2} \right) \tag{5}$$

But what is a_0 and a_1? Now if one chooses, $(a, f(a))$ and $(b, f(b))$ as the two points to approximate $f(x)$ by a straight line from a to b,

$$f(a) = f_1(a) = a_0 + a_1 a \tag{6}$$

$$f(b) = f_1(b) = a_0 + a_1 b \tag{7}$$

Solving the above two equations for a_1 and a_0,

$$a_1 = \frac{f(b) - f(a)}{b - a}$$

$$a_0 = \frac{f(a)b - f(b)a}{b - a} \tag{8a}$$

Hence from Equation (5),

$$\int_a^b f(x)dx \approx \frac{f(a)b - f(b)a}{b - a}(b - a) + \frac{f(b) - f(a)}{b - a}\frac{b^2 - a^2}{2} \tag{8b}$$

$$= (b - a)\left[\frac{f(a) + f(b)}{2}\right] \tag{9}$$

Method 2: Also Derived from Calculus
$f_1(x)$ can also be approximated by using Newton's divided difference polynomial as

$$f_1(x) = f(a) + \frac{f(b) - f(a)}{b - a}(x - a) \tag{10}$$

Hence

$$\int_a^b f(x)dx \approx \int_a^b f_1(x)dx$$

$$= \int_a^b \left[f(a) + \frac{f(b) - f(a)}{b - a}(x - a)\right]dx$$

$$= \left[f(a)x + \frac{f(b) - f(a)}{b - a}\left(\frac{x^2}{2} - ax\right)\right]_a^b$$

$$= f(a)b - f(a)a + \left(\frac{f(b) - f(a)}{b - a}\right)\left(\frac{b^2}{2} - ab - \frac{a^2}{2} + a^2\right)$$

$$= f(a)b - f(a)a + \left(\frac{f(b) - f(a)}{b - a}\right)\left(\frac{b^2}{2} - ab + \frac{a^2}{2}\right)$$

$$= f(a)b - f(a)a + \left(\frac{f(b) - f(a)}{b - a}\right)\frac{1}{2}(b - a)^2$$

$$= f(a)b - f(a)a + \frac{1}{2}(f(b) - f(a))(b - a)$$

$$= f(a)b - f(a)a + \frac{1}{2}f(b)b - \frac{1}{2}f(b)a - \frac{1}{2}f(a)b + \frac{1}{2}f(a)a$$

$$= \frac{1}{2}f(a)b - \frac{1}{2}f(a)a + \frac{1}{2}f(b)b - \frac{1}{2}f(b)a$$

$$= (b-a)\left[\frac{f(a) + f(b)}{2}\right] \tag{11}$$

This gives the same result as Equation (10) because they are just different forms of writing the same polynomial.

Method 3: Derived from Geometry
The trapezoidal rule can also be derived from geometry. Look at Figure 2. The area under the curve $f_1(x)$ is the area of a trapezoid. The integral

$$\int_a^b f(x)dx \approx \text{Area of trapezoid}$$

$$= \frac{1}{2}(\text{Sum of length of parallel sides})(\text{Perpendicular distance between parallel sides})$$

$$= \frac{1}{2}(f(b) + f(a))(b-a)$$

$$= (b-a)\left[\frac{f(a) + f(b)}{2}\right] \tag{12}$$

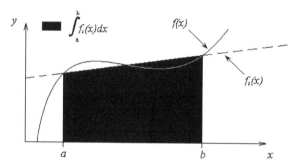

Figure 2 Geometric representation of trapezoidal rule.

Method 4: Derived from Method of Coefficients
The trapezoidal rule can also be derived by the method of coefficients. The formula

$$\int_a^b f(x)dx \approx \frac{b-a}{2}f(a) + \frac{b-a}{2}f(b) \tag{13}$$

$$= \sum_{i=1}^{2} c_i f(x_i)$$

where

$$c_1 = \frac{b-a}{2}$$

$$c_2 = \frac{b-a}{2}$$

$$x_1 = a$$

$$x_2 = b$$

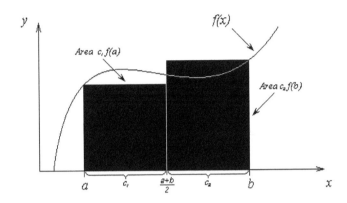

Figure 3 Area by method of coefficients.

The interpretation is that $f(x)$ is evaluated at points a and b, and each function evaluation is given a weight of $\frac{b-a}{2}$. Geometrically, Equation (12) is looked at as the area of a trapezoid, while Equation (13) is viewed as the sum of the area of two rectangles, as shown in Figure 3. How can one derive the trapezoidal rule by the method of coefficients?

Assume

$$\int_a^b f(x)dx = c_1 f(a) + c_2 f(b) \tag{14}$$

Let the right hand side be an exact expression for integrals of $\int_a^b 1\,dx$ and $\int_a^b x\,dx$, that is, the formula will then also be exact for linear combinations of $f(x) = 1$ and $f(x) = x$, that is, for $f(x) = a_0(1) + a_1(x)$.

$$\int_a^b 1\,dx = b - a = c_1 + c_2 \tag{15}$$

$$\int_a^b x\,dx = \frac{b^2 - a^2}{2} = c_1 a + c_2 b \tag{16}$$

Solving the above two equations gives

$$c_1 = \frac{b-a}{2}$$

$$c_2 = \frac{b-a}{2} \tag{17}$$

Hence

$$\int_{a}^{b} f(x)dx \approx \frac{b-a}{2}f(a) + \frac{b-a}{2}f(b) \tag{18}$$

Method 5: Another approach on the Method of Coefficients

The trapezoidal rule can also be derived by the method of coefficients by another approach

$$\int_{a}^{b} f(x)dx \approx \frac{b-a}{2}f(a) + \frac{b-a}{2}f(b)$$

Assume

$$\int_{a}^{b} f(x)dx = c_1 f(a) + c_2 f(b) \tag{19}$$

Let the right hand side be exact for integrals of the form

$$\int_{a}^{b} (a_0 + a_1 x)dx$$

So

$$\int_{a}^{b} (a_0 + a_1 x)dx = \left(a_0 x + a_1 \frac{x^2}{2} \right)_{a}^{b}$$

$$= a_0 (b-a) + a_1 \left(\frac{b^2 - a^2}{2} \right) \tag{20}$$

But we want

$$\int_{a}^{b} (a_0 + a_1 x)dx = c_1 f(a) + c_2 f(b) \tag{21}$$

to give the same result as Equation (20) for $f(x) = a_0 + a_1 x$.

$$\int_{a}^{b} (a_0 + a_1 x)dx = c_1 (a_0 + a_1 a) + c_2 (a_0 + a_1 b)$$

$$= a_0 (c_1 + c_2) + a_1 (c_1 a + c_2 b) \tag{22}$$

Hence from Equations (20) and (22),

$$a_0 (b-a) + a_1 \left(\frac{b^2 - a^2}{2} \right) = a_0 (c_1 + c_2) + a_1 (c_1 a + c_2 b)$$

Since a_0 and a_1 are arbitrary for a general straight line

$$c_1 + c_2 = b - a$$

$$c_1 a + c_2 b = \frac{b^2 - a^2}{2} \tag{23}$$

Again, solving the above two equations (23) gives

$$c_1 = \frac{b-a}{2}$$

$$c_2 = \frac{b-a}{2} \tag{24}$$

Therefore

$$\int_a^b f(x)dx \approx c_1 f(a) + c_2 f(b)$$

$$= \frac{b-a}{2} f(a) + \frac{b-a}{2} f(b) \tag{25}$$

Example 1

The vertical distance covered by a rocket from $t = 8$ to $t = 30$ seconds is given by

$$x = \int_8^{30} \left(2000 \ln\left[\frac{140000}{140000 - 2100t}\right] - 9.8t \right) dt$$

a) Use the single segment trapezoidal rule to find the distance covered for $t = 8$ to $t = 30$ seconds.
b) Find the true error, E_t for part (a).
c) Find the absolute relative true error for part (a).

Solution

a) $\quad I \approx (b-a)\left[\dfrac{f(a) + f(b)}{2}\right]$, where

$a = 8$
$b = 30$

$$f(t) = 2000 \ln\left[\frac{140000}{140000 - 2100t}\right] - 9.8t$$

$$f(8) = 2000 \ln\left[\frac{140000}{140000 - 2100(8)}\right] - 9.8(8)$$

$$= 177.27 \text{ m/s}$$

$$f(30) = 2000 \ln\left[\frac{140000}{140000 - 2100(30)}\right] - 9.8(30)$$

$$= 901.67 \text{ m/s}$$

$$I \approx (30 - 8)\left[\frac{177.27 + 901.67}{2}\right]$$

$$= 11868 \text{ m}$$

b) The exact value of the above integral is

$$x = \int_8^{30} \left(2000 \ln\left[\frac{140000}{140000 - 2100t}\right] - 9.8t \right) dt$$

$$= 11061 \text{ m}$$

so the true error is

$$E_t = \text{True Value} - \text{Approximate Value}$$

$$= 11061 - 11868$$

$$= -807 \text{ m}$$

c) The absolute relative true error, $|\in_t|$, would then be

$$|\in_t| = \left|\frac{\text{True Error}}{\text{True Value}}\right| \times 100$$

$$= \left|\frac{11061 - 11868}{11061}\right| \times 100$$

$$= 7.2958\%$$

Multiple-Segment Trapezoidal Rule

In Example 1, the true error using a single segment trapezoidal rule was large. We can divide the interval [8,30] into [8,19] and [19,30] intervals and apply the trapezoidal rule over each segment.

$$f(t) = 2000\ln\left(\frac{140000}{140000 - 2100t}\right) - 9.8t$$

$$\int_8^{30} f(t)dt = \int_8^{19} f(t)dt + \int_{19}^{30} f(t)dt$$

$$\approx (19-8)\left[\frac{f(8) + f(19)}{2}\right] + (30-19)\left[\frac{f(19) + f(30)}{2}\right]$$

$$f(8) = 177.27 \text{ m/s}$$

$$f(19) = 2000\ln\left(\frac{140000}{140000 - 2100(19)}\right) - 9.8(19) = 484.75 \text{ m/s}$$

$$f(30) = 901.67 \text{ m/s}$$

Hence

$$\int_8^{30} f(t)dt \approx (19-8)\left[\frac{177.27 + 484.75}{2}\right] + (30-19)\left[\frac{484.75 + 901.67}{2}\right]$$

$$= 11266 \text{ m}$$

The true error, E_t is

$$E_t = 11061 - 11266$$

$$= -205 \text{ m}$$

The true error now is reduced from 807 m to 205 m. Extending this procedure to dividing $[a,b]$ into n equal segments and applying the trapezoidal rule over each segment, the sum of the results obtained for each segment is the approximate value of the integral.

Divide $(b-a)$ into n equal segments as shown in Figure 4. Then the width of each segment is

$$h = \frac{b-a}{n} \tag{26}$$

The integral I can be broken into h integrals as

$$I = \int_a^b f(x)dx$$

$$= \int_a^{a+h} f(x)dx + \int_{a+h}^{a+2h} f(x)dx + \dots + \int_{a+(n-2)h}^{a+(n-1)h} f(x)dx + \int_{a+(n-1)h}^{b} f(x)dx \tag{27}$$

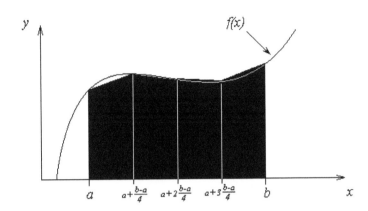

Figure 4 Multiple ($n = 4$) segment trapezoidal rule

Applying trapezoidal rule Equation (27) on each segment gives

$$\int_a^b f(x)dx = [(a+h) - a]\left[\frac{f(a) + f(a+h)}{2}\right]$$

$$+ [(a+2h) - (a+h)]\left[\frac{f(a+h) + f(a+2h)}{2}\right]$$

$$+ \dots\dots\dots + [(a+(n-1)h) - (a+(n-2)h)]\left[\frac{f(a+(n-2)h) + f(a+(n-1)h)}{2}\right]$$

$$+ [b - (a+(n-1)h)]\left[\frac{f(a+(n-1)h) + f(b)}{2}\right]$$

$$= h\left[\frac{f(a) + f(a+h)}{2}\right] + h\left[\frac{f(a+h) + f(a+2h)}{2}\right] + \dots\dots\dots$$

$$+ h\left[\frac{f(a+(n-2)h) + f(a+(n-1)h)}{2}\right] + h\left[\frac{f(a+(n-1)h) + f(b)}{2}\right]$$

$$= h\left[\frac{f(a) + 2f(a+h) + 2f(a+2h) + \dots + 2f(a+(n-1)h) + f(b)}{2}\right]$$

$$= \frac{h}{2}\left[f(a) + 2\left\{\sum_{i=1}^{n-1} f(a+ih)\right\} + f(b)\right]$$

$$= \frac{b-a}{2n}\left[f(a) + 2\left\{\sum_{i=1}^{n-1} f(a+ih)\right\} + f(b)\right] \tag{28}$$

Example 2

The vertical distance covered by a rocket from $t = 8$ to $t = 30$ seconds is given by

$$x = \int_{8}^{30} \left(2000 \ln \left[\frac{140000}{140000 - 2100t} \right] - 9.8t \right) dt$$

    a) Use the two-segment trapezoidal rule to find the distance covered from $t = 8$ to $t = 30$ seconds.

    b) Find the true error, E_t for part (a).

    c) Find the absolute relative true error for part (a).

Solution

a) The solution using 2-segment Trapezoidal rule is

$$I \approx \frac{b-a}{2n} \left[f(a) + 2 \left\{ \sum_{i=1}^{n-1} f(a + ih) \right\} + f(b) \right]$$

$n = 2$

$a = 8$

$b = 30$

$h = \dfrac{b-a}{n}$

$ = \dfrac{30-8}{2}$

$ = 11$

$$I \approx \frac{30-8}{2(2)} \left[f(8) + 2 \left\{ \sum_{i=1}^{2-1} f(8 + 11i) \right\} + f(30) \right]$$

$ = \dfrac{22}{4} \left[f(8) + 2f(19) + f(30) \right]$

$ = \dfrac{22}{4} \left[177.27 + 2(484.75) + 901.67 \right]$

$ = 11266 \text{ m}$

b) The exact value of the above integral is

$$x = \int_{8}^{30} \left(2000 \ln \left[\frac{140000}{140000 - 2100t} \right] - 9.8t \right) dt$$

$ = 11061 \text{ m}$

so the true error is

$ E_t = \text{True Value} - \text{Approximate Value}$

$ = 11061 - 11266$

$ = -205 \text{ m}$

c) The absolute relative true error, $\left| \in_t \right|$, would then be

$$|\epsilon_t| = \left| \frac{\text{True Error}}{\text{True Value}} \right| \times 100$$

$$= \left| \frac{11061 - 11266}{11061} \right| \times 100$$

$$= 1.8537\%$$

Table 1 Values obtained using multiple-segment trapezoidal rule for

$$x = \int_{8}^{30} \left(2000 \ln \left[\frac{140000}{140000 - 2100t} \right] - 9.8t \right) dt$$

n	Approximate Value	E_t	$|\epsilon_t|\%$	$|\epsilon_a|\%$
1	11868	-807	7.296	---
2	11266	-205	1.853	5.343
3	11153	-91.4	0.8265	1.019
4	11113	-51.5	0.4655	0.3594
5	11094	-33.0	0.2981	0.1669
6	11084	-22.9	0.2070	0.09082
7	11078	-16.8	0.1521	0.05482
8	11074	-12.9	0.1165	0.03560

Example 3

Use the multiple-segment trapezoidal rule to find the area under the curve

$$f(x) = \frac{300x}{1 + e^x}$$

from $x = 0$ to $x = 10$.

Solution

Using two segments, we get

$$h = \frac{10 - 0}{2} = 5$$

$$f(0) = \frac{300(0)}{1 + e^0} = 0$$

$$f(5) = \frac{300(5)}{1 + e^5} = 10.039$$

$$f(10) = \frac{300(10)}{1 + e^{10}} = 0.136$$

$$I \approx \frac{b - a}{2n} \left[f(a) + 2 \left\{ \sum_{i=1}^{n-1} f(a + ih) \right\} + f(b) \right]$$

$$= \frac{10 - 0}{2(2)} \left[f(0) + 2 \left\{ \sum_{i=1}^{2-1} f(0 + 5) \right\} + f(10) \right]$$

$$= \frac{10}{4} \left[f(0) + 2f(5) + f(10) \right]$$

$$= \frac{10}{4} \left[0 + 2(10.039) + 0.136 \right] \quad = 50.537$$

So what is the true value of this integral?

$$\int_{0}^{10} \frac{300x}{1 + e^x} dx = 246.59$$

Making the absolute relative true error

$$\left| \epsilon_t \right| = \left| \frac{246.59 - 50.535}{246.59} \right| \times 100$$

$$= 79.506\%$$

Why is the true value so far away from the approximate values? Just take a look at Figure 5. As you can see, the area under the "trapezoids" (yeah, they really look like triangles now) covers a small portion of the area under the curve. As we add more segments, the approximated value quickly approaches the true value.

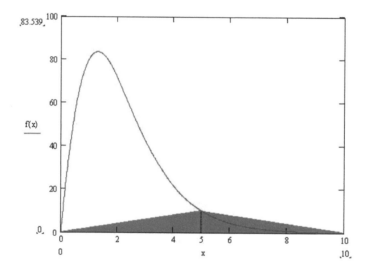

Figure 5 2-segment trapezoidal rule approximation.

Table 2 Values obtained using multiple-segment trapezoidal rule for $\int_{0}^{10} \frac{300x}{1 + e^x} dx$.

n	Approximate Value	E_t	$\left| \epsilon_t \right|$
1	0.681	245.91	99.724%
2	50.535	196.05	79.505%
4	170.61	75.978	30.812%
8	227.04	19.546	7.927%

16	241.70	4.887	1.982%
32	245.37	1.222	0.495%
64	246.28	0.305	0.124%

Example 4

Use multiple-segment trapezoidal rule to find

$$I = \int_0^2 \frac{1}{\sqrt{x}}\, dx$$

Solution

We cannot use the trapezoidal rule for this integral, as the value of the integrand at $x = 0$ is infinite. However, it is known that a discontinuity in a curve will not change the area under it. We can assume any value for the function at $x = 0$. The algorithm to define the function so that we can use the multiple-segment trapezoidal rule is given below.

> Function $f(x)$
> If $x = 0$ Then $f = 0$
> If $x \neq 0$ Then $f = x^{\wedge}(-0.5)$
> End Function

Basically, we are just assigning the function a value of zero at $x = 0$. Everywhere else, the function is continuous. This means the true value of our integral will be just that—true. Let's see what happens using the multiple-segment trapezoidal rule.
Using two segments, we get

$$h = \frac{2-0}{2} = 1$$

$$f(0) = 0$$

$$f(1) = \frac{1}{\sqrt{1}} = 1$$

$$f(2) = \frac{1}{\sqrt{2}} = 0.70711$$

$$I \approx \frac{b-a}{2n}\left[f(a) + 2\left\{\sum_{i=1}^{n-1} f(a+ih)\right\} + f(b) \right]$$

$$= \frac{2-0}{2(2)}\left[f(0) + 2\left\{\sum_{i=1}^{2-1} f(0+1)\right\} + f(2) \right]$$

$$= \frac{2}{4}\left[f(0) + 2f(1) + f(2) \right]$$

$$= \frac{2}{4}\left[0 + 2(1) + 0.70711 \right]$$

$$= 1.3536$$

So what is the true value of this integral?

$$\int_0^2 \frac{1}{\sqrt{x}}\,dx = 2.8284$$

Thus making the absolute relative true error

$$|\in_t| = \left|\frac{2.8284 - 1.3536}{2.8284}\right| \times 100$$

$$= 52.145\%$$

Table 3 Values obtained using multiple-segment trapezoidal rule for $\int_0^2 \frac{1}{\sqrt{x}}\,dx$.

n	Approximate Value	E_t	$|\in_t|$
2	1.354	1.474	52.14%
4	1.792	1.036	36.64%
8	2.097	0.731	25.85%
16	2.312	0.516	18.26%
32	2.463	0.365	12.91%
64	2.570	0.258	9.128%
128	2.646	0.182	6.454%
256	2.699	0.129	4.564%
512	2.737	0.091	3.227%
1024	2.764	0.064	2.282%
2048	2.783	0.045	1.613%
4096	2.796	0.032	1.141%

Error in Multiple-segment Trapezoidal Rule

The true error for a single segment Trapezoidal rule is given by

$$E_t = -\frac{(b-a)^3}{12}f''(\zeta), \quad a < \zeta < b$$

Where ζ is some point in $[a,b]$.

What is the error then in the multiple-segment trapezoidal rule? It will be simply the sum of the errors from each segment, where the error in each segment is that of the single segment trapezoidal rule. The error in each segment is

$$E_1 = -\frac{[(a+h)-a]^3}{12}f''(\zeta_1), \quad a < \zeta_1 < a+h$$

$$= -\frac{h^3}{12}f''(\zeta_1)$$

$$E_2 = -\frac{[(a+2h)-(a+h)]^3}{12}f''(\zeta_2), \quad a+h < \zeta_2 < a+2h$$

$$= -\frac{h^3}{12}f''(\zeta_2)$$

$$E_i = -\frac{[(a+ih)-(a+(i-1)h)]^3}{12} f''(\zeta_i), \quad a+(i-1)h < \zeta_i < a+ih$$

$$= -\frac{h^3}{12} f''(\zeta_i)$$

$$E_{n-1} = -\frac{[\{a+(n-1)h\}-\{a+(n-2)h\}]^3}{12} f''(\zeta_{n-1}), \quad a+(n-2)h < \zeta_{n-1} < a+(n-1)h$$

$$= -\frac{h^3}{12} f''(\zeta_{n-1})$$

$$E_n = -\frac{[b-\{a+(n-1)h\}]^3}{12} f''(\zeta_n), \quad a+(n-1)h < \zeta_n < b$$

$$= -\frac{h^3}{12} f''(\zeta_n)$$

Hence the total error in the multiple-segment trapezoidal rule is

$$E_t = \sum_{i=1}^{n} E_i$$

$$= -\frac{h^3}{12} \sum_{i=1}^{n} f''(\zeta_i)$$

$$= -\frac{(b-a)^3}{12n^3} \sum_{i=1}^{n} f''(\zeta_i)$$

$$= -\frac{(b-a)^3}{12n^2} \frac{\sum_{i=1}^{n} f''(\zeta_i)}{n}$$

The term $\dfrac{\sum_{i=1}^{n} f''(\zeta_i)}{n}$ is an approximate average value of the second derivative $f''(x)$, $a < x < b$.

Hence

$$E_t = -\frac{(b-a)^3}{12n^2} \frac{\sum_{i=1}^{n} f''(\zeta_i)}{n}$$

In Table 4, the approximate value of the integral

$$\int_{8}^{30} \left(2000 \ln\left[\frac{140000}{140000-2100t}\right] - 9.8t \right) dt$$

is given as a function of the number of segments. You can visualize that as the number of segments are doubled, the true error gets approximately quartered.

Table 4 Values obtained using multiple-segment trapezoidal rule for

$$x = \int_{8}^{30} \left(2000\ln\left[\frac{140000}{140000 - 2100t} \right] - 9.8t \right) dt .$$

n	Approximate Value	E_t	$|\epsilon_t|\%$	$|\epsilon_a|\%$
2	11266	-205	1.854	5.343
4	11113	-48	0.4684	0.3594
8	11074	-13	0.1175	0.03560
16	11065	-4	0.03616	0.00401

For example, for the 2-segment trapezoidal rule, the true error is -205, and a quarter of that error is -51.25. That is close to the true error of -48 for the 4-segment trapezoidal rule.

Can you answer the question *why is the true error not exactly -51.25?* How does this information help us in numerical integration? You will find out that this forms the basis of Romberg integration based on the trapezoidal rule, where we use the argument that true error gets approximately quartered when the number of segments is doubled. Romberg integration based on the trapezoidal rule is computationally more efficient than using the trapezoidal rule by itself in developing an automatic integration scheme.

INTEGRATION	
Topic	Trapezoidal Rule
Summary	These are textbook notes of trapezoidal rule of integration
Major	General Engineering
Authors	Autar Kaw, Michael Keltelas
Date	December 23, 2009
Web Site	http://numericalmethods.eng.usf.edu

Multiple Choice Test

Chapter 07.02
Trapezoidal Rule

1. The two-segment trapezoidal rule of integration is exact for integrating at most _____ order polynomials.
    (A) first
    (B) second
    (C) third
    (D) fourth

2. The value of $\int\limits_{0.2}^{2.2} xe^x dx$ by using the one-segment trapezoidal rule is most nearly
    (A) 11.672
    (B) 11.807
    (C) 20.099
    (D) 24.119

3. The value of $\int\limits_{0.2}^{2.2} xe^x dx$ by using the three-segment trapezoidal rule is most nearly
    (A) 11.672
    (B) 11.807
    (C) 12.811
    (D) 14.633

4. The velocity of a body is given by
    $$v(t) = 2t, \qquad 1 \le t \le 5$$
    $$= 5t^2 + 3, \ 5 < t \le 14$$
    where t is given in seconds, and v is given in m/s. Use the two-segment trapezoidal rule to find the distance in meters covered by the body from $t = 2$ to $t = 9$ seconds.
    (A) 935.00
    (B) 1039.7
    (C) 1260.9
    (D) 5048.9

5. The shaded area shows a plot of land available for sale. The units of measurement are in meters. Your best estimate of the area of the land in m² is most nearly
   (A) 2500
   (B) 4775
   (C) 5250
   (D) 6000

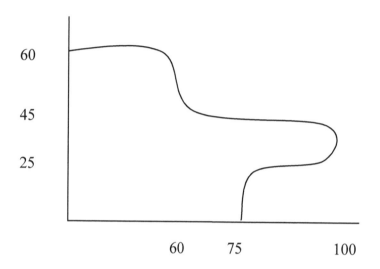

6. The following data of the velocity of a body is given as a function of time.

Time (s)	0	15	18	22	24
Velocity (m/s)	22	24	37	25	123

The distance in meters covered by the body from $t = 12\,s$ to $t = 18\,s$ calculated using the trapezoidal rule with unequal segments is
   (A) 162.90
   (B) 166.00
   (C) 181.70
   (D) 436.50

Complete Solution

Problem Set

Trapezoidal Rule
Chapter 07.02

1. Find the value of $\int_{0.2}^{2.2} xe^x dx$ by using two-segment trapezoidal rule.

2. Find the value of $\int_{-3.4}^{2.2} x^2 e^x dx$ by using four-segment trapezoidal rule.

3. The upward velocity of a rocket is given by
$$v(t) = 200\ln(t+1) - 10t, \quad t > 0$$
where t is given in s and v is given in m/s.
   - (a) Use 2-segment trapezoidal rule to calculate the distance covered by the rocket from $t = 0$ to $t = 5$ s.
   - (b) What is the true value of the distance covered by the rocket from $t = 0$ to $t = 5s$?
   - (c) What is the true error in part (a)?
   - (d) What is the relative true error in part (a)?
   - (e) What is the absolute relative true error in percentage for part (a).
   - (f) Use 4-segment Trapezoidal rule to calculate the distance covered by the rocket from $t = 0$ to $t = 5$ s.
   - (g) What is the absolute relative approximate error in percentage for part (e), assuming the previous approximation is from part (a)?
   - (h) Based on the answer from part (g), how many significant digits are correct in the answer in part (g).

4. Find the value of the integral $\int_{1}^{5} 3e^{-2t} dt$ using 2-segment trapezoidal rule.

5. For the integral $\int_{1}^{4} xe^{-2x} dx$, find the following
   - (a) Exact integral using your calculus knowledge (Hint: $\int u\,dv = uv - \int v\,du + C$)
   - (b) Value of integral using two segment trapezoidal rule.
   - (c) Value of integral using four-segment trapezoidal rule.
   - (d) Calculate the true error for part (b) and part (c). Is the true error for part (c) approximately a quarter of the true error for part (b)? Explain.

6. In multiple-segment trapezoidal rule, if E_n is the true error using n ($n \geq 1$) segments, then the true error using $2n$ segments approximately is _____ of E_n.

7. The upward velocity of a body is given by
    $$v(t) = \ln\left(\frac{160}{160 - 9t}\right), \ t > 0$$
    where t is given in seconds, and v in m/s.
    What is the distance covered by the body from $t = 5$ to $t = 9$ seconds? Use multiple segment trapezoidal rule with 4 segments.

8. The true error for the single segment trapezoidal rule used to calculate the approximate value of the integral $\int_a^b f(x)dx$ is given by

    $$E_t = -\frac{(b-a)^3}{12} f''(\zeta), a \leq \zeta \leq b.$$

    For the integral $\int_3^6 3e^{1.1x}dx$, what is the value of ζ ?

9. The approximate value of the integral of $\int_1^5 f(x)dx$ is found by using 1-segment trapezoidal rule as 0.35958. Given $f(2) = 0.7447$, $f(3) = 0.10454$ and $f(4) = -0.50730$, what is the approximate value of the integral of $\int_1^5 f(x)dx$ using 2-segment trapezoidal rule.

10. The true error for trapezoidal rule used to calculate the approximate value of the integral $\int_a^b f(x)dx$ is given by

    $$E_t = -\frac{(b-a)^3}{12} f''(\zeta), a \leq \zeta \leq b.$$

    For the integral $\int_2^5 (3x^2 + dx + e)dx$, where constants d and e are not given to you, the single segment Trapezoidal rule gives the value of the integral as 201.0. Find the exact value of the integral.

11.   A quadrature rule is developed by a scientist

$$\int_a^b f(x)dx \approx c_1 f(a).$$

The value of c_1 is found by assuming that the formula is exact for integrals of $f(x) = a_0 x^2$, where a_0 is an arbitrary constant. What is the value of c_1 in terms of a and b.

Chapter 07.03

Simpson's 1/3 Rule of Integration

After reading this chapter, you should be able to

1. *derive the formula for Simpson's 1/3 rule of integration,*
2. *use Simpson's 1/3 rule it to solve integrals,*
3. *develop the formula for multiple-segment Simpson's 1/3 rule of integration,*
4. *use multiple-segment Simpson's 1/3 rule of integration to solve integrals, and*
5. *derive the true error formula for multiple-segment Simpson's 1/3 rule.*

What is integration?

Integration is the process of measuring the area under a function plotted on a graph. Why would we want to integrate a function? Among the most common examples are finding the velocity of a body from an acceleration function, and displacement of a body from a velocity function. Throughout many engineering fields, there are (what sometimes seems like) countless applications for integral calculus. You can read about some of these applications in Chapters 07.00A-07.00G.

Sometimes, the evaluation of expressions involving these integrals can become daunting, if not indeterminate. For this reason, a wide variety of numerical methods has been developed to simplify the integral. Here, we will discuss Simpson's 1/3 rule of integral approximation, which improves upon the accuracy of the trapezoidal rule.

Here, we will discuss the Simpson's 1/3 rule of approximating integrals of the form

$$I = \int_a^b f(x)dx$$

where

$f(x)$ is called the integrand,
a = lower limit of integration
b = upper limit of integration

Simpson's 1/3 Rule

The trapezoidal rule was based on approximating the integrand by a first order polynomial, and then integrating the polynomial over interval of integration. Simpson's 1/3 rule is an

07.03.1

extension of Trapezoidal rule where the integrand is approximated by a second order polynomial.

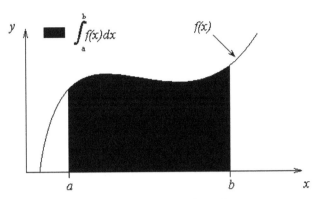

Figure 1 Integration of a function

<u>Method 1:</u>
Hence

$$I = \int_a^b f(x)dx \approx \int_a^b f_2(x)dx$$

where $f_2(x)$ is a second order polynomial given by

$$f_2(x) = a_0 + a_1 x + a_2 x^2.$$

Choose

$$(a, f(a)), \left(\frac{a+b}{2}, f\left(\frac{a+b}{2}\right)\right), \text{ and } (b, f(b))$$

as the three points of the function to evaluate a_0, a_1 and a_2.

$$f(a) = f_2(a) = a_0 + a_1 a + a_2 a^2$$

$$f\left(\frac{a+b}{2}\right) = f_2\left(\frac{a+b}{2}\right) = a_0 + a_1\left(\frac{a+b}{2}\right) + a_2\left(\frac{a+b}{2}\right)^2$$

$$f(b) = f_2(b) = a_0 + a_1 b + a_2 b^2$$

Solving the above three equations for unknowns, a_0, a_1 and a_2 give

$$a_0 = \frac{a^2 f(b) + abf(b) - 4abf\left(\frac{a+b}{2}\right) + abf(a) + b^2 f(a)}{a^2 - 2ab + b^2}$$

$$a_1 = -\frac{af(a) - 4af\left(\frac{a+b}{2}\right) + 3af(b) + 3bf(a) - 4bf\left(\frac{a+b}{2}\right) + bf(b)}{a^2 - 2ab + b^2}$$

$$a_2 = \frac{2\left(f(a) - 2f\left(\dfrac{a+b}{2}\right) + f(b)\right)}{a^2 - 2ab + b^2}$$

Then

$$I \approx \int_a^b f_2(x)\,dx$$

$$= \int_a^b \left(a_0 + a_1 x + a_2 x^2\right)dx$$

$$= \left[a_0 x + a_1 \frac{x^2}{2} + a_2 \frac{x^3}{3}\right]_a^b$$

$$= a_0(b-a) + a_1 \frac{b^2 - a^2}{2} + a_2 \frac{b^3 - a^3}{3}$$

Substituting values of a_0, a_1 and a_2 give

$$\int_a^b f_2(x)\,dx = \frac{b-a}{6}\left[f(a) + 4f\left(\frac{a+b}{2}\right) + f(b)\right]$$

Since for Simpson 1/3 rule, the interval $[a,b]$ is broken into 2 segments, the segment width

$$h = \frac{b-a}{2}$$

Hence the Simpson's 1/3 rule is given by

$$\int_a^b f(x)\,dx \approx \frac{h}{3}\left[f(a) + 4f\left(\frac{a+b}{2}\right) + f(b)\right]$$

Since the above form has 1/3 in its formula, it is called Simpson's 1/3 rule.

Method 2:
Simpson's 1/3 rule can also be derived by approximating $f(x)$ by a second order polynomial using Newton's divided difference polynomial as

$$f_2(x) = b_0 + b_1(x-a) + b_2(x-a)\left(x - \frac{a+b}{2}\right)$$

where

$$b_0 = f(a)$$

$$b_1 = \frac{f\left(\dfrac{a+b}{2}\right) - f(a)}{\dfrac{a+b}{2} - a}$$

$$b_2 = \dfrac{\dfrac{f(b) - f\left(\dfrac{a+b}{2}\right)}{b - \dfrac{a+b}{2}} - \dfrac{f\left(\dfrac{a+b}{2}\right) - f(a)}{\dfrac{a+b}{2} - a}}{b - a}$$

Integrating Newton's divided difference polynomial gives us

$$\int_a^b f(x)dx \approx \int_a^b f_2(x)dx$$

$$= \int_a^b \left[b_0 + b_1(x-a) + b_2(x-a)\left(x - \dfrac{a+b}{2}\right) \right]dx$$

$$= \left[b_0 x + b_1\left(\dfrac{x^2}{2} - ax\right) + b_2\left(\dfrac{x^3}{3} - \dfrac{(3a+b)x^2}{4} + \dfrac{a(a+b)x}{2}\right) \right]_a^b$$

$$= b_0(b-a) + b_1\left(\dfrac{b^2 - a^2}{2} - a(b-a)\right)$$

$$\qquad + b_2\left(\dfrac{b^3 - a^3}{3} - \dfrac{(3a+b)(b^2 - a^2)}{4} + \dfrac{a(a+b)(b-a)}{2}\right)$$

Substituting values of b_0, b_1, and b_2 into this equation yields the same result as before

$$\int_a^b f(x)dx \approx \dfrac{b-a}{6}\left[f(a) + 4f\left(\dfrac{a+b}{2}\right) + f(b) \right]$$

$$= \dfrac{h}{3}\left[f(a) + 4f\left(\dfrac{a+b}{2}\right) + f(b) \right]$$

<u>Method 3:</u>
One could even use the Lagrange polynomial to derive Simpson's formula. Notice any method of three-point quadratic interpolation can be used to accomplish this task. In this case, the interpolating function becomes

$$f_2(x) = \dfrac{\left(x - \dfrac{a+b}{2}\right)(x-b)}{\left(a - \dfrac{a+b}{2}\right)(a-b)} f(a) + \dfrac{(x-a)(x-b)}{\left(\dfrac{a+b}{2} - a\right)\left(\dfrac{a+b}{2} - b\right)} f\left(\dfrac{a+b}{2}\right) + \dfrac{(x-a)\left(x - \dfrac{a+b}{2}\right)}{(b-a)\left(b - \dfrac{a+b}{2}\right)} f(b)$$

Integrating this function gets

$$\int_a^b f_2(x)dx = \left[\frac{\frac{x^3}{3} - \frac{(a+3b)x^2}{4} + \frac{b(a+b)x}{2}}{\left(a - \frac{a+b}{2}\right)(a-b)} f(a) + \frac{\frac{x^3}{3} - \frac{(a+b)x^2}{2} + abx}{\left(\frac{a+b}{2} - a\right)\left(\frac{a+b}{2} - b\right)} f\left(\frac{a+b}{2}\right) \right.$$

$$\left. + \frac{\frac{x^3}{3} - \frac{(3a+b)x^2}{4} + \frac{a(a+b)x}{2}}{(b-a)\left(b - \frac{a+b}{2}\right)} f(b) \right]_a^b$$

$$= \frac{\frac{b^3 - a^3}{3} - \frac{(a+3b)(b^2 - a^2)}{4} + \frac{b(a+b)(b-a)}{2}}{\left(a - \frac{a+b}{2}\right)(a-b)} f(a)$$

$$+ \frac{\frac{b^3 - a^3}{3} - \frac{(a+b)(b^2 - a^2)}{2} + ab(b-a)}{\left(\frac{a+b}{2} - a\right)\left(\frac{a+b}{2} - b\right)} f\left(\frac{a+b}{2}\right)$$

$$+ \frac{\frac{b^3 - a^3}{3} - \frac{(3a+b)(b^2 - a^2)}{4} + \frac{a(a+b)(b-a)}{2}}{(b-a)\left(b - \frac{a+b}{2}\right)} f(b)$$

Believe it or not, simplifying and factoring this large expression yields you the same result as before

$$\int_a^b f(x)dx \approx \frac{b-a}{6}\left[f(a) + 4f\left(\frac{a+b}{2}\right) + f(b) \right]$$

$$= \frac{h}{3}\left[f(a) + 4f\left(\frac{a+b}{2}\right) + f(b) \right].$$

<u>Method 4:</u>
Simpson's 1/3 rule can also be derived by the method of coefficients. Assume

$$\int_a^b f(x)dx \approx c_1 f(a) + c_2 f\left(\frac{a+b}{2}\right) + c_3 f(b)$$

Let the right-hand side be an exact expression for the integrals $\int_a^b 1dx$, $\int_a^b xdx$, and $\int_a^b x^2 dx$. This implies that the right hand side will be exact expressions for integrals of any linear combination of the three integrals for a general second order polynomial. Now

$$\int_a^b 1dx = b - a = c_1 + c_2 + c_3$$

$$\int_a^b x\,dx = \frac{b^2 - a^2}{2} = c_1 a + c_2 \frac{a+b}{2} + c_3 b$$

$$\int_a^b x^2\,dx = \frac{b^3 - a^3}{3} = c_1 a^2 + c_2 \left(\frac{a+b}{2}\right)^2 + c_3 b^2$$

Solving the above three equations for c_0, c_1 and c_2 give

$$c_1 = \frac{b-a}{6}$$

$$c_2 = \frac{2(b-a)}{3}$$

$$c_3 = \frac{b-a}{6}$$

This gives

$$\int_a^b f(x)\,dx \approx \frac{b-a}{6} f(a) + \frac{2(b-a)}{3} f\left(\frac{a+b}{2}\right) + \frac{b-a}{6} f(b)$$

$$= \frac{b-a}{6}\left[f(a) + 4f\left(\frac{a+b}{2}\right) + f(b) \right]$$

$$= \frac{h}{3}\left[f(a) + 4f\left(\frac{a+b}{2}\right) + f(b) \right]$$

The integral from the first method

$$\int_a^b f(x)\,dx \approx \int_a^b (a_0 + a_1 x + a_2 x^2)\,dx$$

can be viewed as the area under the second order polynomial, while the equation from Method 4

$$\int_a^b f(x)\,dx \approx \frac{b-a}{6} f(a) + \frac{2(b-a)}{3} f\left(\frac{a+b}{2}\right) + \frac{b-a}{6} f(b)$$

can be viewed as the sum of the areas of three rectangles.

Example 1

The distance covered by a rocket in meters from $t = 8\,s$ to $t = 30\,s$ is given by

$$x = \int_8^{30} \left(2000 \ln\left[\frac{140000}{140000 - 2100t} \right] - 9.8t \right) dt$$

a) Use Simpson's 1/3 rule to find the approximate value of x.
b) Find the true error, E_t.
c) Find the absolute relative true error, $|\epsilon_t|$.

Solution

a) $x \approx \dfrac{b-a}{6}\left[f(a) + 4f\left(\dfrac{a+b}{2}\right) + f(b)\right]$

$a = 8$

$b = 30$

$\dfrac{a+b}{2} = 19$

$f(t) = 2000\ln\left[\dfrac{140000}{140000 - 2100t}\right] - 9.8t$

$f(8) = 2000\ln\left[\dfrac{140000}{140000 - 2100(8)}\right] - 9.8(8) = 177.27 \, m/s$

$f(30) = 2000\ln\left[\dfrac{140000}{140000 - 2100(30)}\right] - 9.8(30) = 901.67 \, m/s$

$f(19) = 2000\ln\left(\dfrac{140000}{140000 - 2100(19)}\right) - 9.8(19) = 484.75 \, m/s$

$x \approx \dfrac{b-a}{6}\left[f(a) + 4f\left(\dfrac{a+b}{2}\right) + f(b)\right]$

$= \left(\dfrac{30-8}{6}\right)\left[f(8) + 4f(19) + f(30)\right]$

$= \dfrac{22}{6}\left[177.27 + 4 \times 484.75 + 901.67\right]$

$= 11065.72 \, m$

b) The exact value of the above integral is

$x = \displaystyle\int_{8}^{30}\left(2000\ln\left[\dfrac{140000}{140000 - 2100t}\right] - 9.8t\right)dt$

$= 11061.34 \, m$

So the true error is

$E_t = True \, Value - Approximate \, Value$

$= 11061.34 - 11065.72$

$= -4.38 \, m$

c) Absolute Relative true error,

$\left|\epsilon_t\right| = \left|\dfrac{True \, Error}{True \, Value}\right| \times 100$

$= \left|\dfrac{-4.38}{11061.34}\right| \times 100$

$$= 0.0396\%$$

Multiple-segment Simpson's 1/3 Rule

Just like in multiple-segment trapezoidal rule, one can subdivide the interval $[a,b]$ into n segments and apply Simpson's 1/3 rule repeatedly over every two segments. Note that n needs to be even. Divide interval $[a,b]$ into n equal segments, so that the segment width is given by

$$h = \frac{b-a}{n}.$$

Now

$$\int_a^b f(x)dx = \int_{x_0}^{x_n} f(x)dx$$

where

$$x_0 = a$$

$$x_n = b$$

$$\int_a^b f(x)dx = \int_{x_0}^{x_2} f(x)dx + \int_{x_2}^{x_4} f(x)dx + \dots\dots + \int_{x_{n-4}}^{x_{n-2}} f(x)dx + \int_{x_{n-2}}^{x_n} f(x)dx$$

Apply Simpson's 1/3rd Rule over each interval,

$$\int_a^b f(x)dx \cong (x_2 - x_0)\left[\frac{f(x_0) + 4f(x_1) + f(x_2)}{6}\right] + (x_4 - x_2)\left[\frac{f(x_2) + 4f(x_3) + f(x_4)}{6}\right] + \dots$$

$$+ (x_{n-2} - x_{n-4})\left[\frac{f(x_{n-4}) + 4f(x_{n-3}) + f(x_{n-2})}{6}\right] + (x_n - x_{n-2})\left[\frac{f(x_{n-2}) + 4f(x_{n-1}) + f(x_n)}{6}\right]$$

Since

$$x_i - x_{i-2} = 2h$$

$$i = 2, 4, \dots, n$$

then

$$\int_a^b f(x)dx \cong 2h\left[\frac{f(x_0) + 4f(x_1) + f(x_2)}{6}\right] + 2h\left[\frac{f(x_2) + 4f(x_3) + f(x_4)}{6}\right] + \dots$$

$$+ 2h\left[\frac{f(x_{n-4}) + 4f(x_{n-3}) + f(x_{n-2})}{6}\right] + 2h\left[\frac{f(x_{n-2}) + 4f(x_{n-1}) + f(x_n)}{6}\right]$$

$$= \frac{h}{3}\left[f(x_0) + 4\{f(x_1) + f(x_3) + \dots + f(x_{n-1})\} + 2\{f(x_2) + f(x_4) + \dots + f(x_{n-2})\} + f(x_n)\right]$$

$$= \frac{h}{3}\left[f(x_0) + 4\sum_{\substack{i=1\\i=odd}}^{n-1} f(x_i) + 2\sum_{\substack{i=2\\i=even}}^{n-2} f(x_i) + f(x_n) \right]$$

$$\int_a^b f(x)dx \cong \frac{b-a}{3n}\left[f(x_0) + 4\sum_{\substack{i=1\\i=odd}}^{n-1} f(x_i) + 2\sum_{\substack{i=2\\i=even}}^{n-2} f(x_i) + f(x_n) \right]$$

Example 2

Use 4-segment Simpson's 1/3 rule to approximate the distance covered by a rocket in meters from $t = 8$ s to $t = 30$ s as given by

$$x = \int_8^{30}\left(2000\ln\left[\frac{140000}{140000 - 2100t} \right] - 9.8t \right)dt$$

a) Use four segment Simpson's 1/3rd Rule to find the probability.
b) Find the true error, E_t for part (a).
c) Find the absolute relative true error, $|\epsilon_t|$ for part (a).

Solution:

a) Using n segment Simpson's 1/3 rule,

$$x \approx \frac{b-a}{3n}\left[f(t_0) + 4\sum_{\substack{i=1\\i=odd}}^{n-1} f(t_i) + 2\sum_{\substack{i=2\\i=even}}^{n-2} f(t_i) + f(t_n) \right]$$

$$n = 4$$
$$a = 8$$
$$b = 30$$
$$h = \frac{b-a}{n}$$
$$= \frac{30-8}{4}$$
$$= 5.5$$

$$f(t) = 2000\ln\left[\frac{140000}{140000 - 2100t} \right] - 9.8t$$

So

$$f(t_0) = f(8)$$

$$f(8) = 2000\ln\left[\frac{140000}{140000 - 2100(8)} \right] - 9.8(8) = 177.27 m/s$$

$$f(t_1) = f(8 + 5.5) = f(13.5)$$

$$f(13.5) = 2000 \ln\left[\frac{140000}{140000 - 2100(13.5)}\right] - 9.8(13.5) = 320.25 m/s$$

$$f(t_2) = f(13.5 + 5.5) = f(19)$$

$$f(19) = 2000 \ln\left(\frac{140000}{140000 - 2100(19)}\right) - 9.8(19) = 484.75 m/s$$

$$f(t_3) = f(19 + 5.5) = f(24.5)$$

$$f(24.5) = 2000 \ln\left[\frac{140000}{140000 - 2100(24.5)}\right] - 9.8(24.5) = 676.05 m/s$$

$$f(t_4) = f(t_n) = f(30)$$

$$f(30) = 2000 \ln\left[\frac{140000}{140000 - 2100(30)}\right] - 9.8(30) = 901.67 m/s$$

$$x = \frac{b-a}{3n}\left[f(t_0) + 4\sum_{\substack{i=1 \\ i=odd}}^{n-1} f(t_i) + 2\sum_{\substack{i=2 \\ i=even}}^{n-2} f(t_i) + f(t_n)\right]$$

$$= \frac{30-8}{3(4)}\left[f(8) + 4\sum_{\substack{i=1 \\ i=odd}}^{3} f(t_i) + 2\sum_{\substack{i=2 \\ i=even}}^{2} f(t_i) + f(30)\right]$$

$$= \frac{22}{12}\left[f(8) + 4f(t_1) + 4f(t_3) + 2f(t_2) + f(30)\right]$$

$$= \frac{11}{6}\left[f(8) + 4f(13.5) + 4f(24.5) + 2f(19) + f(30)\right]$$

$$= \frac{11}{6}\left[177.27 + 4(320.25) + 4(676.05) + 2(484.75) + 901.67\right]$$

$$= 11061.64 \ m$$

b) The exact value of the above integral is

$$x = \int_{8}^{30}\left(2000 \ln\left[\frac{140000}{140000 - 2100t}\right] - 9.8t\right) dt$$

$$= 11061.34 \ m$$

So the true error is

$$E_t = True \ Value - Approximate \ Value$$

$$E_t = 11061.34 - 11061.64$$

$$= -0.30 \ m$$

c) Absolute Relative true error,

$$\left|\epsilon_t\right| = \left|\frac{\text{True Error}}{\text{True Value}}\right| \times 100$$

$$= \left|\frac{-0.3}{11061.34}\right| \times 100$$

$$= 0.0027\%$$

Table 1 Values of Simpson's 1/3 rule for Example 2 with multiple-segments

n	Approximate Value	E_t	$\left|\epsilon_t\right|$
2	11065.72	-4.38	0.0396%
4	11061.64	-0.30	0.0027%
6	11061.40	-0.06	0.0005%
8	11061.35	-0.02	0.0002%
10	11061.34	-0.01	0.0001%

Error in Multiple-segment Simpson's 1/3 rule

The true error in a single application of Simpson's 1/3rd Rule is given[1] by

$$E_t = -\frac{(b-a)^5}{2880} f^{(4)}(\zeta), \quad a < \zeta < b$$

In multiple-segment Simpson's 1/3 rule, the error is the sum of the errors in each application of Simpson's 1/3 rule. The error in the n segments Simpson's 1/3rd Rule is given by

$$E_1 = -\frac{(x_2 - x_0)^5}{2880} f^{(4)}(\zeta_1), \quad x_0 < \zeta_1 < x_2$$

$$= -\frac{h^5}{90} f^{(4)}(\zeta_1)$$

$$E_2 = -\frac{(x_4 - x_2)^5}{2880} f^{(4)}(\zeta_2), \quad x_2 < \zeta_2 < x_4$$

$$= -\frac{h^5}{90} f^{(4)}(\zeta_2)$$

$$\vdots$$

$$E_i = -\frac{(x_{2i} - x_{2(i-1)})^5}{2880} f^{(4)}(\zeta_i), \quad x_{2(i-1)} < \zeta_i < x_{2i}$$

$$= -\frac{h^5}{90} f^{(4)}(\zeta_i)$$

$$\vdots$$

---

[1] The $f^{(4)}$ in the true error expression stands for the fourth derivative of the function $f(x)$.

$$E_{\frac{n}{2}-1} = -\frac{(x_{n-2} - x_{n-4})^5}{2880} f^{(4)}\left(\varsigma_{\frac{n}{2}-1}\right), \quad x_{n-4} < \varsigma_{\frac{n}{2}-1} < x_{n-2}$$

$$= -\frac{h^5}{90} f^{(4)}\left(\varsigma_{\frac{n}{2}-1}\right)$$

$$E_{\frac{n}{2}} = -\frac{(x_n - x_{n-2})^5}{2880} f^{(4)}\left(\varsigma_{\frac{n}{2}}\right), x_{n-2} < \varsigma_{\frac{n}{2}} < x_n$$

Hence, the total error in the multiple-segment Simpson's 1/3 rule is

$$= -\frac{h^5}{90} f^{(4)}\left(\varsigma_{\frac{n}{2}}\right)$$

$$E_t = \sum_{i=1}^{\frac{n}{2}} E_i$$

$$= -\frac{h^5}{90} \sum_{i=1}^{\frac{n}{2}} f^{(4)}(\varsigma_i)$$

$$= -\frac{(b-a)^5}{90n^5} \sum_{i=1}^{\frac{n}{2}} f^{(4)}(\varsigma_i)$$

$$= -\frac{(b-a)^5}{90n^4} \frac{\sum_{i=1}^{\frac{n}{2}} f^{(4)}(\varsigma_i)}{n}$$

The term $\dfrac{\sum_{i=1}^{\frac{n}{2}} f^{(4)}(\varsigma_i)}{n}$ is an approximate average value of $f^{(4)}(x), a < x < b$. Hence

$$E_t = -\frac{(b-a)^5}{90n^4} \overline{f}^{(4)}$$

where

$$\overline{f}^{(4)} = \frac{\sum_{i=1}^{\frac{n}{2}} f^{(4)}(\varsigma_i)}{n}$$

INTEGRATION	
Topic	Simpson's 1/3 rule
Summary	Textbook notes of Simpson's 1/3 rule
Major	General Engineering
Authors	Autar Kaw, Michael Keteltas
Date	December 23, 2009
Web Site	http://numericalmethods.eng.usf.edu

Multiple-Choice Test

Chapter 07.03
Simpson's 1/3 Rule

1. The highest order of polynomial integrand for which Simpson's 1/3 rule of integration is exact is
    - (A) first
    - (B) second
    - (C) third
    - (D) fourth

2. The value of $\int_{0.2}^{2.2} e^x dx$ by using 2-segment Simpson's 1/3 rule most nearly is
    - (A) 7.8036
    - (B) 7.8423
    - (C) 8.4433
    - (D) 10.246

3. The value of $\int_{0.2}^{2.2} e^x dx$ by using 4-segment Simpson's 1/3 rule most nearly is
    - (A) 7.8036
    - (B) 7.8062
    - (C) 7.8423
    - (D) 7.9655

4. The velocity of a body is given by
    $$v(t) = 2t, \qquad 1 \le t \le 5$$
    $$= 5t^2 + 3, \ 5 < t \le 14$$
    where t is given in seconds, and v is given in m/s. Using two-segment Simpson's 1/3 rule, the distance in meters covered by the body from $t = 2$ to $t = 9$ seconds most nearly is
    - (A) 949.33
    - (B) 1039.7
    - (C) 1200.5
    - (D) 1442.0

5. The value of $\int\limits_{3}^{19} f(x)dx$ by using 2-segment Simpson's 1/3 rule is estimated as

702.039. The estimate of the same integral using 4-segment Simpson's 1/3 rule most nearly is

(A) $702.039 + \dfrac{8}{3}[2f(7) - f(11) + 2f(15)]$

(B) $\dfrac{702.039}{2} + \dfrac{8}{3}[2f(7) - f(11) + 2f(15)]$

(C) $702.039 + \dfrac{8}{3}[2f(7) + 2f(15)]$

(D) $\dfrac{702.039}{2} + \dfrac{8}{3}[2f(7) + 2f(15)]$

6. The following data of the velocity of a body is given as a function of time.

Time (s)	4	7	10	15
Velocity (m/s)	22	24	37	46

The best estimate of the distance in meters covered by the body from $t = 4$ to $t = 15$ using combined Simpson's 1/3 rule and the trapezoidal rule would be

(A) 354.70
(B) 362.50
(C) 368.00
(D) 378.80

Complete Solution

Problem Set

Chapter 07.03
Simpson 1/3 Rule

1. Find the value of $\int\limits_{0.2}^{2.2} xe^x\,dx$ by using two-segment Simpson's 1/3 rule.

2. Find the value of $\int\limits_{-3.4}^{2.2} x^2 e^x\,dx$ by using four-segment Simpson's 1/3 rule.

3. The upward velocity of a rocket is given by
    $$v(t) = 200\ln(t+1) - 10t, \quad t > 0$$
    where t is given in seconds and v is given in m/s.
    a) Use two-segment Simpson's 1/3 rule to calculate the distance covered by the rocket from $t = 0$ to $t = 5$ s.
    b) What is the true value of the distance covered by the rocket from $t = 0$ to $t = 5$ s?
    c) What is the true error in part (a)?
    d) What is the relative true error in part (a)?
    e) What is the absolute relative true error in percentage for part (a).
    f) Use four-segment Simpson's 1/3rd rule to calculate the distance covered by the rocket from $t = 0$ to $t = 5$ s.
    g) What is the absolute relative approximate error in percentage for part (e), assuming the previous approximation is from part (a)?
    h) Based on the answer from part (g), how many significant digits are correct in the answer in part (g).

4. The upward velocity of a body is given by
    $$v(t) = \ln\left(\frac{160}{160-9t}\right), t > 0,$$
    where t is given in seconds, and v in m/s. What is the distance covered by the body from $t = 5$ to $t = 9$ seconds? Use multiple segment Simpson's 1/3 rule with 4 segments.

5. The true error for the two segment Simpson's 1/3 rule used to calculate the approximate value of the integral $\int\limits_a^b f(x)dx$ is given by

$$E_t = -\frac{(b-a)^5}{2880} f^{(4)}(\xi), \ a \le \xi \le b.$$

For the integral $\int\limits_3^6 4e^{2x}dx$, what is the value of ξ?

6. The true error for the two segment Simpson's 1/3 rule used to calculate the approximate value of the integral $\int\limits_a^b f(x)dx$ is given by

$$E_t = -\frac{(b-a)^5}{2880} f^{(4)}(\xi), \ a \le \xi \le b.$$

For the integral $\int\limits_3^6 4e^{2x}dx$,

   a) find the lower and upper estimate of the true error based on the true error formula.
   b) find the exact value of the integral.
   c) verify that the estimates of part (a) bracket the true error.

Chapter 07.05
Gauss Quadrature Rule of Integration

After reading this chapter, you should be able to:

1. *derive the Gauss quadrature method for integration and be able to use it to solve problems, and*
2. *use Gauss quadrature method to solve examples of approximate integrals.*

What is integration?

Integration is the process of measuring the area under a function plotted on a graph. Why would we want to integrate a function? Among the most common examples are finding the velocity of a body from an acceleration function, and displacement of a body from a velocity function. Throughout many engineering fields, there are (what sometimes seems like) countless applications for integral calculus. You can read about some of these applications in Chapters 07.00A-07.00G.

Sometimes, the evaluation of expressions involving these integrals can become daunting, if not indeterminate. For this reason, a wide variety of numerical methods has been developed to simplify the integral.

Here, we will discuss the Gauss quadrature rule of approximating integrals of the form

$$I = \int_a^b f(x)dx$$

where

$f(x)$ is called the integrand,
a = lower limit of integration
b = upper limit of integration

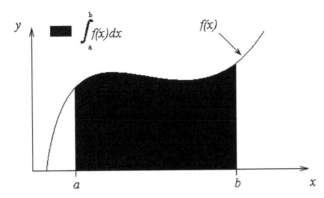

Figure 1 Integration of a function.

Gauss Quadrature Rule

<u>Background:</u>
To derive the trapezoidal rule from the method of undetermined coefficients, we approximated

$$\int_a^b f(x)dx \approx c_1 f(a) + c_2 f(b) \tag{1}$$

Let the right hand side be exact for integrals of a straight line, that is, for an integrated form of

$$\int_a^b (a_0 + a_1 x)dx$$

So

$$\int_a^b (a_0 + a_1 x)dx = \left[a_0 x + a_1 \frac{x^2}{2} \right]_a^b$$

$$= a_0(b-a) + a_1\left(\frac{b^2 - a^2}{2} \right) \tag{2}$$

But from Equation (1), we want

$$\int_a^b (a_0 + a_1 x)dx = c_1 f(a) + c_2 f(b) \tag{3}$$

to give the same result as Equation (2) for $f(x) = a_0 + a_1 x$.

$$\int_a^b (a_0 + a_1 x)dx = c_1(a_0 + a_1 a) + c_2(a_0 + a_1 b)$$

$$= a_0(c_1 + c_2) + a_1(c_1 a + c_2 b) \tag{4}$$

Hence from Equations (2) and (4),

$$a_0(b-a) + a_1\left(\frac{b^2 - a^2}{2} \right) = a_0(c_1 + c_2) + a_1(c_1 a + c_2 b)$$

Since a_0 and a_1 are arbitrary constants for a general straight line

$$c_1 + c_2 = b - a \tag{5a}$$

$$c_1 a + c_2 b = \frac{b^2 - a^2}{2} \tag{5b}$$

Multiplying Equation (5a) by a and subtracting from Equation (5b) gives

$$c_2 = \frac{b - a}{2} \tag{6a}$$

Substituting the above found value of c_2 in Equation (5a) gives

$$c_1 = \frac{b - a}{2} \tag{6b}$$

Therefore

$$\int_a^b f(x)dx \approx c_1 f(a) + c_2 f(b)$$

$$= \frac{b - a}{2} f(a) + \frac{b - a}{2} f(b) \tag{7}$$

Derivation of two-point Gauss quadrature rule

Method 1:

The two-point Gauss quadrature rule is an extension of the trapezoidal rule approximation where the arguments of the function are not predetermined as a and b, but as unknowns x_1 and x_2. So in the two-point Gauss quadrature rule, the integral is approximated as

$$I = \int_a^b f(x)dx$$

$$\approx c_1 f(x_1) + c_2 f(x_2)$$

There are four unknowns x_1, x_2, c_1 and c_2. These are found by assuming that the formula gives exact results for integrating a general third order polynomial, $f(x) = a_0 + a_1 x + a_2 x^2 + a_3 x^3$. Hence

$$\int_a^b f(x)dx = \int_a^b \left(a_0 + a_1 x + a_2 x^2 + a_3 x^3\right)dx$$

$$= \left[a_0 x + a_1 \frac{x^2}{2} + a_2 \frac{x^3}{3} + a_3 \frac{x^4}{4}\right]_a^b$$

$$= a_0(b - a) + a_1\left(\frac{b^2 - a^2}{2}\right) + a_2\left(\frac{b^3 - a^3}{3}\right) + a_3\left(\frac{b^4 - a^4}{4}\right) \tag{8}$$

The formula would then give

$$\int_a^b f(x)dx \approx c_1 f(x_1) + c_2 f(x_2) =$$

$$c_1\left(a_0 + a_1 x_1 + a_2 x_1^2 + a_3 x_1^3\right) + c_2\left(a_0 + a_1 x_2 + a_2 x_2^2 + a_3 x_2^3\right) \tag{9}$$

Equating Equations (8) and (9) gives

$$a_0(b-a)+a_1\left(\frac{b^2-a^2}{2}\right)+a_2\left(\frac{b^3-a^3}{3}\right)+a_3\left(\frac{b^4-a^4}{4}\right)$$

$$= c_1\left(a_0+a_1x_1+a_2x_1^2+a_3x_1^3\right)+c_2\left(a_0+a_1x_2+a_2x_2^2+a_3x_2^3\right)$$

$$= a_0(c_1+c_2)+a_1(c_1x_1+c_2x_2)+a_2\left(c_1x_1^2+c_2x_2^2\right)+a_3\left(c_1x_1^3+c_2x_2^3\right) \qquad (10)$$

Since in Equation (10), the constants a_0, a_1, a_2, and a_3 are arbitrary, the coefficients of a_0, a_1, a_2, and a_3 are equal. This gives us four equations as follows.

$$b-a=c_1+c_2$$

$$\frac{b^2-a^2}{2}=c_1x_1+c_2x_2$$

$$\frac{b^3-a^3}{3}=c_1x_1^2+c_2x_2^2$$

$$\frac{b^4-a^4}{4}=c_1x_1^3+c_2x_2^3 \qquad (11)$$

Without proof (see Example 1 for proof of a related problem), we can find that the above four simultaneous nonlinear equations have only one acceptable solution

$$c_1=\frac{b-a}{2}$$

$$c_2=\frac{b-a}{2}$$

$$x_1=\left(\frac{b-a}{2}\right)\left(-\frac{1}{\sqrt{3}}\right)+\frac{b+a}{2}$$

$$x_2=\left(\frac{b-a}{2}\right)\left(\frac{1}{\sqrt{3}}\right)+\frac{b+a}{2} \qquad (12)$$

Hence

$$\int_a^b f(x)dx \approx c_1 f(x_1)+c_2 f(x_2)$$

$$=\frac{b-a}{2}f\left(\frac{b-a}{2}\left(-\frac{1}{\sqrt{3}}\right)+\frac{b+a}{2}\right)+\frac{b-a}{2}f\left(\frac{b-a}{2}\left(\frac{1}{\sqrt{3}}\right)+\frac{b+a}{2}\right) \qquad (13)$$

Method 2:
We can derive the same formula by assuming that the expression gives exact values for the individual integrals of $\int_a^b 1dx$, $\int_a^b xdx$, $\int_a^b x^2dx$, and $\int_a^b x^3dx$. The reason the formula can also be

derived using this method is that the linear combination of the above integrands is a general third order polynomial given by $f(x) = a_0 + a_1 x + a_2 x^2 + a_3 x^3$.

These will give four equations as follows

$$\int_a^b 1 dx = b - a = c_1 + c_2$$

$$\int_a^b x dx = \frac{b^2 - a^2}{2} = c_1 x_1 + c_2 x_2$$

$$\int_a^b x^2 dx = \frac{b^3 - a^3}{3} = c_1 x_1^2 + c_2 x_2^2$$

$$\int_a^b x^3 dx = \frac{b^4 - a^4}{4} = c_1 x_1^3 + c_2 x_2^3 \tag{14}$$

These four simultaneous nonlinear equations can be solved to give a single acceptable solution

$$c_1 = \frac{b-a}{2}$$

$$c_2 = \frac{b-a}{2}$$

$$x_1 = \left(\frac{b-a}{2}\right)\left(-\frac{1}{\sqrt{3}}\right) + \frac{b+a}{2}$$

$$x_2 = \left(\frac{b-a}{2}\right)\left(\frac{1}{\sqrt{3}}\right) + \frac{b+a}{2} \tag{15}$$

Hence

$$\int_a^b f(x) dx \approx \frac{b-a}{2} f\left(\frac{b-a}{2}\left(-\frac{1}{\sqrt{3}}\right) + \frac{b+a}{2}\right) + \frac{b-a}{2} f\left(\frac{b-a}{2}\left(\frac{1}{\sqrt{3}}\right) + \frac{b+a}{2}\right) \tag{16}$$

Since two points are chosen, it is called the two-point Gauss quadrature rule. Higher point versions can also be developed.

Higher point Gauss quadrature formulas

For example

$$\int_a^b f(x) dx \approx c_1 f(x_1) + c_2 f(x_2) + c_3 f(x_3) \tag{17}$$

is called the three-point Gauss quadrature rule. The coefficients c_1, c_2 and c_3, and the function arguments x_1, x_2 and x_3 are calculated by assuming the formula gives exact expressions for integrating a fifth order polynomial

$$\int_a^b \left(a_0 + a_1 x + a_2 x^2 + a_3 x^3 + a_4 x^4 + a_5 x^5\right) dx .$$

General n-point rules would approximate the integral

$$\int_a^b f(x)dx \approx c_1 f(x_1) + c_2 f(x_2) + \ldots\ldots + c_n f(x_n) \qquad (18)$$

Arguments and weighing factors for n-point Gauss quadrature rules

In handbooks (see Table 1), coefficients and arguments given for n-point Gauss quadrature rule are given for integrals of the form

$$\int_{-1}^{1} g(x)dx \approx \sum_{i=1}^{n} c_i g(x_i) \qquad (19)$$

Table 1 Weighting factors c and function arguments x used in Gauss quadrature formulas

Points	Weighting Factors	Function Arguments
2	$c_1 = 1.000000000$	$x_1 = -0.577350269$
	$c_2 = 1.000000000$	$x_2 = 0.577350269$
3	$c_1 = 0.555555556$	$x_1 = -0.774596669$
	$c_2 = 0.888888889$	$x_2 = 0.000000000$
	$c_3 = 0.555555556$	$x_3 = 0.774596669$
4	$c_1 = 0.347854845$	$x_1 = -0.861136312$
	$c_2 = 0.652145155$	$x_2 = -0.339981044$
	$c_3 = 0.652145155$	$x_3 = 0.339981044$
	$c_4 = 0.347854845$	$x_4 = 0.861136312$
5	$c_1 = 0.236926885$	$x_1 = -0.906179846$
	$c_2 = 0.478628670$	$x_2 = -0.538469310$
	$c_3 = 0.568888889$	$x_3 = 0.000000000$
	$c_4 = 0.478628670$	$x_4 = 0.538469310$
	$c_5 = 0.236926885$	$x_5 = 0.906179846$
6	$c_1 = 0.171324492$	$x_1 = -0.932469514$
	$c_2 = 0.360761573$	$x_2 = -0.661209386$
	$c_3 = 0.467913935$	$x_3 = -0.238619186$
	$c_4 = 0.467913935$	$x_4 = 0.238619186$

	$c_5 = 0.360761573$	$x_5 = 0.661209386$
	$c_6 = 0.171324492$	$x_6 = 0.932469514$

So if the table is given for $\int\limits_{-1}^{1} g(x)dx$ **integrals, how does one solve** $\int\limits_{a}^{b} f(x)dx$ **?**

The answer lies in that any integral with limits of $[a, b]$ can be converted into an integral with limits $[-1, 1]$. Let

$$x = mt + c \tag{20}$$

If $x = a$, then $t = -1$

If $x = b$, then $t = +1$

such that

$$a = m(-1) + c$$
$$b = m(1) + c \tag{21}$$

Solving the two Equations (21) simultaneously gives

$$m = \frac{b-a}{2}$$

$$c = \frac{b+a}{2} \tag{22}$$

Hence

$$x = \frac{b-a}{2}t + \frac{b+a}{2}$$

$$dx = \frac{b-a}{2}dt$$

Substituting our values of x and dx into the integral gives us

$$\int\limits_{a}^{b} f(x)dx = \int\limits_{-1}^{1} f\left(\frac{b-a}{2}x + \frac{b+a}{2}\right)\frac{b-a}{2}dx \tag{23}$$

Example 1

For an integral $\int\limits_{-1}^{1} f(x)dx$, show that the two-point Gauss quadrature rule approximates to

$$\int\limits_{-1}^{1} f(x)dx \approx c_1 f(x_1) + c_2 f(x_2)$$

where

$$c_1 = 1$$
$$c_2 = 1$$

$$x_1 = -\frac{1}{\sqrt{3}}$$

$$x_2 = \frac{1}{\sqrt{3}}$$

Solution

Assuming the formula

$$\int_{-1}^{1} f(x)dx = c_1 f(x_1) + c_2 f(x_2) \tag{E1.1}$$

gives exact values for integrals $\int_{-1}^{1} 1 dx,\ \int_{-1}^{1} x dx,\ \int_{-1}^{1} x^2 dx,$ and $\int_{-1}^{1} x^3 dx$. Then

$$\int_{-1}^{1} 1 dx = 2 = c_1 + c_2 \tag{E1.2}$$

$$\int_{-1}^{1} x dx = 0 = c_1 x_1 + c_2 x_2 \tag{E1.3}$$

$$\int_{-1}^{1} x^2 dx = \frac{2}{3} = c_1 x_1^2 + c_2 x_2^2 \tag{E1.4}$$

$$\int_{-1}^{1} x^3 dx = 0 = c_1 x_1^3 + c_2 x_2^3 \tag{E1.5}$$

Multiplying Equation (E1.3) by x_1^2 and subtracting from Equation (E1.5) gives

$$c_2 x_2 \left(x_1^2 - x_2^2\right) = 0 \tag{E1.6}$$

The solution to the above equation is

$c_2 = 0$, or/and

$x_2 = 0$, or/and

$x_1 = x_2$, or/and

$x_1 = -x_2$.

I. $c_2 = 0$ is not acceptable as Equations (E1.2-E1.5) reduce to $c_1 = 2$, $c_1 x_1 = 0$, $c_1 x_1^2 = \frac{2}{3}$, and $c_1 x_1^3 = 0$. But since $c_1 = 2$, then $x_1 = 0$ from $c_1 x_1 = 0$, but $x_1 = 0$ conflicts with $c_1 x_1^2 = \frac{2}{3}$.

II. $x_2 = 0$ is not acceptable as Equations (E1.2-E1.5) reduce to $c_1 + c_2 = 2$, $c_1 x_1 = 0$, $c_1 x_1^2 = \frac{2}{3}$, and $c_1 x_1^3 = 0$. Since $c_1 x_1 = 0$, then c_1 or x_1 has to be zero but this violates $c_1 x_1^2 = \frac{2}{3} \neq 0$.

III. $x_1 = x_2$ is not acceptable as Equations (E1.2-E1.5) reduce to $c_1 + c_2 = 2$, $c_1 x_1 + c_2 x_1 = 0$, $c_1 x_1^2 + c_2 x_1^2 = \frac{2}{3}$, and $c_1 x_1^3 + c_2 x_1^3 = 0$. If $x_1 \neq 0$, then $c_1 x_1 + c_2 x_1 = 0$

gives $c_1 + c_2 = 0$ and that violates $c_1 + c_2 = 2$. If $x_1 = 0$, then that violates

$$c_1 x_1^2 + c_2 x_1^2 = \frac{2}{3} \neq 0.$$

That leaves the solution of $x_1 = -x_2$ as the only possible acceptable solution and in fact, it does not have violations (see it for yourself)

$$x_1 = -x_2 \tag{E1.7}$$

Substituting (E1.7) in Equation (E1.3) gives

$$c_1 = c_2 \tag{E1.8}$$

From Equations (E1.2) and (E1.8),

$$c_1 = c_2 = 1 \tag{E1.9}$$

Equations (E1.4) and (E1.9) gives

$$x_1^2 + x_2^2 = \frac{2}{3} \tag{E1.10}$$

Since Equation (E1.7) requires that the two results be of opposite sign, we get

$$x_1 = -\frac{1}{\sqrt{3}}$$

$$x_2 = \frac{1}{\sqrt{3}}$$

Hence

$$\int_{-1}^{1} f(x)dx = c_1 f(x_1) + c_2 f(x_2) \tag{E1.11}$$

$$= f\left(-\frac{1}{\sqrt{3}}\right) + f\left(\frac{1}{\sqrt{3}}\right)$$

Example 2

For an integral $\int_{a}^{b} f(x)dx$, derive the one-point Gauss quadrature rule.

Solution

The one-point Gauss quadrature rule is

$$\int_{a}^{b} f(x)dx \approx c_1 f(x_1) \tag{E2.1}$$

Assuming the formula gives exact values for integrals $\int_{-1}^{1} 1 dx$, and $\int_{-1}^{1} x dx$

$$\int_{a}^{b} 1 dx = b - a = c_1$$

$$\int_{a}^{b} x dx = \frac{b^2 - a^2}{2} = c_1 x_1 \tag{E2.2}$$

Since $c_1 = b - a$, the other equation becomes

$$(b-a)x_1 = \frac{b^2 - a^2}{2}$$

$$x_1 = \frac{b+a}{2} \tag{E2.3}$$

Therefore, one-point Gauss quadrature rule can be expressed as

$$\int_a^b f(x)dx \approx (b-a)f\left(\frac{b+a}{2}\right) \tag{E2.4}$$

Example 3

What would be the formula for

$$\int_a^b f(x)dx = c_1 f(a) + c_2 f(b)$$

if you want the above formula to give you exact values of $\int_a^b (a_0 x + b_0 x^2)dx$, that is, a linear

combination of x and x^2.

Solution

If the formula is exact for a linear combination of x and x^2, then

$$\int_a^b x\,dx = \frac{b^2 - a^2}{2} = c_1 a + c_2 b$$

$$\int_a^b x^2\,dx = \frac{b^3 - a^3}{3} = c_1 a^2 + c_2 b^2 \tag{E3.1}$$

Solving the two Equations (E3.1) simultaneously gives

$$\begin{bmatrix} a & b \\ a^2 & b^2 \end{bmatrix} \begin{bmatrix} c_1 \\ c_2 \end{bmatrix} = \begin{bmatrix} \dfrac{b^2 - a^2}{2} \\ \dfrac{b^3 - a^3}{3} \end{bmatrix}$$

$$c_1 = -\frac{1}{6} \frac{1 - ab - b^2 + 2a^2}{a}$$

$$c_2 = -\frac{1}{6} \frac{a^2 + ab - 2b^2}{b} \tag{E3.2}$$

So

$$\int_a^b f(x)dx = -\frac{1}{6}\frac{1 - ab - b^2 + 2a^2}{a}f(a) - \frac{1}{6}\frac{a^2 + ab - 2b^2}{b}f(b) \tag{E3.3}$$

Let us see if the formula works.

Evaluate $\int_2^5 (2x^2 - 3x)dx$ using Equation(E3.3)

$$\int_{2}^{5} \left(2x^2 - 3x\right)dx \approx c_1 f(a) + c_2 f(b)$$

$$= -\frac{1}{6} \frac{1 - (2)(5) - 5^2 + 2(2)^2}{2} \left[2(2)^2 - 3(2)\right] - \frac{1}{6} \frac{2^2 + 2(5) - 2(5)^2}{5} \left[2(5)^2 - 3(5)\right]$$

$$= 46.5$$

The exact value of $\int_{2}^{5} \left(2x^2 - 3x\right)dx$ is given by

$$\int_{2}^{5} \left(2x^2 - 3x\right)dx = \left[\frac{2x^3}{3} - \frac{3x^2}{2}\right]_{2}^{5}$$

$$= 46.5$$

Any surprises?

Now evaluate $\int_{2}^{5} 3dx$ using Equation (E3.3)

$$\int_{2}^{5} 3dx \approx c_1 f(a) + c_2 f(b)$$

$$= -\frac{1}{6} \frac{1 - 2(5) - 5^2 + 2(2)^2}{2}(3) - \frac{1}{6} \frac{2^2 + 2(5) - 2(5)^2}{5}(3)$$

$$= 10.35$$

The exact value of $\int_{2}^{5} 3dx$ is given by

$$\int_{2}^{5} 3dx = \left[3x\right]_{2}^{5}$$

$$= 9$$

Because the formula will only give exact values for linear combinations of x and x^2, it does not work exactly even for a simple integral of $\int_{2}^{5} 3dx$.

Do you see now why we choose $a_0 + a_1 x$ as the integrand for which the formula

$$\int_{a}^{b} f(x)dx \approx c_1 f(a) + c_2 f(b)$$

gives us exact values?

Example 4

Use two-point Gauss quadrature rule to approximate the distance covered by a rocket from $t = 8$ to $t = 30$ as given by

$$x = \int_{8}^{30} \left(2000 \ln\left[\frac{140000}{140000 - 2100t}\right] - 9.8t\right)dt$$

Also, find the absolute relative true error.

Solution

First, change the limits of integration from $[8, 30]$ to $[-1, 1]$ using Equation(23) gives

$$\int_8^{30} f(t)dt = \frac{30-8}{2} \int_{-1}^1 f\left(\frac{30-8}{2}x + \frac{30+8}{2}\right)dx$$

$$= 11\int_{-1}^1 f(11x + 19)dx$$

Next, get weighting factors and function argument values from Table 1 for the two point rule,

$c_1 = 1.000000000.$

$x_1 = -0.577350269$

$c_2 = 1.000000000$

$x_2 = 0.577350269$

Now we can use the Gauss quadrature formula

$$11\int_{-1}^1 f(11x + 19)dx \approx 11[c_1 f(11x_1 + 19) + c_2 f(11x_2 + 19)]$$

$$= 11[f(11(-0.5773503) + 19) + f(11(0.5773503) + 19)]$$
$$= 11[f(12.64915) + f(25.35085)]$$
$$= 11[(296.8317) + (708.4811)]$$
$$= 11058.44 \text{ m}$$

since

$$f(12.64915) = 2000\ln\left[\frac{140000}{140000 - 2100(12.64915)}\right] - 9.8(12.64915)$$

$$= 296.8317$$

$$f(25.35085) = 2000\ln\left[\frac{140000}{140000 - 2100(25.35085)}\right] - 9.8(25.35085)$$

$$= 708.4811$$

The absolute relative true error, $|\epsilon_t|$, is (True value = 11061.34 m)

$$|\epsilon_t| = \left|\frac{11061.34 - 11058.44}{11061.34}\right| \times 100$$

$$= 0.0262\%$$

Example 5

Use three-point Gauss quadrature rule to approximate the distance covered by a rocket from $t = 8$ to $t = 30$ as given by

$$x = \int_8^{30}\left(2000\ln\left[\frac{140000}{140000 - 2100t}\right] - 9.8t\right)dt$$

Also, find the absolute relative true error.

Solution

First, change the limits of integration from $[8, 30]$ to $[-1, 1]$ using Equation (23) gives

$$\int_{8}^{30} f(t)\,dt = \frac{30-8}{2}\int_{-1}^{1} f\left(\frac{30-8}{2}x + \frac{30+8}{2}\right)dx$$

$$= 11\int_{-1}^{1} f(11x+19)\,dx$$

The weighting factors and function argument values are

$$c_1 = 0.555555556$$
$$x_1 = -0.774596669$$
$$c_2 = 0.888888889$$
$$x_2 = 0.000000000$$
$$c_3 = 0.555555556$$
$$x_3 = 0.774596669$$

and the formula is

$$11\int_{-1}^{1} f(11x+19)\,dx \approx 11[c_1 f(11x_1+19) + c_2 f(11x_2+19) + c_3 f(11x_3+19)]$$

$$= 11\left[\begin{array}{l}0.5555556 f(11(-.7745967)+19) + 0.8888889 f(11(0.0000000)+19)\\ + 0.5555556 f(11(0.7745967)+19)\end{array}\right]$$

$$= 11[0.55556 f(10.47944) + 0.88889 f(19.00000) + 0.55556 f(27.52056)]$$

$$= 11[0.55556 \times 239.3327 + 0.88889 \times 484.7455 + 0.55556 \times 795.1069]$$

$$= 11061.31 \text{ m}$$

since

$$f(10.47944) = 2000\ln\left[\frac{140000}{140000-2100(10.47944)}\right] - 9.8(10.47944)$$
$$= 239.3327$$

$$f(19.00000) = 2000\ln\left[\frac{140000}{140000-2100(19.00000)}\right] - 9.8(19.00000)$$
$$= 484.7455$$

$$f(27.52056) = 2000\ln\left[\frac{140000}{140000-2100(27.52056)}\right] - 9.8(27.52056)$$
$$= 795.1069$$

The absolute relative true error, $|\epsilon_t|$, is (True value = 11061.34 m)

$$|\epsilon_t| = \left|\frac{11061.34 - 11061.31}{11061.34}\right| \times 100$$
$$= 0.0003\%$$

INTEGRATION	
Topic	Gauss quadrature rule
Summary	These are textbook notes of Gauss quadrature rule
Major	General Engineering
Authors	Autar Kaw, Michael Keteltas
Date	August 11, 2010
Web Site	http://numericalmethods.eng.usf.edu

Multiple-Choice Test

Chapter 07.05
Gauss Quadrature Rule

1. $\int\limits_{5}^{10} f(x)dx$ is exactly

    (A) $\int\limits_{-1}^{1} f(2.5x + 7.5)dx$

    (B) $2.5\int\limits_{-1}^{1} f(2.5x + 7.5)dx$

    (C) $5\int\limits_{-1}^{1} f(5x + 5)dx$

    (D) $5\int\limits_{-1}^{1} (2.5x + 7.5)f(x)dx$

2. For a definite integral of any third order polynomial, the two-point Gauss quadrature rule will give the same results as the
    (A) 1-segment trapezoidal rule
    (B) 2-segment trapezoidal rule
    (C) 3-segment trapezoidal rule
    (D) Simpson's 1/3 rule

3. The value of $\int\limits_{0.2}^{2.2} xe^x dx$ by using the two-point Gauss quadrature rule is most nearly
    (A) 11.672
    (B) 11.807
    (C) 12.811
    (D) 14.633

07.05.1

4.   A scientist uses the one-point Gauss quadrature rule based on getting exact results of integration for functions $f(x) = 1$ and x. The one-point Gauss quadrature rule approximation for $\int_a^b f(x)dx$ is

   (A) $\dfrac{b-a}{2}\left[f(a) + f(b)\right]$

   (B) $(b-a)f\left(\dfrac{a+b}{2}\right)$

   (C) $\dfrac{b-a}{2}\left[f\left(\dfrac{b-a}{2}\left\{-\dfrac{1}{\sqrt{3}}\right\} + \dfrac{b+a}{2}\right) + f\left(\dfrac{b-a}{2}\left\{\dfrac{1}{\sqrt{3}}\right\} + \dfrac{b+a}{2}\right)\right]$

   (D) $(b-a)f(a)$

5.   A scientist develops an approximate formula for integration as

   $\int_a^b f(x)dx \approx c_1 f(x_1),$ where $a \le x_1 \le b$

   The values of c_1 and x_1 are found by assuming that the formula is exact for functions of the form $a_0 x + a_1 x^2$. The resulting formula would therefore be exact for integrating

   (A) $f(x) = 2$
   (B) $f(x) = 2 + 3x + 5x^2$
   (C) $f(x) = 5x^2$
   (D) $f(x) = 2 + 3x$

6.   You are asked to estimate the water flow rate in a pipe of radius $2\,\text{m}$ at a remote area location with a harsh environment. You already know that velocity varies along the radial location, but you do not know how it varies. The flow rate Q is given by

   $$Q = \int_0^2 2\pi r V dr$$

   To save money, you are allowed to put only two velocity probes (these probes send the data to the central office in New York, NY via satellite) in the pipe. Radial location, r is measured from the center of the pipe, that is $r = 0$ is the center of the pipe and $r = 2\text{m}$ is the pipe radius. The radial locations you would suggest for the two velocity probes for the most accurate calculation of the flow rate are

   (A) $0, 2$
   (B) $1, 2$
   (C) $0, 1$
   (D) $0.42, 1.58$

Complete Solution

Problem Set

Chapter 07.05
Gauss Quadrature Rule

1. Find the value of the integral $\int_{1}^{5} 7e^{-2t} dt$ using

   a) 2-point Gaussian quadrature rule.
   b) 3-point Gaussian quadrature rule

2. The upward velocity of a rocket is given by
$$v(t) = 200\ln(t+1) - 10t, \quad t > 0$$
where t is given in seconds and v is given in m/s.

   a) Use 2-point Gauss quadrature rule to calculate the distance covered by the rocket   from $t = 0$ to $t = 5$ s.
   b) What is the true value of the distance covered by the rocket from $t = 0$ to $t = 5$ s?
   c) What is the true error in part (a)?
   d) What is the relative true error in part (a)?
   e) What is the absolute relative true error in percentage for part (a).
   f) Use 3-point Gauss quadrature rule to calculate the distance covered by the rocket from $t = 0$ to $t = 5$ s.

3. The velocity of a body is given by
$$v(t) = t + 1, 0 < t < 2, \text{ and } v(t) = 33, 2 < t < 5,$$
where the velocity, $v(t)$ is given in m/s and t is in seconds.

   a) Find the distance covered by the body between $1 < t < 1.9$ seconds by using the two-point Gauss quadrature rule. Find the absolute relative true error.
   b) Find the distance covered by the body between $1 < t < 3.9$ seconds by using the four-point Gauss quadrature rule. Find the absolute relative true error.

4. The one-point Gauss quadrature rule is defined as
$$\int_{a}^{b} f(x)dx \approx c_1 f(x_1), \quad a \le x_1 \le b$$

The values of c_1 and x_1 are found by assuming that the one-point formula is exact for any first order polynomial. Find c_1 and x_1 in the above one-point Gauss quadrature rule.

07.05.1

5.   A scientist develops an approximate formula for integration as

$$\int_a^b f(x)dx \approx c_1 f(x_1), \text{ where } a \leq x_1 \leq b$$

The values of c_1 and x_1 are found by assuming that the formula is exact for the functions of the form $a_0 x + a_1 x^2$ polynomial. Find c_1 and x_1.

6.   A scientist develops an approximate formula for integration as

$$\int_a^b f(x)dx \approx c_1 f(a) + c_2 f(b).$$

The values of c_1 and c_2 are found by assuming that the formula is exact for the functions of the form $a_0 x + a_1 x^2$ polynomial.

   a) Find the values of c_1 and c_2.

   b) Verify the formula works exactly for the integral $\int_2^7 (3x^2 + 5x)dx$

   c) Verify the formula does not work exactly for the integral of $\int_2^7 2dx$

Chapter 07.06

Integrating Discrete Functions

After reading this chapter, you should be able to:

1. *integrate discrete functions by several methods,*
2. *derive the formula for trapezoidal rule with unequal segments, and*
3. *solve examples of finding integrals of discrete functions.*

What is integration?

Integration is the process of measuring the area under a function plotted on a graph. Why would we want to integrate a function? Among the most common examples are finding the velocity of a body from an acceleration function, and displacement of a body from a velocity function. Throughout many engineering fields, there are (what sometimes seems like) countless applications for integral calculus. You can read about a few of these applications in different engineering majors in Chapters 07.00A-07.00G.

Sometimes, the function to be integrated is given at discrete data points, and the area under the curve is needed to be approximated. Here, we will discuss the integration of such discrete functions,

$$I = \int_a^b f(x)dx$$

where

$f(x)$ is called the integrand and is given at discrete value of x,

$a =$ lower limit of integration

$b =$ upper limit of integration

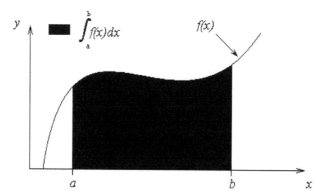

Figure 1 Integration of a function

Integrating discrete functions

Multiple methods of integrating discrete functions are shown below using an example.
Example 1

The upward velocity of a rocket is given as a function of time in Table 1.

Table 1 Velocity as a function of time.

t (s)	$v(t)$ (m/s)
0	0
10	227.04
15	362.78
20	517.35
22.5	602.97
30	901.67

Determine the distance, s, covered by the rocket from $t = 11$ to $t = 16$ using the velocity data provided and use any applicable numerical technique.

Solution

Method 1: Average Velocity Method
The velocity of the rocket is not provided at $t = 11$ and $t = 16$, so we will have to use an interval that includes $[11, 16]$ to find the average velocity of the rocket within that range. In this case, the interval $[10, 20]$ will suffice.

$$v(10) = 227.04$$
$$v(15) = 362.78$$
$$v(20) = 517.35$$

$$Average\ Velocity = \frac{v(10) + v(15) + v(20)}{3}$$

$$= \frac{227.04 + 362.78 + 517.35}{3}$$

$$= 369.06 \text{ m/s}$$

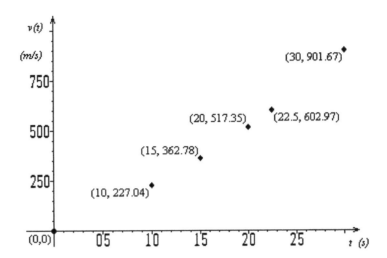

Figure 1 Velocity vs. time data for the rocket example

Using

$$s = \bar{v}\Delta t,$$

we get

$$s = (369.06)(16 - 11) = 1845.3 \text{ m}$$

Method 2: Trapezoidal Rule
If we were finding the distance traveled between times in the data table, we would simply find the area of the trapezoids with the corner points given as the velocity and time data points. For example

$$\int_{10}^{20} v(t)dt = \int_{10}^{15} v(t)dt + \int_{15}^{20} v(t)dt$$

and applying the trapezoidal rule over each of the above integrals gives

$$\int_{10}^{20} v(t)dt \approx \frac{15 - 10}{2}[v(10) + v(15)] + \frac{20 - 15}{2}[v(15) + v(20)]$$

The values of $v(10)$, $v(15)$ and $v(20)$ are given in Table 1.
However, we are interested in finding

$$\int_{11}^{16} v(t)dt = \int_{11}^{15} v(t)dt + \int_{15}^{16} v(t)dt$$

and applying the trapezoidal rule over each of the above integrals gives

$$\int_{11}^{16} v(t)dt \approx \frac{15-11}{2}[v(11)+v(15)]+\frac{16-15}{2}[v(15)+v(16)]$$

$$= \frac{15-11}{2}(v(11)+362.78)+\frac{16-15}{2}(362.78+v(16))$$

How do we find $v(11)$ and $v(16)$? We use linear interpolation. To find $v(11)$,

$$v(t) = 227.04 + 27.148(t-10),\ 10 \le t \le 15$$

$$v(11) = 227.04 + 27.148(11-10)$$

$$= 254.19\ \text{m/s}$$

and to find $v(16)$

$$v(t) = 362.78 + 30.913(t-15),\ 15 \le t \le 20$$

$$v(16) = 362.78 + 30.913(16-15)$$

$$= 393.69\ \text{m/s}$$

Then

$$\int_{11}^{16} v(t)dt \approx \frac{15-11}{2}(v(11)+362.78)+\frac{16-15}{2}(362.78+v(16))$$

$$= \frac{15-11}{2}(254.19+362.78)+\frac{16-15}{2}(362.78+393.69)$$

$$= 1612.2\ \text{m}$$

Method 3: Polynomial interpolation to find the velocity profile

Because we are finding the area under the curve from $[10,\ 20]$, we must use three points, $t = 10$, $t = 15$, and $t = 20$, to fit a quadratic polynomial through the data. Using polynomial interpolation, our resulting velocity function is (refer to notes on direct method of interpolation)

$$v(t) = 12.05 + 17.733t + 0.3766t^2,\ 10 \le t \le 20.$$

Now, we simply take the integral of the quadratic within our limits, giving us

$$s \approx \int_{11}^{16} \left(12.05 + 17.733t + 0.3766t^2\right)dt$$

$$= \left[12.05t + \frac{17.733t^2}{2} + \frac{0.3766t^3}{3}\right]_{11}^{16}$$

$$= 12.05(16-11) + \frac{17.733}{2}\left(16^2 - 11^2\right) + \frac{0.3766}{3}\left(16^3 - 11^3\right)$$

$$= 1604.3\ \text{m}$$

Method 4: Spline interpolation to find the velocity profile

Fitting quadratic splines (refer to notes on spline method of interpolation) through the data results in the following set of quadratics

$$v(t) = 22.704t, \qquad\qquad\qquad 0 \le t \le 10$$

$$= 0.8888t^2 + 4.928t + 88.88, \qquad 10 \le t \le 15$$

$$= -0.1356t^2 + 35.66t - 141.61, \qquad 15 \le t \le 20$$
$$= 1.6048t^2 - 33.956t + 554.55, \qquad 20 \le t \le 22.5$$
$$= 0.20889t^2 + 28.86t - 152.13, \qquad 22.5 \le t \le 30$$

The value of the integral would then simply be

$$s = \int_{11}^{15} v(t)\,dt + \int_{15}^{16} v(t)\,dt$$

$$\approx \int_{11}^{15} \left(0.8888t^2 + 4.928t + 88.88\right)dt + \int_{15}^{16} \left(-0.1356t^2 + 35.66t - 141.61\right)dt$$

$$= \left[\frac{0.8888t^3}{3} + \frac{4.928t^2}{2} + 88.88t\right]_{11}^{15} + \left[\frac{-0.1356t^3}{3} + \frac{35.66t^2}{2} - 141.61t\right]_{15}^{16}$$

$$= \frac{0.8888}{3}\left(15^3 - 11^3\right) + \frac{4.928}{2}\left(15^2 - 11^2\right) + 88.88(15 - 11)$$

$$+ \frac{-0.1356}{3}\left(16^3 - 15^3\right) + \frac{35.66}{2}\left(16^2 - 15^2\right) - 141.61(16 - 15)$$

$$= 1595.9 \; m$$

Example 2

What is the absolute relative true error for each of the four methods used in Example 1 if the data in Table 1 was actually obtained from the velocity profile of

$$v(t) = \left(2000\ln\left[\frac{140000}{140000 - 2100t}\right] - 9.8t\right),$$

where v is given in m/s and t in s.

Solution

The distance covered between $t = 11$ and $t = 16$ is

$$s = \int_{11}^{16} \left(2000\ln\left[\frac{140000}{140000 - 2100t}\right] - 9.8t\right)dt$$
$$= 1604.9 \; m$$

Method 1
The approximate value obtained using average velocity method was $1845.3\,\text{m}$. Hence, the absolute relative true error, $\left|\epsilon_t\right|$, is

$$\left|\epsilon_t\right| = \left|\frac{1604.9 - 1845.3}{1604.9}\right| \times 100\%$$
$$= 14.976\%$$

Method 2:
The approximate value obtained using the trapezoidal rule was $1612.2 \; \text{m}$. Hence, the absolute relative true error, $\left|\epsilon_t\right|$, is

$$|\epsilon_t| = \left|\frac{1604.9 - 1612.2}{1604.9}\right| \times 100\%$$
$$= 0.451\%$$

Method 3:

The approximate value obtained using the direct polynomial was 1604.3 m. Hence, the absolute relative true error, $|\epsilon_t|$, is

$$|\epsilon_t| = \left|\frac{1604.9 - 1604.3}{1604.9}\right| \times 100\%$$
$$= 0.037\%$$

Method 4:

The approximate value obtained using the spline interpolation was 1595.9 m, hence, the absolute relative true error, $|\epsilon_t|$, is

$$|\epsilon_t| = \left|\frac{1604.9 - 1595.9}{1604.9}\right| \times 100\%$$
$$= 0.564\%$$

Table 2 Comparison of discrete function methods of numerical integration

Method	Approximate Value	$|\epsilon_t|$
Average Velocity	1845.3	14.976%
Trapezoidal Rule	1612.2	0.451%
Polynomial Interpolation	1604.3	0.037%
Spline Interpolation	1595.9	0.564%

Trapezoidal Rule for Discrete Functions with Unequal Segments

For a general case of a function given at n data points $(x_1, f(x_1))$, $(x_2, f(x_2))$, $(x_3, f(x_3))$, ..., $(x_n, f(x_n))$, where, $x_1, x_2, ..., x_n$ are in an ascending order, the approximate value of the integral $\int\limits_{x_1}^{x_n} f(x)dx$ is given by

$$\int\limits_{x_1}^{x_n} f(x)dx = \int\limits_{x_1}^{x_2} f(x)dx + \int\limits_{x_2}^{x_3} f(x)dx + ... + \int\limits_{x_{n-1}}^{x_n} f(x)dx$$

$$\approx (x_2 - x_1)\frac{f(x_1) + f(x_2)}{2} + (x_3 - x_2)\frac{f(x_2) + f(x_3)}{2} + ...$$

$$....... + (x_n - x_{n-1})\frac{f(x_{n-1}) + f(x_n)}{2}$$

This approach uses the trapezoidal rule in the intervals $[x_1, x_2]$, $[x_2, x_3]$, ..., $[x_{n-1}, x_n]$ and then adds the obtained values.

Example 3

The upward velocity of a rocket is given as a function of time in Table 3.

Table 3. Velocity as a function of time.

t	v(t)
s	m/s
0	0
10	227.04
15	362.78
20	517.35
22.5	602.97
30	901.67

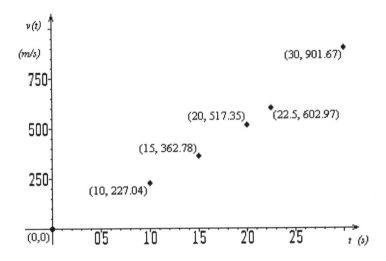

Figure 2 Velocity vs. time data for the rocket example

Determine the distance, s, covered by the rocket from $t = 0$ to $t = 30$ using the velocity data provided and the trapezoidal rule for discrete data with unequal segments.

Solution

$$\int_0^{30} v(t)dt = \int_0^{10} v(t)dt + \int_{10}^{15} v(t)dt + \int_{15}^{20} v(t)dt + \int_{20}^{22.5} v(t)dt + \int_{22.5}^{30} v(t)dt$$

$$= (10-0)\frac{v(0)+v(10)}{2} + (15-10)\frac{v(10)+v(15)}{2}$$
$$+ (20-15)\frac{v(15)+v(20)}{2} + (22.5-20)\frac{v(20)+v(22.5)}{2}$$

$$+ (30 - 22.5)\frac{v(22.5) + v(30)}{2}$$

$$= (10)\frac{0 + 227.04}{2} + (5)\frac{227.04 + 362.78}{2}$$

$$+ (5)\frac{362.78 + 517.35}{2} + (2.5)\frac{517.35 + 602.97}{2}$$

$$+ (7.5)\frac{602.97 + 901.67}{2}$$

$$= 1135.2 + 1474.55 + 2200.325 + 1399.9 + 5642.4$$

$$= 11852\,\text{m}$$

Can you find the value of $\int_{10}^{20} v(t)\,dt$?

INTEGRATION	
Topic	Integrating discrete functions
Summary	Textbook notes on integrating discrete functions
Major	All Majors of Engineering
Authors	Autar Kaw
Last Revised	December 23, 2009
Web Site	http://numericalmethods.eng.usf.edu

Problem Set

Chapter 07.06
Integrating Discrete Functions

1. The following data of the velocity of a body as a function of time is given.

Time (s)	0	15	18	22	24
Velocity (m/s)	22	24	37	25	123

    Use trapezoidal rule with unequal segments OR a better scientific method to find the distance covered by the body from $t = 15$ to 22 seconds.

2. The following data of the velocity of a body as a function of time is given.

Time (s)	0	15	18	22	24
Velocity (m/s)	22	24	37	25	123

    Use trapezoidal rule with unequal segments OR a better scientific method to find the distance covered by the body from $t = 13$ to 18 seconds.

3. Water is flowing out at the end of 20 meter long U-shaped channel and falls into a field at the flow rate given below as a function of time.

Time (s)	2	4	7	10
Flow rate (m^3/s)	12	15	17	14

    Use trapezoidal rule for discrete data to find the amount of water that fell on the field between $t = 3$ and $t = 9$ seconds.

4. Water is flowing out at the end of 20 meter long U-shaped channel and falls into a field at the flow rate given below as a function of time.

Time (s)	2	4	7	10
Flow rate (m^3/s)	12	15	17	14

    Use Simpson's 1/3 rule to find the amount of water that fell on the field between $t = 4$ and $t = 10$ seconds.

5. Water is flowing through a circular pipe of 1/2 ft radius and flow velocity (ft/s) measurements are made from the center to the wall of the pipe as follows

Radial Location, r (ft)	0	0.083	0.17	0.25	0.33	0.42	0.50
Velocity, v (ft/s)	10	9.72	8.88	7.5	5.6	3.1	0

    Estimate the flow rate in the pipe.

6.   Below is the data given for thermal expansion coefficient of steel as a function of temperature.

Temperature			
°F	°C	K	Instantaneous thermal expansion coefficient μin/in/°F
80	26.67	299.67	6.47
60	15.56	288.56	6.36
40	4.44	277.44	6.24
20	-6.67	266.33	6.12
0	-17.78	255.22	6.00
-20	-28.89	244.11	5.86
-40	-40.00	233.00	5.72
-60	-51.11	221.89	5.58
-80	-62.22	210.78	5.43
-100	-73.33	199.67	5.28
-120	-84.44	188.56	5.09
-140	-95.56	177.44	4.91
-160	-106.67	166.33	4.72
-180	-117.78	155.22	4.52
-200	-128.89	144.11	4.30
-220	-140.00	133.00	4.08
-240	-151.11	121.89	3.83
-260	-162.22	110.78	3.58
-280	-173.33	99.67	3.33
-300	-184.44	88.56	3.07
-320	-195.56	77.44	2.76
-340	-206.67	66.33	2.45

A bascule bridge designer needs to shrink fit a solid circular shaft A of diameter a 12.358" in a hollow cylinder B with inner diameter 12.358". His plan is to put the solid shaft A in liquid nitrogen to contract its diameter so that it can be slid through the inner diameter of cylinder B. He also needs a diametral clearance of at least 0.01" so that the shafts do not touch each other before the whole shaft A is slid through. Assume the room temperature is 70°F and that liquid nitrogen boils at $-315°$F.

Solve the following problems.

   a) A consultant on this project assumed the thermal expansion coefficient is constant over the temperature range. He used the value of thermal expansion coefficient at 80°F in all his calculations. Find the contraction of diameter in the shaft A.

   b) Does he calculate enough contraction in the shaft A diameter ? In part (a), does he calculate enough contraction in the shaft A diameter?

c) Is his assumption of assuming constant thermal expansion correct? Why or why not? A single sentence answer will do.

d) How would you solve the problem? Solve by at least two different methods you learned in class. Do you calculate enough contraction in shaft A diameter?

e) If you did not get enough contraction in the diameter in part (d), what would you suggest? Give a quantified solution, not just a qualitative answer.

Chapter 07.07
Integrating Improper Functions

After reading this chapter, you should be able to:

1. *integrate improper functions using methods such as the trapezoidal rule and Gaussian Quadrature schemes.*

What is integration?

Integration is the process of measuring the area under a function plotted on a graph. Why would we want to integrate a function? Among the most common examples are finding the velocity of a body from an acceleration function, and displacement of a body from a velocity function. Throughout many engineering fields, there are (what sometimes seems like) countless applications for integral calculus. You can read about some of these applications in Chapters 07.00A-07.00G.

Sometimes, the evaluation of expressions involving these integrals can become daunting, if not indeterminate. For this reason, a wide variety of numerical methods has been developed to simplify the integral.

Here, we will discuss the incorporation of these numerical methods into improper integrals.

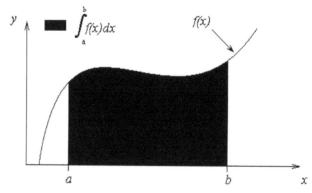

Figure 1 Integration of a function

What is an improper integral?

An integral is improper if
    a) the integrand becomes infinite in the interval of integration (including end points) or/and
    b) the interval of integration has an infinite bound.

Example 1

Give some examples of improper integrals
Solution

The integral

$$I = \int_0^2 \frac{x}{\sqrt{4 - x^2}} dx$$

is improper because the integrand becomes infinite at $x = 2$.

The integral

$$I = \int_0^2 \frac{x}{\sqrt{1 - x}} dx$$

is improper because the integrand becomes infinite at $x = 1$.
The integral

$$I = \int_0^\infty e^{-t} t \, dt$$

is improper because the interval of integration has an infinite bound.
The integral

$$I = \int_0^\infty \frac{e^{-t}}{\sqrt{1 - t}} dt$$

is improper because the interval of integration has an infinite bound and the integrand is infinite at $t = 1$.

    If the integrand is undefined at a finite number of points, the value of the area under the curve does not change. Hence such integrals could theoretically be solved either by assuming any value of the integrand at such points. Also, methods such as Gauss quadrature rule do not use the value of the integrand at end points, and hence integrands that are undefined at end points can be integrated using such methods.

    For the case where there is an infinite interval of integration, one may make a change of variables that transforms the infinite range of integration to a finite one.

    Let us illustrate these two cases with examples.

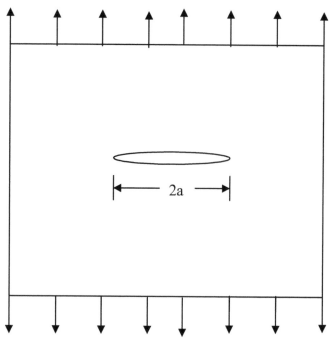

Figure 2 A plate with a crack under a uniform axial load

Example 2

In analyzing fracture of metals, one wants to know the opening displacement of cracks. In a large plate, if there is a crack length of $2a$ meters, then the maximum crack opening displacement (MCOD) is given by

$$\text{MCOD} = \frac{2\sigma}{E} \int_0^a \frac{x}{\sqrt{a^2 - x^2}} \, dx$$

where

$\qquad \sigma = $ remote normal applied stress
$\qquad E = $ Young's modulus

Assume

$\qquad a = 0.02$ m
$\qquad E = 210$ GPa and
$\qquad \sigma = 70$ MPa .

Find the exact value of the maximum crack opening displacement.
Solution

The maximum crack opening displacement (MCOD) is given by

$$\text{MCOD} = \frac{2\sigma}{E} \int_0^a \frac{x}{\sqrt{a^2 - x^2}} \, dx$$

Substituting $a = 0.02$ m , $E = 210$ GPa and $\sigma = 70$ MPa gives

$$\text{MCOD} = \frac{2\left(70 \times 10^6\right)}{210 \times 10^9} \int_0^{0.02} \frac{x}{\sqrt{(0.02)^2 - x^2}}\, dx$$

$$= \frac{1}{1500} \int_0^{0.02} \frac{x}{\sqrt{0.0004 - x^2}}\, dx$$

The exact value of the integral then is

$$MCOD = \frac{1}{1500} \left[-\sqrt{0.0004 - x^2} \right]_0^{0.02}$$

$$= \frac{1}{1500}(-0 + 0.02)$$

$$= 1.3333 \times 10^{-5}\ \text{m}$$

Example 3

Any of the Newton-Cotes formulas, such as Trapezoidal rule and Simpson's 1/3 rule, cannot be used directly for integrals where the integrands become infinite at the ends of the intervals. Since Gauss quadrature rule does not require calculation of the integrand at the end points, it could be used directly to calculate such integrals. Knowing this, find the value of the integral

$$\frac{1}{1500} \int_0^{0.02} \frac{x}{\sqrt{0.0004 - x^2}}\, dx$$

from Example 2 by using two-point Gauss quadrature rule.

Solution

We will change the limits of integration from $[0,0.02]$ to $[-1,1]$, such that we may use the tabulated values of c_1, c_2, x_1, and x_2. Assigning

$$f(x) = \frac{x}{\sqrt{0.0004 - x^2}},$$

we get

$$\frac{1}{1500} \int_0^{0.02} f(x)\, dx = \frac{1}{1500} \frac{0.02 - 0}{2} \int_{-1}^{1} f\left(\frac{0.02 - 0}{2}x + \frac{0.02 + 0}{2}\right) dx$$

$$= \frac{1}{150000} \int_{-1}^{1} f(0.01x + 0.01)\, dx$$

The function arguments and weighting factors for two-point Gauss quadrature rule are

$c_1 = 1.000000000$

$x_1 = -0.577350269$

$c_2 = 1.000000000$

$x_2 = 0.577350269$

Giving us a formula of

$$\frac{1}{150000}\int\limits_{-1}^{1}f(0.01x+0.01)dx \approx \frac{1}{150000}c_1 f(0.01x_1+0.01)+\frac{1}{150000}c_2 f(0.01x_2+0.01)$$

$$=\frac{1}{150000}f(0.01(-0.57735)+0.01)+\frac{1}{150000}f(0.01(0.57735)+0.01)$$

$$=\frac{1}{150000}f(0.0042265)+\frac{1}{150000}f(0.0157735)$$

$$=\frac{1}{150000}(0.21621)+\frac{1}{150000}(1.28279)$$

$$=9.9934\times10^{-6}\ \text{m}$$

since

$$f(0.0042265)=\frac{0.0042265}{\sqrt{0.0004-(0.0042265)^2}}=0.21621$$

$$f(0.0157735)=\frac{0.0157735}{\sqrt{0.0004-(0.0157735)^2}}=1.28279$$

The absolute relative true error, $|\epsilon_t|$, is

$$|\epsilon_t|=\left|\frac{1.3333\times10^{-5}-9.9934\times10^{-6}}{1.3333\times10^{-5}}\right|\times100\%$$

$$=25.048\%$$

Example 4

The value of the integral

$$\frac{1}{1500}\int\limits_{0}^{0.02}\frac{x}{\sqrt{0.0004-x^2}}dx$$

in Example 3 by using two-point Gauss quadrature rule has a large absolute relative true error of more than 25%. Use the double-segment two-point Gauss quadrature rule to find the value of the integral. Take the interval $[0, 0.02]$ and split it into two equal segments of $[0, 0.01]$ and $[0.01, 0.02]$, and then apply the two-point Gauss quadrature rule over each segment.

Solution

Write the integral with interval of [0,0.02] as sum of two integrals with intervals [0,0.01] and [0.01,0.02] gives

$$\frac{1}{1500}\int\limits_{0}^{0.02}f(x)dx=\frac{1}{1500}\int\limits_{0}^{0.01}f(x)dx+\frac{1}{1500}\int\limits_{0.01}^{0.02}f(x)dx$$

$$=\frac{1}{1500}\frac{0.01-0}{2}\int\limits_{-1}^{1}f\left(\frac{0.01-0}{2}x+\frac{0.01+0}{2}\right)dx$$

$$+\frac{1}{1500}\frac{0.02-0.01}{2}\int\limits_{-1}^{1}f\left(\frac{0.02-0.01}{2}x+\frac{0.02+0.01}{2}\right)dx$$

$$= \frac{1}{300000} \int_{-1}^{1} f(0.005x + 0.005)dx + \frac{1}{300000} \int_{-1}^{1} f(0.005x + 0.015)dx$$

Using the two-point Gauss quadrature rule, this becomes

$$\frac{1}{1500} \int_{0}^{0.02} f(x)dx \approx \frac{1}{300000} c_1 f(0.005x_1 + 0.005) + \frac{1}{300000} c_2 f(0.005x_2 + 0.005)$$

$$+ \frac{1}{300000} c_1 f(0.005x_1 + 0.015) + \frac{1}{300000} c_2 f(0.005x_2 + 0.015)$$

Using the same arguments and weighting factors as before

$$\frac{1}{1500} \int_{0}^{0.02} f(x)dx \approx \frac{1}{300000} f(0.005(-0.57735) + 0.005) + \frac{1}{300000} f(0.005(0.57735) + 0.005)$$

$$+ \frac{1}{300000} f(0.005(-0.57735) + 0.015) + \frac{1}{300000} f(0.005(0.57735) + 0.015)$$

$$= \frac{1}{300000} f(0.0021132) + \frac{1}{300000} f(0.0078868)$$

$$+ \frac{1}{300000} f(0.0121132) + \frac{1}{300000} f(0.0178868)$$

$$= \frac{1}{300000} (0.10626 + 0.42911 + 0.76115 + 1.99900)$$

$$= 1.0985 \times 10^{-5} \text{ m}$$

since

$$f(0.0021133) = \frac{0.0021133}{\sqrt{0.0004 - (0.0021133)^2}} = 0.10626$$

$$f(0.0078868) = \frac{0.0078868}{\sqrt{0.0004 - (0.0078868)^2}} = 0.42911$$

$$f(0.0121133) = \frac{0.0121133}{\sqrt{0.0004 - (0.0121133)^2}} = 0.76115$$

$$f(0.0178868) = \frac{0.0178868}{\sqrt{0.0004 - (0.0178868)^2}} = 1.99900$$

The absolute relative true error, $|\epsilon_t|$, is

$$|\epsilon_t| = \left| \frac{1.3333 \times 10^{-5} - 1.0985 \times 10^{-5}}{1.3333 \times 10^{-5}} \right| \times 100\%$$

$$= 17.610\%$$

Repeating this process by splitting the interval into progressively more equal segments and applying the two-point Gaussian quadrature rule over each segment will obtain the data displayed in Table 1.

Table 1 Gauss quadrature rule on an improper integral

$$\left(\frac{1}{1500}\int\limits_{0}^{0.02}\frac{x}{\sqrt{0.0004-x^2}}\,dx\right)$$

Number of Segments	Value	$\lvert\in_t\rvert\%$
1	9.9934×10^{-6}	25.05
2	1.0985×10^{-5}	17.61
3	1.1420×10^{-5}	14.35
4	1.1679×10^{-5}	12.41
5	1.1855×10^{-5}	11.09
6	1.1984×10^{-5}	10.12
7	1.2085×10^{-5}	9.365
8	1.2166×10^{-5}	8.758

As evident from Table 1, the integral does not converge rapidly to the true value with an increase in number of quadrature points. Since the integrand becomes infinite at the end point $x = 0.02$, its value changes rapidly near $x = 0.02$. Since the multiple-segment two-point Gauss quadrature rule is non-adaptive, it will take a large number of segments to reach a converging value.

Example 5

Euler's constant in mathematics is defined as

$$\Gamma(x) = \int\limits_{0}^{\infty}e^{-t}t^{x-1}dt$$

Find $\Gamma(2.4)$ using two and three-point Gauss quadrature rules. Also, find the absolute relative true error for each case.

Solution

$$\Gamma(2.4) = \int\limits_{0}^{\infty}e^{-t}t^{2.4-1}dt$$

$$= \int\limits_{0}^{\infty}e^{-t}t^{1.4}dt$$

To solve the above improper integral, one may make a change of variables as

$$y = \frac{1}{1+t}$$

giving

$$t = \frac{1}{y}-1$$

$$dt = -\frac{1}{y^2}dy$$

At $t = 0, y = 1$, at $t = \infty, y = 0$. So the integral can be re-written as

$$\Gamma(2.4) = \int_1^0 e^{-\left(\frac{1}{y}-1\right)}\left(\frac{1}{y}-1\right)^{1.4}\left(-\frac{1}{y^2}\right)dy$$

First, assigning

$$f(y) = e^{-\left(\frac{1}{y}-1\right)}\left(\frac{1}{y}-1\right)^{1.4}\left(-\frac{1}{y^2}\right)$$

and then changing the limits of integration, we get

$$\Gamma(2.4) = \frac{0-1}{2}\int_{-1}^1 f\left(\frac{0-1}{2}y+\frac{0+1}{2}\right)dy$$

$$= -0.5\int_{-1}^1 f(-0.5y+0.5)dy$$

Now, one can use two-point Gauss Quadrature Rule to find the value of $\Gamma(2.4)$ with weighting factors and function arguments of

$c_1 = 1.000000000$

$y_1 = -0.577350269$

$c_2 = 1.000000000$

$y_2 = 0.577350269$

$$\Gamma(2.4) \approx -0.5c_1 f(-0.5y_1+0.5) - 0.5c_2 f(-0.5y_2+0.5)$$
$$= -0.5f(-0.5(-0.57735)+0.5) - 0.5f(-0.5(0.57735)+0.5)$$
$$= -0.5f(0.78868) - 0.5f(0.21133)$$
$$= -0.5(-0.19458) - 0.5(-3.38857)$$
$$= 1.7916$$

since

$$f(0.78868) = e^{-\left(\frac{1}{0.78868}-1\right)}\left(\frac{1}{0.78868}-1\right)^{1.4}\left(-\frac{1}{(0.78868)^2}\right)$$
$$= -0.19458$$

$$f(0.21133) = e^{-\left(\frac{1}{0.21133}-1\right)}\left(\frac{1}{0.21133}-1\right)^{1.4}\left(-\frac{1}{(0.21133)^2}\right)$$
$$= -3.38857$$

The true value of the integral

$$\Gamma(2.4) = \int_0^\infty e^{-t}t^{1.4}dt = 1.2422$$

so the absolute relative true error, $|\epsilon_t|$, is

$$|\epsilon_t| = \left|\frac{1.2422-1.7916}{1.2422}\right|\times 100\%$$

$$= 44.230\%$$

For three-point Gauss Quadrature Rule, the weighting factors and function arguments are

$$c_1 = 0.555555556$$
$$y_1 = -0.774596669$$
$$c_2 = 0.888888889$$
$$y_2 = 0.000000000$$
$$c_3 = 0.555555556$$
$$y_3 = 0.774596669$$

The limits of integration and $f(y)$ remain the same as for the two-point rule, so

$$\Gamma(2.4) \approx -0.5c_1 f(-0.5y_1 + 0.5) - 0.5c_2 f(-0.5y_2 + 0.5) - 0.5c_3 f(-0.5y_3 + 0.5)$$
$$= -0.5(0.55556) f(-0.5(-0.77460) + 0.5)$$
$$-0.5(0.88889) f(-0.5(0) + 0.5) - 0.5(0.55556) f(-0.5(0.77460) + 0.5)$$
$$= -0.27778 f(0.88730) - 0.44444 f(0.5) - 0.27778 f(0.11270)$$
$$= -0.27778(-0.06224) - 0.44444(-1.47152) - 0.27778(-0.53890)$$
$$= 0.82100$$

since

$$f(0.88730) = e^{-\left(\frac{1}{0.88730} - 1\right)} \left(\frac{1}{0.88730} - 1\right)^{1.4} \left(-\frac{1}{(0.88730)^2}\right)$$
$$= -0.06224$$

$$f(0.5) = e^{-\left(\frac{1}{0.5} - 1\right)} \left(\frac{1}{0.5} - 1\right)^{1.4} \left(-\frac{1}{(0.5)^2}\right)$$
$$= -1.47152$$

$$f(0.11270) = e^{-\left(\frac{1}{0.11270} - 1\right)} \left(\frac{1}{0.11270} - 1\right)^{1.4} \left(-\frac{1}{(0.11270)^2}\right)$$
$$= -0.53894$$

The absolute relative true error, $|\epsilon_t|$, is

$$|\epsilon_t| = \left|\frac{1.2422 - 0.82099}{1.2422}\right| \times 100\%$$
$$= 33.906\%$$

Example 6

As you can see from the plot given in Figure 3 for the integrand in $\int_0^{\infty} e^{-t} t^{1.4} dt$ of Example 5, once the value of t exceeds 10, the area under the curve looks insignificant. What would happen if you used the two-segment two-point Gauss quadrature rule within the significant range of $[0,10]$?

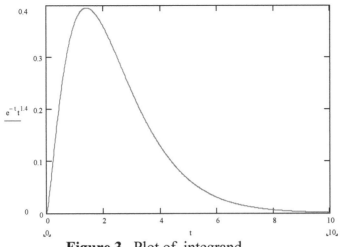

Figure 3 Plot of integrand

Solution

In doing this, no change of variables is necessary—only a change in the limits of each segment is needed to apply Gauss quadrature rule. Observe

$$\Gamma(2.4) = \int_0^\infty e^{-t} t^{1.4} dt$$

$$\approx \int_0^{10} e^{-t} t^{1.4} dt$$

$$= \int_0^{2.4} e^{-t} t^{1.4} dt + \int_{2.4}^{10} e^{-t} t^{1.4} dt$$

Setting $f(t) = e^{-t} t^{1.4}$ to make the change of variables, we get

$$\Gamma(2.4) \approx \frac{2.4-0}{2} \int_{-1}^1 f\left(\frac{2.4-0}{2} t + \frac{2.4+0}{2}\right) dt + \frac{10-2.4}{2} \int_{-1}^1 f\left(\frac{10-2.4}{2} t + \frac{10+2.4}{2}\right) dt$$

$$= 1.2 \int_{-1}^1 f(1.2t + 1.2) dt + 3.8 \int_{-1}^1 f(3.8t + 6.2) dt$$

Applying two-point Gauss quadrature rule gets

$$c_1 = 1.000000000$$
$$t_1 = -0.577350269$$
$$c_2 = 1.000000000$$
$$t_2 = 0.577350269$$

$$\Gamma(2.4) \approx 1.2c_1 f(1.2t_1 + 1.2) + 1.2c_2 f(1.2t_2 + 1.2) + 3.8c_1 f(3.8t_1 + 6.2) + 3.8c_2 f(3.8t_2 + 6.2)$$
$$= 1.2 f(1.2(-0.57735) + 1.2) + 1.2 f(1.2(0.57735) + 1.2)$$
$$+ 3.8 f(3.8(-0.57735) + 6.2) + 3.8 f(3.8(0.57735) + 6.2)$$
$$= 1.2 f(0.50718) + 1.2 f(1.89282) + 3.8 f(4.00607) + 3.8 f(8.39393)$$
$$= 1.2(0.23279) + 1.2(0.36805) + 3.8(0.12706) + 3.8(0.00445)$$
$$= 1.2207$$

since

$$f(0.50718) = e^{-0.50718}0.50718^{1.4} = 0.23279$$

$$f(1.89282) = e^{-1.89282}1.89282^{1.4} = 0.36805$$

$$f(4.00607) = e^{-4.00607}4.00607^{1.4} = 0.12706$$

$$f(8.39393) = e^{-8.39393}8.39393^{1.4} = 0.00445$$

The absolute relative true error, $|\epsilon_t|$, is

$$|\epsilon_t| = \left|\frac{1.2422 - 1.2207}{1.2422}\right| \times 100\%$$

$$= 1.731\%$$

INTEGRATION	
Topic	Integrating improper functions
Summary	These are textbook notes of integrating improper functions
Major	General Engineering
Authors	Autar Kaw, Michael Keteltas
Last Revised	December 23, 2009
Web Site	http://numericalmethods.eng.usf.edu

Problem Set

Chapter 07.07
Improper Integrals

1. Integrate the following integral numerically using any technique

$$\int_{-2}^{\infty} y e^{-y} dy$$

2. Use two-point Gauss quadrature rule to integrate $\int_{-2}^{\infty} e^{-x^2} dx$. You may make a change of variables before applying the Gauss quadrature rule.

3. Integrate $\int_{-2}^{\infty} e^{-x^2} dx$ by breaking the integral interval to [–2,0], [0,2], and [2,∞]. Apply the two-point Gauss quadrature rule over each of the three intervals. Do you get a value close to the exact answer of 1.7683?

4. Integrate numerically $\int_{1}^{\infty} \frac{1}{x(x+3)} dx$. Compare with the exact value.

5. Integrate numerically $\int_{2}^{11} \frac{1}{\sqrt{x-2}} dx$. Compare with the exact value.

6. The cumulative normal distribution is given by $\int_{-\infty}^{x} \frac{1}{\sqrt{2\pi}} e^{-t^2} dt$. Use numerical integration to find the value of the integral for $x \to \infty$ $\int_{-\infty}^{x} \frac{1}{\sqrt{2\pi}} e^{-t^2} dt$

Chapter 08.00A

Physical Problem for Ordinary Differential Equations
General Engineering

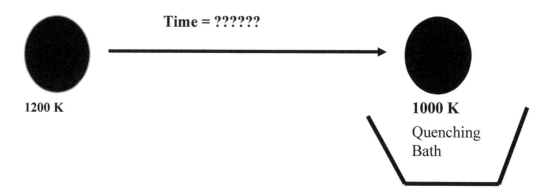

Problem

You are working for a ball bearing company - Ralph's Bearings. For long lasting life of some spherical bearings made in this company, they need to be quenched for 30 seconds in water that is maintained at a room temperature of 300K after heating them to a high temperature of 1000K. However, it takes time to take the ball from the furnace to the quenching bath and its temperature falls. If the temperature of the furnace is 1200K and it takes 10 seconds to take the ball to the quenching bath. Is less or more time needed to get to a temperature of 1000K?

Mathematical model

To keep the mathematical simple, one can assume the spherical bearing to be a lumped mass system. What does a lumped system mean? It implies that the internal conduction in the sphere is large enough that the temperature throughout the ball is uniform. This allows us to make the assumption that the temperature is only a function of time and not of the location in the spherical ball. This means that if a differential equation governs this physical problem, it would be an ordinary differential equation for a lumped system and a partial differential equation for a non-lumped system. In your heat transfer course, you will learn when a system can be considered lumped or nonlumped. In simplistic terms, this distinction is based on the material, geometry and heat exchange factors of the ball with its surroundings.

Now assuming a lumped-mass system, let us develop the mathematical model for the above problem. When the ball is taken out of the furnace at the initial temperature of θ_0 and is cooled by radiation to its surroundings at the temperature of θ_a, the rate at which heat is lost to radiation is

Rate of heat lost due to radiation $= A \in \sigma\left(\theta^4 - \theta_a{}^4\right)$

where

A = surface area of ball, m^2
$\in$ = emittance[1]
σ = Stefan-Boltzmann[2] constant, $5.67 \times 10^{-8} \dfrac{\text{J}}{\text{s.m}^2.\text{K}^4}$
θ = temperature of the ball at a given time, K

The energy stored in the mass is given by

Energy stored by mass $= mC\theta$

where

m = mass of ball, kg
C = specific heat of the ball, $\text{J}/(\text{kg} - \text{K})$

From an energy balance,

Rate at which heat is gained - Rate at which heat is lost
=Rate at which heat is stored

gives

$$-A \in \sigma\left(\theta^4 - \theta_a^4\right) = mC\frac{d\theta}{dt}$$

Given the

Radius of ball, $r = 2.0$ cm
Density of ball, $\rho = 7800 \text{ kg/m}^3$
Specific heat, C = 420 J/(kg.K)
Emittance, $\in$ = 0.85
Stefan-Boltzmann Constant, $\sigma = 5.67 \times 10^{-8} \text{ J}/(\text{s.m}^2.\text{K}^4)$
Initial temperature of the ball, $\theta(0) = 1200 \text{ K}$,
Ambient temperature, $\theta_a = 300 \text{ K}$,

we have

Surface area of the ball

$$A = 4\pi r^2$$
$$= 4\pi (0.02)^2$$

---

[1] Emittance is defined as the total radiation emitted divided by total radiation that would be emitted by a blackbody at the same temperature. The emittance is always between 0 and 1. A black body is a body that emits and absorbs at any temperature the maximum possible amount of radiation at any given wavelength.
[2] Stefan-Botzmann constant was discovered by two Austrian scientists – J. Stefan and L. Boltzmann. Stefan found it experimentally in 1879 and Boltzmann derived it theoretically in 1884.

$$= 5.02654 \times 10^{-3} \, \text{m}^2$$

Mass of the ball

$$M = pV$$

$$= \rho \left[\frac{4}{3} \pi r^3 \right]$$

$$= 7800 \times \left(\frac{4}{3} \right) \pi (0.02)^3$$

$$= 0.261380 kg$$

Hence

$$- A \in \sigma(\theta^4 - \theta_a^{\ 4}) = mC \frac{d\theta}{dt}$$

reduces to

$$- (5.02654 \times 10^{-3}) \, (0.85) \, (5.67 \times 10^{-8}) \, (\theta^4 - 300^4) = (0.261380) \, (420) \frac{d\theta}{dt}$$

$$\frac{d\theta}{dt} = -2.20673 \times 10^{-12} \, (\theta^4 - 81 \times 10^8)$$

An improved mathematical model
The heat from the ball can also be lost due to convection. The rate of heat lost due to convection is

Rate of heat lost due to convection $= hA(\theta - \theta_a)$,

where

$h =$ the convective cooling coefficient $\left[\text{W} / (\text{m}^2 - \text{K}) \right]$.

Hence the heat is lost is due to both, convection and radiation and is given by

Rate of heat lost due to convection and radiation $= A \in \sigma(\theta^4 - \theta_a^4) + hA(\theta - \theta_a)$

Energy stored by mass $= mC\theta$

From an energy balance,

Rate at which heat is gained -Rate at which heat is lost
=Rate at which heat is stored

gives

$$- A \in \sigma(\theta^4 - \theta_a^4) - hA(\theta - \theta_a) = mC \frac{d\theta}{dt}$$

Given $h = 350 \dfrac{\text{J}}{\text{s} - \text{m}^2 - \text{K}}$ and considering both convection and radiation, and substituting
the values of the constants given before

$$- (5.02654 \times 10^{-3}) \, (0.85) \, (5.67 \times 10^{-8}) \, (\theta^4 - 300^4)$$

$$- (350) \, (5.02654 \times 10^{-3}) \, (\theta - 300) = (0.261380) \, (420) \frac{d\theta}{dt}$$

$$\frac{d\theta}{dt} = -2.20673 \times 10^{-13} (\theta^4 - 81 \times 10^8) - 1.60256 \times 10^{-2} \, (\theta - 300)$$

The solution to the above ordinary differential equation with the initial condition of $\theta(0) = 1200\text{K}$ would give us the temperature of the ball as a function of time. We can then find at what time the ball temperature drops to 1000K.

Questions
1. Note that the above ordinary differential equation is non-linear. Is there is an exact solution to the problem?
2. You are asked to solve the inverse problem, that is, when is the dependent variable temperature 1000K. How would you go about solving the inverse problem using different numerical methods such as Euler's and Runge-Kutta methods
3. Can you find if convection or radiation can be neglected? How would you quantify the effect of neglecting one or the other?
4. Find the following at $t = 5\,\text{s}$
   a) Rate of change of temperature,
   b) Rate at which heat is lost due to convection,
   c) Rate at which heat is lost due to radiation,
   d) Rate at which heat is stored in the ball.

ORDINARY DIFFERENTIAL EQUATIONS	
Topic	Ordinary differential equations
Summary	To find the temperature of a heated ball as a function of time, a first-order ordinary differential equation must be solved.
Major	General Engineering
Authors	Autar Kaw
Date	October 16, 2008
Web Site	http://numericalmethods.eng.usf.edu

Chapter 08.00B

Physical Problem for Ordinary Differential Equations
Chemical Engineering

Soap is prepared through a reaction known as saponification. In saponification, tallow (fats from animals such as cattle) or vegetable fat (e.g. coconut) is reacted with potassium or sodium hydroxide to produce glycerol and fatty acid salt known as "soap". The soap is separated from the glycerol through precipitation by the addition of sodium chloride. Water layer on top of the mixture that contains dissolved sodium chloride is drawn-off the mixture as a waste. This method of soap making is still being practiced in many villages in the developing countries where the price of mass produced soap maybe too expensive for the average villager.

Two chemical engineering students used knowledge of saponification acquired in their organic chemistry class to organize and produce "home made" soap. The local ordinance requires that the minimum concentration level for sodium chloride waste in any liquid that is discharged into the environment must not exceed 11.00g/L. Sodium chloride laden liquid water is the major waste of the process. The company has only one 15-liter tank for waste storage. On filling the waste tank, the tank contained 15 liters of water and 750 grams of sodium chloride. To continue production and meet local ordinance, it is desired to pump in fresh water into the tank at the rate of 2.0 liters per minute while waste salt water containing 25 grams of salt per liter is added at the rate of 1.5 liters per minute. To keep the solution level at 15 liters, 3.5 liters per minute of the waste is discharged. A sketch Figure 1 of the flows is given below where A represents the waste stream from the process, B is the fresh water stream and C is the discharge stream to the environment. Here, it is assumed that as the two streams, A and B enter into the tank, instantaneously the chloride concentration in the tank changes to the exit concentration, x_1.

The material (sodium chloride) balance on the tank system can be written as

Accumulation = input – output + removal by reaction   (1)

Noting that no chemical reaction occurs in the storage tank (i.e. the third term on the right hand side of (1) is zero), the above equation can be written as

$$\frac{dx_1}{dt} = (25\text{g/L})(1.5\text{L/min}) + (0\text{g/L})(2\text{L/min}) - (x_1\text{g/L})(3.5\text{L/min}) + 0 \qquad (2)$$

Simplifying Equation (2), we obtain

$$\frac{dx_1}{dt} + 3.5x_1 = 37.5 \qquad (3)$$

For the initial conditions of the ordinary differential equations in Equation (3), recall that at $t = 0$, the salt concentration in the tank was given as 750 g/15L (50g/L), that is,

$$t = 0, \ x_1(0) = \frac{750}{15} = 50\text{g/L} \qquad (4)$$

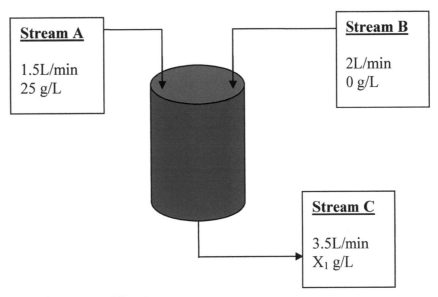

Figure 1 Sketch of flow for a saponification process.

QUESTIONS

1. Using Equations (3) and (4), numerically determine how the concentration of salt being discharged changes with time.
2. Plot the solution obtained.
3. How long did it take to achieve the minimum required local ordinance? At steady state, what is the concentration of salt being discharged from this local soap factory?

Ordinary Differential Equation	
Topic	Ordinary Differential Equations
Summary	Sodium chloride waste control while making soap
Major	Chemical Engineering
Authors	Egwu Eric Kalu
Date	December 23, 2009
Web Site	http://numericalmethods.eng.usf.edu

Chapter 08.00C

Physical Problem for Civil Engineering
Ordinary Differential Equations

When is it safe to return to the lake?

Pollution in lakes can be a serious issue as they are used for recreation use. Pollution resulting from sewage, runoff from suburban yards that is loaded with fertilizers and pesticides to keep the homeowner's associations off your back can be a safety hazard for people. One is generally interested in knowing that if the concentration of a particular pollutant is above acceptable levels, how long will it take for the pollution level to decrease to an acceptable level.

Figure 1 Pollutant in a lake

Mass of pollutant = Mass of pollutant entering – Mass of pollutant leaving

which also gives

Rate of change of mass of pollutant = Rate of change of mass of pollutant entering – Rate of change of mass of pollutant leaving.

If the concentration of pollutant is given by

$$C(t) = \frac{M(t)}{V}$$

where

$M(t) =$ mass of pollutant at time, t

$V =$ Volume of lake.

Rate of change of mass of pollutant entering is QC_o, where Q is the flow rate of the water into the lake, and the rate of change of mass of pollutant leaving the lake is $\frac{QM(t)}{V}$.

The above assumes that the flow rate of water going in and out of lake is the same. We also assuming that the pollutant is uniformly distributed in the lake. Also, no reaction is assumed. This gives

$$\frac{dM(t)}{dt} = QC_o - \frac{QM(t)}{V}$$

Now

$$M(t) = VC_o(t)$$

giving

$$V\frac{dC}{dt} = \dot{Q}C_o - \dot{Q}C$$

$$V\frac{dC}{dt} + \dot{Q}C = \dot{Q}C_o$$

Assume a weekly flow rate of fresh water as $1.5 \times 10^6 \, \text{m}^3$. $C_o = 0$ as we are assuming only fresh water coming in. The volume of the lake is $25 \times 10^6 \, \text{m}^3$. If the initial concentration of the pollutant is $10^7 \, \text{parts/m}^3$, and the acceptable level is $5 \times 10^6 \, \text{parts/m}^3$, how much time would it take for the pollutant to reach acceptable levels.

$$25 \times 10^6 \frac{dC}{dt} + 1.5 \times 10^6 C = 0$$

$$\frac{dC}{dt} + 0.06C = 0, C(0) = 10^7$$

ORDINARY DIFFERENTIAL EQUATION	
Topic	Ordinary Differential Equations
Summary	A physical problem of finding how much time it would take a lake to have safe levels of pollutant. To find the time, the problem is modeled as an ordinary differential equation.
Major	Civil Engineering
Authors	Autar Kaw
Date	December 23, 2009
Web Site	http://numericalmethods.eng.usf.edu

Chapter 08.00D

Physical Problem for Computer Engineering
Ordinary Differential Equations

Problem Statement

Resistors and capacitors are fundamental elements of any circuit. Even the behavior of semiconductor devices in your computer can be modeled employing these basis elements (along with some others). A transistor is comprised of junctions of different kinds of materials, giving rise to interesting electrical properties. The electrical properties at these semiconductor junctions can be characterized using resistors (R) and capacitors (C), giving rise to the name "RC-model". In this module we will consider the electrical behavior of the simplest configuration of the RC elements and see how it can characterized using ordinary differential elements.

Two quantities that are important in electrical circuits are voltage (denoted here by V) and current (denoted here by I). The current through a resistor has a linear relationship with voltage and is defined by $V = IR$, where R, is constant used to quantify the resistor. This is called the Ohms law and you should have seen it one of your physics classes. A capacitor is a bit stranger element for which the rate of change of voltage across it is proportional to the current. Or in other words: $C\dfrac{dV}{dt} = I$, where C is called the capacitance. Voltage changes slowly across high capacitance. These elements are represented by diagrams as shown below.

R V_1 $V_1 - V_0 = I\,R$ V_0

C V_1 $C\,d(V_1 - V_0)/dt = I$ V_0

Resistor:
$V_1 - V_0$ = Voltage drop
I = Current

Capacitor:
$V_1 - V_0$ = Voltage drop
I = Current

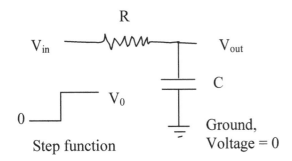

Figure 1. A simple RC circuit. As the input voltage is switched on at t=0, what happens to the output voltage.

Consider the simple combination of resistor and capacitor, as shown above. This kind of configuration is not rare and occurs in all power supplies to your computer. There are other components in addition to this, but this is one of the basic arrangements. The voltage at one end of the resistor is denoted by Vin and the voltage at the other end is denoted by Vout. The latter end is also connected to the capacitor, whose other end of which is connected to ground, which can be taken to be at zero voltage. The question we ask is what happens to the output voltage Vout when the input voltage Vin is switched on suddenly?

The voltage and current relationship across the resistor and the capacitor can be expressed, respectively as

$$V_{in} - V_{out} = IR \qquad \text{and} \qquad C\frac{dV_{out}}{dt} = I$$

where I is the current through the circuit. Eliminating this quantity from the above two equations, we have

$$V_{in} - V_{out} = RC\frac{dV_{out}}{dt}$$

For any input voltage profile we can solve this equation to arrive at the output voltage profile.

Worked Out Example

The sudden change in the input voltage can be modeled using the following function

$$V_{in} = \begin{cases} V_0 & \forall t \geq 0 \\ 0 & \forall t < 0 \end{cases}$$

This is also called a "step" function. For this input the differential equation modeling the output voltage for t > 0 is given by

$$RC\frac{dV_{out}}{dt} = V_0 - V_{out}$$

The solution of this equation we need some boundary conditions. We know the voltage at $t = 0$ is zero, i.e. $V_{out}(0) = 0$, and the voltage after a long time should be equal to the new input voltage, i.e $V_{out}(\infty) = V_0$. Using boundary conditions, in along with general solution form: $V_{out}(t) = c_o \exp(at) + c_1 \exp(-at) + c_2$, we can arrive at the following solution for the output voltage

$$V_{out}(t) = V_o(1 - \exp(-\frac{t}{RC}))$$

In the Figure 2 we see the plot of the transient output voltage for various values of the product RC. The output starts at zero and gradually converges to V0 = 1. The rate of convergence is dependent on the product RC.

QUESTIONS

1. If the for $V_{in} = x_1(t)$, the output voltage is given by the function $y_1(t)$, and for $V_{in} = x_2(t)$, the output voltage is given by the function $y_2(t)$, show that the output for the input $V_{in} = x_1(t) + x_2(t)$, is given by $y_1(t) + y_2(t)$.

2. If the for $V_{in} = x_1(t)$, the output voltage is given by the function $y_1(t)$, show that the output for the input $V_{in} = ax_1(t)$, is given by $ay_1(t)$.

3. Consider a pulse shaped input that is defined by:

$$V_{in}(t) = \begin{cases} 0 & \forall t < 0 \\ V_0 & 0 \le t \le T \\ 0 & t > T \end{cases}$$

What is the form of the output?
Hint: Express this input of in the form $x_1(t) - x_2(t)$ and then use the properties you have derived so far to arrive at the solution.

4. What can you say about the output as the ratio $\dfrac{T}{RC}$ is varied?

5. What can say about the behavior of this circuit when there is a voltage "spike" at the input?

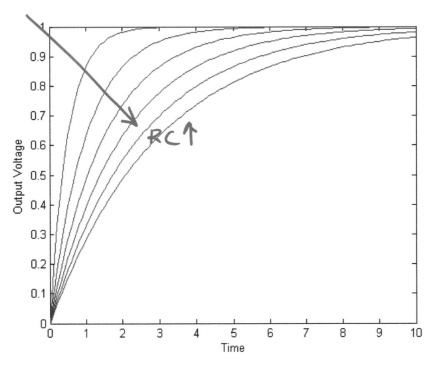

Figure 2. Output voltage, Vout(t), for various values of the product RC.

ORDINARY DIFFERENTIAL EQUATIONS	
Topic	Ordinary Differential Equations
Summary	Transient analysis of resistor-capacitor system
Major	Computer Engineering
Authors	Sudeep Sarkar
Date	December 23, 2009
Web Site	http://numericalmethods.eng.usf.edu

Chapter 08.00E

Physical Problem for Electrical Engineering
Ordinary Differential Equations

Problem Statement

Small non-switching power supplies such as AC power bricks are typically built around a small transformer, rectifier, and voltage regulator as shown in Figure 1.

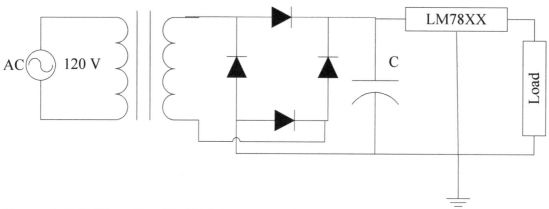

Figure 1. Full-Wave Rectified DC Power Supply

The transformer is used to reduce the AC voltage levels to a more reasonable range (e.g. 12 VAC or 18 VAC) and the bridge rectifier will take the negative half cycle of the AC waveform and convert it to a positive half cycle. A typical full-wave rectified waveform is shown in Figure 2. This waveform was generated assuming an ideal diode operating under no-load conditions and can be modeled with the following equation:

$$V_{full} = \max\left(\left|18 \times \cos(t) - 1.4\right|, 0\right)$$

For a half-wave rectified system built using only a single diode, the equation would become:

$$V_{half} = \max\left(18 \times \cos(t) - 0.7, 0\right)$$

and the waveform would look similar to Figure 2 except every other hump would be replaced with 0.

08.00E.1

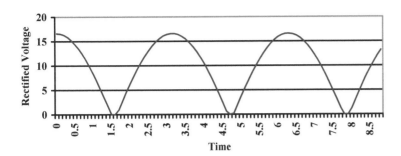

Figure 2 Full-Wave Rectified AC Signal.

This is clearly not suitable as a DC power source since the load is looking for a constant DC value. This is where the capacitor, C, and the LM78XX voltage regulator of Figure 1 become important. A typical voltage regulator requires that the voltage on the input pin maintain a certain margin above the regulated output voltage. This is typically in the range of 2.5 to 3 V and for the LM7805, which provides 5 VDC, it is 2.5 V [1]. This means that the minimum voltage at the input pin of the LM7805 must not drop below 7.5 V. Clearly, the waveform in Figure 2 does that regularly.

The task of the capacitor, C, in the power supply is to store up charge when the rectifier provides voltage in excess of the required minimum and then support the voltage when the regulated voltage is below the minimum by providing stored charge to the voltage regulator. Thus, the circuit has two distinct phases of operation.

Phase 1

When the rectified voltage is above the voltage across the capacitor V_c, then the rectifier provides current to the capacitor and the voltage regulator, and the capacitor charges. The ideal model of a diode will not be adequate here since we need to know how much current the diode can supply. A better model of the diode can be found from its VI characteristic such as the one shown in Figure 3. A model for this will be developed shortly.

Phase 2

When the rectified voltage drops below V_c current ceases to flow between the rectifier diodes and the capacitor. The capacitor then becomes the sole source of current to the voltage regulator by bleeding off its charge. This has the additional effect of continually reducing the voltage across the capacitor. As long as it does not fall below the required threshold, the regulator can successfully do its job.

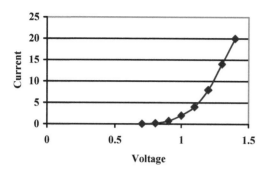

Figure 3 VI Characteristic of a 1N4001 Diode [2].

Diode Model

The diode of Figure 3 must be modeled to account properly for the current it can supply during the Phase 1 charging phase of the capacitor. It is reasonable to model a diode under these conditions as a voltage drop and a series resistance. This essentially treats the Figure 3 curve as piece-wise linear model and it can only be applied when the diode is on (that is, it does not properly model an under-biased or reverse-biased diode) [3, pp. 67-74]. This model is shown in Figure 4 and for the 1N4001 of Figure 3 suitable values are $V_d = 1.0\,V$ and $R_d = 0.02\,\Omega$. Other diodes will have similar numbers.

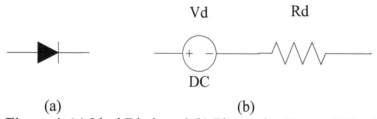

(a)   (b)

Figure 4 (a) Ideal Diode and (b) Piece-wise Forward Bias Model.

Load Model

The final piece to the picture is how to model the load represented by the voltage regulator. Rather than get into the details of the internal structure of the voltage regulator it is sufficient to model the worst-case scenario when choosing the appropriate capacitor. This is represented by the peak continuous current that the power-supply is expected to provide. For this problem, it will be assumed to be 100 mA.

Circuit Models

With the Phase 1 charging, and Phase 2 discharging, circuit models of the power supply circuit can now be built. They are shown in Figure 5. In both cases, the circuit must provide 100 mA to the load. It will be additionally assumed that a transformer will be chosen that provides sufficient AC power at 18 VAC running at 60 Hz.

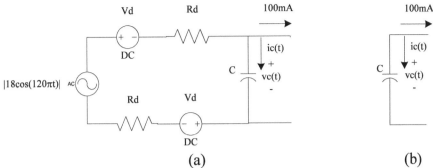

(a)   (b)

Figure 5 (a)Phase 1 (Charging) and (b) Phase 2 (Discharging) Circuit Models

Analysis

The analysis of these two circuits is rather straight-forward once the VI characteristic of the capacitor is substituted. In the time-domain, this is represented by the differential equation

$$i_c(t) = C \frac{dv_c(t)}{dt} \qquad \text{subject to initial conditions on } v_c .$$

During the charging of Phase 1, the operative circuit equation is found by writing a Kirchoff's Current Law equation for the node at the top of the capacitor. Doing this yields

$$C \frac{dv_c(t)}{dt} + 100mA = \frac{|18\cos(120\pi t)| - 2V_d - v_c(t)}{2R_d} ,$$

when

$$v_c(t) \le |18\cos(120\pi t)| - 2V_d .$$

During the discharging of Phase 2, the circuit is a bit simpler and the equation is

$$C \frac{dv_c(t)}{dt} + 100mA = 0 ,$$

when

$$v_c(t) > |18\cos(120\pi t)| - 2V_d .$$

These are essentially the same differential equation it is just that the forcing function has two cases that must be monitored as the equation is solved. Substituting the previously derived values for V_d and R_d will yield the following equation in standard form.

$$\frac{dv_c(t)}{dt} = \frac{1}{C} \left\{ -0.1 + \max\left(\frac{|18\cos(120\pi t)| - 2 - v_c(t)}{0.04}, 0 \right) \right\} .$$

Assuming that the capacitor is initially discharged (i.e. $v_c(0+) = 0$) it is simply a matter of trying various standard capacitors (e.g. 100, 150, 220, 330, 470, and 680 μF or other powers of 10 [4]) into the equation and simulating it for a few cycles of the AC source. Pick the smallest value where $v_c(t)$ never drops below the required 7.5 V.

QUESTIONS

1. Most capacitors are marked with a tolerance of $\pm 20\%$. How would your analysis handle the case that a 100 μF capacitor could be as high as 120 μF or as low as 80 μF ?

2. What effect would it have on the differential equation to use a more complex model for the diode?

3. Is it necessary to have a more detailed model of the voltage regulator? Alternatively, is it suitable to model it simply as a maximum current sink?

4. Modify the model to account for an AC brownout, that is, what would happen if the AC power source saw a temporary drop in voltage?

References

[1]   LM340/LM78XX Data Sheet, National Semiconductor, http://www.national.com/ds/LM/LM340.pdf, accessed May 11, 2005.

[2]   1N4001 Data Sheet, Fairchild Semiconductor, http://www.fairchildsemi.com/ds/1N/1N4007.pdf, accessed May 12, 2005.

[3]   Malvino, A., Electronic Principles, Sixth Edition, Glencoe McGraw-Hill, 1999.

[4]   Standard Capacitor Values, RF Café, http://www.rfcafe.com/references/electrical/capacitor_values.htm, accessed May 12, 2005.

ORDINARY DIFFERENTIAL EQUATIONS	
Topic	Ordinary Differential Equations
Summary	A rectifier-based power supply requires a capacitor to store power temporarily when the rectified waveform from the AC source drops below the target voltage. To size this capacitor properly, a first-order ordinary differential equation must be solved.
Major	Electrical Engineering
Authors	Henry Welch
Date	May 24,2005
Web Site	http://numericalmethods.eng.usf.edu

Chapter 08.00F

Physical Problem for Industrial Engineering Ordinary Differential Equations

Speed control of DC motors

In this example we will discuss the closed loop speed control of a DC motor. Figure 1 shows three different DC motors and Figure 2 depicts the inside of a DC motor. Universal Motors which are essentially DC motors are widely used in applications where the speed of a process needs to be controlled. Such applications are encountered frequently in our daily lives such as controlling the speed of fans or controlling the speed of hand-held tools such as drills, and in industrial automation applications such as controlling the speed of conveyor belts.

Figure 1 A variety of DC motors

Figure 2 The inside of a DC motor

Before we can discuss the speed control of a DC motor, it is important to understand the physical time varying relationships that determine the operating characteristics of a DC motor.

Equation (1) below describes the linear relationship between the torque T and the current i_a applied to the motor. The slope of the line is the torque constant K_t. Equation (2) describes the linear relationship between the back emf E_B and the armature speed w. The slope of the line K_B is the voltage constant. Equation (3) describes the components of the armature voltage V as sum of the back emf and the voltage drop across armature resistance Ri_a. Finally, Equation (4) describes the relationship between torque, acceleration and speed of the motor in a no-load system as the sum of the angular acceleration dw/dt multiplied by the inertia of the motor and the load, and the damping of the system f multiplied by the armature speed.

$$T(t) = K_T i_a(t) \tag{1}$$
$$E_B(t) = K_B w(t) \tag{2}$$
$$V(t) = Ri_a(t) + E_B(t) \tag{3}$$
$$T(t) = I\frac{dw}{dt} + fw(t) \tag{4}$$

The equation for the speed of the motor in relation to the voltage input can be derived from these relationships as follows. Substitute the value of back emf from Equation (2) into Equation (3) as:

$$V(t) = Ri_a(t) + K_B w(t) \tag{5}$$

Equating Equations (1) and (4) and solving for ia results in

$$i_a = \frac{I\dfrac{dw}{dt} + fw(t)}{K_T} \tag{6}$$

Finally substitute the value for ia from Equation (6) into Equation (5) as

$$K_T V(t) = RI\frac{dw}{dt} + (Rf + K_T K_B)w(t) \tag{7}$$

Equation (7) is a first order differential equation which describes the open-loop response of the motor to a voltage input where the output variable system (speed of the motor) is not considered in the control mechanism. In the next section we will consider the closed-loop control of the motor.

Closed loop control

Figure 3 illustrates the block diagram of a proportional control system used to control the speed of a DC motor where KP is the proportional gain. The "C" block is the summing point which generates an error term e equal to the difference between the desired speed set by the operator (w_d) and the actual speed of the motor. The "DC Motor" block transforms the amplified error input from the "Control Action" block to the output speed of the motor.

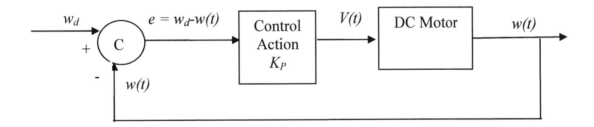

Figure 3 Block diagram of a DC motor control systems

Based on the control system block diagram

$$V(t) = K_P[w_d - w(t)] \tag{8}$$

Substituting the value of $V(t)$ from Equation (8) in to Equation (7) and rearranging terms results in the differential Equation (9) which describes the relationship of the actual speed of the motor to the desired speed.

$$K_T K_P w_d = RI \frac{dw}{dt} + [Rf + K_T (K_B + K_P)]w(t) \tag{9}$$

Example application

Consider a machine vision quality inspection system which inspects parts for defects shown in Figure 4. The parts are positioned in fixtures on a conveyor driven by a DC motor. The conveyor is required to ramp up to a certain speed within a specific time (before a part enters the field of view of the camera), maintain a constant speed while the part is under the camera and finally come to a stop once the inspection of the part is completed. Many such applications which utilize DC motors have requirements associated with the steady-state speed and/or a ramp up time for the motor to reach this speed.

Consider a DC motor which has the following specifications:

Voltage constant $K_B = 0.06$ V·s/rad

Torque constant $K_t = 0.06$ N·m/A

Armature resistance $R = 2\,\Omega$

Moment of inertia $I = 6 \times 10^{-4}$ N.m.s^2/rad

The open loop response of the motor to a voltage input using Equation (7) and assuming a system without damping (($f = 0$ N·m·s /rad)) is

$$V(t) = (0.02)\frac{dw}{dt} + (0.06)w(t).$$

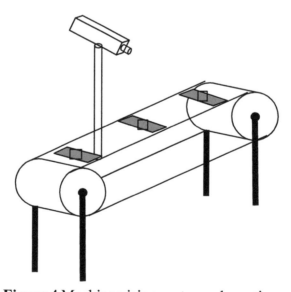

Figure 4 Machine vision system schematic

The speed of the motor $w(t)$ can therefore be controlled by changing the magnitude of this input voltage ($v(t)$). Assuming the initial condition $w(0) = 0$ and a specific input voltage, the above ordinary differential equation can be solved to determine the stead-state speed of the motor as well as the time it takes for the motor to ramp up to this speed. The information obtained from the solution is important in selection of the appropriate voltage input and/or motor for a particular application to assure that the motor response time and speed is sufficient for the task.

Similarly, the design of a closed loop controller to control the speed of the motor requires the solution to the ordinary differential Equation (9) to determine the user settings to obtain the necessary output from the motor. This application is posed as Exercise Problem 5 below.

Exercise problems

For the DC motor in the Example Problem, answer the following questions:

1. Draw the speed response graph $w(t)$ vs t for a step input of 20 Volts without the damping of the system ($f = 0$ N·m·s /rad)

2. Draw the speed response graph for a step input of 20 Volts considering the damping of the system where $f = 1.0 \times 10^{-4}$ N.m.s/rad .

3. What is the difference between the steady-state speed of the motor with and without damping?

4. Consider a closed loop control system with gain $K_P = 10$. What is the closed loop speed response graph of motor to a desired setting of 100 rad/s?

5. The answer to Question#4 is less than 100 rad/s due to the steady state error present in first order systems. What should be the desired speed setting for the motor speed response to be 100 rad/s?

Additional reading

[1] Boucher, T.O., Computer Automation in Manufacturing: An Introduction, Chapman & Hall, London, 1996.
[2] Bateson, R.N., Introduction to Control System Technology, 6th Edition, Prentice Hall, New Jersey, 1999.

ORDINARY DIFFERENTIAL EQUATIONS	
Topic	Ordinary Differential Equations
Summary	Many appliances used in our daily lives as well as numerous applications in industrial automation require controlling speed of a DC motor to function properly. Classical control theory requires solving differential equations to control these types of motors.
Major	Industrial Engineering
Author	Ali Yalcin
Date	October 16, 2008
Website	http://numericalmethods.eng.usf.edu/

Chapter 08.00G

Physical Problem for Mechanical Engineering
Ordinary Differential Equations

Problem Statement

To make the fulcrum (Figure 1) of a bascule bridge, a long hollow steel shaft called the trunnion is shrink fit into a steel hub. The resulting steel trunnion-hub assembly is then shrink fit into the girder of the bridge.

Figure 1 Trunnion-Hub-Girder (THG) assembly.

This is done by first immersing the trunnion in a cold medium such as liquid nitrogen. After the trunnion reaches the steady state temperature of the cold medium, the trunnion outer diameter contracts. The trunnion is taken out of the medium and slid though the hole of the hub (Figure 1).

When the trunnion heats up, it expands and creates an interference fit with the hub. Because of the large thermal shock that the trunnion undergoes, it is suggested that the trunnion be cooled in stages. First, put the trunnion in a refrigerated chamber, then dip it in dry-ice/alcohol mixture and then immerse it in a bath of liquid nitrogen. However, this approach will take more time. One is mainly concerned about the cool down time in the refrigerated chamber. Assuming that the room temperature is 27°C and the refrigerated chamber is set is -33°C, how much time would it take for the trunnion to cool down to -33°C.

Let us do a simplified problem of a trunnion that is solid and assume the trunnion can be treated as a lumped-mass system. What does a lumped system mean[1]?

Let us develop the mathematical model for the above problem. When the trunnion is placed in the refrigerated chamber, the trunnion loses heat to its surroundings by convection.

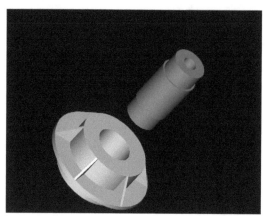

Figure 2 Trunnion slide through the hub after contracting

$$\text{Rate of heat lost due to convection} = h(\theta)A(\theta - \theta_a). \tag{1}$$

where

$h(\theta)$ = the convective cooling coefficient, $\text{W/m}^2.\text{K}$ and is a function of temperature

A = surface area

θ_a = ambient temperature of refrigerated chamber

The energy stored in the mass is given by

$$\text{Energy stored by mass} = mC\theta \tag{2}$$

where

m = mass of the trunnion, kg

C = specific heat of the trunnion, J/(kg-K)

From an energy balance,

Rate at which heat is gained - Rate at which heat is lost =
= Rate at which heat is stored

gives

---

[1] It implies that the internal conduction in the trunnion is large enough that the temperature throughout the trunnion is uniform. This allows us to make the assumption that the temperature is only a function of time and not of the location in the trunnion. This means that if a differential equation governs this physical problem, it would be an ordinary differential equation for a lumped system and a partial differential equation for a non-lumped system. In your heat transfer course, you will learn when a system can be considered lumped or non-lumped. In simplistic terms, this distinction is based on the material, geometry, and heat exchange factors of the ball with its surroundings. *We will prove later that the trunnion can be treated as a lumped system.*

$$-h(\theta)A(\theta-\theta_a)=mC\frac{d\theta}{dt} \tag{3}$$

Note that the convective cooling coefficient is a function of temperature. Other material parameters such as density (affecting mass), specific heat and thermal conductivity (affecting whether the system can be considered lumped or not) of the trunnion material are functions of temperature as well, but within our temperature range of 27°C to -33°C these vary by only 10% from the room temperature values. So we will assume these parameters to be constant. Let us now determine the constants needed for the above ordinary differential equation.

Convection coefficient of air

The convection coefficient of air, $h(\theta)$ is not a constant function of temperature and is given by

$$h=\frac{Nu\times k}{D} \tag{4}$$

where

Nu is the Nusselt number,

k is the thermal conductivity of air,

D is the characteristic diameter and in this case is taken as the outer diameter of the trunnion.

The Nusselt number for a vertical cylinder is given by the empirical formula [1]:

$$Nu=\left(0.825+\frac{0.387Ra^{\frac{1}{6}}}{\left(1+\left(\frac{0.492}{\Pr}\right)^{\frac{9}{16}}\right)^{\frac{8}{27}}}\right)^2 \tag{5}$$

where

Pr is the Prandtl number given by

$$\Pr=\frac{v_k}{\alpha} \tag{6}$$

v_k is the kinematic viscosity of the fluid,

α is the thermal diffusivity,

R_a is the Rayleigh number given by:

$$R_a=G_r\times\Pr \tag{7}$$

G_r is the Grashoff number given by:

$$Gr=\frac{g\beta(T_{wall}-T_{fluid})D^3}{v_k^2} \tag{8}$$

g is the gravitational constant,

β is the volumetric thermal expansion coefficient,

T_{wall} is the temperature of the wall,

T_{fluid} is the temperature of the fluid.

To calculate the convection coefficient, we use the following value for kinematics viscosity , ν thermal conductivity , k and thermal diffusivity , α and volumetric coefficient, β of air as a function of temperature, T [Ref. 1] .

Table 1 Properties of air as a function of temperature.

T_{lookup}	ν	k	α	β
°C	m²/s	W/(m-K)	m²/s	1/K
-173.15	2.00×10^{-6}	9.34×10^{-3}	2.54×10^{-6}	1.00×10^{-2}
-123.15	4.43×10^{-6}	1.38×10^{-2}	5.84×10^{-6}	6.67×10^{-3}
-73.15	7.59×10^{-6}	1.81×10^{-2}	1.03×10^{-5}	5.00×10^{-3}
-23.15	1.14×10^{-5}	2.23×10^{-2}	1.59×10^{-5}	4.00×10^{-3}
26.85	1.59×10^{-5}	2.63×10^{-2}	2.25×10^{-5}	3.33×10^{-3}

Other constants needed are:

$D = 0.25\,\text{m}$

$g = 9.8\,\text{m/s}^2$

$T_{fluid} = -33^\circ\text{C}$

Table 2 Convection coefficient of air as a function of temperature.

T_{wall}	$T_{average}$ [= ½(T fluid + T wall)]	h
°C	°C	W/(m².K)
-33	-16.50	5.846E-02
-18	-9.00	4.527E+00
-8	-4.00	5.214E+00
2	1.00	5.702E+00
27	13.50	6.533E+00

The values in Table 2 are interpolated from Table 1 where temperatures are chosen as the average value for the wall and ambient temperature. The above data is interpolated as:

$$h(\theta) = -3.69 \times 10^{-6}\theta^4 + 2.33 \times 10^{-5}\theta^3 + 1.35 \times 10^{-3}\theta^2 + 5.42 \times 10^{-2}\theta + 5.59 \qquad (9)$$

Area, A

  Outer radius of trunnion, $a = 0.125\,\text{m}$.
  Length, of trunnion, $L = 1.36\,\text{m}$.

gives

$$A = (2\pi a)L + 2\pi a^2 \qquad (10)$$
$$= 2\pi(.125)(1.36) + 2\pi(0.125)^2$$
$$= 1.166\ m^2$$

Mass, m

  Length of the trunnion, $L = 1.36\,\text{m}$

Density of trunnion material, $\rho = 7800$ kg/m^3

gives

$$m = \rho V \tag{11}$$
$$= \rho(\pi r^2 L)$$
$$= 7800\pi(0.125)^2 1.36$$
$$= 520.72 \text{ kg}$$

Other constants

Specific heat, $C = 420$ J/ (kg-K)

Initial temperature of the trunnion, $T(0) = 27°$ C,

Ambient temperature, $T_a = -33°$C

The first order ordinary differential equation:

$$-h(\theta)A(\theta - \theta_a) = mC\frac{d\theta}{dt}$$

is given by

$$-\left(-3.69\times10^{-6}\theta^4 + 2.33\times10^{-5}\theta^3 + 1.35\times10^{-3}\theta^2 + 5.42\times10^{-2}\theta + 5.588\right)\times$$

$$\times(1.166)\times(\theta + 33) = (520.72)\times(420)\times\frac{d\theta}{dt}$$

$$\frac{d\theta}{dt} = -5.331\times10^{-6}(-3.69\times10^{-6}\theta^4 + 2.33\times10^{-5}\theta^3 + 1.35\times10^{-3}\theta^2 + \tag{12}$$

$$+ 5.42\times10^{-2}\theta + 5.588)(\theta + 33)$$

$$\theta(0) = 27°C$$

Is the assumption of the trunnion considered as a lumped system correct?

To determine whether a system is lumped, we calculate the Biot number which defined as

$$\text{Bi} = \frac{hL}{k_s} \tag{13}$$

where

h = average surface conductance,

L = significant length dimension (volume of body/surface area),

k_s = thermal conductivity of solid body.

If $B_i < 0.1$, the temperature in the body is uniform within 5% error.

In our case:

$$h = 4.407\frac{W}{m^2.K}$$

$$L = 1.36m$$

$$k_s = 81\frac{W}{m.K} \qquad \text{[Ref. 2]}$$

$$Bi = \frac{4.407\times1.36}{81}$$

$$= 0.074 < 0.1$$

This gives us a Biot number that is less than 0.1. One can hence assume the trunnion to be a lumped mass system.

References

[1]. F. B. Incropera, D. P. Dewitt, Introduction to Heat Transfer, 3rd Ed, John Wiley & Sons, Inc., New York, NY, 2000, Chap. 9.

[2]. F. Kreith, M. S. Bohn, Principle of Heat Transfer, 4th Ed, Harper & Row, Publishers, New York, NY, 1993, Appendix 2.

ORDINARY DIFFERENTIAL EQUATION	
Topic	Ordinary Differential Equations
Summary	A physical problem of finding how much time it would take a trunnion to cool down in a refrigerated chamber. To find the time, the problem would be modeled as a ordinary differential equation.
Major	Mechanical Engineering
Authors	Autar Kaw
Date	December 23, 2009
Web Site	http://numericalmethods.eng.usf.edu

Multiple-Choice Test

Chapter 08.01
Background

1. The differential equation $2\dfrac{dy}{dx} + x^2 y = 2x + 3, \; y(0) = 5$ is

    (A) linear
    (B) nonlinear
    (C) linear with fixed constants
    (D) undeterminable to be linear or nonlinear

2. A differential equation is considered to be ordinary if it has

    (A) one dependent variable
    (B) more than one dependent variable
    (C) one independent variable
    (D) more than one independent variable

3. Given
$$2\dfrac{dy}{dx} + 3y = \sin 2x, \; y(0) = 6$$
$y(2)$ most nearly is

    (A) 0.17643
    (B) 0.29872
    (C) 0.32046
    (D) 0.58024

4. The form of the exact solution to
$$2\dfrac{dy}{dx} + 3y = e^{-x}, \; y(0) = 5$$
is

    (A) $Ae^{-1.5x} + Be^{-x}$
    (B) $Ae^{-1.5x} + Bxe^{-x}$
    (C) $Ae^{1.5x} + Be^{-x}$
    (D) $Ae^{1.5x} + Bxe^{-x}$

5. The following nonlinear differential equation can be solved exactly by separation of variables.

$$\frac{d\theta}{dt} = -10^{-6}\left(\theta^2 - 81\right),\ \theta(0) = 1000$$

The value of $\theta(100)$ most nearly is

(A) -99.99
(B) 909.10
(C) 1000.32
(D) 1111.10

6. A solid spherical ball taken out of a furnace at 1200 K is allowed to cool in air. Given the following,

   radius of the ball $= 2$ cm
   density of the ball $= 7800$ kg/m^3
   specific heat of the ball $= 420$ J/kg$\cdot$K
   emmittance $= 0.85$
   Stefan-Boltzman constant $= 5.67 \times 10^{-8}$ J/s$\cdot$m$^2\cdot$K^4
   ambient temperature $= 300$ K
   convection coefficient to air $= 350$ J/s$\cdot$m$^2\cdot$K

the differential equation governing the temperature θ of the ball as a function of time t is given by

(A) $\dfrac{d\theta}{dt} = -2.2067 \times 10^{-12}\left(\theta^4 - 81 \times 10^8\right)$

(B) $\dfrac{d\theta}{dt} = -1.6026 \times 10^{-2}\left(\theta - 300\right)$

(C) $\dfrac{d\theta}{dt} = 2.2067 \times 10^{-12}\left(\theta^4 - 81 \times 10^8\right) + 1.6026 \times 10^{-12}\left(\theta - 300\right)$

(D) $\dfrac{d\theta}{dt} = -2.2067 \times 10^{-12}\left(\theta^4 - 81 \times 10^8\right) - 1.6026 \times 10^{-2}\left(\theta - 300\right)$

Complete Solution

Problem Set

Chapter 08.01
Background of Ordinary Differential Equations

1. Solve the ordinary differential equation exactly

    $$2\frac{dy}{dx} + 0.4\,y = 3e^{-x}, y(0) = 5.$$

2. For the ordinary differential equation

    $$2\frac{dy}{dx} + 3\,y = e^{-1.5x}, y(0) = 5,$$

    solve exactly to find
    a) $y(0)$,

    b) $\frac{dy}{dx}(0)$,

    c) $y(2.5)$,

    d) $\frac{dy}{dx}(2.5)$.

3. Solve the ordinary differential equation exactly

    $$2\frac{d^2 y}{dx^2} + 10\frac{dy}{dx} + 12y = 6e^x, \ y(0) = 7, \ \frac{dy}{dx}(0) = 11$$

4. Solve the ordinary differential equations exactly

    $$2\frac{d^2 y}{dx^2} + 8\frac{dy}{dx} + 8y = 3\sin(2x), \ y(0) = 7, \ \frac{dy}{dx}(0) = 11$$

5. Solve the ordinary differential equations exactly

    $$2\frac{d^2 y}{dx^2} + 8\frac{dy}{dx} + 26y = x^2, \ y(0) = 7, \ \frac{dy}{dx}(0) = 11$$

6.   A spherical ball is taken out of a furnace at 2500 K. It loses heat due to radiation and
        convection. Given the following,

        Radius of ball, $r = 1.0\,\text{cm}$

        Density of ball, $\rho = 3000\,\text{kg/m}^3$

        Specific heat, $C = 1000\,\text{J}/(\text{kg}\cdot\text{K})$

        Emittance, $\epsilon = 0.5$

        Stefan-Boltzmann Constant, $\sigma = 5.67\times10^{-8}\,\text{J}/(\text{s}\cdot\text{m}^2\cdot\text{K}^4)$

        Initial temperature of the ball, $\theta(0) = 2500\,\text{K}$

        Ambient temperature, $\theta_a = 300\,\text{K}$

        Convective cooling coefficient, $h = 500\,\text{J}/(\text{s}\cdot\text{m}^2\cdot\text{K})$

        the ordinary differential equation that governs the temperature of the ball, θ as a
        function of time, t is given by

        $$\frac{d\theta}{dt} = -2.8349\times10^{-12}(\theta^4 - 81\times10^8) - 0.05\,(\theta - 300).$$

        Hint: The above formula was calculated by using the knowledge that

        Rate of heat lost due to radiation $= A\,\epsilon\,\sigma(\theta^4 - \theta_a^4)$

        Rate of heat lost due to convection $= hA(\theta - \theta_a)$

        Heat stored $= mc\theta$

        a) Note that the above ODE is nonlinear. Is there an exact solution to the
            problem? If so, find it by hand or by using a mathematical package.
        b) The exact solution in part (a) is not explicit. To solve for temperature at a
            particular time, one needs to solve a nonlinear equation. Find the
            temperature at $t = 10$ seconds.
        c) What are following at $t = 0\text{s}$?
             i. temperature,
             ii. rate of change of temperature,
             iii. rate of heat loss due to radiation,
             iv. rate of heat loss due to convection,
             v. rate of heat stored.
        d) Can either convection or radiation be neglected if we are interested in
            finding the temperature profile between 0 and 10 s?

Chapter 08.02
Euler's Method for Ordinary Differential Equations

After reading this chapter, you should be able to:

1. *develop Euler's Method for solving ordinary differential equations,*
2. *determine how the step size affects the accuracy of a solution,*
3. *derive Euler's formula from Taylor series, and*
4. *use Euler's method to find approximate values of integrals.*

What is Euler's method?

Euler's method is a numerical technique to solve ordinary differential equations of the form

$$\frac{dy}{dx} = f(x,y), y(0) = y_0 \tag{1}$$

So only first order ordinary differential equations can be solved by using Euler's method. In another chapter we will discuss how Euler's method is used to solve higher order ordinary differential equations or coupled (simultaneous) differential equations. How does one write a first order differential equation in the above form?

Example 1

Rewrite

$$\frac{dy}{dx} + 2y = 1.3e^{-x}, y(0) = 5$$

in

$$\frac{dy}{dx} = f(x,y), \ y(0) = y_0 \ \text{form.}$$

Solution

$$\frac{dy}{dx} + 2y = 1.3e^{-x}, y(0) = 5$$

$$\frac{dy}{dx} = 1.3e^{-x} - 2y, y(0) = 5$$

In this case

08.03.1

$$f(x,y)=1.3e^{-x}-2y$$

Example 2

Rewrite

$$e^y \frac{dy}{dx} + x^2 y^2 = 2\sin(3x), \ y(0)=5$$

in

$$\frac{dy}{dx} = f(x,y), \ y(0) = y_0 \text{ form.}$$

Solution

$$e^y \frac{dy}{dx} + x^2 y^2 = 2\sin(3x), \ y(0)=5$$

$$\frac{dy}{dx} = \frac{2\sin(3x) - x^2 y^2}{e^y}, \ y(0)=5$$

In this case

$$f(x,y) = \frac{2\sin(3x) - x^2 y^2}{e^y}$$

Derivation of Euler's method

At $x=0$, we are given the value of $y=y_0$. Let us call $x=0$ as x_0. Now since we know the slope of y with respect to x, that is, $f(x,y)$, then at $x=x_0$, the slope is $f(x_0,y_0)$. Both x_0 and y_0 are known from the initial condition $y(x_0)=y_0$.

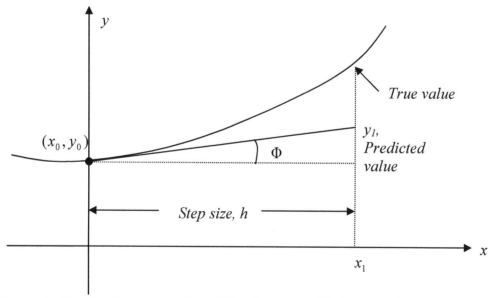

Figure 1 Graphical interpretation of the first step of Euler's method.

So the slope at $x = x_0$ as shown in Figure 1 is

$$\text{Slope} = \frac{Rise}{Run}$$

$$= \frac{y_1 - y_0}{x_1 - x_0}$$

$$= f(x_0, y_0)$$

From here

$$y_1 = y_0 + f(x_0, y_0)(x_1 - x_0)$$

Calling $x_1 - x_0$ the step size h, we get

$$y_1 = y_0 + f(x_0, y_0)h \qquad (2)$$

One can now use the value of y_1 (an approximate value of y at $x = x_1$) to calculate y_2, and that would be the predicted value at x_2, given by

$$y_2 = y_1 + f(x_1, y_1)h$$

$$x_2 = x_1 + h$$

Based on the above equations, if we now know the value of $y = y_i$ at x_i, then

$$y_{i+1} = y_i + f(x_i, y_i)h \qquad (3)$$

This formula is known as Euler's method and is illustrated graphically in Figure 2. In some books, it is also called the Euler-Cauchy method.

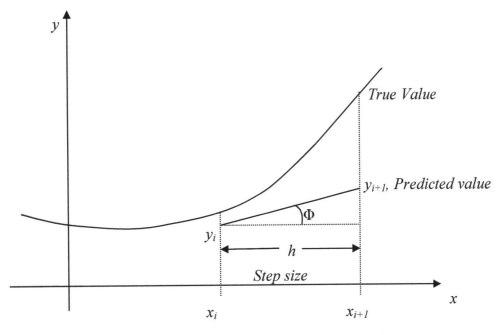

Figure 2 General graphical interpretation of Euler's method.

Example 3

A ball at 1200K is allowed to cool down in air at an ambient temperature of 300K. Assuming heat is lost only due to radiation, the differential equation for the temperature of the ball is given by

$$\frac{d\theta}{dt} = -2.2067 \times 10^{-12}\left(\theta^4 - 81 \times 10^8\right), \ \theta(0) = 1200\text{K}$$

where θ is in K and t in seconds. Find the temperature at $t = 480$ seconds using Euler's method. Assume a step size of $h = 240$ seconds.

Solution

$$\frac{d\theta}{dt} = -2.2067 \times 10^{-12}\left(\theta^4 - 81 \times 10^8\right)$$

$$f(t,\theta) = -2.2067 \times 10^{-12}\left(\theta^4 - 81 \times 10^8\right)$$

Per Equation (3), Euler's method reduces to

$$\theta_{i+1} = \theta_i + f(t_i,\theta_i)h$$

For $i = 0$, $t_0 = 0$, $\theta_0 = 1200$

$$\begin{aligned}
\theta_1 &= \theta_0 + f(t_0,\theta_0)h \\
&= 1200 + f(0,1200) \times 240 \\
&= 1200 + \left(-2.2067 \times 10^{-12}\left(1200^4 - 81 \times 10^8\right)\right) \times 240 \\
&= 1200 + (-4.5579) \times 240 \\
&= 106.09\,\text{K}
\end{aligned}$$

θ_1 is the approximate temperature at

$$t = t_1 = t_0 + h = 0 + 240 = 240$$

$$\theta_1 = \theta(240) \approx 106.09\,\text{K}$$

For $i = 1$, $t_1 = 240$, $\theta_1 = 106.09$

$$\begin{aligned}
\theta_2 &= \theta_1 + f(t_1,\theta_1)h \\
&= 106.09 + f(240,106.09) \times 240 \\
&= 106.09 + \left(-2.2067 \times 10^{-12}\left(106.09^4 - 81 \times 10^8\right)\right) \times 240 \\
&= 106.09 + (0.017595) \times 240 \\
&= 110.32\,\text{K}
\end{aligned}$$

θ_2 is the approximate temperature at

$$t = t_2 = t_1 + h = 240 + 240 = 480$$

$$\theta_2 = \theta(480) \approx 110.32\,\text{K}$$

Figure 3 compares the exact solution with the numerical solution from Euler's method for the step size of $h = 240$.

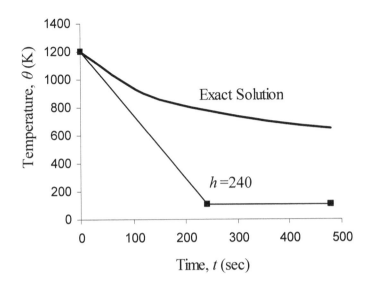

Figure 3 Comparing the exact solution and Euler's method.

The problem was solved again using a smaller step size. The results are given below in Table 1.

Table 1 Temperature at 480 seconds as a function of step size, h.

Step size, h	$\theta(480)$	E_t	$\lvert \in_t \rvert \%$
480	-987.81	1635.4	252.54
240	110.32	537.26	82.964
120	546.77	100.80	15.566
60	614.97	32.607	5.0352
30	632.77	14.806	2.2864

Figure 4 shows how the temperature varies as a function of time for different step sizes.

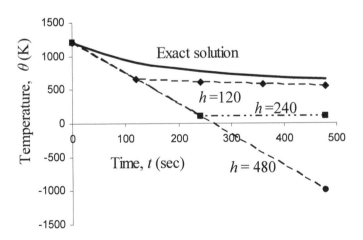

Figure 4 Comparison of Euler's method with the exact solution for different step sizes.

The values of the calculated temperature at $t = 480\,\text{s}$ as a function of step size are plotted in Figure 5.

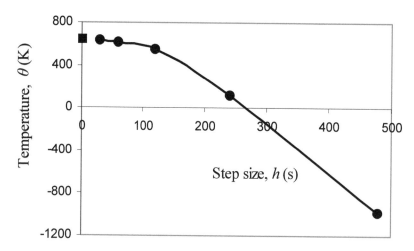

Figure 5 Effect of step size in Euler's method.

The exact solution of the ordinary differential equation is given by the solution of a non-linear equation as

$$0.92593\ln\frac{\theta-300}{\theta+300}-1.8519\tan^{-1}\!\left(0.333\times10^{-2}\,\theta\right)=-0.22067\times10^{-3}t-2.9282 \qquad (4)$$

The solution to this nonlinear equation is

$$\theta = 647.57\,\text{K}$$

It can be seen that Euler's method has large errors. This can be illustrated using the Taylor series.

$$y_{i+1}=y_i+\left.\frac{dy}{dx}\right|_{x_i,y_i}\!\!(x_{i+1}-x_i)+\frac{1}{2!}\left.\frac{d^2y}{dx^2}\right|_{x_i,y_i}\!\!(x_{i+1}-x_i)^2+\frac{1}{3!}\left.\frac{d^3y}{dx^3}\right|_{x_i,y_i}\!\!(x_{i+1}-x_i)^3+\ldots \qquad (5)$$

$$=y_i+f(x_i,y_i)(x_{i+1}-x_i)+\frac{1}{2!}f'(x_i,y_i)(x_{i+1}-x_i)^2+\frac{1}{3!}f''(x_i,y_i)(x_{i+1}-x_i)^3+\ldots \qquad (6)$$

As you can see the first two terms of the Taylor series

$$y_{i+1}=y_i+f(x_i,y_i)h$$

are Euler's method.

The true error in the approximation is given by

$$E_t=\frac{f'(x_i,y_i)}{2!}h^2+\frac{f''(x_i,y_i)}{3!}h^3+\ldots \qquad (7)$$

The true error hence is approximately proportional to the square of the step size, that is, as the step size is halved, the true error gets approximately quartered. However from Table 1, we see that as the step size gets halved, the true error only gets approximately halved. This is because the true error, being proportioned to the square of the step size, is the local truncation error, that is, error from one point to the next. The global truncation error is however proportional only to the step size as the error keeps propagating from one point to another.

Can one solve a definite integral using numerical methods such as Euler's method of solving ordinary differential equations?

Let us suppose you want to find the integral of a function $f(x)$

$$I = \int_a^b f(x)dx.$$

Both fundamental theorems of calculus would be used to set up the problem so as to solve it as an ordinary differential equation.

The first fundamental theorem of calculus states that if f is a continuous function in the interval [a,b], and F is the antiderivative of f, then

$$\int_a^b f(x)dx = F(b) - F(a)$$

The second fundamental theorem of calculus states that if f is a continuous function in the open interval D, and a is a point in the interval D, and if

$$F(x) = \int_a^x f(t)dt$$

then

$$F'(x) = f(x)$$

at each point in D.

Asked to find $\int_a^b f(x)dx$, we can rewrite the integral as the solution of an ordinary differential equation (here is where we are using the second fundamental theorem of calculus)

$$\frac{dy}{dx} = f(x), \ y(a) = 0,$$

where then $y(b)$ (here is where we are using the first fundamental theorem of calculus) will give the value of the integral $\int_a^b f(x)dx$.

Example 4

Find an approximate value of

$$\int_5^8 6x^3 dx$$

using Euler's method of solving an ordinary differential equation. Use a step size of $h = 1.5$.

Solution

Given $\int_5^8 6x^3 dx$, we can rewrite the integral as the solution of an ordinary differential equation

$$\frac{dy}{dx} = 6x^3, \; y(5) = 0$$

where $y(8)$ will give the value of the integral $\int\limits_5^8 6x^3 dx$.

$$\frac{dy}{dx} = 6x^3 = f(x, y), \; y(5) = 0$$

The Euler's method equation is

$$y_{i+1} = y_i + f(x_i, y_i)h$$

<u>Step 1</u>

$$i = 0, \; x_0 = 5, \; y_0 = 0$$
$$h = 1.5$$
$$\begin{aligned} x_1 &= x_0 + h \\ &= 5 + 1.5 \\ &= 6.5 \end{aligned}$$
$$\begin{aligned} y_1 &= y_0 + f(x_0, y_0)h \\ &= 0 + f(5,0) \times 1.5 \\ &= 0 + (6 \times 5^3) \times 1.5 \\ &= 1125 \\ &\approx y(6.5) \end{aligned}$$

<u>Step 2</u>

$$i = 1, \; x_1 = 6.5, \; y_1 = 1125$$
$$\begin{aligned} x_2 &= x_1 + h \\ &= 6.5 + 1.5 \\ &= 8 \end{aligned}$$
$$\begin{aligned} y_2 &= y_1 + f(x_1, y_1)h \\ &= 1125 + f(6.5, 1125) \times 1.5 \\ &= 1125 + (6 \times 6.5^3) \times 1.5 \\ &= 3596.625 \\ &\approx y(8) \end{aligned}$$

Hence

$$\begin{aligned} \int\limits_5^8 6x^3 dx &= y(8) - y(5) \\ &\approx 3596.625 - 0 \\ &= 3596.625 \end{aligned}$$

ORDINARY DIFFERENTIAL EQUATIONS	
Topic	Euler's Method for ordinary differential equations
Summary	Textbook notes on Euler's method for solving ordinary differential equations
Major	General Engineering
Authors	Autar Kaw
Last Revised	December 23, 2009
Web Site	http://numericalmethods.eng.usf.edu

Multiple-Choice Test

Chapter 08.02
Euler's Method

1. To solve the ordinary differential equation

    $$3\frac{dy}{dx} + 5y^2 = \sin x, \, y(0) = 5$$

    by Euler's method, you need to rewrite the equation as

    (A) $\frac{dy}{dx} = \sin x - 5y^2, \, y(0) = 5$

    (B) $\frac{dy}{dx} = \frac{1}{3}(\sin x - 5y^2), \, y(0) = 5$

    (C) $\frac{dy}{dx} = \frac{1}{3}\left(-\cos x - \frac{5y^3}{3}\right), \, y(0) = 5$

    (D) $\frac{dy}{dx} = \frac{1}{3}\sin x, \, y(0) = 5$

2. Given

    $$3\frac{dy}{dx} + 5y^2 = \sin x, \, y(0.3) = 5$$

    and using a step size of $h = 0.3$, the value of $y(0.9)$ using Euler's method is most nearly

    (A) -35.318
    (B) -36.458
    (C) -658.91
    (D) -669.05

3. Given

    $$3\frac{dy}{dx} + \sqrt{y} = e^{0.1x}, \, y(0.3) = 5$$

    and using a step size of $h = 0.3$, the best estimate of $\frac{dy}{dx}(0.9)$ using Euler's method is most nearly

    (A) -0.37319
    (B) -0.36288
    (C) -0.35381
    (D) -0.34341

08.02.1

4.   The velocity (m/s) of a body is given as a function of time (seconds) by
$$v(t) = 200\ln(1+t) - t,\ t \geq 0$$
Using Euler's method with a step size of 5 seconds, the distance in meters traveled by the body from $t = 2$ to $t = 12$ seconds is most nearly
(A) 3133.1
(B) 3939.7
(C) 5638.0
(D) 39397

5.   Euler's method can be derived by using the first two terms of the Taylor series of writing the value of y_{i+1}, that is the value of y at x_{i+1}, in terms of y_i and all the derivatives of y at x_i. If $h = x_{i+1} - x_i$, the explicit expression for y_{i+1} if the first three terms of the Taylor series are chosen for the ordinary differential equation
$$2\frac{dy}{dx} + 3y = e^{-5x}, y(0) = 7$$
would be

(A) $y_{i+1} = y_i + \frac{1}{2}\left(e^{-5x_i} - 3y_i\right)h$

(B) $y_{i+1} = y_i + \frac{1}{2}\left(e^{-5x_i} - 3y_i\right)h - \frac{1}{2}\left(\frac{5}{2}e^{-5x_i}\right)h^2$

(C) $y_{i+1} = y_i + \frac{1}{2}\left(e^{-5x_i} - 3y_i\right)h + \frac{1}{2}\left(-\frac{13}{4}e^{-5x_i} + \frac{9}{4}y_i\right)h^2$

(D) $y_{i+1} = y_i + \frac{1}{2}\left(e^{-5x_i} - 3y_i\right)h - \frac{3}{2}y_i h^2$

6.   A homicide victim is found at 6:00 PM in an office building that is maintained at $72\ ^\circ F$. When the victim was found, his body temperature was at $85\ ^\circ F$. Three hours later at 9:00 PM, his body temperature was recorded at $78\ ^\circ F$. Assume the temperature of the body at the time of death is the normal human body temperature of $98.6\ ^\circ F$.
The governing equation for the temperature θ of the body is
$$\frac{d\theta}{dt} = -k(\theta - \theta_a)$$
where,
     $\theta =$ temperature of the body, $^\circ F$
     $\theta_a =$ ambient temperature, $^\circ F$
     $t =$ time, hours
     $k =$ constant based on thermal properties of the body and air.
The estimated time of death most nearly is
(A) 2:11 PM
(B) 3:13 PM
(C) 4:34 PM

(D)   5:12 PM

Complete Solution

Problem Set

Chapter 08.02
Euler's Method for Ordinary Differential Equations

1. For the ordinary differential equation

$$2\frac{dy}{dx} + 3xy = e^{-1.5x}, \quad y(0) = 5,$$

use a step size of $h = 2$ and Euler's method to find $y(6)$.

2. For the ordinary differential equation

$$2\frac{dy}{dx} + 3y = e^{-1.5x}, \quad y(0) = 5$$

   a) use Euler's method to find $y(2.5)$ using $h = 1.25$,

   b) use Euler's method to find $\frac{dy}{dx}(2.5)$ using $h = 1.25$,

   c) true value of $y(2.5)$,

   d) absolute relative true error for part (a),

   e) true value of $\frac{dy}{dx}(2.5)$,

   f) absolute relative true error for part (b).

3. Find the approximate value of the integral $\int_{3}^{8} 2e^{0.6x} dx$ using Euler's method.

   a) Use $h = 2.5$ and compare the value with the exact value.

   b) Use $h = 1.25$ and compare the value with the exact value.

4. From problem (3a), is the value obtained using Euler's method the same as 2-segment LRAM (Left Endpoint Rectangular Approximation), or 2-segment MRAM (Midpoint Rectangular Approximation), or 2-segment RRAM (Right Endpoint Rectangular Approximation) method of integration? Explain.

5.   A water tank with a hole at the top and a circular hole at the bottom is shown in the figure.

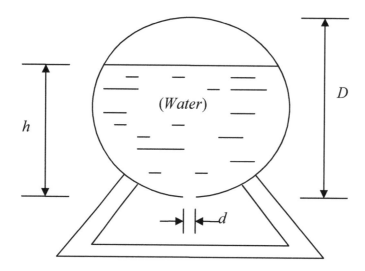

Given

         Diameter of tank, $D = 6\,\text{m}$
         Initial height of water, $h = 5\,\text{m}$
         Diameter of hole, $d = 4.95\,\text{cm}$

The flow rate $\dot{Q}$ of water through the bottom hole is given by

$$\dot{Q} = -Av,$$

where

         A = cross-sectional area of the hole,
         v = velocity of the water flowing through the hole.

Since

$$v = \sqrt{2gh}$$

where

         h = height of water from the bottom of the tank,
         g = acceleration due to gravity.

From this, we get

$$\dot{Q} = -A\sqrt{2gh}$$

Also, since the volume V of the water at height h is given by

$$V = \frac{1}{3}\pi h^2 \left(\frac{3D}{2} - h \right)$$

where

$$\frac{dV}{dt} = \left(\pi h D - \pi h^2 \right)\frac{dh}{dt}$$

Since

$$\dot{Q} = \frac{dV}{dt}$$

$$\left(\pi hD - \pi h^2\right)\frac{dh}{dt} = -A\sqrt{2gh}$$

$$\left(\pi hD - \pi h^2\right)\frac{dh}{dt} = -\frac{\pi d^2}{4}\sqrt{2gh}$$

$$\frac{dh}{dt} = -\frac{d^2\sqrt{2gh}}{4\left(hD - h^2\right)}$$

a) Use Euler's method with a step size of 10 minutes to find the height of water at $t = 50$ minutes.
b) Based on the results from part (a), estimate the time when the height of the water is 2 m.
c) Compare the results of part(a) and part (b) with the exact values.

6. A spherical ball is taken out of a furnace at 2500 K. It loses heat due to radiation and convection. Given the following,

Radius of ball, $r = 1.0\,\text{cm}$
Density of the ball, $\rho = 3000\,\text{kg/m}^3$
Specific heat, $C = 1000\,\text{J/(kg}\cdot\text{K)}$
Emittance, $\epsilon = 0.5$
Stefan-Boltzmann Constant, $\sigma = 5.67\times10^{-8}\,\text{J/(s}\cdot\text{m}^2\cdot\text{K}^4)$
Convective cooling coefficient, $h = 500\,\text{J/(s}\cdot\text{m}^2\cdot\text{K)}$
Initial temperature of the ball, $\theta(0) = 2500\,\text{K}$,
Ambient temperature, $\theta_a = 300\,\text{K}$,

the ordinary differential equation that governs the temperature of the ball is given by

$$\frac{d\theta}{dt} = -2.8349\times10^{-12}\,(\theta^4 - 81\times10^8) - 0.05\,(\theta - 300).$$

Hint: The above formula was calculated by using the knowledge that
Rate of heat lost due to radiation $= A\,\epsilon\,\sigma(\theta^4 - \theta_a^4)$
Rate of heat lost due to convection $= hA(\theta - \theta_a)$
Heat stored $= mc\theta$

where
$A =$ surface area of the ball,
$m =$ mass of the ball.

a) What are following at $t = 0\,\text{s}$?
   i. temperature,
   ii. rate of change of temperature,
   iii. rate of heat loss due to radiation,
   iv. rate of heat loss due to convection,
   v. rate of heat stored.
b) Find the following at $t = 10\,\text{s}$ using Euler's method and a step size of $h = 2.5$.
   i. temperature,

      ii. rate of change of temperature,
     iii. rate of heat loss due to radiation,
     iv. rate of heat loss due to convection,
      v. rate of heat stored.

c) Can either convection or radiation be neglected if we are interested in finding the temperature profile between 0 and 10 s? Base your answer on quantitative reasoning.

d) Find the time when the temperature will be 2000 K using Euler's method with a step size of $h = 2.5$.

Chapter 08.03
Runge-Kutta 2nd Order Method for Ordinary Differential Equations

After reading this chapter, you should be able to:

1. *understand the Runge-Kutta 2nd order method for ordinary differential equations and how to use it to solve problems.*

What is the Runge-Kutta 2nd order method?

The Runge-Kutta 2nd order method is a numerical technique used to solve an ordinary differential equation of the form

$$\frac{dy}{dx} = f(x, y), y(0) = y_0$$

Only first order ordinary differential equations can be solved by using the Runge-Kutta 2nd order method. In other sections, we will discuss how the Euler and Runge-Kutta methods are used to solve higher order ordinary differential equations or coupled (simultaneous) differential equations.

How does one write a first order differential equation in the above form?

Example 1

Rewrite

$$\frac{dy}{dx} + 2y = 1.3e^{-x}, y(0) = 5$$

in

$$\frac{dy}{dx} = f(x, y), \ y(0) = y_0 \ \text{form.}$$

Solution

$$\frac{dy}{dx} + 2y = 1.3e^{-x}, y(0) = 5$$

$$\frac{dy}{dx} = 1.3e^{-x} - 2y, y(0) = 5$$

In this case

08.04.1

$$f(x, y) = 1.3e^{-x} - 2y$$

Example 2

Rewrite

$$e^y \frac{dy}{dx} + x^2 y^2 = 2\sin(3x), \ y(0) = 5$$

in

$$\frac{dy}{dx} = f(x, y), \ y(0) = y_0 \ \text{form.}$$

Solution

$$e^y \frac{dy}{dx} + x^2 y^2 = 2\sin(3x), \ y(0) = 5$$

$$\frac{dy}{dx} = \frac{2\sin(3x) - x^2 y^2}{e^y}, \ y(0) = 5$$

In this case

$$f(x, y) = \frac{2\sin(3x) - x^2 y^2}{e^y}$$

Runge-Kutta 2nd order method

Euler's method is given by

$$y_{i+1} = y_i + f(x_i, y_i)h \tag{1}$$

where

$$x_0 = 0$$

$$y_0 = y(x_0)$$

$$h = x_{i+1} - x_i$$

To understand the Runge-Kutta 2nd order method, we need to derive Euler's method from the Taylor series.

$$y_{i+1} = y_i + \frac{dy}{dx}\bigg|_{x_i, y_i} (x_{i+1} - x_i) + \frac{1}{2!} \frac{d^2 y}{dx^2}\bigg|_{x_i, y_i} (x_{i+1} - x_i)^2 + \frac{1}{3!} \frac{d^3 y}{dx^3}\bigg|_{x_i, y_i} (x_{i+1} - x_i)^3 + \ldots$$

$$= y_i + f(x_i, y_i)(x_{i+1} - x_i) + \frac{1}{2!} f'(x_i, y_i)(x_{i+1} - x_i)^2 + \frac{1}{3!} f''(x_i, y_i)(x_{i+1} - x_i)^3 + \ldots \tag{2}$$

As you can see the first two terms of the Taylor series

$$y_{i+1} = y_i + f(x_i, y_i)h$$

are Euler's method and hence can be considered to be the Runge-Kutta 1st order method. The true error in the approximation is given by

$$E_t = \frac{f'(x_i, y_i)}{2!} h^2 + \frac{f''(x_i, y_i)}{3!} h^3 + \ldots \tag{3}$$

So what would a 2nd order method formula look like. It would include one more term of the Taylor series as follows.

$$y_{i+1} = y_i + f(x_i, y_i)h + \frac{1}{2!}f'(x_i, y_i)h^2 \tag{4}$$

Let us take a generic example of a first order ordinary differential equation

$$\frac{dy}{dx} = e^{-2x} - 3y, y(0) = 5$$

$$f(x, y) = e^{-2x} - 3y$$

Now since y is a function of x,

$$f'(x, y) = \frac{\partial f(x, y)}{\partial x} + \frac{\partial f(x, y)}{\partial y}\frac{dy}{dx} \tag{5}$$

$$= \frac{\partial}{\partial x}(e^{-2x} - 3y) + \frac{\partial}{\partial y}[(e^{-2x} - 3y)](e^{-2x} - 3y)$$

$$= -2e^{-2x} + (-3)(e^{-2x} - 3y)$$

$$= -5e^{-2x} + 9y$$

The 2nd order formula for the above example would be

$$y_{i+1} = y_i + f(x_i, y_i)h + \frac{1}{2!}f'(x_i, y_i)h^2$$

$$= y_i + (e^{-2x_i} - 3y_i)h + \frac{1}{2!}(-5e^{-2x_i} + 9y_i)h^2$$

However, we already see the difficulty of having to find $f'(x, y)$ in the above method. What Runge and Kutta did was write the 2nd order method as

$$y_{i+1} = y_i + (a_1k_1 + a_2k_2)h \tag{6}$$

where

$$k_1 = f(x_i, y_i)$$

$$k_2 = f(x_i + p_1h, y_i + q_{11}k_1h) \tag{7}$$

This form allows one to take advantage of the 2nd order method without having to calculate $f'(x, y)$.

So how do we find the unknowns a_1, a_2, p_1 and q_{11}. Without proof (see Appendix for proof), equating Equation (4) and (6), gives three equations.

$$a_1 + a_2 = 1$$

$$a_2 p_1 = \frac{1}{2}$$

$$a_2 q_{11} = \frac{1}{2}$$

Since we have 3 equations and 4 unknowns, we can assume the value of one of the unknowns. The other three will then be determined from the three equations. Generally the value of a_2 is chosen to evaluate the other three constants. The three values generally used for a_2 are $\frac{1}{2}$, 1 and $\frac{2}{3}$, and are known as Heun's Method, the midpoint method and Ralston's method, respectively.

Heun's Method

Here $a_2 = \dfrac{1}{2}$ is chosen, giving

$$a_1 = \frac{1}{2}$$
$$p_1 = 1$$
$$q_{11} = 1$$

resulting in

$$y_{i+1} = y_i + \left(\frac{1}{2}k_1 + \frac{1}{2}k_2\right)h \tag{8}$$

where

$$k_1 = f(x_i, y_i) \tag{9a}$$
$$k_2 = f(x_i + h, y_i + k_1 h) \tag{9b}$$

This method is graphically explained in Figure 1.

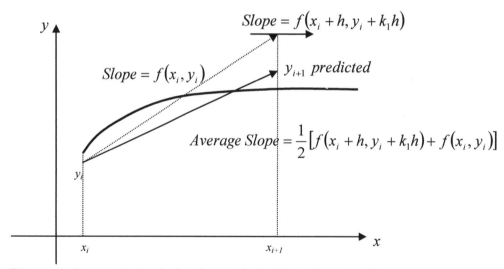

Figure 1 Runge-Kutta 2nd order method (Heun's method).

Midpoint Method

Here $a_2 = 1$ is chosen, giving

$$a_1 = 0$$
$$p_1 = \frac{1}{2}$$
$$q_{11} = \frac{1}{2}$$

resulting in

$$y_{i+1} = y_i + k_2 h \tag{10}$$

where

$$k_1 = f(x_i, y_i) \tag{11a}$$

$$k_2 = f\left(x_i + \frac{1}{2}h, y_i + \frac{1}{2}k_1 h\right) \tag{11b}$$

<u>Ralston's Method</u>

Here $a_2 = \dfrac{2}{3}$ is chosen, giving

$$a_1 = \frac{1}{3}$$

$$p_1 = \frac{3}{4}$$

$$q_{11} = \frac{3}{4}$$

resulting in

$$y_{i+1} = y_i + \left(\frac{1}{3}k_1 + \frac{2}{3}k_2\right)h \tag{12}$$

where

$$k_1 = f(x_i, y_i) \tag{13a}$$

$$k_2 = f\left(x_i + \frac{3}{4}h, y_i + \frac{3}{4}k_1 h\right) \tag{13b}$$

Example 3

A ball at $1200\,\mathrm{K}$ is allowed to cool down in air at an ambient temperature of $300\,\mathrm{K}$. Assuming heat is lost only due to radiation, the differential equation for the temperature of the ball is given by

$$\frac{d\theta}{dt} = -2.2067 \times 10^{-12}\left(\theta^4 - 81 \times 10^8\right)$$

where θ is in K and t in seconds. Find the temperature at $t = 480$ seconds using Runge-Kutta 2nd order method. Assume a step size of $h = 240$ seconds.

Solution

$$\frac{d\theta}{dt} = -2.2067 \times 10^{-12}\left(\theta^4 - 81 \times 10^8\right)$$

$$f(t, \theta) = -2.2067 \times 10^{-12}\left(\theta^4 - 81 \times 10^8\right)$$

Per Heun's method given by Equations (8) and (9)

$$\theta_{i+1} = \theta_i + \left(\frac{1}{2}k_1 + \frac{1}{2}k_2\right)h$$

$$k_1 = f(t_i, \theta_i)$$

$$k_2 = f(t_i + h, \theta_i + k_1 h)$$

$$i = 0, t_0 = 0, \theta_0 = \theta(0) = 1200$$

$$k_1 = f(t_0, \theta_o)$$

$$= f(0,1200)$$

$$= -2.2067 \times 10^{-12} \left(1200^4 - 81 \times 10^8\right)$$

$$= -4.5579$$

$$k_2 = f\left(t_0 + h, \theta_0 + k_1 h\right)$$

$$= f\left(0 + 240, 1200 + (-4.5579)240\right)$$

$$= f(240, 106.09)$$

$$= -2.2067 \times 10^{-12} \left(106.09^4 - 81 \times 10^8\right)$$

$$= 0.017595$$

$$\theta_1 = \theta_0 + \left(\frac{1}{2} k_1 + \frac{1}{2} k_2\right) h$$

$$= 1200 + \left(\frac{1}{2}(-4.5579) + \frac{1}{2}(0.017595)\right)240$$

$$= 1200 + (-2.2702)240$$

$$= 655.16 \, \text{K}$$

$$i = 1, t_1 = t_0 + h = 0 + 240 = 240, \theta_1 = 655.16 \text{K}$$

$$k_1 = f(t_1, \theta_1)$$

$$= f(240, 655.16)$$

$$= -2.2067 \times 10^{-12} \left(655.16^4 - 81 \times 10^8\right)$$

$$= -0.38869$$

$$k_2 = f\left(t_1 + h, \theta_1 + k_1 h\right)$$

$$= f\left(240 + 240, 655.16 + (-0.38869)240\right)$$

$$= f(480, 561.87)$$

$$= -2.2067 \times 10^{-12} \left(561.87^4 - 81 \times 10^8\right)$$

$$= -0.20206$$

$$\theta_2 = \theta_1 + \left(\frac{1}{2} k_1 + \frac{1}{2} k_2\right) h$$

$$= 655.16 + \left(\frac{1}{2}(-0.38869) + \frac{1}{2}(-0.20206)\right)240$$

$$= 655.16 + (-0.29538)240$$

$$= 584.27 \, \text{K}$$

$$\theta_2 = \theta(480) = 584.27 \, \text{K}$$

The results from Heun's method are compared with exact results in Figure 2.

The exact solution of the ordinary differential equation is given by the solution of a non-linear equation as

$$0.92593 \ln \frac{\theta - 300}{\theta + 300} - 1.8519 \tan^{-1}(0.0033333\theta) = -0.22067 \times 10^{-3} t - 2.9282$$

The solution to this nonlinear equation at $t = 480 \, \text{s}$ is

$$\theta(480) = 647.57 \, \text{K}$$

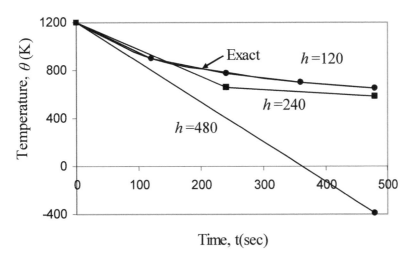

Figure 2 Heun's method results for different step sizes.

Using a smaller step size would increase the accuracy of the result as given in Table 1 and Figure 3 below.

Table 1 Effect of step size for Heun's method

Step size, h	$\theta(480)$	E_t	$|\in_t|\%$
480	-393.87	1041.4	160.82
240	584.27	63.304	9.7756
120	651.35	-3.7762	0.58313
60	649.91	-2.3406	0.36145
30	648.21	-0.63219	0.097625

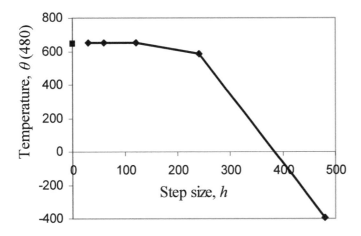

Figure 3 Effect of step size in Heun's method.

In Table 2, Euler's method and the Runge-Kutta 2nd order method results are shown as a function of step size,

Table 2 Comparison of Euler and the Runge-Kutta methods

Step size,	$\theta(480)$			
h	Euler	Heun	Midpoint	Ralston
480	-987.84	-393.87	1208.4	449.78
240	110.32	584.27	976.87	690.01
120	546.77	651.35	690.20	667.71
60	614.97	649.91	654.85	652.25
30	632.77	648.21	649.02	648.61

while in Figure 4, the comparison is shown over the range of time.

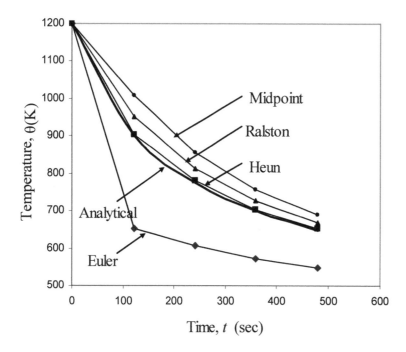

Figure 4 Comparison of Euler and Runge Kutta methods with exact results over time.

How do these three methods compare with results obtained if we found $f'(x, y)$ directly?

Of course, we know that since we are including the first three terms in the series, if the solution is a polynomial of order two or less (that is, quadratic, linear or constant), any of the three methods are exact. But for any other case the results will be different.

Let us take the example of

$$\frac{dy}{dx} = e^{-2x} - 3y, y(0) = 5.$$

If we directly find $f'(x, y)$, the first three terms of the Taylor series gives

$$y_{i+1} = y_i + f(x_i, y_i)h + \frac{1}{2!}f'(x_i, y_i)h^2$$

where

$$f(x,y) = e^{-2x} - 3y$$
$$f'(x,y) = -5e^{-2x} + 9y$$

For a step size of $h = 0.2$, using Heun's method, we find

$$y(0.6) = 1.0930$$

The exact solution

$$y(x) = e^{-2x} + 4e^{-3x}$$

gives

$$y(0.6) = e^{-2(0.6)} + 4e^{-3(0.6)}$$
$$= 0.96239$$

Then the absolute relative true error is

$$|\epsilon_t| = \left| \frac{0.96239 - 1.0930}{0.96239} \right| \times 100$$
$$= 13.571\%$$

For the same problem, the results from Euler's method and the three Runge-Kutta methods are given in Table 3.

Table 3 Comparison of Euler's and Runge-Kutta 2nd order methods

	\multicolumn{6}{c}{y(0.6)}					
	Exact	Euler	Direct 2nd	Heun	Midpoint	Ralston
Value	0.96239	0.4955	1.0930	1.1012	1.0974	1.0994
$\|\epsilon_t\|$ %		48.514	13.571	14.423	14.029	14.236

Appendix A

How do we get the 2nd order Runge-Kutta method equations?

We wrote the 2nd order Runge-Kutta equations without proof to solve

$$\frac{dy}{dx} = f(x,y), \ y(0) = y_0 \tag{A.1}$$

as

$$y_{i+1} = y_i + (a_1 k_1 + a_2 k_2)h \tag{A.2}$$

where

$$k_1 = f(x_i, y_i) \tag{A.3a}$$

$$k_2 = f(x_i + p_1 h, y_i + q_{11} k_1 h) \tag{A.3b}$$

and

$$a_1 + a_2 = 1$$
$$a_2 p_2 = \frac{1}{2}$$

$$a_2 q_{11} = \frac{1}{2} \tag{A.4}$$

The advantage of using 2nd order Runge-Kutta method equations is based on not having to find the derivative of $f(x, y)$ symbolically in the ordinary differential equation

So how do we get the above three Equations (A.4)? This is the question that is answered in this Appendix.

Writing out the first three terms of Taylor series are

$$y_{i+1} = y_i + \left.\frac{dy}{dx}\right|_{x_i, y_i} h + \frac{1}{2!}\left.\frac{d^2 y}{dx^2}\right|_{x_i, y_i} h^2 + O(h^3) \tag{A.5}$$

where

$$h = x_{i+1} - x_i$$

Since

$$\frac{dy}{dx} = f(x, y)$$

we can rewrite the Taylor series as

$$y_{i+1} = y_i + f(x_i, y_i) h + \frac{1}{2!} f'(x_i, y_i) h^2 + O(h^3) \tag{A.6}$$

Now

$$f'(x, y) = \frac{\partial f(x, y)}{\partial x} + \frac{\partial f(x, y)}{\partial y} \frac{dy}{dx}. \tag{A.7}$$

Hence

$$y_{i+1} = y_i + f(x_i, y_i) h + \frac{1}{2!}\left(\left.\frac{\partial f}{\partial x}\right|_{x_i, y_i} + \left.\frac{\partial f}{\partial y}\right|_{x_i, y_i} \times \left.\frac{dy}{dx}\right|_{x_i, y_i} \right) h^2 + O(h^3)$$

$$= y_i + f(x_i, y_i) h + \frac{1}{2}\left.\frac{\partial f}{\partial x}\right|_{x_i, y_i} h^2 + \frac{1}{2}\left.\frac{\partial f}{\partial y}\right|_{x_i, y_i} f(x_i, y_i) h^2 + O(h^3) \tag{A.8}$$

Now the term used in the Runge-Kutta 2nd order method for k_2 can be written as a Taylor series of two variables with the first three terms as

$$k_2 = f(x_i + p_1 h, y_i + q_{11} k_1 h)$$

$$= f(x_i, y_i) + p_1 h \left.\frac{\partial f}{\partial x}\right|_{x_i, y_i} + q_{11} k_1 h \left.\frac{\partial f}{\partial y}\right|_{x_i, y_i} + O(h^2) \tag{A.9}$$

Hence

$$y_{i+1} = y_i + (a_1 k_1 + a_2 k_2) h$$

$$= y_i + \left(a_1 f(x_i, y_i) + a_2 \left\{ f(x_i, y_i) + p_1 h \left.\frac{\partial f}{\partial x}\right|_{x_i, y_i} + q_{11} k_1 h \left.\frac{\partial f}{\partial y}\right|_{x_i, y_i} + O(h^2) \right\} \right) h$$

$$= y_i + (a_1 + a_2) h f(x_i, y_i) + a_2 p_1 h^2 \left.\frac{\partial f}{\partial x}\right|_{x_i, y_i} + a_2 q_{11} f(x_i, y_i) h^2 \left.\frac{\partial f}{\partial y}\right|_{x_i, y_i} + O(h^3)$$

$$(A.10)$$

Equating the terms in Equation (A.8) and Equation (A.10), we get

$$a_1 + a_2 = 1$$

$$a_2 p_1 = \frac{1}{2}$$

$$a_2 q_{11} = \frac{1}{2}$$

ORDINARY DIFFERENTIAL EQUATIONS	
Topic	Runge 2nd Order Method for Ordinary Differential Equations
Summary	Textbook notes on Runge 2nd order method for ODE
Major	General Engineering
Authors	Autar Kaw
Last Revised	December 23, 2009
Web Site	http://numericalmethods.eng.usf.edu

Multiple-Choice Test

Chapter 08.03
Runge-Kutta 2nd Order Method

1. To solve the ordinary differential equation

$$3\frac{dy}{dx} + xy^2 = \sin x, \ y(0) = 5$$

by the Runge-Kutta 2nd order method, you need to rewrite the equation as

(A) $\dfrac{dy}{dx} = \sin x - xy^2, \ y(0) = 5$

(B) $\dfrac{dy}{dx} = \dfrac{1}{3}\left(\sin x - xy^2\right), \ y(0) = 5$

(C) $\dfrac{dy}{dx} = \dfrac{1}{3}\left(-\cos x - \dfrac{xy^3}{3}\right), \ y(0) = 5$

(D) $\dfrac{dy}{dx} = \dfrac{1}{3}\sin x, \ y(0) = 5$

2. Given

$$3\frac{dy}{dx} + 5y^2 = \sin x, \ y(0.3) = 5$$

and using a step size of $h = 0.3$, the value of $y(0.9)$ using the Runge-Kutta 2nd order Heun method is most nearly

(A) -4297.4

(B) -4936.7

(C) -0.21336×10^{14}

(D) -0.24489×10^{14}

3. Given

$$3\frac{dy}{dx} + 5\sqrt{y} = e^{0.1x}, \ y(0.3) = 5$$

and using a step size of $h = 0.3$, the best estimate of $\dfrac{dy}{dx}(0.9)$ using the Runge-Kutta 2nd order midpoint method most nearly is

(A) -2.2473

(B) -2.2543

(C) -2.6188

(D) -3.2045

4.   The velocity (m/s) of a body is given as a function of time (seconds) by
$$v(t) = 200\ln(1+t) - t, \ t \geq 0$$
Using the Runge-Kutta 2nd order Ralston method with a step size of 5 seconds, the distance in meters traveled by the body from $t = 2$ to $t = 12$ seconds is estimated most nearly as
(A)   3904.9
(B)   3939.7
(C)   6556.3
(D)   39397

5.   The Runge-Kutta 2nd order method can be derived by using the first three terms of the Taylor series of writing the value of y_{i+1} (that is the value of y at x_{i+1}) in terms of y_i (that is the value of y at x_i) and all the derivatives of y at x_i. If $h = x_{i+1} - x_i$, the explicit expression for y_{i+1} if the first three terms of the Taylor series are chosen for solving the ordinary differential equation
$$\frac{dy}{dx} + 5y = 3e^{-2x}, y(0) = 7$$
would be

(A) $y_{i+1} = y_i + \left(3e^{-2x_i} - 5y_i\right)h + 5\dfrac{h^2}{2}$

(B) $y_{i+1} = y_i + \left(3e^{-2x_i} - 5y_i\right)h + \left(-21e^{-2x_i} + 25y_i\right)\dfrac{h^2}{2}$

(C) $y_{i+1} = y_i + \left(3e^{-2x_i} - 5y_i\right)h + \left(-6e^{-2x_i}\right)\dfrac{h^2}{2}$

(D) $y_{i+1} = y_i + \left(3e^{-2x_i} - 5y_i\right)h + \left(-6e^{-2x_i} + 5\right)\dfrac{h^2}{2}$

6.   A spherical ball is taken out of a furnace at 1200 K and is allowed to cool in air. You are given the following

  radius of ball = 2 cm
  specific heat of ball = 420 J/kg · K
  density of ball = 7800 kg/m³
  convection coefficient = 350 J/s · m² · K
  ambient temperature = 300 K

The ordinary differential equation that is given for the temperature θ of the ball is

$$\frac{d\theta}{dt} = -2.20673 \times 10^{-13} \left(\theta^4 - 81 \times 10^8 \right)$$

if only radiation is accounted for. The ordinary differential equation if convection is accounted for in addition to radiation is

(A) $\dfrac{d\theta}{dt} = -2.20673 \times 10^{-13} \left(\theta^4 - 81 \times 10^8 \right) - 1.6026 \times 10^{-2} \left(\theta - 300 \right)$

(B) $\dfrac{d\theta}{dt} = -2.20673 \times 10^{-13} \left(\theta^4 - 81 \times 10^8 \right) - 4.3982 \times 10^{-2} \left(\theta - 300 \right)$

(C) $\dfrac{d\theta}{dt} = -1.6026 \times 10^{-2} \left(\theta - 300 \right)$

(D) $\dfrac{d\theta}{dt} = -4.3982 \times 10^{-2} \left(\theta - 300 \right)$

Complete Solution

Problem Set

Chapter 08.03
Runge-Kutta 2nd order method for Ordinary Differential Equations

1.   For the ordinary differential equation

$$2\frac{dy}{dx} + 3xy = e^{-1.5x}, \quad y(0) = 5$$

use a step size of $h = 2$ and Ralston's Runge-Kutta 2nd order method to find $y(6)$.

2.   For the ordinary differential equation

$$2\frac{dy}{dx} + 3y = e^{-1.5x}, \quad y(0) = 5$$

a) use midpoint Runge-Kutta 2nd order method to find $y(2.5)$ using $h = 1.25$,

b) use midpoint Runge-Kutta 2nd order method to find $\frac{dy}{dx}(2.5)$ using $h = 1.25$,

c) true value of $y(2.5)$,

d) absolute relative true error for part (a),

e) true error of $\frac{dy}{dx}(2.5)$,

f) absolute relative true error for part (b).

3.   Find the approximate value of the integral $\int_{3}^{8} 2e^{0.6x} dx$ using Heun's Runge-Kutta 2nd order method.

a) Use $h = 2.5$ and compare the value with the exact value.

b) Use $h = 1.25$ and compare the value with the exact value.

4.   From problem (3a), is the value obtained using Heun's Runge-Kutta 2nd order method same as 2-segment LRAM (Left Endpoint Rectangular Approximation), or 2-segment MRAM (Midpoint Rectangular Approximation), or 2-segment RRAM (Right Endpoint Rectangular Approximation) method of integration? Explain.

08.03.1

5.   A water tank with a hole at the top and a circular hole at the bottom is shown in the figure.

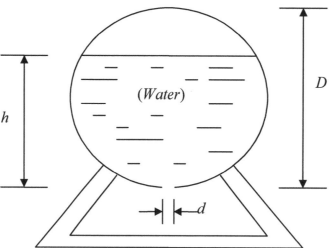

Given
        Diameter of tank, $D = 6\,\text{m}$
        Initial height of water, $h = 5\,\text{m}$
        Diameter of hole, $d = 4.95\,\text{cm}$
The flow rate $\dot{Q}$ of water through the bottom hole is given by
        $\dot{Q} = -Av$,
where
        A = cross-sectional area of the hole,
        v = velocity of the water flowing through the hole.
Since
        $v = \sqrt{2gh}$
where
        h = height of water from the bottom of the tank,
        g = acceleration due to gravity.
From this, we get
        $\dot{Q} = -A\sqrt{2gh}$
Also, since the volume V of the water at height h is given by
        $V = \dfrac{1}{3}\pi h^2\left(\dfrac{3D}{2} - h\right)$
where
        $\dfrac{dV}{dt} = \left(\pi h D - \pi h^2\right)\dfrac{dh}{dt}$
Since
        $\dot{Q} = \dfrac{dV}{dt}$

$$\left(\pi h D - \pi h^2\right)\frac{dh}{dt} = -A\sqrt{2gh}$$

$$\left(\pi h D - \pi h^2\right)\frac{dh}{dt} = -\frac{\pi d^2}{4}\sqrt{2gh}$$

$$\frac{dh}{dt} = -\frac{d^2\sqrt{2gh}}{4\left(hD - h^2\right)}$$

a) Use Heun's method with a step size of 10 minutes to find the height of water at $t = 50$ minutes.

b) Based on the results from part (a), estimate the time when the height of the water is 2 m.

c) Compare the results of part(a) and part (b) with the exact values.

6. Given the following for a spherical ball taken out of furnace at 2500 K that loses heat due to radiation and convection.

Radius of ball, $r = 1.0\,\text{cm}$,

Density of the ball, $\rho = 3000\,\text{kg/m}^3$,

Specific heat, $C = 1000\,\text{J}/(\text{kg}\cdot\text{K})$,

Emittance, $\epsilon = 0.5$,

Stefan-Boltzmann Constant, $\sigma = 5.67 \times 10^{-8}\,\text{J}/(\text{s}\cdot\text{m}^2\cdot\text{K}^4)$,

Convective cooling coefficient, $h = 500\,\text{J}/(\text{s}\cdot\text{m}^2\cdot\text{K})$,

Initial temperature of the ball, $\theta(0) = 2500\,\text{K}$,

Ambient temperature, $\theta_a = 300\,\text{K}$,

the ordinary differential equation that governs the temperature of the ball is given by

$$\frac{d\theta}{dt} = -2.8349 \times 10^{-12}\left(\theta^4 - 81 \times 10^8\right) - 0.05\left(\theta - 300\right).$$

Hint: The above formula was calculated by using the knowledge that

Rate of heat lost due to radiation $= A\,\epsilon\,\sigma(\theta^4 - \theta_a^4)$

Rate of heat lost due to convection $= hA(\theta - \theta_a)$

Heat stored $= mc\theta$

where

$A =$ surface area of the ball,

$m =$ mass of the ball.

a) What are following at $t = 0\,\text{s}$?
   i. temperature,
   ii. rate of change of temperature,
   iii. rate of heat loss due to radiation,
   iv. rate of heat loss due to convection,
   v. rate of heat stored,

b) Find the following at $t = 10\,\text{s}$ using Ralston's method and a step size of $h = 2.5$.
   i. temperature,

      ii. rate of change of temperature,

     iii. rate of heat loss due to radiation,

     iv. rate of heat loss due to convection,

      v. rate of heat stored,

c) Can either convection or radiation be neglected if we are interested in finding the temperature profile between 0 and 10 s? Base your answer on quantitative reasoning.

d) Find the time when the temperature will be 2000 K using Ralston's method and a step size of $h = 2.5\,\text{s}$.

Chapter 08.04
Runge-Kutta 4th Order Method for Ordinary Differential Equations

After reading this chapter, you should be able to
1. *develop Runge-Kutta 4th order method for solving ordinary differential equations,*
2. *find the effect size of step size has on the solution,*
3. *know the formulas for other versions of the Runge-Kutta 4th order method*

What is the Runge-Kutta 4th order method?

Runge-Kutta 4th order method is a numerical technique used to solve ordinary differential equation of the form

$$\frac{dy}{dx} = f(x, y), y(0) = y_0$$

So only first order ordinary differential equations can be solved by using the Runge-Kutta 4th order method. In other sections, we have discussed how Euler and Runge-Kutta methods are used to solve higher order ordinary differential equations or coupled (simultaneous) differential equations.

How does one write a first order differential equation in the above form?

Example 1

Rewrite

$$\frac{dy}{dx} + 2y = 1.3e^{-x}, y(0) = 5$$

in

$$\frac{dy}{dx} = f(x, y), \ y(0) = y_0 \text{ form.}$$

Solution

$$\frac{dy}{dx} + 2y = 1.3e^{-x}, \, y(0) = 5$$

$$\frac{dy}{dx} = 1.3e^{-x} - 2y, \, y(0) = 5$$

In this case

$$f(x, y) = 1.3e^{-x} - 2y$$

Example 2

Rewrite

$$e^{y}\frac{dy}{dx} + x^{2}y^{2} = 2\sin(3x), \, y(0) = 5$$

in

$$\frac{dy}{dx} = f(x, y), \, y(0) = y_{0} \text{ form.}$$

Solution

$$e^{y}\frac{dy}{dx} + x^{2}y^{2} = 2\sin(3x), \, y(0) = 5$$

$$\frac{dy}{dx} = \frac{2\sin(3x) - x^{2}y^{2}}{e^{y}}, \, y(0) = 5$$

In this case

$$f(x, y) = \frac{2\sin(3x) - x^{2}y^{2}}{e^{y}}$$

The Runge-Kutta 4th order method is based on the following

$$y_{i+1} = y_{i} + (a_{1}k_{1} + a_{2}k_{2} + a_{3}k_{3} + a_{4}k_{4})h \qquad (1)$$

where knowing the value of $y = y_{i}$ at x_{i}, we can find the value of $y = y_{i+1}$ at x_{i+1}, and

$$h = x_{i+1} - x_{i}$$

Equation (1) is equated to the first five terms of Taylor series

$$y_{i+1} = y_{i} + \frac{dy}{dx}\Big|_{x_{i}, y_{i}}(x_{i+1} - x_{i}) + \frac{1}{2!}\frac{d^{2}y}{dx^{2}}\Big|_{x_{i}, y_{i}}(x_{i+1} - x_{i})^{2} + \frac{1}{3!}\frac{d^{3}y}{dx^{3}}\Big|_{x_{i}, y_{i}}(x_{i+1} - x_{i})^{3}$$

$$+ \frac{1}{4!}\frac{d^{4}y}{dx^{4}}\Big|_{x_{i}, y_{i}}(x_{i+1} - x_{i})^{4} \qquad (2)$$

Knowing that $\frac{dy}{dx} = f(x, y)$ and $x_{i+1} - x_{i} = h$

$$y_{i+1} = y_{i} + f(x_{i}, y_{i})h + \frac{1}{2!}f'(x_{i}, y_{i})h^{2} + \frac{1}{3!}f''(x_{i}, y_{i})h^{3} + \frac{1}{4!}f'''(x_{i}, y_{i})h^{4} \qquad (3)$$

Based on equating Equation (2) and Equation (3), one of the popular solutions used is

$$y_{i+1} = y_{i} + \frac{1}{6}(k_{1} + 2k_{2} + 2k_{3} + k_{4})h \qquad (4)$$

$$k_1 = f(x_i, y_i) \tag{5a}$$

$$k_2 = f\left(x_i + \frac{1}{2}h, y_i + \frac{1}{2}k_1 h\right) \tag{5b}$$

$$k_3 = f\left(x_i + \frac{1}{2}h, y_i + \frac{1}{2}k_2 h\right) \tag{5c}$$

$$k_4 = f(x_i + h, y_i + k_3 h) \tag{5d}$$

Example 3

A ball at 1200 K is allowed to cool down in air at an ambient temperature of 300 K. Assuming heat is lost only due to radiation, the differential equation for the temperature of the ball is given by

$$\frac{d\theta}{dt} = -2.2067 \times 10^{-12}\left(\theta^4 - 81 \times 10^8\right), \theta(0) = 1200\,\text{K}$$

where θ is in K and t in seconds. Find the temperature at $t = 480$ seconds using Runge-Kutta 4th order method. Assume a step size of $h = 240$ seconds.

Solution

$$\frac{d\theta}{dt} = -2.2067 \times 10^{-12}\left(\theta^4 - 81 \times 10^8\right)$$

$$f(t, \theta) = -2.2067 \times 10^{-12}\left(\theta^4 - 81 \times 10^8\right)$$

$$\theta_{i+1} = \theta_i + \frac{1}{6}(k_1 + 2k_2 + 2k_3 + k_4)h$$

For $i = 0$, $t_0 = 0$, $\theta_0 = 1200\text{K}$

$$\begin{aligned}
k_1 &= f(t_0, \theta_0) \\
&= f(0, 1200) \\
&= -2.2067 \times 10^{-12}\left(1200^4 - 81 \times 10^8\right) \\
&= -4.5579
\end{aligned}$$

$$\begin{aligned}
k_2 &= f\left(t_0 + \frac{1}{2}h, \theta_0 + \frac{1}{2}k_1 h\right) \\
&= f\left(0 + \frac{1}{2}(240), 1200 + \frac{1}{2}(-4.5579) \times 240\right) \\
&= f(120, 653.05) \\
&= -2.2067 \times 10^{-12}\left(653.05^4 - 81 \times 10^8\right) \\
&= -0.38347
\end{aligned}$$

$$\begin{aligned}
k_3 &= f\left(t_0 + \frac{1}{2}h, \theta_0 + \frac{1}{2}k_2 h\right) \\
&= f\left(0 + \frac{1}{2}(240), 1200 + \frac{1}{2}(-0.38347) \times 240\right) \\
&= f(120, 1154.0)
\end{aligned}$$

$$= -2.2067 \times 10^{-12} \left(1154.0^4 - 81 \times 10^8 \right)$$

$$= -3.8954$$

$$k_4 = f\left(t_0 + h, \theta_0 + k_3 h\right)$$

$$= f\left(0 + 240, 1200 + (-3.894) \times 240\right)$$

$$= f(240, 265.10)$$

$$= -2.2067 \times 10^{-12} \left(265.10^4 - 81 \times 10^8 \right)$$

$$= 0.0069750$$

$$\theta_1 = \theta_0 + \frac{1}{6}(k_1 + 2k_2 + 2k_3 + k_4)h$$

$$= 1200 + \frac{1}{6}\left(-4.5579 + 2(-0.38347) + 2(-3.8954) + (0.069750)\right)240$$

$$= 1200 + (-2.1848) \times 240$$

$$= 675.65 \, \text{K}$$

θ_1 is the approximate temperature at

$$t = t_1$$

$$= t_0 + h$$

$$= 0 + 240$$

$$= 240$$

$$\theta_1 = \theta(240)$$

$$\approx 675.65 \, \text{K}$$

For $i = 1, t_1 = 240, \theta_1 = 675.65 \, \text{K}$

$$k_1 = f(t_1, \theta_1)$$

$$= f(240, 675.65)$$

$$= -2.2067 \times 10^{-12} \left(675.65^4 - 81 \times 10^8 \right)$$

$$= -0.44199$$

$$k_2 = f\left(t_1 + \frac{1}{2}h, \theta_1 + \frac{1}{2}k_1 h\right)$$

$$= f\left(240 + \frac{1}{2}(240), 675.65 + \frac{1}{2}(-0.44199)240\right)$$

$$= f(360, 622.61)$$

$$= -2.2067 \times 10^{-12} \left(622.61^4 - 81 \times 10^8 \right)$$

$$= -0.31372$$

$$k_3 = f\left(t_1 + \frac{1}{2}h, \theta_1 + \frac{1}{2}k_2 h\right)$$

$$= f\left(240 + \frac{1}{2}(240), 675.65 + \frac{1}{2}(-0.31372) \times 240\right)$$

$$= f(360, 638.00)$$

$$= -2.2067 \times 10^{-12} \left(638.00^4 - 81 \times 10^8 \right)$$

$$= -0.34775$$

$$k_4 = f(t_1 + h, \theta_1 + k_3 h)$$
$$= f(240 + 240, 675.65 + (-0.34775) \times 240)$$
$$= f(480, 592.19)$$
$$= 2.2067 \times 10^{-12} (592.19^4 - 81 \times 10^8)$$
$$= -0.25351$$

$$\theta_2 = \theta_1 + \frac{1}{6}(k_1 + 2k_2 + 2k_3 + k_4)h$$

$$= 675.65 + \frac{1}{6}(-0.44199 + 2(-0.31372) + 2(-0.34775) + (-0.25351)) \times 240$$

$$= 675.65 + \frac{1}{6}(-2.0184) \times 240$$

$$= 594.91 \text{K}$$

θ_2 is the approximate temperature at

$$t = t_2$$
$$= t_1 + h$$
$$= 240 + 240$$
$$= 480$$

$$\theta_2 = \theta(480)$$
$$\approx 594.91 \text{K}$$

Figure 1 compares the exact solution with the numerical solution using the Runge-Kutta 4th order method with different step sizes.

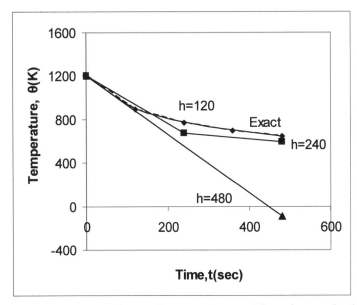

Figure 1 Comparison of Runge-Kutta 4th order method with exact solution for different step sizes.

Table 1 and Figure 2 show the effect of step size on the value of the calculated temperature at $t = 480$ seconds.

Table 1 Value of temperature at time, $t = 480\,\text{s}$ for different step sizes

Step size, h	$\theta(480)$	E_t	$\lvert \varepsilon_t \rvert \%$
480	-90.278	737.85	113.94
240	594.91	52.660	8.1319
120	646.16	1.4122	0.21807
60	647.54	0.033626	0.0051926
30	647.57	0.00086900	0.00013419

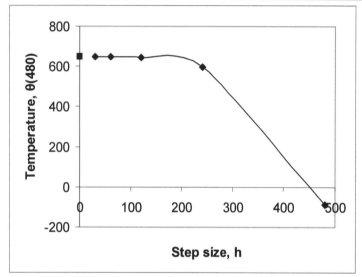

Figure 2 Effect of step size in Runge-Kutta 4th order method.

In Figure 3, we are comparing the exact results with Euler's method (Runge-Kutta 1st order method), Heun's method (Runge-Kutta 2nd order method), and Runge-Kutta 4th order method.

The formula described in this chapter was developed by Runge. This formula is same as Simpson's 1/3 rule, if $f(x, y)$ were only a function of x. There are other versions of the 4th order method just like there are several versions of the second order methods. The formula developed by Kutta is

$$y_{i+1} = y_i + \frac{1}{8}\left(k_1 + 3k_2 + 3k_3 + k_4\right)h \qquad (6)$$

where

$$k_1 = f\left(x_i, y_i\right) \qquad (7a)$$

$$k_2 = f\left(x_i + \frac{1}{3}h, y_i + \frac{1}{3}hk_1\right) \qquad (7b)$$

$$k_3 = f\left(x_i + \frac{2}{3}h, y_i - \frac{1}{3}hk_1 + hk_2\right) \qquad (7c)$$

$$k_4 = f\left(x_i + h, y_i + hk_1 - hk_2 + hk_3\right) \qquad (7d)$$

This formula is the same as the Simpson's 3/8 rule, if $f(x, y)$ is only a function of x.

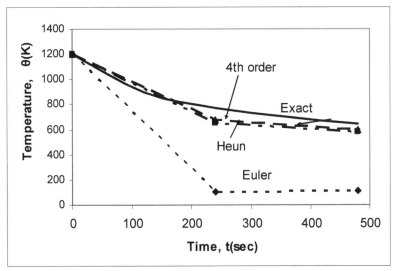

Figure 3 Comparison of Runge-Kutta methods of 1st (Euler), 2nd, and 4th order.

ORDINARY DIFFERENTIAL EQUATIONS	
Topic	Runge-Kutta 4th order method
Summary	Textbook notes on the Runge-Kutta 4th order method for solving ordinary differential equations.
Major	General Engineering
Authors	Autar Kaw
Last Revised	December 23, 2009
Web Site	http://numericalmethods.eng.usf.edu

Multiple-Choice Test

Chapter 08.04
Runge-Kutta 4th Order Method

1. To solve the ordinary differential equation

$$3\frac{dy}{dx} + xy^2 = \sin x, y(0) = 5,$$

by Runge-Kutta 4th order method, you need to rewrite the equation as

(A) $\frac{dy}{dx} = \sin x - xy^2, y(0) = 5$

(B) $\frac{dy}{dx} = \frac{1}{3}\left(\sin x - xy^2\right), y(0) = 5$

(C) $\frac{dy}{dx} = \frac{1}{3}\left(-\cos x - \frac{xy^3}{3}\right), y(0) = 5$

(D) $\frac{dy}{dx} = \frac{1}{3}\sin x, y(0) = 5$

2. Given $3\frac{dy}{dx} + 5y^2 = \sin x, y(0.3) = 5$ and using a step size of $h = 0.3$, the value of $y(0.9)$ using Runge-Kutta 4th order method is most nearly

(A) -0.25011×10^{40}
(B) -4297.4
(C) -1261.5
(D) 0.88498

3. Given $3\frac{dy}{dx} + y^2 = e^x, y(0.3) = 5$, and using a step size of $h = 0.3$, the best estimate of $\frac{dy}{dx}(0.9)$ Runge-Kutta 4th order method is most nearly

(A) -1.6604
(B) -1.1785
(C) -0.45831
(D) 2.7270

08.04.1

4.   The velocity (m/s) of a parachutist is given as a function of time (seconds) by

$$v(t) = 55.8\tanh(0.17t),\ t \geq 0$$

Using Runge-Kutta 4th order method with a step size of 5 seconds, the distance in meters traveled by the body from $t = 2$ to $t = 12$ seconds is estimated most nearly as

        (A) 341.43
        (B) 428.97
        (C) 429.05
        (D) 703.50

5.   Runge-Kutta method can be derived from using first three terms of Taylor series of writing the value of y_{i+1}, that is the value of y at x_{i+1}, in terms of y_i and all the derivatives of y at x_i. If $h = x_{i+1} - x_i$, the explicit expression for y_{i+1} if the first five terms of the Taylor series are chosen for the ordinary differential equation

$$\frac{dy}{dx} + 5y = 3e^{-2x}, y(0) = 7,$$

would be

(A) $y_{i+1} = y_i + \left(3e^{-2x_i} - 5y_i\right)h + \dfrac{5h^2}{2}$

(B)
$$y_{i+1} = y_i + \left(3e^{-2x_i} - 5y_i\right)h + \left(-21e^{-2x_i} + 25y_i\right)\frac{h^2}{2}$$
$$+ \left(-483e^{-2x_i} + 625y_i\right)\frac{h^3}{6} + \left(-300909e^{-2x_i} + 390625y_i\right)\frac{h^4}{24}$$

(C)
$$y_{i+1} = y_i + \left(3e^{-2x_i} - 5y_i\right)h + \left(-6e^{-2x_i}\right)\frac{h^2}{2} + \left(12e^{-2x_i}\right)\frac{h^3}{6}$$
$$+ \left(-24e^{-2x_i}\right)\frac{h^4}{24}$$

(D)
$$y_{i+1} = y_i + \left(3e^{-2x_i} - 5y_i\right)h + \left(-6e^{-2x_i} + 5\right)\frac{h^2}{2} + \left(12e^{-2x_i}\right)\frac{h^3}{6}$$
$$+ \left(-24e^{-2x_i}\right)\frac{h^4}{24}$$

6.   A hot solid cylinder is immersed in a cool oil bath as part of a quenching process. This process makes the temperature of the cylinder, θ_c, and the bath, θ_b, change with time. If the initial temperature of the bar and the oil bath is given as 600° C and 27°C, respectively, and

  Length of cylinder = 30 cm
  Radius of cylinder = 3 cm
  Density of cylinder = 2700 kg/m³
  Specific heat of cylinder = 895 J/kg · K
  Convection heat transfer coefficient = 100 W/m² · K
  Specific heat of oil = 1910 J/kg · K
  Mass of oil = 2 kg

the coupled ordinary differential equation giving the heat transfer are given by

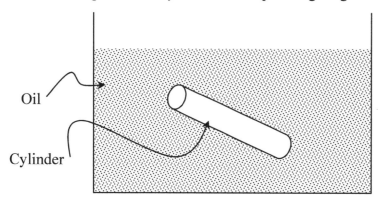

(A)
$$362.4\frac{d\theta_c}{dt} + \theta_c = \theta_b$$
$$675.5\frac{d\theta_b}{dt} + \theta_b = \theta$$

(B)
$$362.4\frac{d\theta_c}{dt} - \theta_c = \theta_b$$
$$675.5\frac{d\theta_b}{dt} - \theta_b = \theta_c$$

(C)
$$675.5\frac{d\theta_c}{dt} + \theta_c = \theta_b$$
$$362.4\frac{d\theta_b}{dt} + \theta_b = \theta_c$$

(D) $$675.5\frac{d\theta_c}{dt} - \theta_c = \theta_b$$

Complete Solution

Problem Set

Chapter 08.04
Runge-Kutta 4th order method for Ordinary Differential Equations

1. For the ordinary differential equation

$$2\frac{dy}{dx} + 3\,xy = e^{-1.5x}, y(0) = 5$$

use a step size of $h = 2$ and Runge-Kutta 4th order method to find $y(6)$.

2. For the ordinary differential equation

$$2\frac{dy}{dx} + 3\,y = e^{-1.5x}, y(0) = 5$$

a) use Runge-Kutta 4th order method to find $y(2.5)$ using $h = 1.25$,

b) use Runge-Kutta 4th order method to find $\frac{dy}{dx}(2.5)$ using $h = 1.25$,

c) true value of $y(2.5)$,

d) absolute relative true error for part (a),

e) true error of $\frac{dy}{dx}(2.5)$,

f) absolute relative true error for part (b).

3. Find the approximate value of the integral $\int_{3}^{8} 2e^{0.6x} dx$ using Runge-Kutta 4th order method.

a) Use $h = 2.5$ and compare the value with the exact value.

b) Use $h = 1.25$ and compare the value with the exact value.

4. From problem (3a), is the value obtained using Runge-Kutta 4th order method same as 2-segment LRAM (Left Endpoint Rectangular Approximation), or 2-segment MRAM (Midpoint Rectangular Approximation), or 2-segment RRAM (Right Endpoint Rectangular Approximation) method of integration? Explain.

5. A water tank with a hole at the top and a circular hole at the bottom is shown in the figure.

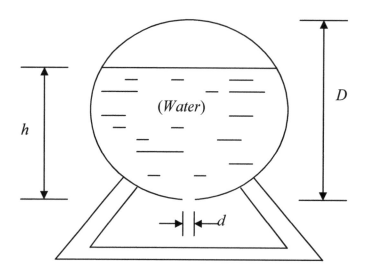

Given

      Diameter of tank, $D = 6\,\text{m}$
      Initial height of water, $h = 5\,\text{m}$
      Diameter of hole, $d = 4.95\,\text{cm}$

The flow rate $\dot{Q}$ of water through the bottom hole is given by

$$\dot{Q} = -Av,$$

where

      $A =$ cross-sectional area of the hole,
      $v =$ velocity of the water flowing through the hole.

Since

$$v = \sqrt{2gh}$$

where

      $h =$ height of water from the bottom of the tank,
      $g =$ acceleration due to gravity.

From this, we get

$$\dot{Q} = -A\sqrt{2gh}$$

Also, since the volume V of the water at height h is given by

$$V = \frac{1}{3}\pi h^2 \left(\frac{3D}{2} - h\right)$$

where

$$\frac{dV}{dt} = \left(\pi hD - \pi h^2\right)\frac{dh}{dt}$$

Since

$$\dot{Q} = \frac{dV}{dt}$$

$$\left(\pi hD - \pi h^2\right)\frac{dh}{dt} = -A\sqrt{2gh}$$

$$\left(\pi hD - \pi h^2\right)\frac{dh}{dt} = -\frac{\pi d^2}{4}\sqrt{2gh}$$

$$\frac{dh}{dt} = -\frac{d^2\sqrt{2gh}}{4\left(hD - h^2\right)}$$

a) Use Runge-Kutta 4th order method with a step size of 10 minutes to find the height of water at $t = 50$ minutes.
b) Based on the results from part (a), estimate the time when the height of the water is 2 m.
c) Compare the results of part(a) and part (b) with the exact values.

6. Given the following for a spherical ball taken out of furnace at 2500 K that loses heat due to radiation and convection.

Radius of ball, $r = 1.0$ cm,
Density of the ball, $\rho = 3000$ kg/m^3 ,
Specific heat, $C = 1000$ J/(kg $\cdot$ K),
Emittance, $\epsilon = 0.5$,
Stefan-Boltzmann Constant, $\sigma = 5.67 \times 10^{-8}$ J/(s $\cdot$ m^2 $\cdot$ K^4),
Convective cooling coefficient, $h = 500$ J/(s $\cdot$ m^2 $\cdot$ K),
Initial temperature of the ball, $\theta(0) = 2500$ K,
Ambient temperature, $\theta_a = 300$ K,

the ordinary differential equation that governs the temperature of the ball is given by

$$\frac{d\theta}{dt} = -2.8349 \times 10^{-12}(\theta^4 - 81 \times 10^8) - 0.05\,(\theta - 300).$$

Hint: The above formula was calculated by using the knowledge that

Rate of heat lost due to radiation $= A\,\epsilon\,\sigma(\theta^4 - \theta_a^4)$

Rate of heat lost due to convection $= hA(\theta - \theta_a)$

Heat stored $= mc\theta$

where

A = surface area of the ball,
m = mass of the ball.

a) What are following at $t = 0$ s?
    i. temperature,
    ii. rate of change of temperature,
    iii. rate of heat loss due to radiation,
    iv. rate of heat loss due to convection,
    v. rate of heat stored,
b) Find the following at $t = 10$ s using Runge-Kutta 4th order method and a step size of $h = 2.5$.
    i. temperature,
    ii. rate of change of temperature,
    iii. rate of heat loss due to radiation,

        iv. rate of heat loss due to convection,

        v. rate of heat stored,

c) Can either convection or radiation be neglected if we are interested in finding the temperature profile between 0 and 10 s? Base your answer on quantitative reasoning.

d) Find the time when the temperature will be 2000 K using Runge-Kutta 4th order method and a step size of $h = 2.5\,\text{s}$.

Chapter 08.05
On Solving Higher Order Equations for Ordinary Differential Equations

After reading this chapter, you should be able to:
    1. *solve higher order and coupled differential equations,*

We have learned Euler's and Runge-Kutta methods to solve first order ordinary differential equations of the form

$$\frac{dy}{dx} = f(x, y), \ y(0) = y_0 \tag{1}$$

What do we do to solve simultaneous (coupled) differential equations, or differential equations that are higher than first order? For example an nth order differential equation of the form

$$a_n \frac{d^n y}{dx^n} + a_{n-1} \frac{d^{n-1} y}{dx^{n-1}} + \ldots + a_1 \frac{dy}{dx} + a_o y = f(x) \tag{2}$$

with $n-1$ initial conditions can be solved by assuming

$$y = z_1 \tag{3.1}$$

$$\frac{dy}{dx} = \frac{dz_1}{dx} = z_2 \tag{3.2}$$

$$\frac{d^2 y}{dx^2} = \frac{dz_2}{dx} = z_3 \tag{3.3}$$

$$\vdots$$

$$\frac{d^{n-1} y}{dx^{n-1}} = \frac{dz_{n-1}}{dx} = z_n \tag{3.n}$$

$$\begin{aligned}
\frac{d^n y}{dx^n} = \frac{dz_n}{dx} \\
= \frac{1}{a_n} \left(-a_{n-1} \frac{d^{n-1} y}{dx^{n-1}} \ldots - a_1 \frac{dy}{dx} - a_0 y + f(x) \right) \\
= \frac{1}{a_n} \left(-a_{n-1} z_n \ldots - a_1 z_2 - a_0 z_1 + f(x) \right)
\end{aligned} \tag{3.n+1}$$

The above Equations from (3.1) to (3.n+1) represent n first order differential equations as follows

08.08.1

$$\frac{dz_1}{dx} = z_2 = f_1(z_1, z_2, \ldots, x) \tag{4.1}$$

$$\frac{dz_2}{dx} = z_3 = f_2(z_1, z_2, \ldots, x) \tag{4.2}$$

$$\vdots$$

$$\frac{dz_n}{dx} = \frac{1}{a_n}\left(-a_{n-1}z_n \ldots - a_1 z_2 - a_0 z_1 + f(x)\right) \tag{4.n}$$

Each of the n first order ordinary differential equations are accompanied by one initial condition. These first order ordinary differential equations are simultaneous in nature but can be solved by the methods used for solving first order ordinary differential equations that we have already learned.

Example 1

Rewrite the following differential equation as a set of first order differential equations.

$$3\frac{d^2 y}{dx^2} + 2\frac{dy}{dx} + 5y = e^{-x}, \; y(0) = 5, \; y'(0) = 7$$

Solution

The ordinary differential equation would be rewritten as follows. Assume

$$\frac{dy}{dx} = z,$$

Then

$$\frac{d^2 y}{dx^2} = \frac{dz}{dx}$$

Substituting this in the given second order ordinary differential equation gives

$$3\frac{dz}{dx} + 2z + 5y = e^{-x}$$

$$\frac{dz}{dx} = \frac{1}{3}\left(e^{-x} - 2z - 5y\right)$$

The set of two simultaneous first order ordinary differential equations complete with the initial conditions then is

$$\frac{dy}{dx} = z, \; y(0) = 5$$

$$\frac{dz}{dx} = \frac{1}{3}\left(e^{-x} - 2z - 5y\right), \; z(0) = 7.$$

Now one can apply any of the numerical methods used for solving first order ordinary differential equations.

Example 2

Given

$$\frac{d^2 y}{dt^2} + 2\frac{dy}{dt} + y = e^{-t}, \; y(0) = 1, \; \frac{dy}{dt}(0) = 2, \text{ find by Euler's method}$$

a) $y(0.75)$

b) the absolute relative true error for part(a), if $y(0.75)|_{exact} = 1.668$

c) $\dfrac{dy}{dt}(0.75)$

Use a step size of $h = 0.25$.

Solution

First, the second order differential equation is written as two simultaneous first-order differential equations as follows. Assume

$$\frac{dy}{dt} = z$$

then

$$\frac{dz}{dt} + 2z + y = e^{-t}$$

$$\frac{dz}{dt} = e^{-t} - 2z - y$$

So the two simultaneous first order differential equations are

$$\frac{dy}{dt} = z = f_1(t,y,z),\; y(0) = 1 \tag{E2.1}$$

$$\frac{dz}{dt} = e^{-t} - 2z - y = f_2(t,y,z),\; z(0) = 2 \tag{E2.2}$$

Using Euler's method on Equations (E2.1) and (E2.2), we get

$$y_{i+1} = y_i + f_1(t_i, y_i, z_i)h \tag{E2.3}$$

$$z_{i+1} = z_i + f_2(t_i, y_i, z_i)h \tag{E2.4}$$

a) To find the value of $y(0.75)$ and since we are using a step size of 0.25 and starting at $t = 0$, we need to take three steps to find the value of $y(0.75)$.

For $i = 0, t_0 = 0,\; y_0 = 1,\; z_0 = 2$,

From Equation (E2.3)

$$\begin{aligned}
y_1 &= y_0 + f_1(t_0, y_0, z_0)h \\
&= 1 + f_1(0,1,2)(0.25) \\
&= 1 + 2(0.25) \\
&= 1.5
\end{aligned}$$

y_1 is the approximate value of y at

$$t = t_1 = t_0 + h = 0 + 0.25 = 0.25$$

$$y_1 = y(0.25) \approx 1.5$$

From Equation (E2.4)

$$\begin{aligned}
z_1 &= z_0 + f_2(t_0, y_0, z_0)h \\
&= 2 + f_2(0,1,2)(0.25) \\
&= 2 + (e^{-0} - 2(2) - 1)(0.25) \\
&= 1
\end{aligned}$$

z_1 is the approximate value of z (same as $\dfrac{dy}{dt}$) at $t = 0.25$

$$z_1 = z(0.25) \approx 1$$

For $i = 1$, $t_1 = 0.25$, $y_1 = 1.5$, $z_1 = 1$,

From Equation (E2.3)

$$\begin{aligned}
y_2 &= y_1 + f_1(t_1, y_1, z_1)h \\
&= 1.5 + f_1(0.25, 1.5, 1)(0.25) \\
&= 1.5 + (1)(0.25) \\
&= 1.75
\end{aligned}$$

y_2 is the approximate value of y at

$$t = t_2 = t_1 + h = 0.25 + 0.25 = 0.50$$
$$y_2 = y(0.5) \approx 1.75$$

From Equation (E2.4)

$$\begin{aligned}
z_2 &= z_1 + f_2(t_1, y_1, z_1)h \\
&= 1 + f_2(0.25, 1.5, 1)(0.25) \\
&= 1 + (e^{-0.25} - 2(1) - 1.5)(0.25) \\
&= 1 + (-2.7211)(0.25) \\
&= 0.31970
\end{aligned}$$

z_2 is the approximate value of z at

$$t = t_2 = 0.5$$
$$z_2 = z(0.5) \approx 0.31970$$

For $i = 2$, $t_2 = 0.5$, $y_2 = 1.75$, $z_2 = 0.31970$,

From Equation (E2.3)

$$\begin{aligned}
y_3 &= y_2 + f_1(t_2, y_2, z_2)h \\
&= 1.75 + f_1(0.50, 1.75, 0.31970)(0.25) \\
&= 1.75 + (0.31970)(0.25) \\
&= 1.8299
\end{aligned}$$

y_3 is the approximate value of y at

$$t = t_3 = t_2 + h = 0.5 + 0.25 = 0.75$$
$$y_3 = y(0.75) \approx 1.8299$$

From Equation (E2.4)

$$\begin{aligned}
z_3 &= z_2 + f_2(t_2, y_2, z_2)h \\
&= 0.31972 + f_2(0.50, 1.75, 0.31970)(0.25) \\
&= 0.31972 + (e^{-0.50} - 2(0.31970) - 1.75)(0.25) \\
&= 0.31972 + (-1.7829)(0.25) \\
&= -0.1260
\end{aligned}$$

z_3 is the approximate value of z at

$$t = t_3 = 0.75$$
$$z_3 = z(0.75) \approx -0.12601$$
$$y(0.75) \approx y_3 = 1.8299$$

b) The exact value of $y(0.75)$ is

$$y(0.75)\big|_{exact} = 1.668$$

The absolute relative true error in the result from part (a) is

$$|\in_t| = \left|\frac{1.668 - 1.8299}{1.668}\right| \times 100$$

$$= 9.7062\%$$

c) $\dfrac{dy}{dx}(0.75) = z_3 \approx -0.12601$

Example 3
Given

$$\frac{d^2 y}{dt^2} + 2\frac{dy}{dt} + y = e^{-t}, y(0) = 1, \frac{dy}{dt}(0) = 2,$$

find by Heun's method

    a) $y(0.75)$

    b) $\dfrac{dy}{dx}(0.75)$.

Use a step size of $h = 0.25$.

Solution

First, the second order differential equation is rewritten as two simultaneous first-order differential equations as follows. Assume

$$\frac{dy}{dt} = z$$

then

$$\frac{dz}{dt} + 2z + y = e^{-t}$$

$$\frac{dz}{dt} = e^{-t} - 2z - y$$

So the two simultaneous first order differential equations are

$$\frac{dy}{dt} = z = f_1(t, y, z), y(0) = 1 \tag{E3.1}$$

$$\frac{dz}{dt} = e^{-t} - 2z - y = f_2(t, y, z), z(0) = 2 \tag{E3.2}$$

Using Heun's method on Equations (1) and (2), we get

$$y_{i+1} = y_i + \frac{1}{2}\left(k_1^y + k_2^y\right)h \tag{E3.3}$$

$$k_1^y = f_1\left(t_i, y_i, z_i\right) \tag{E3.4a}$$

$$k_2^y = f_1\left(t_i + h, y_i + hk_1^y, z_i + hk_1^z\right) \tag{E 3.4b}$$

$$z_{i+1} = z_i + \frac{1}{2}\left(k_1^z + k_2^z\right)h \tag{E3.5}$$

$$k_1^z = f_2\left(t_i, y_i, z_i\right) \qquad \text{(E3.6a)}$$
$$k_2^z = f_2\left(t_i + h, y_i + hk_1^y, z_i + hk_1^z\right) \qquad \text{(E3.6b)}$$

For $i = 0, t_o = 0, y_o = 1, z_o = 2$

From Equation (E3.4a)

$$k_1^y = f_1\left(t_o, y_o, z_o\right)$$
$$= f_1\left(0,1,2\right)$$
$$= 2$$

From Equation (E3.6a)

$$k_1^z = f_2\left(t_0, y_0, z_0\right)$$
$$= f_2\left(0,1,2\right)$$
$$= e^{-0} - 2(2) - 1$$
$$= -4$$

From Equation (E3.4b)

$$k_2^y = f_1\left(t_0 + h, y_0 + hk_1^y, z_0 + hk_1^z\right)$$
$$= f_1\left(0 + 0.25, 1 + (0.25)(2), 2 + (0.25)(-4)\right)$$
$$= f_1\left(0.25, 1.5, 1\right)$$
$$= 1$$

From Equation (E3.6b)

$$k_2^z = f_2\left(t_0 + h, y_0 + hk_1^y, z_0 + hk_1^z\right)$$
$$= f_2\left(0 + 0.25, 1 + (0.25)(2), 2 + (0.25)(-4)\right)$$
$$= f_2\left(0.25, 1.5, 1\right)$$
$$= e^{-0.25} - 2(1) - 1.5$$
$$= -2.7212$$

From Equation (E3.3)

$$y_1 = y_0 + \frac{1}{2}\left(k_1^y + k_2^y\right)h$$
$$= 1 + \frac{1}{2}(2 + 1)(0.25)$$
$$= 1.375$$

y_1 is the approximate value of y at

$$t = t_1 = t_0 + h = 0 + 0.25 = 0.25$$
$$y_1 = y(0.25) \cong 1.375$$

From Equation (E3.5)

$$z_1 = z_0 + \frac{1}{2}\left(k_1^z + k_2^z\right)h$$
$$= 2 + \frac{1}{2}(-4 + (-2.7212))(0.25)$$
$$= 1.1598$$

z_1 is the approximate value of z at

$$t = t_1 = 0.25$$

$$z_1 = z(0.25) \approx 1.1598$$

For $i = 1$, $t_1 = 0.25$, $y_1 = 1.375$, $z_1 = 1.1598$

From Equation (E3.4a)

$$k_1^y = f_1(t_1, y_1, z_1)$$
$$= f_1(0.25, 1.375, 1.1598)$$
$$= 1.1598$$

From Equation (E3.6a)

$$k_1^z = f_2(t_1, y_1, z_1)$$
$$= f_2(0.25, 1.375, 1.1598)$$
$$= e^{-0.25} - 2(1.1598) - 1.375$$
$$= -2.9158$$

From Equation (E3.4b)

$$k_2^y = f_1(t_1 + h, y_1 + hk_1^y, z_1 + hk_1^z)$$
$$= f_1(0.25 + 0.25, 1.375 + (0.25)(1.1598), 1.1598 + (0.25)(-2.9158))$$
$$= f_1(0.50, 1.6649, 0.43087)$$
$$= 0.43087$$

From Equation (E3.6b)

$$k_2^z = f_2(t_1 + h, y_1 + hk_1^y, z_1 + hk_1^z)$$
$$= f_2(0.25 + 0.25, 1.375 + (0.25)(1.1598), 1.1598 + (0.25)(-2.9158))$$
$$= f_2(0.50, 1.6649, 0.43087)$$
$$= e^{-0.50} - 2(0.43087) - 1.6649$$
$$= -1.9201$$

From Equation (E3.3)

$$y_2 = y_1 + \frac{1}{2}(k_1^y + k_2^y)h$$
$$= 1.375 + \frac{1}{2}(1.1598 + 0.43087)(0.25)$$
$$= 1.5738$$

y_2 is the approximate value of y at

$$t = t_2 = t_1 + h = 0.25 + 0.25 = 0.50$$
$$y_2 = y(0.50) \approx 1.5738$$

From Equation (E3.5)

$$z_2 = z_1 + \frac{1}{2}(k_1^z + k_2^z)h$$
$$= 1.1598 + \frac{1}{2}(-2.9158 + (-1.9201))(0.25)$$
$$= 0.55533$$

z_2 is the approximate value of z at

$$t = t_2 = 0.50$$
$$z_2 = z(0.50) \approx 0.55533$$

For $i = 2$, $t_2 = 0.50$, $y_2 = 1.57384$, $z_2 = 0.55533$

From Equation (E3.4a)

$$k_1^y = f_1(t_2, y_2, z_2)$$
$$= f_1(0.50, 1.5738, 0.55533)$$
$$= 0.55533$$

From Equation (E3.6a)

$$k_1^z = f_2(t_2, y_2, z_2)$$
$$= f_2(0.50, 1.5738, 0.55533)$$
$$= e^{-0.50} - 2(0.55533) - 1.5738$$
$$= -2.0779$$

From Equation (E3.4b)

$$k_2^y = f_2(t_2 + h, y_2 + hk_1^y, z_2 + hk_1^z)$$
$$= f_1(0.50 + 0.25, 1.5738 + (0.25)(0.55533), 0.55533 + (0.25)(-2.0779))$$
$$= f_1(0.75, 1.7126, 0.035836)$$
$$= 0.035836$$

From Equation (E3.6b)

$$k_2^z = f_2(t_2 + h, y_2 + hk_1^y, z_2 + hk_1^z)$$
$$= f_2(0.50 + 0.25, 1.5738 + (0.25)(0.55533), 0.55533 + (0.25)(-2.0779))$$
$$= f_2(0.75, 1.7126, 0.035836)$$
$$= e^{-0.75} - 2(0.035836) - 1.7126$$
$$= -1.3119$$

From Equation (E3.3)

$$y_3 = y_2 + \frac{1}{2}(k_1^y + k_2^y)h$$

$$= 1.5738 + \frac{1}{2}(0.55533 + 0.035836)(0.25)$$

$$= 1.6477$$

y_3 is the approximate value of y at

$$t = t_3 = t_2 + h = 0.50 + 0.25 = 0.75$$
$$y_3 = y(0.75) \approx 1.6477$$

b) From Equation (E3.5)

$$z_3 = z_2 + \frac{1}{2}(k_1^z + k_2^z)h$$

$$= 0.55533 + \frac{1}{2}(-2.0779 + (-1.3119))(0.25)$$

$$= 0.13158$$

z_3 is the approximate value of z at

$$t = t_3 = 0.75$$
$$z_3 = z(0.75) \cong 0.13158$$

The intermediate and the final results are shown in Table 1.

Table 1 Intermediate results of Heun's method.

i	0	1	2
t_i	0	0.25	0.50
y_i	1	1.3750	1.5738
z_i	2	1.1598	0.55533
k_1^y	2	1.1598	0.55533
k_1^z	-4	-2.9158	-2.0779
k_2^y	1	0.43087	0.035836
k_2^z	-2.7211	-1.9201	-1.3119
y_{i+1}	1.3750	1.5738	1.6477
z_{i+1}	1.1598	0.55533	0.13158

ORDINARY DIFFERENTIAL EQUATIONS	
Topic	Higher Order Equations
Summary	Textbook notes on higher order differential equations
Major	General Engineering
Authors	Autar Kaw
Last Revised	December 23, 2009
Web Site	http://numericalmethods.eng.usf.edu

Problem Set

Chapter 08.05
Higher Order Ordinary Differential Equations

1. Reduce the following 2nd order ordinary differential equation to a set of first order differential equations complete with initial conditions and in the form required to solve them numerically.

$$5\frac{d^2y}{dt^2} + 3\frac{dy}{dt} + 7y = e^{-t} + t^2, \quad y(0) = 6, \quad \frac{dy}{dt}(0) = 11.$$

2. Reduce the following coupled ordinary differential equations to a set of first order differential equations complete with initial conditions and in the form required for solving them numerically.

$$10\frac{d^2x_1}{dt^2} - 15(-2x_1 + x_2) = 0,$$

$$20\frac{d^2x_2}{dt^2} - 15(x_1 - 2x_2) = 0,$$

$$x_1(0) = 2, \quad x_2(0) = 3, \quad \frac{dx_1}{dt}(0) = 4, \quad \frac{dx_2}{dt}(0) = 5.$$

3. The acceleration of a spring mass system is given by $(t > 0)$

$$\frac{d^2x}{dt^2} + x = e^{-t}$$

where x is the displacement of the mass given in meters and t is the time given in seconds. The initial conditions are given as $x(0) = 3$, $\frac{dx}{dt}(0) = 2$.

   a) What is the value of displacement, velocity and acceleration at $t = 0+$ seconds.
   b) Use Euler's method to find the value of displacement, velocity and acceleration at $t = 0.5$ seconds. Use a step size of 0.25 seconds.
   c) What is the exact value of displacement, velocity and acceleration at $t = 0.5$ seconds.

4.   The acceleration of a spring mass system is given by

$$\frac{d^2x}{dt^2} + x = e^{-t}$$

where x is the displacement of the mass given in meters and t is the time given in seconds. The initial conditions are given as $x(0) = 3$, $\frac{dx}{dt}(0) = 2$. Use Ralston's method to find the value of displacement, velocity and acceleration at $t = 0.5$ seconds. Use a step size of 0.25 seconds.

Chapter 08.07
Finite Difference Method for Ordinary Differential Equations

After reading this chapter, you should be able to

1. *Understand what the finite difference method is and how to use it to solve problems.*

What is the finite difference method?

The finite difference method is used to solve ordinary differential equations that have conditions imposed on the boundary rather than at the initial point. These problems are called boundary-value problems. In this chapter, we solve second-order ordinary differential equations of the form

$$\frac{d^2 y}{dx^2} = f(x, y, y'), a \le x \le b,$$ (1)

with boundary conditions

$$y(a) = y_a \text{ and } y(b) = y_b$$ (2)

Many academics refer to boundary value problems as position-dependent and initial value problems as time-dependent. That is not necessarily the case as illustrated by the following examples.

The differential equation that governs the deflection y of a simply supported beam under uniformly distributed load (Figure 1) is given by

$$\frac{d^2 y}{dx^2} = \frac{qx(L-x)}{2EI}$$ (3)

where

$x =$ location along the beam (in)
$E =$ Young's modulus of elasticity of the beam (psi)
$I =$ second moment of area (in^4)
$q =$ uniform loading intensity (lb/in)
$L =$ length of beam (in)

The conditions imposed to solve the differential equation are

$$y(x = 0) = 0$$ (4)
$$y(x = L) = 0$$

Clearly, these are boundary values and hence the problem is considered a boundary-value problem.

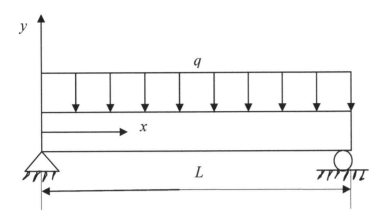

Figure 1 Simply supported beam with uniform distributed load.

Now consider the case of a cantilevered beam with a uniformly distributed load (Figure 2). The differential equation that governs the deflection y of the beam is given by

$$\frac{d^2 y}{dx^2} = \frac{q(L-x)^2}{2EI} \tag{5}$$

where

$\quad x =$ location along the beam (in)
$\quad E =$ Young's modulus of elasticity of the beam (psi)
$\quad I =$ second moment of area (in^4)
$\quad q =$ uniform loading intensity (lb/in)
$\quad L =$ length of beam (in)

The conditions imposed to solve the differential equation are

$$y(x = 0) = 0 \tag{6}$$

$$\frac{dy}{dx}(x = 0) = 0$$

Clearly, these are initial values and hence the problem needs to be considered as an initial value problem.

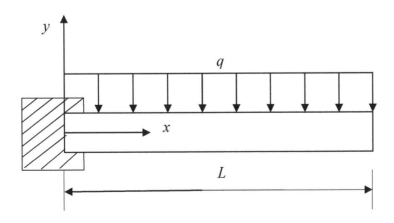

Figure 2 Cantilevered beam with a uniformly distributed load.

Example 1

The deflection y in a simply supported beam with a uniform load q and a tensile axial load T is given by

$$\frac{d^2 y}{dx^2} - \frac{Ty}{EI} = \frac{qx(L-x)}{2EI} \qquad\qquad (E1.1)$$

where

x = location along the beam (in)
T = tension applied (lbs)
E = Young's modulus of elasticity of the beam (psi)
I = second moment of area (in^4)
q = uniform loading intensity (lb/in)
L = length of beam (in)

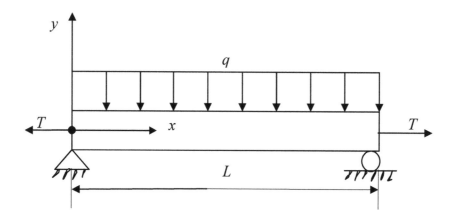

Figure 3 Simply supported beam for Example 1.

Given,

$$T = 7200 \text{ lbs}, \ q = 5400 \text{ lbs/in}, \ L = 75 \text{ in}, \ E = 30 \text{ Msi}, \text{ and } I = 120 \text{ in}^4,$$

a) Find the deflection of the beam at $x = 50"$. Use a step size of $\Delta x = 25"$ and approximate the derivatives by central divided difference approximation.
b) Find the relative true error in the calculation of $y(50)$.

Solution

a) Substituting the given values,

$$\frac{d^2 y}{dx^2} - \frac{7200 y}{(30 \times 10^6)(120)} = \frac{(5400)x(75-x)}{2(30 \times 10^6)(120)}$$

$$\frac{d^2 y}{dx^2} - 2 \times 10^{-6} y = 7.5 \times 10^{-7} x(75-x) \qquad\qquad (E1.2)$$

Approximating the derivative $\dfrac{d^2 y}{dx^2}$ at node i by the central divided difference approximation,

Figure 4 Illustration of finite difference nodes using central divided difference method.

$$\frac{d^2y}{dx^2} \approx \frac{y_{i+1} - 2y_i + y_{i-1}}{(\Delta x)^2}$$ (E1.3)

We can rewrite the equation as

$$\frac{y_{i+1} - 2y_i + y_{i-1}}{(\Delta x)^2} - 2\times10^{-6}y_i = 7.5\times10^{-7}x_i(75 - x_i)$$ (E1.4)

Since $\Delta x = 25$, we have 4 nodes as given in Figure 3

$$\begin{array}{cccc}
i=1 & i=2 & i=3 & i=4 \\
\bullet & \bullet & \bullet & \bullet \\
x=0 & x=25 & x=50 & x=75
\end{array}$$

Figure 5 Finite difference method from $x = 0$ to $x = 75$ with $\Delta x = 25$.

The location of the 4 nodes then is

$$x_0 = 0$$
$$x_1 = x_0 + \Delta x = 0 + 25 = 25$$
$$x_2 = x_1 + \Delta x = 25 + 25 = 50$$
$$x_3 = x_2 + \Delta x = 50 + 25 = 75$$

Writing the equation at each node, we get

<u>Node 1:</u> From the simply supported boundary condition at $x = 0$, we obtain

$$y_1 = 0$$ (E1.5)

<u>Node 2:</u> Rewriting equation (E1.4) for node 2 gives

$$\frac{y_3 - 2y_2 + y_1}{(25)^2} - 2\times10^{-6}y_2 = 7.5\times10^{-7}x_2(75 - x_2)$$

$$0.0016y_1 - 0.003202y_2 + 0.0016y_3 = 7.5\times10^{-7}(25)(75 - 25)$$

$$0.0016y_1 - 0.003202y_2 + 0.0016y_3 = 9.375\times10^{-4}$$ (E1.6)

<u>Node 3:</u> Rewriting equation (E1.4) for node 3 gives

$$\frac{y_4 - 2y_3 + y_2}{(25)^2} - 2\times10^{-6}y_3 = 7.5\times10^{-7}x_3(75 - x_3)$$

$$0.0016y_2 - 0.003202y_3 + 0.0016y_3 = 7.5\times10^{-7}(50)(75 - 50)$$

$$0.0016y_2 - 0.003202y_3 + 0.0016y_3 = 9.375\times10^{-4}$$ (E1.7)

<u>Node 4:</u> From the simply supported boundary condition at $x = 75$, we obtain

$$y_4 = 0$$ (E1.8)

Equations (E1.5-E1.8) are 4 simultaneous equations with 4 unknowns and can be written in matrix form as

$$\begin{bmatrix} 1 & 0 & 0 & 0 \\ 0.0016 & -0.003202 & 0.0016 & 0 \\ 0 & 0.0016 & -0.003202 & 0.0016 \\ 0 & 0 & 0 & 1 \end{bmatrix} \begin{bmatrix} y_1 \\ y_2 \\ y_3 \\ y_4 \end{bmatrix} = \begin{bmatrix} 0 \\ 9.375 \times 10^{-4} \\ 9.375 \times 10^{-4} \\ 0 \end{bmatrix}$$

The above equations have a coefficient matrix that is tridiagonal (we can use Thomas' algorithm to solve the equations) and is also strictly diagonally dominant (convergence is guaranteed if we use iterative methods such as the Gauss-Siedel method). Solving the equations we get,

$$\begin{bmatrix} y_1 \\ y_2 \\ y_3 \\ y_4 \end{bmatrix} = \begin{bmatrix} 0 \\ -0.5852 \\ -0.5852 \\ 0 \end{bmatrix}$$

$$y(50) = y(x_2) \approx y_2 = -0.5852"$$

The exact solution of the ordinary differential equation is derived as follows. The homogeneous part of the solution is given by solving the characteristic equation

$$m^2 - 2 \times 10^{-6} = 0$$
$$m = \pm 0.0014142$$

Therefore,

$$y_h = K_1 e^{0.0014142x} + K_2 e^{-0.0014142x}$$

The particular part of the solution is given by

$$y_p = Ax^2 + Bx + C$$

Substituting the differential equation (E1.2) gives

$$\frac{d^2 y_p}{dx^2} - 2 \times 10^{-6} y_p = 7.5 \times 10^{-7} x(75 - x)$$

$$\frac{d^2}{dx^2}(Ax^2 + Bx + C) - 2 \times 10^{-6}(Ax^2 + Bx + C) = 7.5 \times 10^{-7} x(75 - x)$$

$$2A - 2 \times 10^{-6}(Ax^2 + Bx + C) = 7.5 \times 10^{-7} x(75 - x)$$

$$-2 \times 10^{-6} Ax^2 - 2 \times 10^{-6} Bx + (2A - 2 \times 10^{-6} C) = 5.625 \times 10^{-5} x - 7.5 \times 10^{-7} x^2$$

Equating terms gives

$$-2 \times 10^{-6} A = -7.5 \times 10^{-7}$$
$$-2 \times 10^{-6} B = -5.625 \times 10^{-5}$$
$$2A - 2 \times 10^{-6} C = 0$$

Solving the above equation gives

$$A = 0.375$$
$$B = -28.125$$
$$C = 3.75 \times 10^5$$

The particular solution then is
$$y_p = 0.375x^2 - 28.125x + 3.75 \times 10^5$$
The complete solution is then given by
$$y = 0.375x^2 - 28.125x + 3.75 \times 10^5 + K_1 e^{0.0014142x} + K_2 e^{-0.0014142x}$$
Applying the following boundary conditions
$$y(x = 0) = 0$$
$$y(x = 75) = 0$$
we obtain the following system of equations
$$K_1 + K_2 = -3.75 \times 10^5$$
$$1.1119K_1 + 0.89937K_2 = -3.75 \times 10^5$$
These equations are represented in matrix form by
$$\begin{bmatrix} 1 & 1 \\ 1.1119 & 0.89937 \end{bmatrix}\begin{bmatrix} K_1 \\ K_2 \end{bmatrix} = \begin{bmatrix} -3.75 \times 10^5 \\ -3.75 \times 10^5 \end{bmatrix}$$
A number of different numerical methods may be utilized to solve this system of equations such as the Gaussian elimination. Using any of these methods yields
$$\begin{bmatrix} K_1 \\ K_2 \end{bmatrix} = \begin{bmatrix} -1.775656226 \times 10^5 \\ -1.974343774 \times 10^5 \end{bmatrix}$$
Substituting these values back into the equation gives
$$y = 0.375x^2 - 28.125x + 3.75 \times 10^5 - 1.775656266 \times 10^5 e^{0.0014142x} - 1.974343774 \times 10^5 e^{-0.0014142x}$$
Unlike other examples in this chapter and in the book, the above expression for the deflection of the beam is displayed with a larger number of significant digits. This is done to minimize the round-off error because the above expression involves subtraction of large numbers that are close to each other.

b) To calculate the relative true error, we must first calculate the value of the exact solution at $y = 50$.
$$y(50) = 0.375(50)^2 - 28.125(50) + 3.75 \times 10^5 - 1.775656266 \times 10^5 e^{0.0014142(50)}$$
$$- 1.974343774 \times 10^5 e^{-0.0014142(50)}$$
$$y(50) = -0.5320$$
The true error is given by
$$E_t = \text{Exact Value} - \text{Approximate Value}$$
$$E_t = -0.5320 - (-0.5852)$$
$$E_t = 0.05320$$
The relative true error is given by
$$\epsilon_t = \frac{\text{True Error}}{\text{True Value}} \times 100\%$$
$$\epsilon_t = \frac{0.05320}{-0.5320} \times 100\%$$
$$\epsilon_t = -10\%$$

Example 2

Take the case of a pressure vessel that is being tested in the laboratory to check its ability to withstand pressure. For a thick pressure vessel of inner radius a and outer radius b, the differential equation for the radial displacement u of a point along the thickness is given by

$$\frac{d^2u}{dr^2}+\frac{1}{r}\frac{du}{dr}-\frac{u}{r^2}=0 \qquad (E2.3)$$

The inner radius $a = 5''$ and the outer radius $b = 8''$, and the material of the pressure vessel is ASTM A36 steel. The yield strength of this type of steel is 36 ksi. Two strain gages that are bonded tangentially at the inner and the outer radius measure normal tangential strain as

$$\in_{t/r=a} = \quad 0.00077462$$

$$\in_{t/r=b} = \quad 0.00038462 \qquad (E2.4a,b)$$

at the maximum needed pressure. Since the radial displacement and tangential strain are related simply by

$$\in_t = \frac{u}{r}, \qquad (E2.5)$$

then

$$u\big|_{r=a} = \quad 0.00077462 \times 5 \quad = \quad 0.0038731''$$

$$u\big|_{r=b} = \quad 0.00038462 \times 8 \quad = \quad 0.0030769''$$

The maximum normal stress in the pressure vessel is at the inner radius $r = a$ and is given by

$$\sigma_{max} = \frac{E}{1-v^2}\left(\frac{u}{r}\bigg|_{r=a}+v\frac{du}{dr}\bigg|_{r=a}\right) \qquad (E2.7)$$

where

$E =$ Young's modulus of steel (E= 30 Msi)
$v =$ Poisson's ratio ($v = 0.3$)

The factor of safety, FS is given by

$$FS = \frac{\text{Yield strength of steel}}{\sigma_{max}} \qquad (E2.8)$$

a) Divide the radial thickness of the pressure vessel into 6 equidistant nodes, and find the radial displacement profile
b) Find the maximum normal stress and factor of safety as given by equation (E2.8)
c) Find the exact value of the maximum normal stress as given by equation (E2.8) if it is given that the exact expression for radial displacement is of the form

$$u = C_1 r + \frac{C_2}{r}.$$

Calculate the relative true error.

Solution

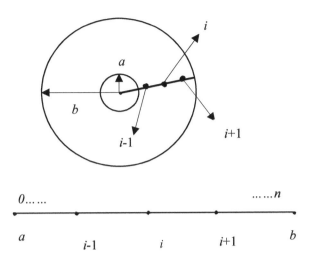

Figure 4 Nodes along the radial direction.

a) The radial locations from $r = a$ to $r = b$ are divided into n equally spaced segments, and hence resulting in $n+1$ nodes. This will allow us to find the dependent variable u numerically at these nodes.

At node i along the radial thickness of the pressure vessel,

$$\frac{d^2u}{dr^2} \approx \frac{u_{i+1} - 2u_i + u_{i-1}}{(\Delta r)^2} \tag{E2.9}$$

$$\frac{du}{dr} \approx \frac{u_{i+1} - u_i}{\Delta r} \tag{E2.10}$$

Such substitutions will convert the ordinary differential equation into a linear equation (but with more than one unknown). By writing the resulting linear equation at different points at which the ordinary differential equation is valid, we get simultaneous linear equations that can be solved by using techniques such as Gaussian elimination, the Gauss-Siedel method, etc.

Substituting these approximations from Equations (E2.9) and (E2.10) in Equation (E2.3)

$$\frac{u_{i+1} - 2u_i + u_{i-1}}{(\Delta r)^2} + \frac{1}{r_i}\frac{u_{i+1} - u_i}{\Delta r} - \frac{u_i}{r_i^2} = 0 \tag{E2.11}$$

$$\left(\frac{1}{(\Delta r)^2} + \frac{1}{r_i \Delta r}\right)u_{i+1} + \left(-\frac{2}{(\Delta r)^2} - \frac{1}{r_i \Delta r} - \frac{1}{r_i^2}\right)u_i + \frac{1}{(\Delta r)^2}u_{i-1} = 0 \tag{E2.12}$$

Let us break the thickness, $b - a$, of the pressure vessel into $n+1$ nodes, that is $r = a$ is node $i = 0$ and $r = b$ is node $i = n$. That means we have $n+1$ unknowns.

We can write the above equation for nodes $1, ..., n-1$. This will give us $n-1$ equations. At the edge nodes, $i = 0$ and $i = n$, we use the boundary conditions of

$$u_0 = u\big|_{r=a}$$

$$u_n = u\big|_{r=b}$$

This gives a total of $n+1$ equations. So we have $n+1$ unknowns and $n+1$ linear equations. These can be solved by any of the numerical methods used for solving simultaneous linear equations.

We have been asked to do the calculations for $n=5$, that is a total of 6 nodes. This gives

$$\Delta r = \frac{b-a}{n}$$

$$= \frac{8-5}{5}$$

$$= 0.6"$$

At node $i = 0, r_0 = a = 5", u_0 = 0.0038731"$ (E2.13)

At node $i = 1, r_1 = r_0 + \Delta r = 5 + 0.6 = 5.6"$ (E2.14)

$$\frac{1}{0.6^2}u_0 + \left(-\frac{2}{0.6^2} - \frac{1}{(5.6)(0.6)} - \frac{1}{(5.6)^2}\right)u_1 + \left(\frac{1}{0.6^2} + \frac{1}{(5.6)(0.6)}\right)u_2 = 0$$

$$2.7778u_0 - 5.8851u_1 + 3.0754u_2 = 0$$ (E2.15)

At node $i = 2, \quad r_2 = r_1 + \Delta r = 5.6 + 0.6 = 6.2"$

$$\frac{1}{0.6^2}u_1 + \left(-\frac{2}{0.6^2} - \frac{1}{(6.2)(0.6)} - \frac{1}{6.2^2}\right)u_2 + \left(\frac{1}{0.6^2} + \frac{1}{(6.2)(0.6)}\right)u_3 = 0$$

$$2.7778u_1 - 5.8504u_2 + 3.0466u_3 = 0$$ (E2.16)

At node $i = 3, \quad r_3 = r_2 + \Delta r = 6.2 + 0.6 = 6.8"$

$$\frac{1}{0.6^2}u_2 + \left(-\frac{2}{0.6^2} - \frac{1}{(6.8)(0.6)} - \frac{1}{6.8^2}\right)u_3 + \left(\frac{1}{0.6^2} + \frac{1}{(6.8)(0.6)}\right)u_4 = 0$$

$$2.7778u_2 - 5.8223u_3 + 3.0229u_4 = 0$$ (E2.17)

At node $i = 4, \quad r_4 = r_3 + \Delta r = 6.8 + 0.6 = 7.4"$

$$\frac{1}{0.6^2}u_3 + \left(-\frac{2}{0.6^2} - \frac{1}{(7.4)(0.6)} - \frac{1}{(7.4)^2}\right)u_4 + \left(\frac{1}{0.6^2} + \frac{1}{(7.4)(0.6)}\right)u_5 = 0$$

$$2.7778u_3 - 5.7990u_4 + 3.0030u_5 = 0$$ (E2.18)

At node $i = 5, \quad r_5 = r_4 + \Delta r = 7.4 + 0.6 = 8"$

$$u_5 = u\big|_{r=b} = 0.0030769"$$ (E2.19)

Writing Equation (E2.13) to (E2.19) in matrix form gives

$$
\begin{bmatrix}
1 & 0 & 0 & 0 & 0 & 0 \\
2.7778 & -5.8851 & 3.0754 & 0 & 0 & 0 \\
0 & 2.7778 & -5.8504 & 3.0466 & 0 & 0 \\
0 & 0 & 2.7778 & -5.8223 & 3.0229 & 0 \\
0 & 0 & 0 & 2.7778 & -5.7990 & 3.0030 \\
0 & 0 & 0 & 0 & 0 & 1
\end{bmatrix}
\begin{bmatrix}
u_0 \\ u_1 \\ u_2 \\ u_3 \\ u_4 \\ u_5
\end{bmatrix}
=
\begin{bmatrix}
0.0038731 \\ 0 \\ 0 \\ 0 \\ 0 \\ 0.0030769
\end{bmatrix}
$$

The above equations are a tri-diagonal system of equations and special algorithms such as Thomas' algorithm can be used to solve such a system of equations.

$u_0 = 0.0038731''$

$u_1 = 0.0036165''$

$u_2 = 0.0034222''$

$u_3 = 0.0032743''$

$u_4 = 0.0031618''$

$u_5 = 0.0030769''$

b) To find the maximum stress, it is given by Equation (E2.7) as

$$
\sigma_{max} = \frac{E}{1-v^2}\left(\frac{u}{r}\bigg|_{r=a} + v\frac{du}{dr}\bigg|_{r=a} \right)
$$

$E = 30 \times 10^6 \, \text{psi}$

$v = 0.3$

$u\big|_{r=a} = u_0 = 0.0038731''$

$$
\frac{du}{dr}\bigg|_{r=a} \approx \frac{u_1 - u_0}{\Delta r}
$$
$$
= \frac{0.0036165 - 0.0038731}{0.6}
$$
$$
= -0.00042767
$$

The maximum stress in the pressure vessel then is

$$
\sigma_{max} = \frac{30 \times 10^6}{1-0.3^2}\left(\frac{0.0038731}{5} + 0.3(-0.00042767) \right)
$$
$$
= 2.1307 \times 10^4 \, \text{psi}
$$

So the factor of safety FS from Equation (E2.8) is

$$
FS = \frac{36 \times 10^3}{2.1307 \times 10^4} = 1.6896
$$

c) The differential equation has an exact solution and is given by the form

$$
u = C_1 r + \frac{C_2}{r} \tag{E2.20}
$$

where C_1 and C_2 are found by using the boundary conditions at $r = a$ and $r = b$.

$$u(r = a) = u(r = 5) = 0.0038731 = C_1(5) + \frac{C_2}{5}$$

$$u(r = b) = u(r = 8) = 0.0030769 = C_1(8) + \frac{C_2}{8}$$

giving

$$C_1 = 0.00013462$$
$$C_2 = 0.016000$$

Thus

$$u = 0.00013462r + \frac{0.016000}{r} \tag{E2.21}$$

$$\frac{du}{dr} = 0.00013462 - \frac{0.016000}{r^2} \tag{E2.22}$$

$$\sigma_{max} = \frac{E}{1-v^2}\left(\left.\frac{u}{r}\right|_{r=a} + v\left.\frac{du}{dr}\right|_{r=a}\right)$$

$$= \frac{30 \times 10^6}{1 - 0.3^2}\left(\frac{0.00013462(5) + \dfrac{0.01600}{5}}{5} + 0.3\left(0.0013462 - \frac{0.016000}{5^2}\right)\right)$$

$$= 2.0538 \times 10^4 \, \text{psi}$$

The true error is

$$E_t = 2.0538 \times 10^4 - 2.1307 \times 10^4$$
$$= -7.6859 \times 10^2$$

The absolute relative true error is

$$|\epsilon_t| = \left|\frac{2.0538 \times 10^4 - 2.1307 \times 10^4}{2.0538 \times 10^4}\right| \times 100$$
$$= 3.744\%$$

Example 3

The approximation in Example 2

$$\frac{du}{dr} \approx \frac{u_{i+1} - u_i}{\Delta r}$$

is first order accurate, that is , the true error is of $O(\Delta r)$.
The approximation

$$\frac{d^2u}{dr^2} \approx \frac{u_{i+1} - 2u_i + u_{i-1}}{(\Delta r)^2} \tag{E3.1}$$

is second order accurate, that is , the true error is $O\left((\Delta r)^2\right)$

Mixing these two approximations will result in the order of accuracy of $O(\Delta r)$ and $O\left((\Delta r)^2\right)$, that is $O(\Delta r)$.

So it is better to approximate

$$\frac{du}{dr} \approx \frac{u_{i+1} - u_{i-1}}{2(\Delta r)} \tag{E3.2}$$

because this equation is second order accurate. Repeat Example 2 with the more accurate approximations.

Solution

a) Repeating the problem with this approximation, at node i in the pressure vessel,

$$\frac{d^2 u}{dr^2} \approx \frac{u_{i+1} - 2u_i + u_{i-1}}{(\Delta r)^2} \tag{E3.3}$$

$$\frac{du}{dr} \approx \frac{u_{i+1} - u_{i-1}}{2\Delta r} \tag{E3.4}$$

Substituting Equations (E3.3) and (E3.4) in Equation (E2.3) gives

$$\frac{u_{i+1} - 2u_i + u_{i-1}}{(\Delta r)^2} + \frac{1}{r_i} \frac{u_{i+1} - u_{i-1}}{2(\Delta r)} - \frac{u_i}{r_i^2} = 0$$

$$\left(-\frac{1}{2r_i(\Delta r)} + \frac{1}{(\Delta r)^2}\right) u_{i-1} + \left(-\frac{2}{(\Delta r)^2} - \frac{1}{r_i^2}\right) u_i + \left(\frac{1}{(\Delta r)^2} + \frac{1}{2r_i \Delta r}\right) u_{i+1} = 0 \tag{E3.5}$$

At node $i = 0$, $r_0 = a = 5$ "

$$u_0 = 0.0038731 \text{"} \tag{E3.6}$$

At node $i = 1$, $r_1 = r_0 + \Delta r = 5 + 0.6 = 5.6$"

$$\left(-\frac{1}{2(5.6)(0.6)} + \frac{1}{(0.6)^2}\right) u_0 + \left(-\frac{2}{(0.6)^2} - \frac{1}{(5.6)^2}\right) u_1 + \left(\frac{1}{0.6^2} + \frac{1}{2(5.6)(0.6)}\right) u_2 = 0$$

$$2.6297 u_0 - 5.5874 u_1 + 2.9266 u_2 = 0 \tag{E3.7}$$

At node $i = 2$, $r_2 = r_1 + \Delta r = 5.6 + 0.6 = 6.2$ "

$$\left(-\frac{1}{2(6.2)(0.6)} + \frac{1}{0.6^2}\right) u_1 + \left(-\frac{2}{0.6^2} - \frac{1}{6.2^2}\right) u_2 + \left(\frac{1}{0.6^2} + \frac{1}{2(6.2)(0.6)}\right) u_3 = 0 \tag{E3.8}$$

$$2.6434 u_1 - 5.5816 u_2 + 2.9122 u_3 = 0$$

At node $i = 3$, $r_3 = r_2 + \Delta r = 6.2 + 0.6 = 6.8$ "

$$\left(-\frac{1}{2(6.8)(0.6)} + \frac{1}{0.6^2}\right) u_2 + \left(-\frac{2}{0.6^2} - \frac{1}{6.8^2}\right) u_3 + \left(\frac{1}{0.6^2} + \frac{1}{2(6.8)(0.6)}\right) u_4 = 0 \tag{E3.9}$$

$$2.6552 u_2 - 5.5772 u_3 + 2.9003 u_4 = 0$$

At node $i = 4$, $r_4 = r_3 + \Delta r = 6.8 + 0.6 = 7.4$ "

$$\left(-\frac{1}{2(7.4)(0.6)} + \frac{1}{0.6^2}\right) u_3 + \left(-\frac{2}{0.6^2} - \frac{1}{(7.4)^2}\right) u_4 + \left(\frac{1}{0.6^2} + \frac{1}{2(7.4)(0.6)}\right) u_5 = 0 \tag{E3.10}$$

$$2.66511 u_3 - 5.5738 u_4 + 2.8903 u_5 = 0$$

At node $i = 5$, $r_5 = r_4 + \Delta r = 7.4 + 0.6 = 8$ "

$$u_5 = u/_{r=b} = 0.0030769 \text{"} \tag{E3.11}$$

Writing Equations (E3.6) thru (E3.11) in matrix form gives

$$\begin{bmatrix} 1 & 0 & 0 & 0 & 0 & 0 \\ 2.6297 & -5.5874 & 2.9266 & 0 & 0 & 0 \\ 0 & 2.6434 & -5.5816 & 2.9122 & 0 & 0 \\ 0 & 0 & 2.6552 & -5.5772 & 2.9003 & 0 \\ 0 & 0 & 0 & 2.6651 & -5.5738 & 2.8903 \\ 0 & 0 & 0 & 0 & 0 & 1 \end{bmatrix} \begin{bmatrix} u_0 \\ u_1 \\ u_2 \\ u_3 \\ u_4 \\ u_5 \end{bmatrix} = \begin{bmatrix} 0.0038731 \\ 0 \\ 0 \\ 0 \\ 0 \\ 0.0030769 \end{bmatrix}$$

The above equations are a tri-diagonal system of equations and special algorithms such as Thomas' algorithm can be used to solve such equations.

$u_0 = 0.0038731"$

$u_1 = 0.0036115"$

$u_2 = 0.0034159"$

$u_3 = 0.0032689"$

$u_4 = 0.0031586"$

$u_5 = 0.0030769"$

b) $\left. \dfrac{du}{dr} \right|_{r=a} \approx \dfrac{-3u_0 + 4u_1 - u_2}{2(\Delta r)}$

$= \dfrac{-3 \times 0.0038731 + 4 \times 0.0036115 - 0.0034159}{2(0.6)}$

$= -4.925 \times 10^{-4}$

$\sigma_{max} = \dfrac{30 \times 10^6}{1 - 0.3^2} \left(\dfrac{0.0038731}{5} + 0.3\left(-4.925 \times 10^{-4}\right) \right)$

$= 2.0666 \times 10^4 \, psi$

Therefore, the factor of safety FS is

$FS = \dfrac{36 \times 10^3}{2.0666 \times 10^4}$

$= 1.7420$

c) The true error in calculating the maximum stress is

$E_t = 2.0538 \times 10^4 - 2.0666 \times 10^4$

$= -128 \, psi$

The relative true error in calculating the maximum stress is

$\left| \epsilon_t \right| = \left| \dfrac{-128}{2.0538 \times 10^4} \right| \times 100$

$= 0.62323\%$

Table 1 Comparisons of radial displacements from two methods.

r	u_{exact}	$u_{1st \, order}$	$\left| \epsilon_t \right|$	$u_{2nd \, order}$	$\left| \epsilon_t \right|$

5	0.0038731	0.0038731	0.0000	0.0038731	0.0000
5.6	0.0036110	0.0036165	1.5160×10^{-1}	0.0036115	1.4540×10^{-2}
6.2	0.0034152	0.0034222	2.0260×10^{-1}	0.0034159	1.8765×10^{-2}
6.8	0.0032683	0.0032743	1.8157×10^{-1}	0.0032689	1.6334×10^{-2}
7.4	0.0031583	0.0031618	1.0903×10^{-1}	0.0031586	9.5665×10^{-3}
8	0.0030769	0.0030769	0.0000	0.0030769	0.0000

ORDINARY DIFFERENTIAL EQUATIONS	
Topic	Finite Difference Methods of Solving Ordinary Differential Equations
Summary	Textbook notes of Finite Difference Methods of solving ordinary differential equations
Major	General Engineering
Authors	Autar Kaw, Cuong Nguyen, Luke Snyder
Date	December 23, 2009
Web Site	http://numericalmethods.eng.usf.edu

Multiple-Choice Test

Chapter 08.07
Finite Difference Method

1. The exact solution to the boundary value problem
    $$\frac{d^2 y}{dx^2} = 6x - 0.5x^2, \ y(0) = 0, \ y(12) = 0$$
    for $y(4)$ is
    (A) -234.67
    (B) 0.00
    (C) 16.000
    (D) 37.333

2. Given
    $$\frac{d^2 y}{dx^2} = 6x - 0.5x^2, \ y(0) = 0, \ y(12) = 0$$

    the value of $\frac{d^2 y}{dx^2}$ at $y(4)$ using the finite difference method and a step size of $h = 4$
    can be approximated by

    (A) $\dfrac{y(8) - y(0)}{8}$

    (B) $\dfrac{y(8) - 2y(4) + y(0)}{16}$

    (C) $\dfrac{y(12) - 2y(8) + y(4)}{16}$

    (D) $\dfrac{y(4) - y(0)}{4}$

3. Given
    $$\frac{d^2 y}{dx^2} = 6x - 0.5x^2, \ y(0) = 0, \ y(12) = 0,$$

    the value of $y(4)$ using the finite difference method with a second order accurate central divided difference method and a step size of $h = 4$ is
    (A) 0.000
    (B) 37.333
    (C) -234.67
    (D) -256.00

4.   The transverse deflection u of a cable of length L that is fixed at both ends, is given as a solution to

$$\frac{d^2u}{dx^2} = \frac{Tu}{R} + \frac{qx(x-L)}{2R}$$

where
   T = tension in cable
   R = flexural stiffness
   q = distributed transverse load

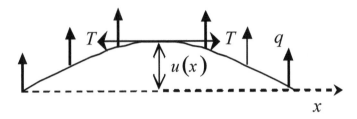

Given $L = 50"$, $T = 2000$ lbs, $q = 75\dfrac{\text{lbs}}{\text{in}}$, and $R = 75 \times 10^6$ lbs·in^2

Using finite difference method modeling with second order central divided difference accuracy and a step size of $h = 12.5"$, the value of the deflection at the center of the cable most nearly is
   (A)   0.072737"
   (B)   0.080832"
   (C)   0.081380"
   (D)   0.084843"

5.   The radial displacement u of a pressurized hollow thick cylinder (inner radius = 5″, outer radius = 8″) is given at different radial locations.

Radius (in)	Radial Displacement (in)
5.0	0.0038731
5.6	0.0036165
6.2	0.0034222
6.8	0.0032743
7.4	0.0031618
8.0	0.0030769

The maximum normal stress, in psi, on the cylinder is given by

$$\sigma_{max} = 3.2967 \times 10^6 \left(\frac{u(5)}{5} + 0.3 \frac{du}{dr}(5) \right)$$

The maximum stress, in psi, with second order accuracy is
    (A) 2079.6
    (B) 2104.5
    (C) 2130.7
    (D) 2182.0

6.   For a simply supported beam (at $x = 0$ and $x = L$) with a uniform load q, the vertical deflection $v(x)$ is described by the boundary value ordinary differential equation as

$$\frac{d^2v}{dx^2} = \frac{qx(x-L)}{2EI}, \quad 0 \le x \le L$$

where
E = Young's modulus of the beam
I = second moment of area

This ordinary differential equation is based on assuming that $\frac{dv}{dx}$ is small. If $\frac{dv}{dx}$ is not small, then the ordinary differential equation is given by

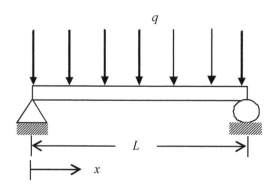

(A) $$\frac{\dfrac{d^2v}{dx^2}}{\sqrt{1+\left(\dfrac{dv}{dx}\right)^2}} = \frac{qx(x-L)}{2EI}$$

(B) $$\frac{\dfrac{d^2v}{dx^2}}{\left(1+\left(\dfrac{dv}{dx}\right)^2\right)^{3/2}} = \frac{qx(x-L)}{2EI}$$

(C) $$\frac{\dfrac{d^2v}{dx^2}}{\sqrt{1+\left(\dfrac{dv}{dx}\right)}} = \frac{qx(x-L)}{2EI}$$

(D) $$\frac{\dfrac{d^2v}{dx^2}}{1+\dfrac{dv}{dx}} = \frac{qx(x-L)}{2EI}$$

Problem Set

Chapter 08.07
Finite Difference Method of Solving Boundary Value Problems

1. Given the boundary value ordinary differential equation as

$$\frac{d^2u}{dr^2} + \frac{1}{r}\frac{du}{dr} - \frac{u}{r^2} = 0, \ u(5) = 0.004", \ u(10.1) = 0.003".$$

Using finite divided difference approximations of

$$\frac{dy}{dx} \approx \frac{y_{i+1} - y_i}{\Delta x},$$

$$\frac{d^2y}{dx^2} \approx \frac{y_{i+1} - 2y_i + y_{i-1}}{(\Delta x)^2},$$

and using 4 equidistant nodes from $r = 5$ to $r = 10.1$, find
a) the value of $u(r)$ at the 4 nodes,
b) the absolute relative true error in your results if the exact solution for $u(r)$

is of the form $u(r) = c_1 r + \dfrac{c_2}{r}$, where c_1 and c_2 are obtained from the

values of $u(r)$ at the boundaries.

2. Given the boundary value ordinary differential equation as

$$\frac{d^2u}{dr^2} + \frac{1}{r}\frac{du}{dr} - \frac{u}{r^2} = 0, \ u(5) = 0.004", \ u(10.1) = 0.003".$$

Using finite divided difference approximations of

$$\frac{dy}{dx} \approx \frac{y_{i+1} - y_{i-1}}{2\Delta x},$$

$$\frac{d^2y}{dx^2} \approx \frac{y_{i+1} - 2y_i + y_{i-1}}{(\Delta x)^2},$$

and using 4 equidistant nodes from $r = 5$ to $r = 10.1$, find
a) the value of $u(r)$ at the 4 nodes.
b) the absolute relative true error in your results if the exact solution for $u(r)$

is of the form $u(r) = c_1 r + \dfrac{c_2}{r}$, where c_1 and c_2 are obtained from the

values of $u(r)$ at the boundaries.

3.   Given the boundary value ordinary differential equation as

$$\frac{d^2u}{dr^2} + \frac{1}{r}\frac{du}{dr} - \frac{u}{r^2} = 0, \; u(5) = 0.004", \; u(10.1) = 0.003".$$

Using finite divided difference approximations of

$$\frac{dy}{dx} \approx \frac{y_i - y_{i-1}}{\Delta x},$$

$$\frac{d^2y}{dx^2} \approx \frac{y_{i+1} - 2y_i + y_{i-1}}{(\Delta x)^2},$$

and using 4 equidistant nodes from $r = 5$ to $r = 10.1$, find
   a) the value of $u(r)$ at the 4 nodes,
   b) the absolute relative true error in your results if the exact solution for $u(r)$

        is of the form $u(r) = c_1 r + \dfrac{c_2}{r}$, where c_1 and c_2 are obtained from the

        values of $u(r)$ at the boundaries.

4.   The simply supported beam is subjected to a uniform load q. The differential
     equation governing the vertical deflection, y in the beam is given by

$$EI\frac{d^2y}{dx^2} = \frac{qx}{2}(L-x)$$

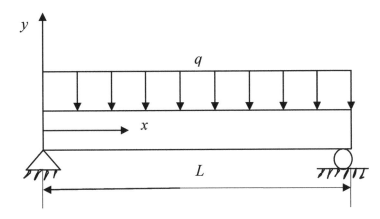

     Given
              $L = 0.5\,\mathrm{m}$
              $E = 210\,\mathrm{GPa}$
              $I = 125\,\mathrm{cm}^4$
     find
              a) the exact solution of the ordinary differential equation,
              b) $y(x)$ at 4 nodes equally spaced along the length of the beam using the

                  finite difference approximation for $\dfrac{d^2y}{dx^2}$,

c) the absolute relative true error in the value of y at the non-boundary nodes for part (b).

Index

True error, 11-13, 49, 64, 66, 95-96, 98-101, 106, 109, 120, 169, 170, 183, 192, 375, 421, 533, 534, 536, 538, 540, 542, 558-559, 587-588, 644, 656, 703

Truncation error, 22-26, 64, 526, 644

Trunnion-Hub-Girder (THG) assembly, 1, 86, 147, 218, 323, 407, 518, 629

Two-point Gauss quadrature rule, 566-568, 570-572, 574-575, 597-598, 602-604

U

Unequal segments, 588

Unequal segments, trapezoidal rule, 588

Upper triangular matrix, 226, 267, 274, 278, 286

V

Variable costs, 141-144

Variables, dependent, 418, 476, 609, 635, 705

Variables, independent, 399, 418, 421, 635

Variance, 412-416, 422-423, 480

Vector, 206-208, 228-237, 239-240, 276, 286, 294, 295, 298, 498-501, 507-508

Z

Zener diode, 404, 509

Zero matrix, 227-228